MICROORGANISMS
INDIGENOUS TO MAN

ABOUT THE AUTHOR

THEODOR ROSEBURY, D.D.S. is currently Professor of Bacteriology at the Washington University School of Dentistry, St. Louis, Missouri. His research since 1928, when he began professionally as Gies Fellow in Biochemistry at the College of Physicians and Surgeons, Columbia University, has dealt with the subject of this book except for the wartime period, when he served as chief of the airborne infection project at Camp Detrick, Maryland.

A graduate of the Dental School of the University of Pennsylvania, Dr. Rosebury was successively Instructor, Assistant Professor, and Associate Professor of Bacteriology at Columbia University Medical School from 1930 until 1951 when he took over the position he currently holds.

Theodor Rosebury, an authority on the normal flora, has not only conducted extensive research in this area, but has also authored over one-hundred papers on the topics in his field of special interest.

MICROORGANISMS INDIGENOUS TO MAN

Theodor Rosebury

Professor of Bacteriology
Washington University
School of Dentistry

The Blakiston Division
McGRAW-HILL BOOK COMPANY, INC.
New York   Toronto   London

MICROORGANISMS INDIGENOUS TO MAN

Library of Congress Catalog Card Number: 61-18314

53620

THE MAPLE PRESS COMPANY, YORK, PA.

In nature's infinite book of secrecy
A little I can read.

And I can speak of the disturbances
That nature works, and of her cures; which
doth give me
A more content in course of true delight
Than to be thirsty after tottering honour,
Or tie my treasure up in silken bags,
To please the fool and death.

To Amy

PREFACE

In this book I have undertaken to collect and organize the large and scattered literature on what microbiologists usually call the "normal flora" of man. "Microbiota" is a more accurate word, especially since I have chosen to include protozoa. Nobody else, to my knowledge, has ever attempted such a book before. In fact, this seems to be the first time, except for my own earlier essays, that the subject has been treated as an organic unit. Doing so required that I cross many boundaries, and I have let the subject lead me over them with little hesitation. Perhaps I have trespassed. The job seemed to me to need doing, and nobody else had done it.

Anything seen from a new perspective is likely to reveal aspects previously hidden. By bringing material together in a new way in this book and exploring some aspects of the subject more deeply than I had ever done before I have gained new insights. Persons with a specialized interest, microbiologic or clinical, including teachers, students, and investigators—the audience for whom I have been writing—may find their own problems duplicated in unexpected places. Perhaps light from such places will be reflected back into dark corners of their own domains and help to clarify them.

Organization of knowledge also exposes gaps and raises questions. I have tried to point these out explicitly as I found them so as to make this book useful to those looking for research problems. To further this end I have included sources fully both as documentation and as a guide to the literature.

The "microorganisms indigenous to man" happen to coincide in many instances with the lesser pathogens or presumed nonpathogens that have often received negligent and sometimes inaccurate treatment in medical textbooks. It happens, therefore, that this book has come to deal with the more neglected microorganisms of medical importance, for many of which even reviews, especially of the more recent literature, are not available. This book may therefore serve as a supplement to the larger texts of medical microbiology.

A long history may be worth a brief recounting. The idea for this book came to me at some time between 1935 and 1938, while I was a member of the bacteriology department at Columbia University. As the dental member of a medical department I had begun to explore the bacteriology of the mouth, which even then seemed to me to demand treatment in a larger context. In 1935 our departmental text appeared, F. P. Gay's *Agents of Disease and Host Resistance* (Charles C Thomas) —a bulky volume the medical students fondly nicknamed "Gay's Anatomy of Bacteriology." Three years later that early example of the now ubiquitous symposium, S. M. Gordon's *Dental Science and Dental Art* (Lea & Febiger) emerged as the dental student's guide to research on the mouth. I had a hand in both books. Dr. Gay, for whose warm critical guidance I shall always be grateful, assigned topics to me that were far enough from my immediate interest to give me new perspectives. Among the consequences traceable back to that enterprise was my wartime stint at Camp Detrick, where an interval in the technologic antipodes of the normal flora provided more perspective—and a long detour. Both Gay and Gordon encouraged and prodded me toward the writing of this book. I made a start on it in 1942, and the war quickly intervened. The writing done that year came to be published as three reviews in 1944, duly mentioned in the pages that follow. The war, which changed so many things, delayed my return to a book on the normal flora.

I have been collecting the literature for this book since 1928, more and more assiduously and systematically. Nearly all my research has pointed toward it. My contributions to the successive editions of R. J. Dubos' *Bacterial and Mycotic Infections of Man* (Lippincott) were preliminary sketches. A year's leave from Washington University in 1958–1959, and subsequently a research grant from the National Institute of Allergy and Infectious Diseases that helped pay much of the cost of preparing the manuscript, have made it possible to bring this book to completion.

I owe thanks to many, including the secretaries who have helped maintain and organize my literature files through the years, especially Sophia Effren, Lois Lunin, Caroline Pinkers, Evelyn Rosenburg, and Ann Browne; to Dr. J. B. Macdonald and the staff of the Forsyth Dental Infirmary for hospitality and many courtesies, in early 1959, that got me started on the writing; to all who sent me reprints of their work; to the medical library staffs at Columbia, Harvard, and Washington Universities and of the New York Academy of Medicine, and especially to Harriet Steuernagel, dental librarian at Washington University; to Elizabeth O. King for critical readings of the section on *Moraxella-Mima;* and to Miss King, Dr. D. I. Annear, Dr. A. Lwoff, Dr. M. Solotorovsky, Dr. G. H. G. Davis, and others who graciously sent me unpublished material; to Dr. F. W. Kraus for reading the manuscript and making many helpful suggestions; to Bozena Kallus for

German translations; to Gale Feldmann for typing most of the manuscript; and to Elinor Watson, Nanci Hoffman, and Richard Simmers for help in spotting errors; and above all to my wife, Amy, who helped me sweat through the travail that only others who have given birth to a book can understand. The errors that remain in spite of everything are, of course, mine alone.

THEODOR ROSEBURY

July 30, 1961

CONTENTS

PREFACE ix

1 INTRODUCTION: CERTAIN GENERAL PRINCIPLES 1
   References, 7

2 THE INDIGENOUS COCCI 9
   Staphylococci, 9 The pathogenic staphylococci, 10 The
   nonpathogenic staphylococci, 23 Anaerobic micrococci, 25
   Streptococci, 26 Enterococci, 26 The viridans group, 31
   Anaerobic streptococci, 33 Neisseriae, 36 Veillonellae, 38
   References, 40

3 INDIGENOUS GRAM-POSITIVE BACILLI 48
   Lactobacilli, 48 Actinomyces, 57 The bifidus group
   (*Lactobacillus bifidus*), 58 The israelii group, 63 Leptotrichiae, 69 *Leptotrichia buccalis*, 69 *Leptotrichia dentium*
   (*Bacterionema matruchotii*), 73 Corynebacteria, 77 Aerobic diphtheroids, 77 Anaerobic diphtheroid-like bacteria, 79
   Mycobacteria, 82 *Mycobacterium smegmatis*, 82 Atypical,
   anonymous, or unclassified mycobacteria, 83 Spore-bearing
   bacilli, 87 *Clostridium perfringens*, 87 References, 90

4 INDIGENOUS AEROBIC GRAM-NEGATIVE BACILLI 99
   Enterobacteria, 99 The *Neisseria*-like bacilli: *Moraxella*,
   Mima, 110 Pseudomonads and alcaligenes, 121 *Ps. aeruginosa*, 124 *Alcaligenes faecalis*, 131 Vibrios, 132 Hemophili, 133 References, 135

5 BACTEROIDES, FUSOBACTERIUM, AND THE MOTILE ANAEROBES 144
   Historical, 145 Bacteroides, 148 Fusobacteria, 166 Anaerobic spirilla and vibrios, 173 References, 179

6 THE INDIGENOUS SPIROCHETES 186
   References, 216

7 INDIGENOUS FUNGI. 222
   Fungi in general, 222 *Pityrosporum*, 225 *Torulopsis*, 227
   Dermatophytes, 228 The genus *Candida*, 230 Pathogenic
   Candida, especially *C. albicans*, 239 References, 250

8 THE INDIGENOUS PROTOZOA 257

Indigenous species, 258   Incidence of the protozoa in man, 264   Summary: protozoa as indigenous to man, 277   Growth of indigenous protozoa, 278   Infectivity and pathogenicity, 281   *Trichomonas vaginalis,* 285   Serology, 290   References, 291

9 PLEUROPNEUMONIA-LIKE ORGANISMS, SPHEROPLASTS, AND PROTOPLASTS 297

References, 306

10 DISTRIBUTION AND DEVELOPMENT OF THE MICROBIOTA OF MAN 310

The inhabited areas, 310   Development of the indigenous biota, 312   Concentrations of the total bacterial flora in different areas, 313   Biotas of the different areas, 316   The indigenous biota in general, 342   References, 343

11 NONPATHOGENIC ACTIVITIES OF THE NORMAL FLORA . . 351

The indigenous biota in host nutrition, 353   Host-biota interactions not leading to disease, 355   Effects of the indigenous biota on man, 355   Effects of the host, particularly man, on the indigenous biota, 357   Antibody formation against indigenous microorganisms, 360   Interactions of indigenous microorganisms, 369   Cooperative interactions, 370   Competitive interactions, 371   References, 384

AUTHOR INDEX 393

SUBJECT INDEX 423

CHAPTER I

INTRODUCTION: CERTAIN GENERAL PRINCIPLES

The interaction of man with his microbe-laden environment leads to the establishment in certain regions of the human body of a characteristic group of microorganisms. This book is concerned with the study of these indigenous or autochthonous microbes—the so-called "normal flora" (and fauna) of man, and with the beginning of an inquiry into their significance.

Contamination and Its Consequences. During the process of birth and continuously thereafter through life, man is exposed to environmental contamination. In the uterus the fetus is bacteriologically sterile; but microorganisms impinge upon it from the birth canal itself, and then from attendants via direct and more or less remote indirect contact, and from multifarious nonhuman sources. The process of contamination (the word is not intended to be invidious) is greatly abetted by the infant's use of his mouth as a primary organ for testing the physical and chemical properties of the outside world.

Contamination leads to several consequences. Many—probably the great majority—of the microbic species that find their way to human body surfaces linger only briefly, either because they fail to find appropriate living conditions, especially food (as would be true, for instance, of autotrophic bacteria); or because they are removed or destroyed by mechanical, biochemical, or immunologic activities of the host or by antagonistic behavior of other microorganisms already present. Other microbic species, finding appropriate food and living conditions and being equipped to withstand, repel, or evade the more inhospitable phenomena of the terrain, survive for longer periods in one or more host locations, some perhaps permanently. A few of these surviving species, by producing soluble noxious products of their metabolism as they proliferate in an isolated locus, or by penetrating host tissues and provoking damage, elicit in the previously unharmed host the appreciable reaction characterized as disease. Disease is an unbalanced state that tends to be resolved, whether in elimination of the microbe or death of the host or attainment of balance, which in turn may be more or less precarious or stable, continuous or interrupted.

Sometimes a microbic species that is characteristically disease-provoking achieves balance at the outset, of varying duration and not necessarily culminating in disease.

These phenomena are, of course, part of the traditional subject matter of pathogenic bacteriology, from latency in syphilis or tuberculosis to the convalescent or recovered carrier state in typhoid fever or diphtheria to the healthy carrier of the meningococcus or the staphylococcus. The staphylococcus is a bridge to another category, the one with which this book is to deal. Overtly pathogenic staphylococci, identified with those of serious disease by refined as well as grosser criteria, have come to achieve the balance under discussion with so large a proportion of the human population that we can exclude them only arbitrarily from the normal flora. By including them we may serve several useful purposes, one of which is to impose caution on the use of the word "normal." In this context the term is appropriate only in the statistical sense.

The Indigenous Biota. In addition, then, to environmental transients and overt pathogens there is a category of microbes, blending without distinct boundaries with both of the other groups, even though the category itself in its middle or most typical region is as different from the others as green is from yellow and blue. These microbes make up the indigenous biota. Impinging upon man from the human and nonhuman environment, they are able to survive and multiply and to persist for appreciable periods in one or more locations—on or in skin, or on or in a mucous surface not far from an external orifice—without eliciting a violent reaction in the otherwise healthy host. The balance sometimes achieved precariously by more overt pathogens is reached by these microbes as a statistically normal state. It may be assumed that such a balance is never static or merely passively neutral, but rather that it is the resultant of an active metabolic interchange between microbial population and host cells or cell products. The resultant is likely to be inappreciable to the host because its effects are below a threshold of awareness or because positive and negative effects seem to cancel out, or only because the host is habituated to the effect and would recognize it only if it were to disappear or to change. Such a change may continue to be inappreciable—as when a microbic population is displaced by the host or replaced by another microbe—or it may emerge as disease, in consequence mainly of host alterations stimulated by something other than the microbic population in question. Disease of this sort differs from that in which more overt pathogens participate, but only by virtue of a different position in a continuous gradient.

The Indigenous Biota as a Unit. The survey of microbic species of the indigenous biota in succeeding chapters reveals a characteristic but highly variable collection of microbes which differ from one locus to another, although such differences seem to be more quantitative than has perhaps been thought. The number of species and the total numbers of microorganisms vary characteristically in the different areas, but, with some exceptions, species found in one locus are likely also to be found in others. Hence we may speak, broadly but not vaguely, of the indigenous biota of man as collectively a unit. And it may be profitable to look within such a unit for unifying features of the biota.

Commensals, Pathogens, Saprophytes. Infection. Certain members of the biota are not found elsewhere in nature, except perhaps in comparable locations in animals other than man. These microbes—which include such familiar bacterial species as viridans streptococci, nonpathogenic neisseriae, *Lactobacillus acidophilus*, *Actinomyces israelii*, *Veillonella alcalescens*, bacteroides, and spirochetes, as well as certain fungi and protozoa—may be considered typically or obligately indigenous, and it will be useful to have a general name for them. They are commonly called "commensals" to distinguish them from "pathogens" and "saprophytes." All three words are used ambiguously, and increasing knowledge may indicate a need to replace or modify all of them. From our present standpoint the word commensal is objectionable because of its imprecise overtones, especially when it implies a mutually neutral or passive relationship between host and microbe which we assume does not exist. A good discussion of the semantics of this question in a related but not identical context will be found in a symposium on the general problem of *symbiosis* [Thornton (1952)] in which it appears that notions of mutual "benefit" and of "infection" are inextricably mingled. Thornton speaks of the classic symbiotic relationship of *Rhizobium* with legumes as infection in the general sense that "both partners must have their effects on the mutual relationship." In the "infected" but nevertheless "healthy and apparently active" root nodule, moreover, the bacteria are described as nonmultiplying and swollen "or otherwise deformed," while the plant cells are hypertrophied, cease to divide, and may show degenerated nuclei; yet these characteristics "are features of the symbiosis and correlated with the nitrogen fixation." This conception may be generalized in full accord with present-day usage (and so as to include viruses as infective agents) by defining "infection" as an interaction of a host organism with a smaller self-replicating agent such that both are modified in the process [Rosebury and Sonnenwirth (1958)].[1] Under this definition such circumstances as the occurrence in healthy human serum of antibodies to indigenous microbes (Chap. 11) place the relationship of these forms

[1] Ravin (1955) has pointed out that *fertilization* can be excluded only arbitrarily from the scope of infection thus defined.

to man well within the limits of the term infection. It appears, moreover, that the attributes of pathogenicity, commensalism, and saprophytism are not mutually exclusive, but may actually all be combined in a
single species (e.g., *Pseudomonas aeruginosa*).

Amphibiosis. It is suggested that the word commensal be discarded in
favor of a term without overtones of prejudice, borrowed from verte-
brate zoology, namely *amphibiont*, signifying a spectral position between symbiosis (or probiosis) and antibiosis (or pathogenicity) and
merging with both. Amphibiosis also blends in another dimension with
saprophytism, that is, with a capacity to multiply (in nature) apart
from a living host, for example in soil. The typical amphibiont, lying
close to the middle of the distribution, is obligately parasitic (non-
saprophytic) and not overtly, actively, or obligately pathogenic (but not
necessarily nonpathogenic). There seems no reason to exclude microbes
that might be actively symbiotic, if such were found.

Criteria of Autochthony. Microorganisms showing typically amphibiotic characteristics in relation to man fall unambiguously within the
scope of this book, but the absence of boundaries around this category
implies that we must also include in the indigenous biota microbes with
less typical or less unambiguous characteristics. What is to determine
whether they are to be included or excluded? How, in other words, shall
we decide whether or not a given microbic species is indigenous to man?
The decision must be made arbitrarily, but it ought not to be made
capriciously. Rules or criteria are needed. In situations apart from man
himself such rules have been clearly formulated and apparently agreed
upon. Thus, Winogradsky (1949) defined the autochthonous micro-
flora of soil to include only those species that persisted in fallow soil for
a period of years without exogenous organic matter—a rigid, basic
definition. Similarly, Gall and Huhtanen (1951) developed as criteria
for "true *rumen* bacteria" that they be (1) anaerobic; (2) found in a
concentration of 10^6 or more per gram of fresh rumen contents; (3)
isolated at least ten times from at least two animals; (4) isolated from
animals in at least two geographic locations; and (5) that they form end
products found in the rumen from substrates in the rumen. Here is a
strict operational formula consistent with the economic foundations of
rumen microbiology. Neither of these approaches could be applied without change to the microbiota of loci of sheep or cattle other than the
rumen, and similarly but even more emphatically the purposes of any
study of man permit no such rigidity or precision in the criteria we now
seek. Previous students of the normal flora of man seem to have been
content to accept the notion of "normality" or "abnormality" or—on
skin—of a "resident" or "transient" flora [e.g., Pillsbury and Rebell
(1952)] without defining these terms except vaguely or by implica-

tion. Connell and Skinner (1953) seem to have come closest to a definition in suggesting that the human skin is a habitat for certain yeasts: "Repeated isolation of certain species from the same source, especially when these species are rare or unknown elsewhere, suggests that this source may well be a true habitat for these species."

But this, after all, only approaches our criteria of amphibiosis. The amphibionts, as has already been noted, will give us no trouble. What we need are rules to determine how far inside the territories of overt pathogenicity and of saprophytism we may draw lines to demark our chosen field. Perhaps we can best do so, not judicially or restrictively— the chosen species do not by such choice become members of an exclusive club (or a ghetto!)—but rather as a matter of convenience. We shall thus attempt to include, in addition to those species that are clearly amphibiotic in man, those that are (1) frequently encountered in one or more typical locations (but no precise limiting frequency need be set); (2) found at least as often in the absence of disease as in its presence; and (3) in practical need of treatment in this book because of inadequate treatment elsewhere. The last criterion stems from the general neglect that has been visited upon this field and is considered further in a later paragraph.

Excluded Forms. Viruses. Excluded, then, from systematic consideration in this book are overt pathogens adequately covered in standard texts of microbiology (with exceptions, notably staphylococci; see Chap. 2); saprophytes found only occasionally in an indigenous locus (as any microbe may be found by chance in a given sample); and rickettsiae and viruses. Our attention is limited to bacteria, fungi, and protozoa, with brief consideration of pleuropneumonia-like and related forms. Rickettsiae are not known to occur amphibiotically in man as they do in arthropods. Viruses do occur under seemingly analogous conditions, as is suggested by expressions such as "enteric viral flora of . . . normal children" [Gelfand, Fox, and LeBlanc (1957)] or "the human cell itself must be regarded as having a considerable viral flora" [Huebner (1957); see also Moscovici and Maisel (1961)]. It is perhaps puristic to suggest that the word "flora" is misapplied in this usage. What is more significant is the wealth of accumulating data leading to a crystallization of opinion around the concept of a virus put forward, for example, by Lwoff (1957) and Lwoff, Anderson and Jacob (1959); see also Dmochowski (1959).

In the frame of reference of this book the essential result of this growing consensus is that viruses, despite their obvious relationship with the biological world, can be sharply and clearly distinguished from *cells* (including microorganisms) of which they can constitute no more than parts, whether normal or pathologic. It seems immaterial in this connection that the parts they constitute may profoundly influence the basic nature and the life or death of the cell. The point seems to be that viruses are not cells. Hence, without any prejudice to the notion that there may well be viruses "normal" to cells and hence to the hosts of which those cells make part, such a subject is intrinsically different from that of normal microorganisms. It is tempting to pursue the question further, for it is extremely interesting in its own right. But it is irrelevant.

Orientation. The history of studies of indigenous microbiology, or more narrowly of the normal bacterial flora of man, has common roots with the parent field in the writings of Leeuwenhoek [Dobell (1932); Schierbeek (1959)] and in many scattered observations during the bacteriologic era. An outstanding early pioneer was W. D. Miller (1889, 1890). It is of interest that Bulloch (1938), in his otherwise detailed history of bacteriology, makes no mention of the normal flora as such. The emerging germ theory, now recognizably simplistic, was explosively productive in the late nineteenth century. It was perhaps inevitable that as attention was focused on the active disease-producing microbes, the other microbes that accompanied and often outnumbered the pathogens (the nonconformists to Koch's postulates, especially to his third) should have been neglected. At that time, to be sure, a phenomenon such as the ability of the mouse peritoneum to filter a pneumococcus out of saliva and present it to the observer in a matter of hours in "pure culture" in the heart blood must have seemed ample justification for regarding the rest of the wealth in the inoculum as trash. But times have changed considerably. The need for the old emphasis on overtly pathogenic microbes has decreased, and the original germ theory has needed amendment. The focus of microbiology has shifted, but to other areas (whose significance is not to be denied); and much of the neglect that came to be visited long ago on the normal flora has never been made good.

It is part of the purpose of this book to suggest that it ought to be. There is enough evidence of participation of amphibionts in disease, despite some difficulties with the third postulate, to warrant reconsideration of the whole question of their pathogenicity in all its subtlety. There are as well enough indications that the activities of the normal flora may be favorable to man rather than the reverse so as, all in all, to reward search in this area. The present book treats this question of favorable activities (Chap. 11), but the question of disease in which the normal flora participates, except for mention of pathogenic activities under the head of separate microbic species, is deferred for extended treatment in a separate volume.

Approach to a Theory of the Indigenous Biota. Evidence of neglect in the development of our knowledge of the indigenous microorganisms is pointed out in the following pages. It will be apparent that the need is not merely or necessarily *more* research. What seems to be lacking is coordination. Individual aspects of the larger subject are explored, often enthusiastically and effectively, but too often as well in a kind of isolation, a lack of awareness of the kinship of the findings to other closely or more distantly related observations. What is needed is a general theory of the indigenous microbiota. The data now at hand and the level of their organization achieved in this book are insufficient to formulate such a theory but may serve as a step in that direction.

Previous Studies. Unity and Diversity. Previous attempts to deal with the whole subject of the normal flora of man [other than those of Rosebury (1948, 1952); and Rosebury and Sonnenwirth (1958)] are represented in the German *Handbuch* [Küster (1913, 1929); Nissle (1929)], in the British *System* [Cruickshank and Cruickshank (1931)], and in the successive editions of Topley and Wilson [Wilson and Miles (1955)]. They have all dealt with the subject piecemeal, as though the various inhabited loci in man are ecologically different continents. Indeed, the use of habitat in terms of indigenous locus as a taxonomic criterion (e.g., see Chap. 6) is evidently a corollary of the tacit assumption that the biota of each locus is necessarily distinctive. That differences exist is, of course, plain; but similarities that may also be present have been largely overlooked. Exclusive focus on separate areas by the medical specialties (as of dentistry on the mouth) has abetted this tendency but cannot be held responsible for it, since the basic problem is microbiologic rather than specifically medical or dental. It seems conceivable that deep-seated inhibitions—Victorian vestiges not entirely abolished by the efforts of Freud and his followers—may have played a hidden role in shaping the manner in which this subject has come to be handled. If this be true, perhaps the effort made in this book to deal with the subject as a unit, not overlooking differences but searching for similarities, on the premise that we are dealing with a single aspect of human biology, will serve another end besides the more obvious ones— as a contribution, however small, to human emancipation.

References

Bulloch, W., 1938, *The History of Bacteriology*, Oxford University Press, New York.

Connell, G. H., and Skinner, C. E., 1953, *J. Bacteriol.*, **66**:627.

Cruickshank, J., and Cruickshank, R., 1931, *A System of Bacteriology in Relation to Medicine (London)*, **8**:334.

Dmochowski, L., 1959, *Bacteriol. Revs.*, **23**:18.
Dobell, C., 1932, *Antony van Leeuwenhoek and His "Little Animals,"* Harcourt, Brace and Company, Inc., New York, p. 241 (reprinted 1960, Dover Publications, New York).
Gall, L. S., and Huhtanen, C. N., 1951, *J. Dairy Sci.*, **34**:353.
Gelfand, H. M., Fox, J. P., and LeBlanc, D. R., 1957, *Am. J. Trop. Med. Hyg.*, **6**:521.
Huebner, R. J., 1957, *Public Health Repts.*, **72**:377.
Küster, E., 1913, in Kolle, W., and Wassermann, A. von, *Handbuch der pathogenen Mikroorganismen*, Gustav Fischer, Jena, **6**:435, 450, 458, 468.
———, 1929, in Kolle, W., Kraus, R., and Uhlenhuth, P., *ibid.*, **6**:355.
Lwoff, A., 1957, *J. Gen. Microbiol.*, **17**:239.
———, Anderson, T. F., and Jacob, F., 1959, *Ann. Inst. Pasteur*, **97**:281.
Miller, W. D., 1889, *Die Mikroorganismen der Mundhöhle*, George Thieme, Leipzig.
———, 1890, *The Micro-Organisms of the Human Mouth*, S. S. White, Philadelphia.
Moscovici, C., and Maisel, J., 1961, *Am. J. Dis. Child.*, **101**:771.
Nissle, A., 1929, in Kolle, W., Kraus, R., and Uhlenhuth, P., *op. cit.*, **6**:391, 415.
Pillsbury, D. M., and Rebell, G., 1952, *J. Invest. Dermatol.*, **18**:173.
Ravin, A. W., 1955, *Am. Scientist*, **43**:468.
Rosebury, T., 1948, in Dubos, R. J., *Bacterial and Mycotic Infections of Man*, 1st ed., J. B. Lippincott Company, Philadelphia, p. 628.
———, 1952, *ibid.*, 2d ed., p. 690.
———, and Sonnenwirth, A. C., 1958, *ibid.*, 3d ed., p. 626.
Schierbeek, A., 1959, *Measuring the Invisible World. The Life and Work of Antoni van Leeuwenhoek FRS*, Abelard-Schuman, Inc., New York, p. 72.
Thornton, H. G., et al., 1952, *Proc. Roy. Soc. (London)*, B, **139**:170.
Wilson, G. S., and Miles, A. A., 1955, *Topley and Wilson's Principles of Bacteriology and Immunity*, 4th ed., The Williams & Wilkins Company, Baltimore, **2**:2249.
Winogradsky, S., 1949, *Microbiologie du sol. Problèmes et méthodes. Cinquant ans de recherches. Oeuvres complètes*, Masson et Cie, Paris, p. 418.

CHAPTER 2

THE INDIGENOUS COCCI

Staphylococci

Current practice tends to classify staphylococci of medical interest into 2 groups mainly on the basis of *coagulase* production, the producing group being called, variously, "coagulase-positive" or "pathogenic" staphylococci, *Staphylococcus aureus* or *Staph. pyogenes;* and the negative group being designated by the converse descriptions or as *Staph. albus* and other species names. The pathogenic group is subject to further refinements of classification (including types based on lysis by a range of bacteriophages, on serologic methods, and in part on sensitivity to antibiotic drugs, the "antibiogram"). We are interested in both groups as members of the normal flora. The pathogenic group is obviously aberrant in this position. Its propensities as a disease-producer, including a common capacity for eliciting generalized and fatal illness, make it as atypical as any species we shall consider. Moreover, basic information on it is available in standard texts, and need not be repeated here in detail. The group is, however, widely distributed in the normal human population all over the world; there is some evidence that it often sets up long-term if not permanent residence in man without producing disease. Its pathogenesis seems to be dependent upon host components in a manner that differs from the comparable activities of more obligate amphibionts perhaps only in degree. Two ancillary reasons may be given for including these organisms in this book; that their epidemiology, far better understood than that of most true amphibionts, may help to elucidate aspects of the development and maintenance of the normal flora generally; and that, since they constitute a problem of great current practical interest, the staphylococci have been generating a torrent of literature which it may be useful to review, albeit briefly and from a restricted viewpoint. The last comprehensive review known to the writer is that of Elek (1959), an immensely valuable work in which, however, there are few references more recent than 1956.

The Pathogenic Staphylococci

The pathogenic staphylococci, then, are distinguished by the production of toxic or aggressive substances lacking among the more clearly amphibiotic varieties of staphylococci. The pathogens are, in fact, identified by the correlation of pathogenicity particularly with two bacterial products: (1) the antigenic substance, coagulase, which, when activated by a prothrombin-like agent in human or rabbit plasma, brings about clotting, and (2) a soluble antigenic toxin (α-toxin or α-hemolysin) which hemolyzes rabbit or sheep erythrocytes, is lethal for rabbits, and is skin-necrotizing. Such strains are usually distinguished as well by the formation of acid from mannite. A battery of other substances is also produced which, however, are less well correlated with pathogenicity; a golden-yellow pigment responsible for the designation *Staphylococcus aureus;* and, in roughly decreasing order of apparent pathogenic significance, a fibrinolysin (staphylokinase), a leukocidin (possibly the same as α-toxin), an enterotoxin (in food-poisoning strains), hemotoxins other than α, and a hyaluronidase, among other distinctive enzymes [e.g., urease, Fusillo and Jaffurs (1955)]. Among other procedures put forward as helping to distinguish pathogenic from nonpathogenic staphylococci are the egg-yolk opacity test of Gillespie and Adler (1952); see also Faber et al. (1960); the ammonium molybdate test of Myers (1959); resistance to mercuric chloride [Moore (1960)]; and growth on EMB agar [Menolasino, Grieves, and Payne (1960)]. Schaub and Merritt (1960) have devised a single broth medium permitting both coagulase and mannite tests. Finegold and Sweeney (1961) have described a selective plating medium based on polymyxin. Innes (1960) has presented a tellurite-egg medium said to be useful for isolation of coagulase-positive staphylococci present in low concentrations in the source, and Runnels and Wilson (1960) have adapted the replica plating technique of Lederberg and Lederberg (1952) to facilitate a range of tests on all staphylococcus colonies on an initial plate [see also Angyal (1961a)].

Phage Typing. The finer classification of coagulase-positive staphylococci is based principally on patterns of lysis by a standard battery of bacteriophages spotted on an agar plate seeded with the test culture. Details have been given by Williams and Rippon (1952), Anderson and Williams (1956), Blair and Carr (1960b), and Blair and Williams (1961). An international committee has recommended that the following basic phages be the minimum set used for routine typing [Blair and Williams (1961)]:

Group I: 29, 52, 52A, 79, 80
Group II: 3A, 3B, 3C, 55, 71

Group III: 6, 7, 42E, 47, 53, 54, 73, 75, 77
Group IV: 42D
Miscellaneous: 81, 187

Groups I, II, and III were established as being roughly correlated with the correspondingly numbered groups of Cowan (1939) based on slide agglutination with absorbed serums. A phage type 81, identified by Bynoe, Elder, and Comtois (1956), has been found associated with members of group I (52, 52A, and 80); and the designation 80/81 has come to be applied to an epidemiologically important group of staphylococci lysed by either phage 80 or 81 (or both), with or without lysis as well by 52, 52A, or both. Wallmark and Finland (1961b) included types 81 and KS6 in group I. They found the phage type 80/81/KS6 to be the most frequent at Boston City Hospital since 1955. That phage pattern 80/81/52/52A is not new has been shown by Rountree (1959) who identified the staphylococcus responsible for the Australian Bundaberg disaster in 1928 as being lysed by all 4 of these phages; and Blair and Carr (1960a) have identified members of the 80/81 group in 53 of 194 typable strains of staphylococci isolated between 1927 and 1947. That changes of phage patterns may occur, however, has been shown especially in the 80/81 group by Asheshov and Rippon (1959), who found that lysogenization of a staphylococcus with a temperate phage (287) changed the lytic pattern from 80/81 to 52/52A/80. Similar results have been reported by Rountree (1959), Blair and Carr (1960), and Rosenblum and Jackson (1960). Comtois (1960) has also been able to induce changes in the pattern of lysis of staphylococci within this phage group, including phage 82 in the formula as well as the other four, by lysogenization with related phages [see also Hurst and Grossman (1960); Sakurai et al. (1961)].

Wallmark and Finland (1961a) have isolated 5 new phages, designated A to E, with which they were able to type 78 per cent of 158 otherwise nontypable staphylococci.

Serologic Typing. Cowan (1939) was able to classify 59 of 86 strains of *Staphylococcus pyogenes* into 3 groups by slide agglutination with either or both of 2 absorbed rabbit antiserums. The other strains showed irregular reactions. Christie and Keogh (1940) found that 62.3 per cent of 122 coagulase-positive staphylococci fell into Cowan's groups; they distinguished 6 additional types (4 through 9) among the remaining 46 strains. Oeding (1952) described 9 antigens in pathogenic staphylococci by cross-absorption of immune serums. This worker (1953) has shown that there is a general correspondence between the 3 principal phage types and Cowan's 3 serologic types. More recently, Oeding and Sompolinsky (1958) and others have found that the two methods, compared with each other and with patterns of antibiotic sensitivity, tend to give somewhat different information. Lachowicz (1959) reported that most of 249 strains of staphylococci fell into Oeding's first 4 types, of which the second and fourth were most common; type 2 strains tended to be sensitive to penicillin, the others resistant. In another study this worker [Lachowicz (1959b)] reported no correlation between typing by means of phages and by serologic means. Pereira (1961) has reported that additional antigens demonstrated by Cowan's method in freshly isolated strains of *Staph. aureus* may disappear during daily subculture, whereupon the antigens of old laboratory strains become demonstrable; phage patterns were not affected. Such difficulties were thought to have hindered application of serologic typing. Most epidemiologic studies have been based on bacteriophage typing, but antibiograms are commonly determined for clinical purposes, and the data, as will be seen, are also epidemiologically significant. The feasibility of serologic typing with fluorescent antibody has been suggested by Cohen and Oeding (1961).

Incidence in General. The high incidence of coagulase-positive staphylococci on healthy human body surfaces is the principal reason for including them in this book. Their common presence, especially on skin and in the nasal passages, preceded the antibiotic era [see Gillespie, Devenish, and Cowan (1939); Miles, Williams, and Clayton-Cooper (1940); Rebell (1947); and for other references, Gould and McKillop (1954)]. The following data are representative. Laurell and Wallmark (1953) found them in the nose and throat in a children's hospital in Stockholm in 87.9 per cent of 874 patients and in 92.2 per cent of 166 members of the hospital staff. Gould and McKillop (1954) gave the nasal carrier rate as averaged from an extensive literature between 1937 and 1951 as about 85 per cent for infants, 57 per cent for children, 45 per cent for adolescents and young adults, 50 per cent for adults, and 65 per cent for hospital staffs. In their own studies these workers observed that 39 per cent of more than 500 medical students at Edinburgh University were persistent or intermittent carriers, while another 42 per cent were occasional carriers. In Chicago 76 per cent of 161 hospital ward personnel were reported by Lepper, Jackson, and Dowling (1955) to have these microbes in their noses at least once when studied monthly for 6 to 12 months, while Hinton and Orr (1957), in Kingston, Ontario, noted that 66 per cent of nasal carriers among hospital personnel had staphylococci in large numbers as compared with 38 per cent of Queens University students.

Similar findings have been reported by Vogelsang and Haaland (1959) in Norway, and from such widely scattered countries as Mexico [Guaolalupe Mayer Tanguma (1959)]; Romania [Nestoresco, Popovici, and Alexenco (1960)]; Israel [Rozansky et al. (1960)]; and China [Cheng and Liu (1959)]. Millian et al. (1960) found, in a study of 577 members of the general population of Ohio State University and a nearby air base, that the nasal carrier rate of coagulase-positive staphylococci was, for women and men, respectively, in whites, 37 and 38 per cent, and in Negroes, 20 and 10 per cent—a difference between the two groups that seemed statistically significant.

Antibiotic Resistance and Hospital Contact. That the carrier rate of coagulase-positive staphylococci tends to be higher in hospitals than elsewhere, as indicated in the preceding paragraphs, has been made abundantly clear by more recent data, which indicate as well that "hospital strains" are much more often resistant to penicillin and other antibiotics than "street strains." As early as 1949 Forbes found that 68.4 per cent of strains of staphylococci from hospital inpatients were penicillin-resistant, as compared with 12.5 per cent of strains from outpatients. Forbes attributed the increased frequency in the hospital group to selection resulting from the widespread use of penicillin.

Other early literature has been reviewed by Lepper et al. (1953), who showed that the nasopharyngeal carrier rate of penicillin-resistant staphylococci, apparently derived from hospital personnel, increased in patients during their stay in a hospital. Hinton and Orr (1957) reported that the proportion of antibiotic-resistant staphylococci recovered from various groups or sources increased in the order, university students, 8.6 (per cent); hospital outpatients, 28.9; hospital dust, 58.9; hospital inpatients, 75.4; and hospital staff, 80 6. Vogelsang and Haaland (1959) found that members of clinical hospital staffs harbored antibiotic-resistant staphylococci more often than those in nonclinical departments. Buhr and Scott (1959) reported that whereas no penicillin-resistant staphylococci were found among 82 strains isolated from hand infections in Oxford in 1952, 81 of 267, or 30 per cent, of the strains recovered in the same unit in 1957 were penicillin-resistant. Resistant organisms were more common in hand infections of nurses than in those of the general population. Of 602 patients in a men's surgical ward studied by Williams et al. (1959), 13 per cent carried penicillin-resistant *Staph. aureus* on admission, but 52 per cent of a small group were found to harbor such strains after 8 weeks in the ward. Noncarriers tended to acquire resistant strains more readily than those initially carrying penicillin-sensitive strains. Of patients treated with antibiotics, 64 of 165 tested acquired penicillin-resistant strains in their noses, while 39 acquired tetracycline-resistant strains. Hinton, Taggart, and Orr (1960) presented data pointing to a direct relationship between duration of stay in a hospital and acquisition of staphylococci in the stool, an appreciable proportion of the strains being penicillin-resistant. Winblad (1960) reported that the incidence of penicillin resistance of hospital strains of staphylococci in Malmo, Sweden, increased from 28.6 per cent in 1951–1952 to 75.8 per cent in 1958; corresponding percentages for streptomycin resistance were 8.5 and 48.4, and for sulfonamide resistance 28.8 and 41.

Even more striking findings have been reported by several workers for carrier rates of infants born in hospital nurseries. Hurst (1957a) reported that almost all such babies carried coagulase-positive penicillin-resistant staphylococci in their throats; although 72 per cent of babies born at home were also found to become carriers, only 18 per cent had penicillin-resistant organisms. The same worker [Hurst (1957b)] found that of 106 newborn babies in a hospital, 99 per cent carried coagulase-positive staphylococci when they left the hospital; 97 per cent of 34 cultures were penicillin-resistant. Such staphylococci were considered to become components of the normal flora, remaining more persistently in the throat than in the nose. Plueckhahn and Banks (1958) recovered coagulase-positive staphylococci from 96 per cent of infants aged more than 2 days in a maternity hospital in Australia. Sanchez-Torres et al. (1959) reported a carrier rate of 90 per cent in the noses and throats of babies in a maternity hospital in Mexico, as compared with 50 per cent among mothers. Hinton, Taggart, and Orr (1960) found that 81.5 per cent of newborn infants acquired coagulase-positive staphylococci in the stool after 4 days in the hospital, with the following percentages of strains resistant to antibiotics: penicillin, 60; streptomycin, 56.9; chloramphenicol, 24.6; tetracycline, 20; and erythromycin, 15.4. Manfield, Shooter, and Lidwell (1960) reported that in the absence of special measures all newborn babies in the nursery of a London hospital carried *Staph. aureus* in the nose by the twelfth day of life.

While coagulase-positive staphylococci are most often looked for in throat and nose and on skin, they have also been recovered in appreciable incidence from saliva [Taplin and Goldsworthy (1958, 1959)]; from feces [Hancock, Dulaney, and Caldwell (1959); Hinton, Taggart, and Orr (1960); see also Ridley (1959)]; in human milk [Rantasalo (1959)]; and in the vagina during pregnancy [Bret et al. (1959); see also Lang, Israel, and Fritz (1958)]. It may be noted that the problem of antibiotic-resistant staphylococci has also been met with among veterinarians and their animal charges [e.g., Pagano et al. (1960); Smith and Crabb (1960)]; and contact with man has been suggested as a basis of staphylococcal infection in wild jackrabbits [Osebold and Gray (1960)]. Live and Nichols (1961) found that the nasal carrier rate of antibiotic-resistant staphylococci of phage types 80/81 and 52/52A increased markedly in hospitalized dogs.

Staphylococci and Nosocomial Disease. The staphylococcus problem today is, of course, essentially one of disease acquired in hospitals. While the details of this question are beyond the province of this book, brief treatment is necessary because of its intimate bearing on other aspects of the subject. The widespread prevalence of coagulase-positive staphylococci, particularly in hospitals, is important because in a minority of instances contact with the organism leads to disease which is frequently serious, and in a small but alarming proportion of instances, fatal. The high frequency of antibiotic resistance among the offending staphylococci aggravates the problem.

The ratio of frequencies of disease to infection (symptomatic illness to carrier state) is low and clearly depends in considerable part on host susceptibility. Staphylococcal disease is most commonly superimposed upon traumatic injury (e.g., surgery) or tissue damage induced in other ways, or it occurs in the very young and sometimes in the very old. Among the clinical problems are a severe cholera-like enteritis or enterocolitis, usually postsurgical and associated directly with antibiotic treatment [see Sanders and Kinnaird (1955); Prohaska, Long, and Nelson (1956); Turnbull (1957); Prohaska (1959); Hinton, Taggart, and Orr (1960)]; impetigo in both adults and children [Parker, Tomlinson, and Williams (1955); Barrow (1955)]; pneumonia in infancy and childhood [Harley (1957)]; and parotitis principally in the aged [Petersdorf, Forsyth, and Bernanke (1958)]. Most common have been postsurgical wound infections [e.g., Williams et al. (1959)], many of which seem to have been associated with unremoved suture. Also significant are bacteremia [Hassal and Rountree (1959); Holloway and Scott (1959); Waisbren and Abboud (1960); Shooter et al. (1960); Hay (1960); Faber et al. (1960)]; breast abscesses perhaps often transmitted by the nurseling [Monro and Markham (1958); Soltau and Hatcher (1960)]; infection of burns [Haynes, Jones, and Gibson (1959–60); Lowbury (1960)]; and, of course, furunculosis, frequently indolent or recurrent over periods of years [e.g., Roodyn (1960a,b)].

Data on the incidence of nosocomial staphylococcal disease include the following. Williams et al. (1959) reported postoperative staphylococcus sepsis in 2 per cent of 342 cases who had never been nasal carriers and in 7.1 per cent of 380 who had been carriers at some time. In about half of these the incriminated strain had the same phage type as that found in the nose. Of 1,319 male surgical patients, 4.5 per cent developed disease elsewhere than in the wound. These workers suggested that the incidence of such disease might be reduced if acquisition of staphylococci in the nose could be prevented. Koch et al. (1959), who cited Jeffrey and Sklaroff (1958) as having reported a staphylococcal wound infection rate of 9 per cent, themselves reported a rate of 4 per cent, including 4 deaths among 51 cases. Thirty-eight of these patients had had major surgery with operations lasting 2 to 5 hours, all were men, 70 per cent were over 50, and 36 had received antibiotics prophylactically, therapeutically, or both. Weinstein (1959) reported the following data for a tuberculosis hospital: 43 per cent of elective surgical patients who had positive nose cultures developed complications of surgery, as compared with 26 per cent of those with negative nose cultures. The over-all surgical failure rate was 23.3 per cent in the carrier group and 7.3 per cent in those that were not carriers. The data of Weinstein (1959) and Williams et al. (1959) raise the question of whether the disease resulted from autoinfection or special patient susceptibility, which might have led both to the carrier state and to disease.

Farrer et al. (1959) studied an outbreak of staphylococcal disease in newborn infants and mothers that began in an 84-bed community general hospital in Lakewood, New Jersey. Most of the lesions were cutaneous. During a 16-month period the infection rate was 25.6 per cent among the newborn and 3.7 per cent among the mothers; 37.1 per cent of deliveries were associated with infection during the interval, only 6.8 per cent at other times. Most of the disease developed after discharge from the hospital—65.8 per cent among the infants and 93.3 per cent among the mothers.

A British commission [Anonymous (1960)] reported on 3,276 surgical operations in 21 hospitals in England and Wales. Of 2,860 studied bacteriologically during convalescence, 9.7 per cent had sepsis yielding pathogenic bacteria in culture. The rate varied in different hospitals from 4.7 to 21.8 per cent, highest after clean operations for cholecystectomy (21 per cent), lowest in orthopedic cases (2 per cent). The rate increased with increasing age, length of hospital stay, length of incision, and duration of operation and showed an association with the use of a drainage tube. While *Staph. aureus* was the commonest causative agent, coliform bacteria were also common. Nasal carriers of staphylococci had only a slightly higher rate of postoperative disease than noncarriers (8.9 compared with 7.1 per cent), but nasal carriers of a few phage types had a considerably higher sepsis rate.

Staphylococcal bacteremia (septicemia and pyemia) was reported by Hay (1960) in New Zealand to have increased during 1957 and 1958. Both incidence and mortality were highest at the extremes of life. Penicillin-resistant staphylococci were responsible for 51 of 71 (72 per cent) of the cases; 29 of these (57 per cent) were fatal. Hospital infection accounted for 27 of the cases. Faber et al. (1960) reported from Copenhagen that 94 of a group of 201 epidemiologically unrelated cases of staphylococcal bacteremia had been contracted in hospital. Of these 94 cases, 47 (50 per cent) originated from surgical procedures; 29 of the 47 (62 per cent) died; 31 of the 94 originated from cutaneous boils; of these 13, or 42 per cent, were fatal. In others the origin was various or unknown; the over-all mortality was 55 per cent.

Pathogenicity. The staphylococcus was one of the first pathogenic bacteria to be recognized. The effort expended through the years toward understanding the manner in which it produces disease has hardly been exceeded by that given to any other microbe, yet the secret of its pathogenicity (assuming, as we probably ought not to do, that there is a single one) remains hidden. It is neither necessary nor appropriate that we stop to consider the wealth of detail that makes up this subject, for background material is available in standard texts [for additional details see Rogers (1956) and Elek (1959)]. Our purpose will be served if we limit our attention principally to the more recent data on experimental disease in animals and man. It may be worth noting beforehand, however, that the staphylococcus is one of the most complex of pathogenic bacteria in terms of factors it produces which are associated with virulence in other microbic species but neither individually nor collectively account adequately for the virulence of this one: a battery of toxins and toxic enzymes, with antigens among these and beyond them, and capsules. Of these factors coagulase and α-toxin seem most important, with enterotoxin participating in gastrointestinal disease in those strains that form it.

An additional element in the complex of staphylococcal pathogenicity is the evidently great significance of *host factors*. These are clearly implied by the clinical features of staphylococcal disease and are unmistakable in experimental findings.

Experimental staphylococcal disease in man seems to have required either parenteral inoculation of relatively large doses of organisms or tissue damage at the inoculated site. This pattern may be compared with that of more typical amphibionts such as *Pseudomonas aeruginosa* (Chap. 4) or *Candida albicans* (Chap. 7). In 1885 Garré produced multiple pustules and a carbuncle in the skin of his forearm after rubbing an entire slant culture of staphylococci into the site. As Foster and Hutt (1960) have pointed out, this dramatic observation tended to discourage the subsequent use of human subjects in experiments with staphylococci. With the advent of antibiotic therapy, Elek (1956) and Elek and Conen (1957) restudied the question with 26 human volunteer subjects. Intradermal injections failed to lead to suppuration with doses of less than 10^6 organisms in a volume of 0.1 ml. The average pus-forming dose by this means was 2 to 8×10^6 staphylococci. Smaller doses were not effective by the subcutaneous route or when inoculated into skin cut through its full thickness; nor was infectivity enhanced by addition of α-toxin, mucin or human plasma. Strains from lesions in man or from healthy carriers were not clearly different in virulence. On the other hand, inoculation by inserting a piece of silk suture into the skin, tying it and leaving it in place, led to suppuration with an estimated dose of as little as 100 staphylococci, and to severe suppuration with 3×10^4 organisms. No lesion developed when a suture charged with the latter dosage was inserted and pulled through, although four-fifths of the inoculum was estimated to have been left in situ by this means. Foster and Hutt (1960) have extended these experiments. When pathogenic staphylococci were inoculated by means of a platinum loop on areas of forearm skin that had been scarified with a small scalpel without inducing bleeding, and the inoculum covered under a sealed cover slip, as few as 15 organisms yielded a lesion in which after 24 hours the bacterial count became similar to those inoculated with larger doses.[1] Among 5 strains of *Staph. aureus* tested—a phage type 52/80, 3 others from carriers, and a phage group II strain from a lesion—no evidence of differences in virulence could be obtained. These experiments had to be terminated because of the development of pustules and furuncles in two of the three subjects in sites other than those inoculated.

Certain experiments in animals seem to support and amplify the suggestions implied in the preceding paragraph. In the mouse, the observation has been made in recent years that striking differences in lethality are associated with route of inoculation. Dutton (1955) reported that the intraperitoneal route was more often fatal than the subcutaneous. Stefanesco et al. (1959) have observed that intrapleural inoculation of pathogenic strains may lead to symptoms in as short a time as 3 or 4 hours and to death in 7 or 8 hours, with a 94 per cent mortality in 24 hours. I. M. Smith and his coworkers (1960) have shown that injection of a uniform number of staphylococci by the intracerebral, intracardiac, intraperitoneal, intrahepatic, or intrasplenic routes is much more often fatal than injection by the intravenous route, which in turn was found to be more lethal than the intramuscular or subcutaneous routes. Except for the intracerebrally inoculated mice the dosage in the inoculum appears to have exceeded 10^7 organisms in all instances. Counts of mouse organs and whole mouse homogenates suggested that death resulted from an increase of the total bacterial population in the host above a critical threshold, no matter how or

---

[1] It is of passing interest and worthy of further study that by this procedure Foster and Hutt also recorded seropurulent lesions without erythema after inoculation of a coagulase-negative *Staph. albus*.

where such increase occurred. The more innocuous routes of infection became lethal when the inoculum concentration was sufficiently increased. With increasing dosage the time from injection to death could be decreased to an apparent limit of 60 minutes.

James and MacLeod (1961) have been able to produce local skin abscesses in young mice with small doses of staphylococci on suture materials, among which silicone-treated silk and Dacron were most effective. With these materials less than 10 organisms infected approximately half the mice inoculated; while 10^2 to 10^3 organisms were active in 97 to 100 per cent of animals. Steel wire was also effective but was found difficult to handle in mice. No difference in virulence could be detected between a phage type 52/80/81 and other types of coagulase-positive staphylococci; coagulase-negative strains were ineffectual. The potentiating effect of the suture materials seemed related to the severity of the polymorphonuclear inflammatory reaction induced by the sterile suture material in mouse skin, and by its capacity to pick up staphylococci from broth cultures. No evidence of increased resistance to homologous or heterologous strains was observed in recovered mice.

A group of studies that appeared in 1961 of staphylococcal disease in rabbits bears directly on questions of altered tissue susceptibility. Johnson, Cluff, and Goshi (1961) observed that increased infectivity of staphylococci in rabbit skin was associated with delayed hypersensitivity induced either by repeated skin infection or with washed heat-killed staphylococci. In further studies [Goshi et al. (1961)], it appeared that skin inflammation brought about by burning at 75 to 100°, by application of croton oil, by intradermal injection of group A streptococci, or by inducing Arthus or tuberculin sensitivity, led similarly to enhanced susceptibility to staphylococcal disease as compared with normal skin, provided that the infecting dose was given within 2 or 3 days after the injury. Necrosis of rabbit skin resulting from burns was further found by Goshi, Cluff, and Johnson (1961) to lead to a striking increase in local infectivity of coagulase-positive staphylococci. Such infection extended beyond the area of the burn but did not lead to bacteremia or metastatic abscesses, nor was the healthy skin of the burned animal altered in susceptibility when tested directly. Recovery in these animals was associated with a high titer of serum antibodies to α-toxin. Thirty to one hundred days after the initial burn infection the animal could no longer be infected in a necrotic burn, although infection of healthy skin occurred as it did in normal rabbits. Immunity to infection by pathogenic staphylococci in necrotic burns could also be induced by vaccination with potent α-toxoid and was found passively transferable with rabbit serum; it was neither strain-nor phage-type-specific. Conti, Cluff, and Scheder (1961) found that pyrogenic but nonlethal doses of purified lipopolysaccharide endotoxin from either *Shigella flexneri* or *Escherichia coli*, given to rabbits intracutaneously or intravenously, increased the infectivity of coagulase-positive staphylococci. The effect could be controlled by antibody to α-toxin. Further studies along similar lines will be awaited with great interest.

Epidemiology. The mode or modes of transmission of both infection and disease due to pathogenic staphylococci are, of course, of central importance for control of the nosocomial problem. They are of additional interest in the context of this book as they bear on questions of establishment and maintenance of the normal flora. The former stimulus has brought forward a large volume of research, facilitated by the availability of refined means for identification of strains, particularly by phage typing. The data reviewed above (see page 13) make it plain that antibiotic-resistant pathogenic staphylococci emerge in hospitals, presumably by mutation and selection under the influence of the drugs, and become indigenous to inhabitants of the hospital, especially to infants, and otherwise in general proportion to human contact with the sick and length of stay in the hospital. Up to 1957 Griffith et al. (1957–58) had found no evidence of a reservoir of antibiotic-resistant staphylococci in the general population [see also Oeding and Sompolinsky (1958) and Rozansky et al. (1960)]. Evidently the epidemiologic problem continues predominantly nosocomial with quantitatively unimportant exceptions [e.g., Roodyn (1960*a,b*)], implying that the organisms, which are obviously being seeded continually into the extra-hospital environment with all its world-wide variations, may find something particularly suitable for their propagation in hospitals which they do not often find elsewhere. An exception may be suggested for the notorious 80/81 hospital phage type of antibiotic-resistant staphylococcus, which has been clearly implicated in disease that originated in a hospital, but nevertheless continued to be transmitted and emerged clinically in the postnosocomial environment [e.g., Hurst and Grossman (1960)].

Our immediate concern, however, is with the persistence of indigenous status, or the carrier state. Gould and McKillop (1954) found in the study of Edinburgh students previously mentioned (see page 12) that repeated examinations over a period of 3 months to 1 year yielded the same phage type on each occasion from persistent or intermittent carriers; whereas, when a staphylococcus was recovered more than once from an occasional carrier it was of a different phage type each time. In other studies of adults, Lepper, Jackson, and Dowling (1955) found that although the tendency to carry a coagulase-positive staphylococcus in the nose seemed to be characteristic of certain persons and not of others, many persistent carriers tended to replace one phage type by another. A given phage type persisted more than 1 month in only one-third of the carriers; in these instances of strain persistence, the original strain tended to disappear more slowly thereafter, at the rate of 1 to 1.5 per cent per month. Hofstad and Vogelsang (1960) have reported that permanent carriers tend to retain strains having the same antibiogram as well as phage type. Hurst (1957*b*) studied the persistence of specific phage types of staphylococci in the nose and throat of 34 infants who had acquired the organism in a hospital nursery. Thirty-three of these carried at least one penicillin-resistant strain. After 6 months, 11 of 21 still under observation (53 per cent) were still carrying one or more of the original hospital strains; and of the babies still being studied after one year, at least 50 per cent continued to carry hospital strains. The organisms were found to persist for longer periods in the throat than in the nose. In a similar study of 26 babies born at home, Hurst (1957*a*) found that 72 per cent acquired *Staph. aureus* in the nose and throat during the first 2 weeks of life, but only 18 per cent had penicillin-resistant organisms. Phage typing indicated that the acquired strains persisted during an observation period of 12 to 25 weeks. The suggestion implied in these findings that strain persistence may be more common in infancy than in later life needs further exploration.

The more particular question of the origin and means of transmission of staphylococcus infections within hospitals is the heart of the great staphylococcus problem. Its voluminous literature cannot be surveyed adequately here but is worth touching upon for its bearing, immediate or remote, on our principal theme. It may be taken as axiomatic that no single source or type of source—infant or adult, patient or attendant, carrier or case—can be incriminated solely and, similarly, that no single route of transmission can be invariably blamed. It seems certain that the question is one of frequency. To consider route of transmission first: while several workers have presented evidence that airborne transmission via droplet-nuclei or dust may participate [e.g., Hurst et al. (1958); Wolf, Harris, and Dyer (1959); Hart (1960); Foster (1960); Anderson, Coulter, and Looke (1960)], others have either failed to find such evidence or have emphasized other routes [e.g., Koch et al. (1959); Williams, Talbot, and Maughan (1959); Manfield, Shooter, and Lidwell (1960); Wolinsky et al. (1960)]. It has been reported that desiccation simulating natural drying such as might occur during indirect transfer in air or dust leads to impairment of both viability and mouse virulence of pathogenic staphylococci [Maltman, Orr, and Hinton (1960); Hinton, Maltman, and

Orr (1960)], suggesting to these workers that more or less direct contact is probably required for effective transmission. Attempts to infect rabbits, mice, and guinea pigs with *Staph. aureus* aerosols at Fort Detrick [Berendt et al. (1961)] have yielded essentially negative results.

If the implications of these findings are accepted provisionally, they help to narrow the search for the most frequent sources of infection to those who (1) most frequently harbor the infecting agent and (2) come most frequently into a relationship with susceptibles such that more or less direct contact can occur. First to be mentioned under these criteria are newborn infants, who have indeed been found guilty of transmitting infection and disease to their mothers and to others [e.g., Hurst and Grossman (1958); Monro and Markham (1958); Stenderup et al. (1959)]. But infants are obviously not the principal source, or even a comparatively frequent source of nosocomial staphylococcal infection. They are to be looked upon objectively primarily as recipients and only secondarily as donors. Next in line, as the data reviewed previously indicate, are the clinical personnel of hospitals. Additional evidence pointing to the epidemiologic importance of this group is by no means complete. Sanchez-Torres et al. (1959) suggested that their findings confirmed those of earlier workers in pointing to a dissemination route in a maternity hospital starting in personnel, spreading to babies and mothers, and thence to household contacts. The observations of Wolinsky et al. (1960) also point to dissemination of staphylococci in nurseries as passing principally from personnel to infant via the hands of the carrier. Shooter, et al. (1960) found no apparent spread of staphylococci from patient to patient in a medical ward, but a dissenting opinion—that the primary source of nosocomial staphylococcal disease is the open lesion—is presented by Burke and Corrigan (1961). White (1961) found that the proportion of hospital-acquired staphylococcal infections due to type 80/81 was larger than and could not be explained by the prevalence of these organisms in the noses of hospitalized patients.

One of the more significantly successful attempts to control nosocomial staphylococcal disease appears to be that reported from Norway by Vogelsang and his coworkers [Vogelsang (1958, 1959); Vogelsang and Haaland (1959); Hofstad and Vogelsang (1960)], based upon decreased use of antibiotics (associated with a decreased prevalence of resistant strains), improved hygiene, and the granting of leaves to personnel found to be carriers [see also Gillespie et al. (1961)].

The occurrence in normal serum of antistaphylococcal antibodies or antibody-like phenomena is considered in Chap. 11.

The Nonpathogenic Staphylococci

The more distinctively amphibiotic staphylococci are typically coagulase-negative,[2] do not ferment mannite, are nonhemolytic, and form either white or, uncommonly, yellow or pink colonies. True amphibionts, as distinguished from saphrophytes, are likely to be unpigmented (white), and the commonly used designation *Staphylococcus albus* is not inappropriate for them. The substitution as a name for this group of *Staphylococcus epidermidis* [Breed, Murray, and Smith (1957)] is not in accord with usage (and is not forced by priority); it can only increase confusion. The suggestion advanced by British workers and reviewed by Elek (1959) that all aerobic Gram-positive spherical bacteria commonly included within the genera *Staphylococcus* or *Micrococcus* can be grouped into 5 species of *Staphylococcus* [*aureus, saprophyticus* (syn. *albus*), *lactis, roseus,* and *afermentans* (syn. *Micrococcus lysodeikticus*)] has much merit and is worthy of further consideration. The present writer objects to the designation *saprophyticus* as not truly descriptive (see Chap. 1); priority considerations again do not apply.

Staphylococcus albus. The term *Staphylococcus albus* will be used here as generally synonymous with coagulase-negative parasitic staphylococci, with the understanding that in this instance as elsewhere in bacteriologic taxonomy no sharp line divides it from adjoining categories, pathogenic on one side and truly saprophytic on the other. Typically, these coagulase-negative organisms fail to produce capsules or any of the toxins or toxic enzymes that characterize *Staph. aureus.* In addition, as with the streptococci (see below and Chap. 11), the more typically amphibiotic staphylococci fail to survive incubation in whole human blood [Spink and Vivino (1942)]. In general contrast to the coagulase-positive forms they are destroyed after ingestion by leukocytes [Rogers and Tompsett (1952); Kapral and Shayegani (1959); Melly, Thomison, and Rogers (1960); Mackaness (1960); see also Rogers and Melly (1960)]. They have been found susceptible to lysozyme [Thompson (1940)]. *Staph. albus* is usually nonpathogenic for laboratory animals when administered by means that demonstrate pathogenicity of coagulase-positive staphylococci (but see page 18). They are probably never true pathogens in man; but staphylococci, including the amphibiotic varieties, have been second only to nonhemolytic streptococci as agents of subacute bacterial endocarditis

[2] Findings briefly reported by Sword et al. (1961) suggest that the difference in coagulase activity between pathogenic and nonpathogenic staphylococci may be quantitative rather than absolute.

[Jones (1950); see also Smith et al. (1958); Rosebury and Sonnen-wirth (1958)].

Other Staphylococci. At the other end of their range the parasitic coagulase-negative staphylococci evidently merge with other aerobic mass-forming Gram-positive cocci that are probably more typical of a saprophytic habitat—the so-called micrococci. Van Eseltine (1955) has suggested that the characteristics of the *Micrococcus-Staphylococcus* group do not warrant their generic separation, while Reimann (1957) could find no clear distinction between a white staphylococcus (derived from a yellow colony) and the so-called *Gaffkya tetragena* (or *Micrococcus tetragenus*). The generic name *Gaffkya* has been ruled "indeterminate" by the Judicial Commission (1954). Reimann notes that "the myth of pathogenicity for mice" of *G. tetragena* is perpetuated [see Blair (1958)]. Similar conclusions have been reached by British workers who, as noted previously, would include all these forms within the genus *Staphylococcus* [see Elek (1959); Angyal (1961a,b)].

Coagulase-negative staphylococci seem to be constant or nearly constant inhabitants of human skin and several mucous membrane areas, although their concentrations do not appear to be high. On skin, Rebell (1947), who cited earlier literature, isolated them from 88 to 98 per cent of normal areas (toes, dorsum of foot, palm, groin). Evans et al. (1950) found white staphylococci to be the predominant aerobic member of the biota of healthy skin in the scapular and deltoid areas, but reported that these forms were greatly outnumbered by anaerobes (principally *Corynebacterium acnes,* see Chap. 3) in the ratio 352: 55,384 per sq cm. In the nose and throat, Lepper, Jackson, and Dowling (1955) found that repeated cultures yielded micrococci in 100 per cent on one or more occasions, and even in these areas coagulase-negative strains were distinctly more common than the more pathogenic varieties. Griffith et al. (1957–58) recovered coagulase-negative staphylococci from nearly all[3] of a series of single nose and throat cultures in 200 subjects 4 to 40 years of age who visited a hospital only briefly for polio vaccination. In the vagina, Hite, Hesseltine, and Goldstein (1947) isolated *Staph. albus* from 34.4 per cent of 61 subjects prenatally, while the normal postpartum uterus yielded these organisms in 84 per cent of 50 cases. Comparable findings for *Staph. aureus* in this study were 6.5 and 6.0 per cent, respectively; and it is of interest that in pathologic states in these areas, other than vaginal trichomoniasis, the incidence of white staphylococci was significantly lower than in the normals. In the mouth, Jordan, Fitzgerald, and Faber (1956),

---

[3] These data are given thus: 193/200 (97 per cent) yielded *Staph. albus,* of which 177 were coagulase-negative; 113/200 yielded *Staph. aureus,* of which 12 were coagulase-negative; and 3 yielded *Staph. citreus.*

in a study of micrococci that grow out on the pH 5 plates used for lactobacillus counts of saliva, recovered 92 coagulase-negative strains (of which 12 were described as tetrad formers) as compared with 17 coagulase-positive cultures. Richardson and Jones (1958) recorded total micrococcus counts from saliva of 14 subjects on the Chapman-Stone medium (BBL) as ranging from 10^1 to 4.2×10^4 per ml, average 5×10^3.

Anaerobic Micrococci

Obligately anaerobic, distinctly Gram-positive mass-forming cocci have been described infrequently as members of the indigenous biota or in cultures from pathologic sources. There is little agreement on any of their characteristics. The first serious study of these forms was made by Prévot (1933); in 1948 this worker listed 9 species as anaerobic members of the genera *Staphylococcus*, *Micrococcus*, or *Sarcina*. Foubert and Douglas (1948) attempted to classify 52 cultures, of which 36 had been isolated from human skin and from the tonsils or uterus, the remainder having been obtained from other workers, including Prévot. The Foubert-Douglas cultures were described as all strictly anaerobic with no tendency to become facultative, but all produced catalase (see page 39). All were Gram-positive except for the lactate fermenters which are considered on pages 38–40 under the generic name *Veillonella*. The group was subdivided into 8 species of which 5 coincided with Prévot's designations, the others being given as new species. In a more recent extensive study, Hare et al. (1952) undertook to classify the anaerobic parasitic cocci in general, including streptococci and Gram-negative cocci as well as those here in question. They worked with 99 cultures, of which 71 were derived from the human vagina and 23 from the respiratory tract, many from pathologic material; the source of 5 cultures was not indicated. Out of this total only 15 seem to have been unambiguous micrococci; these resembled the *Staphylococcus* (or *Micrococcus*) *anaerobius* of the previous workers. This organism was characterized by apparent biochemical inactivity. It fermented neither hexoses nor disaccharides and formed no gas in thiosulfate broth or in a thioglycollate broth containing pyruvate, lactate, malate, fumarate, tartrate, or citrate. An anaerobic coccus that seems to have been similar to the preceding was reported as isolated from 10 of 19 cases of tropical ulcer by Magara et al. (1948).

Among other Gram-positive cocci recovered by Hare and not easily classified, 10 strains listed as mass or tetrad formers (group VIb) were biochemically identical with a group of streptococci (VIa); while 7 other mass-forming cultures (group II) could not be identified with those of other workers. It is noted that although these latter were "suggestive of staphylococci, diplococcal forms, tetrads and short chains are sometimes seen. . . . " Anaerobic micrococci were noted in passing as having been isolated from the vagina and uterus by Hite, Hesseltine, and Goldstein (1947); from the skin by Evans et al. (1950); and from the mouth by Morris (1954).

Micrococcus niger. A black-pigment-producing staphylococcus-like organism described as obligately anaerobic was isolated from urine and called *Micrococcus niger* by Hall (1930). The organism grew best in deep infusion agar, formed gas, and showed pigmented colonies on the fifth or sixth day. According to Prévot and Taffanel (1942) it fails to reduce nitrate, does not attack carbohydrates, produces H_2S, NH_3, indole, ketones, and acetic, butyric, and lactic acids. Digeon and Raynaud (1952) found this organism in the stools of normal nurselings frequently and nearly as abundantly as *Actinomyces bifidus* (Chap. 3). Prévot, Cadore, and Thouvenot (1959) isolated the organism from the healthy vagina as well as from nurseling stools and studied 19 strains. Black pigment, described as intracellular and thought to be a melanin, was formed principally in mixed cultures, and the power to form it could be lost irreversibly.

Streptococci

The more actively pathogenic streptococci and the pneumococci have been omitted here even though their occurrence on healthy tissues, especially of the pharynx, might have warranted their inclusion. We are concerned with the remaining parasitic streptococci, which are numerically prominent among the aerobic biota of mucous surfaces, especially the mouth, pharynx, and lower intestine. In the two former areas they are often considered the most characteristic and important bacteria, but this opinion deserves reconsideration. These streptococci have been dealt with in an early extensive review by the writer [Rosebury (1944)].

Indigenous Gram-positive aerobic chain-forming cocci are usually subdivided in 2 groups, the enterococci and the viridans streptococci [Sherman (1937)].

Enterococci

Streptococcus faecalis and other enterococci are distinguished from other streptococci by the presence of the group D polysaccharide of Lancefield (1933). The D-specific antigen has been located in the cell contents rather than in the cell wall [Jones and Shattock (1960); Cummins and Slade (1961)]. The further subdivision of these forms by

TABLE 2-1

DISTINGUISHING FEATURES OF SPECIES OF ENTEROCOCCI
(AFTER SHATTOCK, 1955)

	Strepto-coccus faecalis	Str. faecalis var. zymogenes	Str. faecalis var. liquefaciens	Str. faecium	Str. durans	Str. bovis
β hemolysis	−	+	−	−	±V	−*
Growth at 10°	+	+	+	+	+$_x$	−
Growth at 45°	+	+	+	+	+$_x$	+
Growth at pH 9.6	+	+	+	+	±V	−
Growth in 6.5% NaCl	+	+	+	+	+	−
Growth in 40% bile	+	+	+	+	+	+
Resists 60° 30 min	+	+	+	+	+	−
Strong reduction of litmus milk	+	±V	+	−	−	−
Gelatin liquefied	−	±V	+	−	−	−
Mannitol, acid	+	+	+	±V	−	∓
Sucrose, acid	+	+	+	±V	−	+
Raffinose, acid	−	−	−	∓	−	+
Sorbitol, acid	+	+	+	∓	−	−
Arabinose, acid	−	−	−	+	−	±V
Growth in ½₅₀₀ potassium tellurite	+	+	+	−	−	−
Tyrosine decarboxylase	+	+	+	±V	±m	−

+, positive; −, negative; +$_x$, usually +; ∓, usually −; ±V, variable; ±m, moderate activity.

* Dain et al. (1957) reported that certain strains of S. bovis are hemolytic in poured horse blood agar (not with bovine or sheep blood) when incubated with 5% or more of CO_2.

serologic typing is practicable [Foley and Wheeler (1945); Skadhauge (1950); Sharpe and Shattock (1952); see also Elliott (1960)]. Bacteriophages specific for enterococci have also been described and suggested as a basis for type classification [Ciuca et al. (1960); see also Akhmedov (1959)].

Subdivision into species and varieties is commonly based at present on resistance to deleterious agencies and on biochemical criteria. The enterococci are usually the most resistant of the streptococci. Typically they grow at both 10 and 45°, at pH 9.6, in 6.5 per cent NaCl, and in 40 per cent bile. They usually withstand 60° for 30 minutes and tend to be resistant to penicillin and other antibiotics. Other characters, including hemolysis [see Irwin and Seeley (1958)] are variable, as shown in Table 2-1 [Shattock (1955)] and serve to distinguish species and varieties within the group. *Streptococcus bovis*, an organism with intermediate properties formerly included among the viridans forms [Sherman (1937)] was shown by Shattock (1949) to contain the group D antigen. Shattock (1955) has also stated that beyond the well-defined species and varieties given in the table, "not all group D streptococci can be assigned a species name . . . there are no clear cut lines of demarcation between the various species within this group. . . . " Sharpe (1952) reported that 2 strains identified as *Str. faecium* reacted with both group D and group N (lactic streptococcus) antiserums; reciprocal absorption tests revealed a common type antigen also found in a strain of *Str. lactis*. Other examples of interrelationships among the streptococci were noted by Rosebury (1944).

Although streptococci, like other lactobacteria, are characteristically nonmotile and lacking in iron-porphyrin enzymes, enterococci have been described with definite motility [Graudel (1957); Hugh (1959); Akhmedov (1959); Langston, Gutierrez, and Bouma (1960*b*)] and as showing catalase activity [Langston, Gutierrez, and Bouma (1960*a*)]. Such strains appear to be rare.

Methods. Selective media and methods for enterococci have made use of 2,3,5-triphenyltetrazolium chloride (TTC) [Barnes (1956)]; thallium acetate [Barnes (1956)]; potassium tellurite [Szita (1957)]; a combination of sodium azide and TTC used with membrane filters [Slanetz and Bartley (1957)]; and a sodium azide–sorbitol agar medium [Kjellander (1960)—this author has reviewed other earlier media; see also Kenner, Clark, and Kabler (1961)]. A blood agar medium for streptococci in general, containing kanamycin and nystatin, has been recommended by Moustardier et al. (1960). Rosenberger and Elsden (1960) have studied the continuous cultivation of *Str. faecalis* in a defined medium; this medium has been used effectively in the writer's laboratory for static mass culture of this bacterium.

Distribution. The principal locus of enterococci, as the name implies, is the lower intestine. Slanetz and Bartley (1957) reported a mean per gram for enterococci in 20 samples of human feces of 3.0×10^7 as compared with 1.8×10^7 for coliforms. The range for enterococci was from 2×10^3 to 2.7×10^8, for coliforms 1×10^4 to 2.6×10^8. The counts for both groups were not markedly different in 15 samples of bovine feces. Buttiaux (1958), using the medium of Barnes (1956*a,b*) also compared human with animal feces for their content of enterococci, as shown in Table 2-2. Group D streptococci appeared invariably in the samples from man and from swine, and in most instances in those from cattle and sheep. *Str. faecalis* and *Str. faecium* were the commonest species in man, while the latter was distinctly the more common in animals. Lactic streptococci were found in 23 of 32 samples of feces

TABLE 2-2

ENTEROCOCCI AND LACTIC STREPTOCOCCI IN FECES OF MAN
AND ANIMALS (AFTER BUTTIAUX, 1958)

	Man			Animals		
	Nurselings	Children	Adults	Swine	Cattle	Sheep
Number examined	72	9	38	52	32	24
Group D streptococci	72	9	38	52	21	21
Str. faecalis	45	4	22	10	3	2
Str. zymogenes	2	0	4	0	0	0
Str. liquefaciens	4	0	2	18	0	1
Str. faecium	49	9	35	48	17	21
Str. bovis	11	1	4	3	7	1
Lactic streptococci	0	5	7	0	23	10

from cattle. Kjellander (1960), who presented additional data on the
distribution and concentration of enterococci in feces of man and various animal species, suggested that fermentation of sorbitol, which was
exhibited both by a higher proportion of strains and by higher concentrations of enterococci in feces of man than of animals, might be used
to differentiate organisms from the two sources.

Bridson and Brown (1960) have found hemolytic enterococci (*Str.
zymogenes*) in the feces of 81 of 347 healthy infants (23.3 per cent) up
to 4 months old; 32 of these, or 9.2 per cent, showed a "profuse growth"
of these organisms. It is of interest that counts of enterococci in the
environment [e.g., in food, Larkin, Litsky, and Fuller (1956); well
water, Ritter, Shull, and Quinley, (1956); and sewage, Slanetz and
Bartley (1957)] have been found to parallel coliform counts. Larkin,
Litsky, and Fuller (1956) have advocated enterococcus counts as an
index of fecal pollution. This question has been explored at length by
Kjellander (1960), who suggested that the procedure may have distinct
advantages [see also Croft (1959); Kenner, Clark, and Kabler (1960)].
These findings are indications of saprophytism in enterococci, as is
their recovery from vegetation [Mundt and Johnson (1959)].

Enterococci have also been recovered from the genitourinary tract
under both normal and pathologic conditions [Porch (1941); Hite and
Hesseltine (1947); Posada and Perez-Miravete (1958)] and from the
mouth [Williams et al. (1950); Morris (1954); Bahn et al. (1960)].
Williams and his coworkers recovered *Str. faecalis*, *Str. liquefaciens* or
Str. zymogenes from saliva in 45 of 206 subjects ranging in age from

4 to 40 years. Bahn et al. (1960) found group D streptococci in 70 of 303 saliva samples (23.1 per cent) from dental clinic patients, but in only 3.6 per cent of samples from 443 naval recruits. In a group of 64 naval recruits tested during an epidemic of virus infection of the upper respiratory tract 34.1 per cent revealed enterococci in the saliva. Hugh, Klopp, and Ryschenkov (1959) have suggested that enterococci, mainly *Str. faecalis*, recovered in cultures from the tonsillar region, are either transients or are associated with malignancy in this or other body areas. This suggestion should be weighed against the possibility of overgrowth of the oral or pharyngeal flora associated with functional disturbances only indirectly connected with illness in this or other areas (see Chap. 11).

Mann, Masson, and Oxford (1954) found that streptococci isolated from the sheep rumen were all group D; 82 per cent resembled *Str. bovis*, 6 per cent *Str. faecalis*, 12 per cent were unclassifiable. Perry, Newland, and Briggs (1958) reported that of 37 group D streptococci isolated from the young calf rumen, 10 *Str. bovis* and 1 unidentified strain shared a type antigen with group N, a phenomenon previously noted by Sharpe (1952; see page 28). For other studies of enterococci in the rumen see Oxford (1958).

Pathogenicity. Enterococci appear to be primarily amphibionts, with saprophytic proclivities as noted above. They have no known special attributes associated with pathogenicity,[4] but they may nevertheless participate in disease. When they do, their resistance, especially to antibiotics, may give them particular significance. Enterococci have been recovered in 4 per cent or more of cases of subacute bacterial endocarditis [Jones (1950); Toh and Ball (1960); Koenig and Kaye (1961)], far less commonly than the viridans streptococci. *Str. faecalis* has been used to produce endocarditis in high-altitude rats [Highman, Altland, and Eagle (1952)]. Gledhill and Rees (1952) implicated an enterococcus as the causative agent of a spontaneous enterohepatitis of mice and produced the disease experimentally with the organism by intraperitoneal or intravenous inoculation or by feeding. Cortisone increased the susceptibility of the animals. The isolated organism reacted with group D antiserums but was otherwise atypical. Pyelonephritis has been produced with both *Str. faecalis* and *Str. zymogenes* in rats [Braude, Shapiro, and Siemienski (1959)] and in mice [Erlandson et al. (1959, 1961)]. Enterococci have been implicated in a mild form of food poisoning conveyed by milk products or meats [Buchbinder, Osler, and Steffen (1948), Osler, Buchbinder, and Steffen (1948)]. Sharpe (1952), acting on a suggestion by Gale (1940) that tyramine,

---

[4] Coagulase-like activity attributed to a special agent has been reported for group D streptococci by Evans, Buetner, and Niven (1952) and by Wood (1959).

produced by the *Str. faecalis* enzyme tyrosine decarboxylase, seemed to be responsible for an experimental fatal diarrhea in rats, observed that the proportion of group D streptococci in the aerobic fecal biota was 90 to 100 per cent in infants with neonatal diarrhea as compared with 10 to 12 per cent in healthy infants. Although the species and varieties of enterococci were the same in the 2 groups, with *Str. faecalis* predominating, serologic typing suggested a pattern of dissemination reflecting exogenous rather than endogenous infection. The intensity of tyrosine decarboxylase activity was related to serologic type but did not seem to be related to health or disease. A lack of relationship of this enzyme to neonatal diarrhea associated with *Str. zymogenes* has also been reported by Bridson and Brown (1960).

The Viridans Group

Indigenous streptococci lacking either D or A polysaccharides have been grouped [Sherman (1937)] under the general term *Viridans*, replacing the no longer valid specific designation *Streptococcus viridans*. The term signifies greening—the so-called α-change in horse blood agar in the still widely used early classification of Brown (1919)—and as such is misleading, since many members of the group are inactive (γ) on blood and some are fully hemolytic (β). This group is most characteristic of mouth and throat and is often accepted as predominant in the indigenous biota of those areas, but as will be noted, this is clearly an error based on the common use of selective methods of cultivation. Members of this group are also found in the lower intestine [Rodaniche, Palmer, and Kirsner (1943); Berens and Chapman (1944)] and in the female urinary [Schaub and Davis (1945)] and genital tracts [Hite and Hesseltine (1947)].

Concentrations in Saliva. Quantitative data on the concentrations of these bacteria are scarce and difficult to interpret because of wide variations in individual subjects. The careful studies of Kraus and Gaston (1956), which are in general agreement with those of earlier workers [see Douglas (1950)] indicate a rough average ratio in healthy saliva of viable *Str. salivarius* to total (aerobic) streptococci to "total aerobes" of 1:2:4. The average for total aerobes as given by Kraus and Gaston is 2.5×10^7 per ml. The findings of Richardson and Jones (1958) and unpublished data from the writer's laboratory suggest that this value probably represents only a small proportion of a "total" salivary biota estimated under *anaerobic* conditions.[5]

---

[5] Burrows and Hemmens (1943) presented often cited values for "total" bacterial counts of saliva in full as follows: "Observations made by one of us [E. S. H.] in another connection showed that in 43 samples of saliva cultured on blood agar, the total bacterial counts varied from 43 million to 5,500 million per c.c., with an average

Streptococcus salivarius (or *Str. hominis*) is the most clearly defined member of the viridans group. Identified principally by the production of large mucoid colonies on 5 per cent sucrose (or raffinose) agar [Niven, Smiley, and Sherman (1941)]—dependent on production of a soluble levan—it is also usually inactive on blood, grows at 45° but not at 10°, ferments inulin, salicin, and esculin, and acidifies and clots litmus milk. Williams (1956) found that 60 of 103 levan-producing, oropharyngeal streptococci reacted with group K antiserum, whereas none of 13 old group K strains, including 3 from Hare's collection, formed levan. Williams gave cogent reasons, including priority of the specific epithet (proposed by Hlava in 1902) for renaming the levan-producing streptococci *Str. hominis*, independently of the presence of the K polysaccharide.

Streptococcus mitis. The remaining indigenous aerobic streptococci are a heterogeneous group that has not yet been satisfactorily classified. The name *Str. mitis* is applied loosely to those forms, commonest in mouth and throat, that fail to produce levan on sucrose agar and do not ferment inulin. Most strains show the typical α or "viridans" effect on blood, but this is not invariable. Other specific designations among viridans streptococci are of doubtful utility, since no satisfactorily consistent set of criteria has as yet been found for classifying them. The Lancefield polysaccharides C, E, F, G, H, and O, as well as K, not necessarily associated with β-hemolysis or other properties, have been found distributed among some of the apparently indigenous streptococci of mouth and throat [Farmer (1953, 1954); Kraus, Casey, and Johnson (1953); Williams (1956)]. Saslaw et al. (1959) recovered a β-streptococcus from the throat that reacted with both A and F antiserums through successive subcultures. Rifkind and Cole (1961) recovered from 2 cases of subacute endocarditis nonhemolytic group M streptococci one of which cross-reacted in Ouchterlony plates with *Str. mitis.*

Of the other characters, including dextran formation [Hehre and

---

of 750 million." These were evidently aerobic counts. Extremely high plate counts of unstimulated saliva from healthy subjects have appeared in the writer's experience and are considered dubious. If we assume an average bacterial volume in the fresh state of $1\mu^3$, the maximum count of packed bacteria would be 10^{12} per cc. Clumps and chains counted as units, nonviable bacteria, and failure of growth of certain species on any single medium, among other factors, would all reduce this value. The total viable count in healthy unstimulated saliva of young adults (with anaerobes included) nevertheless often appears to be astonishingly high—of the order of 10^9 per ml. Richardson and Jones (1958) have reported the average values of 1.1×10^8 and 4.0×10^7 per ml for total anaerobes and total aerobes, respectively. The former value is almost certainly too low in unstimulated saliva. Their average counts for *Str. salivarius* and "total streptococci" (aerobic) were 1.1×10^7 and 1.8×10^7 per ml respectively. Thus anaerobes probably outnumber aerobes in saliva, as in feces, by a factor of more than 10 (see Chap. 10).

Neill (1946)] from sucrose (which is not associated with mucoid colonies), action on red blood cells, fermentation reactions or other metabolic or nutritional phenomena, and resistance to deleterious agencies, none has been generally accepted as a reliable taxonomic index. *Str. sanguis* [or *Streptococcus* s.b.e., White and Niven (1946)] does not seem to be a valid species [Dodd (1949); Selbie, Simon, and Robinson (1949); Porterfield (1950)]. *Streptococcus* MG [Mirick et al. (1944); Horsfall (1951)] appears to be one of several levan-negative streptococci which otherwise resembles *Str. hominis* and pneumococci in possessing capsules containing type-specific polysaccharides. The separation of the MG organisms as a distinctive type or species may be justified on the practical ground of its usefulness as a diagnostic aid in primary atypical pneumonia [Thomas et al. (1943); Meiklejohn and Hanford (1944); Anderson (1960); see also Harding and Snyder (1960)].

Variation and Heterogeneity. It is of passing interest that these accessible and easily cultivated bacteria remain so inadequately characterized. Lack of overt pathogenicity has doubtless drawn interest away from them. Their established role in subacute bacterial endocarditis [see Rosebury (1944); Rosebury and Sonnenwirth (1958)], by contrast, has stimulated efforts that seem fruitless to identify "pathogens" among them. Subacute bacterial endocarditis seems to be a classic example of amphibiosis transformed into disease by a mechanism almost, if not quite, wholly dependent on the host rather than the parasite. And like many members of the complex indigenous biota, these aerobic streptococci display a heterogeneity that may be intrinsic, the despair of taxonomists notwithstanding. Continual genetic interchange among closely related organisms may underlie the difficulty, possibly including among its consequences the oft-repeated finding (as with anaerobic micrococci; see page 25) that cultures isolated in recent years fail to conform closely with those described in the older literature. Bracco et al. (1957) have presented evidence of genetic interchange among "species" in this group, including pneumococci [see also Pakula, Hulanicka, and Walczak (1958, 1959)]. Such findings may help to explain some of the claims in the older literature on the interconversion of hemolytic and nonhemolytic streptococci as well as pneumococci [see Rosebury (1944)].

Other data on these streptococci are given in Chaps. 10 and 11.

Anaerobic Streptococci

Strictly anaerobic streptococci have been known since 1893, when Veillon isolated, from pathologic processes of the mouth and the urinary tract, an organism which he called *Micrococcus foetidus;* it produced gas and a fetid odor. In the decades immediately following, many workers found anaerobic streptococci on healthy mucous surfaces, in mixed infections on or associated with such surfaces, or in the blood [Veillon (1893); for other early references see Taylor (1929)]. Anaerobic streptococcal bacteremia was found notably in a form of puerperal fever regarded as endogenous, related to severe trauma during labor [Schwarz and Dieckmann (1929); Colebrook (1930, 1931); Brown (1930); Schwarz and Brown (1936)]. Some of the clinical conditions in which these organisms have been implicated bear a striking resemblance to those subsequently attributed to bacteroides [Lemierre (1936); Lemierre, Reilly and Laporte (1938); Stone (1940)], and, indeed, the two kinds of bacteria have been recovered together, often in more complex mixtures [see Wills and Reece (1960), and Chap. 5]. Anaerobic streptococci have also been found in a small proportion of war wounds ("streptococcal myositis"), usually mixed with aerobic hemolytic streptococci and staphylococci but not with clostridia [Mac-Lennan (1943)].

Indigenous Distribution

The indigenous character of anaerobic streptococci is suggested or accepted in many papers, but the emphasis in nearly the whole of the literature on this group has been on disease. White (1933), who reviewed the earlier literature, found anaerobic streptococci in the vagina of 18 of 50 normal women (36 per cent) in the first stage of labor, and of 15 of 50 (30 per cent) in the last month of pregnancy. Hite, Hesseltine, and Goldstein (1947) also isolated them from the healthy vagina and from the postpartum uterus. In the "census of human saliva" reported by Richardson and Jones (1958) these organisms were not mentioned, but unpublished data from the writer's laboratory are in line with the general opinion that anaerobic streptococci are indigenous to the mouth and probably very numerous there, and that they also occur prominently in normal human feces. It may be pointed out that their separation from aerobic streptococci, especially for purposes of counting, is not easy, since both groups grow under anaerobic conditions.

The anaerobic streptococci are virtually lacking in independent pathogenic activity when tested by the usual methods, although they may manifest distinct pathogenicity in certain mixtures [see Rosebury and Sonnenwirth (1958)]. They thus fall afoul of Koch's third postulate, which demands the use of pure cultures; and it is almost certainly for this reason, perhaps augmenting the general unpopularity of parasitic anaerobes other than clostridia, that neglect has descended upon them. At all events our present knowledge of these bacteria is even less abundant than the poor average for indigenous forms as a whole.

Classification

Streptococcus putridus. Prévot, who has long pioneered in the attempt to systematize the anaerobes, listed 6 species of anaerobic streptococci in 1925, and 9 species, with additional varieties, in 1948. He classified them in 2 groups which either (1) produced or (2) failed to produce gas and a fetid odor. This grouping is in line with the findings of Hare et al. (1952), who reported isolating 45 strains, mainly from the vagina, of a member of the first group, *Str. putridus.* This organism, a strict anaerobe, ferments glucose, fructose, and maltose with the production of large volumes of gas, principally CO_2, the gas appearing only in the presence of sulfur-containing compounds. Other metabolic products, according to Prévot, are ammonia, hydrogen sulfide, and formic, butyric, and acetic acids. *Str. putridus* is a rather large coccus with a tendency to pleomorphism, showing clubbed and bacillary forms together with variable cocci in individual chains. This or a closely related streptococcus appears to be the one found under pathologic conditions as well as on healthy tissues.

Streptococcus evolutus, Streptococcus micros. Among the second group, which failed to produce gas or odor, a single species, *Str. evolutus*, is said by Prévot to become adapted to aerobic growth. The name *Str. micros* may be used provisionally to cover the strict anaerobes of Prévot's second group. This latter organism or group, first described by Lewkowicz in 1901, may be characterized as a variably small coccus (0.3 to 0.7 μ in diameter) producing no gas or odor. It fails to liquefy gelatin, does not form indole or H_2S, but produces ammonia. Carbohydrates are attacked with the production of lactic, propionic, and formic acids and usually acetylmethylcarbinol. Strains isolated by Hare et al. (1952) were 0.6 to 0.7 μ in diameter but otherwise agreed with this description. *Str. micros* does not seem to have been implicated in pathologic processes. Mattman and Senos (1957) reported that a strain of *Str. micros* obtained from Prévot differed from his description, perhaps because of an altered basal medium—this strain was now found to produce H_2S and not to ferment glucose or levulose; gelatin was sometimes liquefied after prolonged incubation (26 days). In old cultures, moreover (10 days to 8 weeks or more), colonies on laked blood showed black pigmentation like those of *Micrococcus niger* (page 26) or *Bacteroides nigrescens* (Chap. 5).

Mergenhagen and Scherp (1957) have reported on the nutritional requirements of both groups of anaerobic streptococci. Lefebre and Côté (1958) found an organism regarded as *Str. evolutus* in the blood in bacterial endocarditis.

Anaerobic Streptococci of the Rumen. Among the rumen bacteria described in a review by Bryant (1959) are anaerobic Gram-positive chain-forming cocci listed under the genera *Peptostreptococcus* and *Ruminococcus*. It was noted that some of these forms appear to be related to both gas-forming and non-gas-forming species of human origin. Although the rumen organisms seem to be little better understood than those found in man the former group is under more active investigation [see Provost and Doetsch (1960)]. A comparative study of strains isolated from the two sources might prove rewarding.

Neisseriae

The actively pathogenic species of *Neisseria*, the meningococcus and the gonococcus, are omitted here, even though the former, like group A streptococci and pneumococci, is notoriously subject to the so-called "healthy" carrier state, with little relationship between its presence in the nasopharynx and the occurrence of clinical illness [see Cheever (1958) and Chap. 10].

Common Neisseriae

The more typically indigenous aerobic oxidase-positive Gram-negative cocci are most characteristic of the pharynx but are also found commonly in the mouth, less so in the nose [Wilson and Miles (1955)], and apparently sparsely on other mucous surfaces including urethra and vagina [Wilkinson (1952)]. They may be grouped principally into three species following the recommendation of Warner, Faber, and Pelczar (1952). *N. catarrhalis* is the unpigmented form that fails to produce acid from any of the usual carbohydrate substrates. *N. sicca* is also unpigmented but ferments glucose, maltose, fructose, and sucrose.[6] This species is distinguished from the meningococcus by its more abundant growth and resistance (including growth at 22°, characteristic of the other indigenous forms as well but not of the pathogens), and its dry, rough, cohesive colony. Warner and his coworkers found this organism antigenically distinctive. *N. pharyngis* is the name suggested by Wilson and Miles (1946) and by Warner et al. (1952) for the group of fermentative chromogenic amphibiotic neisseriae. These forms produce

---

[6] Berger (1961*a,b*) has reported that nonpathogenic neisseriae isolated from the mouth may ferment glucose but not fructose and that these strains ferment maltose and sucrose more constantly than they do the monosaccharides.

greenish-yellow colonies, ferment carbohydrates with strain variations, and are antigenically somewhat heterogeneous. On the basis of transformation reactions briefly reported by Catlin (1961), *N. catarrhalis* appears to be genetically distinct from the other members of this group, which in turn seem interrelated with each other and with the meningococcus. An additional species, *N. caviae*, isolated by Pelczar, Hajek, and Faber (1949) and Pelczar (1953) from the pharynx of guinea pigs, is a chromogenic nonfermenter.

Less Common Species

There is evidence for the existence of additional species of true *Neisseria*. Veron, Thibaut, and Second (1959) studied 5 strains, recovered from disease of the upper respiratory tract during a 2-year period, of an organism described as *Neisseria mucosa*, apparently corresponding with the *Diplococcus mucosus* originally described by Weichselbaum and Ghon [(1905); see also Elser and Huntoon (1909)]. This organism was described as a morphologically typical neisseria, catalase- and oxidase-positive, forming acid from glucose, fructose, maltose, and sucrose; it was distinguished by being encapsulated and mucoid, reducing nitrate activity to nitrogen gas, and being pathogenic for mice, some of which died 24 to 48 hours after intraperitoneal injection of 0.5 ml of a heavy 24-hour broth culture. In a later study Veron et al. (1961) distinguished this organism serologically. They found 2 major O antigens in 8 strains, one of which cross-reacted with *N. sicca*; otherwise they observed no cross-reactions with other neisseriae or with *Moraxella* or *Mima* (see Chap. 4). In apparent contrast to these findings, Berger (1961c) has found that approximately 85 per cent of 223 amphibiotic neisseriae from the mouth formed a polysaccharide from sucrose, associated in one-third of the strains with mucoid growth; polysaccharide production was related to, but not dependent upon, ability to form acid from sucrose.

The organism described as *Neisseria haemolysans* by Thjötta and Böe (1938) has been studied more recently by Berger (1960a); Berger and Wezel (1960). Other neisseriae or neisseria-like organisms have also been described by this worker [Berger (1960b,c)].

"Anaerobic" Neisseriae

The generic name *Neisseria* should probably be restricted to oxidase-producing species of Gram-negative cocci, and strictly anaerobic organisms described under this name [e.g., by Prévot (1957)] may more fittingly be placed elsewhere. Langford, Faber, and Pelczar (1950) recommended this procedure. They found that all but one of 61 strains of anaerobic Gram-negative cocci isolated from the mouth or obtained from various collections could be classified as *Veillonella;* the exception resembled a streptococcus.

Veillonellae

Among strictly anaerobic cocci that are Gram-negative in young fully grown cultures, only a single species is clearly recognizable, although other species may well exist.[7] We follow Pelczar (1957) in calling this species *Veillonella alcalescens;* synonyms are *V. gazogenes, Micrococcus gazogenes,* and *M. lactilyticus,* among others.

V. alcalescens was first described in the mouths of nurselings by Lewkowicz in 1901. It was recovered by Holman and Krock (1923) from the mouths of man, rabbits, and guinea pigs, and by Hall and Howitt (1925) from human saliva. It is a highly distinctive and characteristic amphibiont. Foubert and Douglas (1948) found it Grampositive in very young cultures, but it is uniformly Gram-negative after 12 hours' growth. It is a small mass-forming spherical coccus, strictly anaerobic.

Distribution

V. alcalescens occurs in saliva regularly, in concentrations equal to or greater than those of aerobic streptococci. Berger, Kapovics, and Pfeifer (1958) found it in the mouths of infants regularly by the end of the first week of life. Reported mean values for adult saliva per milliliter are 5.3×10^7 for 17 samples [Douglas (1950)]; 3.3×10^7 for 145 samples [Rogosa (1956)]; and 1.7×10^7 for 14 samples [Richardson and Jones (1958)]. This coccus has also been found in the rumen and the saliva of sheep [Johns (1951); Hobson, Mann, and Oxford (1958)], and in the mouths of rats (Rogosa) as well as of rabbits and guinea pigs, as noted in the preceding paragraph.

Biochemical Features

V. alcalescens is principally distinguished by its unusual fermentation. It fails to attack sugars but ferments lactate actively under anaerobic conditions with the production of propionic and acetic acids and large amounts of CO_2 and H_2, accompanied by a rise in pH. Pyruvate, malate, fumarate, oxaloacetate, succinate, and tartrate are also fermented. For biochemical details see Foubert and Douglas (1948)

---

[7] Prévot (1957) listed 3 species; Pelczar (1957) listed 6 species and 6 additional varieties. In a brief report summarizing serologic and other studies, Rogosa, Hampp, and MacKintosh (1961) suggested that only gas-forming, lactate-utilizing organisms should be regarded as veillonellae; others were thought to be "anaerobic streptococci staining ambiguously or negatively with the Gram stain."

and Johns (1951). Anaerobic utilization of lactate as the sole carbon source forms the basis for selective media [Douglas (1950); Rogosa (1956), Rogosa et al. (1958)]. The strains studied by Foubert and Douglas were all described as catalase-positive. Fitzgerald, Parramore, and MacKintosh (1958), on the other hand, made passing reference to "the absence of catalase" in this organism. Johns (1951) found that the succinic dehydrogenase formed by *V. alcalescens* is apparently not associated with a cytochrome. Whiteley and Ordal (1955) characterized its hydrogenase as an iron-containing molybdoflavoprotein. Heme-porphyrin enzymes are not known to occur in obligately anaerobic parasitic bacteria, although they may be produced by forms adaptable to aerobic growth, e.g., *Corynebacterium acnes* (Chap. 3) or by anaerobic autotrophs, e.g., *Chlorobium limicola* [Kamen and Vernon (1954)]. In view of the evidence presented by Gordon, Holman, and McLeod (1953) that anaerobiosis depends on H_2O_2 production in the absence of catalase—although the degree of universality of this mechanism has not been defined—the question of catalase production by *V. alcalescens* merits reinvestigation.

Significance to the Host

V. alcalescens has no claim to pathogenicity beyond that characteristic of typical amphibionts [e.g., it is found rarely in subacute bacterial endocarditis; see Jones (1950)]. It is thought to play a significant role in the ovine rumen in the formation of propionic acid from lactate. Its high concentration in saliva is doubtless related to the presence of intermediate products of the glycolytic activity of other bacteria, although this is not accepted as a full explanation of its prominence. Shiota and Kunkel (1958) found that addition of 0.2 or 0.5 per cent of sodium lactate to whole saliva incubated in vitro at 37° increased the concentration of *V. alcalescens* to 10^8 per ml or more in 24 hours. Addition of glucose had a less marked stimulatory effect, inducing less proliferation of the organism at a higher concentration (0.5 per cent) than at a lower (0.2 per cent). That veillonellae are stimulated by the production of lactate in carious lesions is suggested by their higher concentration in saliva and in dental plaque substance in the presence of dental caries than in its absence [Mazzarella and Shklair (1960)].

Mergenhagen (1960) reported that cell-free filtrates of this organism prepared by tryptic digestion could elicit the dermal Shwartzman reaction in rabbits. Evidence for the presence in veillonellae of a lipopolysaccharide-containing endotoxin lethal for mice and active in provoking the local Shwartzman reaction has been presented by Mergenhagen, Hampp, and Scherp (1961).

Fitzgerald, Parramore, and MacKintosh (1959) have reported on antibiotic sensitivities of 6 strains of *V. alcalescens.*

References

Akhmedov, N. A., 1959, *Med. Zhur. Uz.,* 3:38 (1960, *Abstr. Sov. Med.* 4:71).
Anderson, E. S., and Williams, R. E. O., 1956, *J. Clin. Pathol.,* 9:94.
Anderson, K., Coulter, J., and Looke, E., 1960, *Brit. Med. J.* 1:1925.
Anderson, T. B., 1960, *Lancet,* 1:1375.
Angyal, T., 1961*a, Acta Microbiol. Acad. Sci. Hung.,* 8:127.
———, 1961*b, ibid.,* 8:149.
Anon., 1960, *Lancet,* 2:659.
Asheshov, E. H., and Rippon, J. E., 1959, *J. Gen. Microbiol.,* 20:634.
Bahn, A. N., Shklair, I. L., Mazzarella, M., and Calandra, J. C., 1960, *J. Dental Research,* 39:686.
Barnes, E. M., 1956, *J. Appl. Bacteriol.,* 19:193, 204.
———, 1956, *J. Gen. Microbiol.,* 14:57.
Barrow, F. I., 1955, *J. Hyg.,* 53:485.
Berendt, R. F., Beard, C. W., Johnson, R. F., and Reynolds, R. C., 1961, *Bacteriol. Proc.,* p. 140.
Berens, C., and Chapman, G. H., 1944, *J. Bacteriol.* 47:473.
Berger, U., 1960*a, Z. Hyg. Infektionskrankh.,* 146:253.
———, 1960*b ibid.,* 147:158.
———, 1960*c, Zentr. Bakteriol. Parasitenk., I. Orig.,* 180:147.
———, 1961*a, Arch. Hyg. u. Bakteriol.* 145:190.
———, 1961*b, ibid.,* 145:296.
———, 1961*c, Zentr. Bakteriol. Parasitenk. I Orig.,* 181:345.
———, Kapovitz, M., and Pfeifer, G., 1959, *Z. Hyg. Infektionskrankh.,* 145:564.
———, and Wezel, M., 1960, *ibid.,* 146:244.
Blair, J. E., 1958, in Dubos, R. J. (ed.), *Bacterial and Mycotic Infections of Man,* 3d ed., J. B. Lippincott Company, Philadephia, p. 310.
———, and Carr, M., 1960*a, Science,* 132:1247.
———, and ———, 1960*b, J. Lab. Clin. Med.,* 55:650.
———, and Williams, R. E. O., 1961, *Bull. World Health Organization,* 24:771.
Bracco, R. M., Krauss, M. R., Roe, A. S., and MacLeod, C. M., 1957, *J. Exp. Med.,* 106:247.
Braude, A. I., Shapiro, A. P., and Siemienski, J. 1959, *J. Bacteriol.,* 77:270.
Breed, R. S., Murray, E. G. D., and Smith, N. R., 1957, *Bergey's Manual of Determinative Bacteriology,* 7th ed., The Williams & Wilkins Company, Baltimore, p. 466.
Bret, J., Coupe, C., Pillet, J., Solle, R., and Marchand, H., 1959, *Presse Méd.,* 67:216.
Bridson, E. Y., and Brown, J., 1960, *J. Clin. Pathol.,* 13:195.
Brown, J. H., 1919, Rockefeller Institute for Medical Research, New York Monograph No. 9.
Brown, T. K., 1930, *Am. J. Obstet. Gynecol.,* 20:300.
Bryant, M. P., 1959, *Bacteriol. Rev.,* 23:125.
Buchbinder, L., Osler, A. G., and Steffen, G. I., 1948, *Public Health Repts.,* 63:109.
Buhr, A. J., and Scott, J. C., 1959, *Lancet,* 1:1019.

Burke, J. F., and Corrigan, E. A., 1961, *New Engl. J. Med.*, **264**:321.
Burrows, W., and Hemmens, E. S., 1943, *J. Inf. Dis.*, **73**:180.
Buttiaux, R., 1958, *Ann. Inst. Pasteur*, **94**:778.
Bynoe, E. T., Elder, R. H., and Comtois, R. D., 1956, *Can. J. Microbiol.*, **2**:346.
Catlin, B. W., 1961, *Bacteriol. Proc.*, p. 90.
Cheever, F. S., 1958, in Dubos, R. J. (ed.), *Bacterial and Mycotic Infections of Man*, 3d ed., J. B. Lippincott Company, Philadelphia, p. 495.
Cheng, W. F., and Liu, T. Y., 1959, *Chinese J. Pediat.*, **10**:113 (*Biol. Abstr.*).
Christie, R., and Keogh, E. V., 1940, *J. Pathol. Bacteriol.*, **51**:189.
Ciuca, M., Baldovin-Agapi, C., Mihalco, F., Beloiu, I., and Caffe, I., 1960, *Arch. Roumaines Pathol. Exp. Microbiol.*, **18**:519 (*Biol. Abstr.*).
Cohen, J. O., and Oeding, P., 1961, *Bacteriol. Proc.*, p. 124.
Colebrook, L., 1930, *Brit. Med. J.* **2**:134.
———1931, *ibid.*, **2**:777.
Comtois, R. D., 1960, *Can. J. Microbiol.*, **6**:491.
Conti, C. R., Cluff, L. E., and Scheder, E. P., 1961, *J. Exp. Med.*, **113**:845.
Cowan, S. T., 1939, *J. Pathol. Bacteriol.*, **48**:168.
Croft, C. C., 1959, *Am. J. Public Health*, **49**:1379.
Cummins, C. S., and Slade, H. D., 1961, *Bacteriol. Proc.*, p. 94.
Dain, J. A., Seely, H. W., and Neal, A. L., 1957, *J. Bacteriol.*, **73**:291.
Digeon, M., and Raynaud, M., 1952, *Ann. Inst. Pasteur*, **82**:362.
Dodd, R. L., 1949, *Proc. Soc. Expt. Biol. Med.*, **70**:598.
Douglas, H. C., 1950, *J. Dental Research*, **29**:304.
Dutton, A. A. C., 1955, *Brit. J. Exp. Pathol.*, **36**:128.
Elek, S. D., 1956, *Ann. N.Y. Acad. Sci.*, **65**:85.
———, 1959, *Staphylococcus Pyogenes and Its Relation to Disease*, E. and S. Livingstone, Ltd., Edinburgh and London.
———, and Conen, P. E., 1957, *Brit. J. Exp. Pathol.*, **38**:573.
Elliott, S. D., 1960, *J. Exp. Med.*, **111**:621.
Elser, W. J., and Huntoon, F. M., 1909, *J. Med. Research*, **20**:371 (N. S. 15).
Erlandson, A. L., Jr., and Gagliardi, L. A., 1961, *J. Inf. Dis.*, **108**:181.
———, ———, and Fisher, M. W., 1959, *Nature*, **184**:561.
Evans, C. A., Smith, W. M., Johnston, E. A., and Giblett, E. R., 1950, *J. Invest. Dermatol.*, **15**:305.
Evans, J. B., Buetner, L. G., and Niven, C. F., Jr., 1952, *J. Bacteriol.*, **64**:443.
Faber, V., Jessen, O., Rosendal, K., and Eriksen, K. R., 1960, *Brit. Med. J.* **2**:1832.
Farmer, E. D., 1953, *Proc. Royal Soc. Med.*, **46**:201.
———, 1954, *J. Gen. Microbiol.*, **11**:131.
Farrer, S. M., Russo, R., Bavara, C., and Werthamer, S., 1959, *J. Am. Med. Assoc.*, **171**:1072.
Finegold, S. M., and Sweeney, E. E., 1961, *J. Bacteriol.*, **81**:636.
Fitzgerald, R. J., Parramore, M. L., and MacKintosh, M. E., 1959, *Antibiotics & Chemotherapy*, **9**:145.
Foley, G. E., and Wheeler, F. M., 1945, *Am. J. Diseases Children*, **70**:93.
Forbes, G. B., 1949, *Brit. Med. J.*, **2**:569.
Foster, W. D., 1960, *Lancet*, **1**:670.
———, and Hutt, M. S. R., 1960, *ibid.*, **2**:1373.
Foubert, E. L., Jr., and Douglas, H. C., 1948, *J. Bacteriol.* **56**:25, 35.
Fusillo, M. H., and Jaffurs, W. J., 1955, *ibid.*, **70**:481.

Gale, E. F., 1940, *Biochem. J.*, **34**:846.

Garré, C., 1885, *Fortschr. Med.*, **3**:165, cited by Foster and Hutt (1960).

Gillespie, E. H., Devenish, E. A., and Cowan, S. T., 1939, *Lancet*, **2**:870.

Gillespie, W. A., and Adler, V. G., 1952, *J. Pathol. Bacteriol.*, **64**:187.

———, ———, Ayliffe, G. A. J., Powell, D. E. B., and Wypkema, W., 1961, *Lancet*, **1**:1299.

Gledhill, A. W., and Rees, R. J. W., 1952, *Brit. J. Exp. Pathol.*, **33**:183.

Gordan, J., Holman, R. A., and McLeod, J. W., 1953, *J. Pathol. Bacteriol.*, **66**:527.

Goshi, K., Cluff, L. E., and Johnson, J. E., 1961, *J. Exp. Med.*, **113**:259.

———, ———, ———, and Conti, C. R., 1961, *ibid.*, **113**:249.

Gould, J. C., and McKillop, E. J., 1954, *J. Hyg.*, **52**:304.

Graudel, H., 1957, *Acta Pathol. Microbiol. Scand.*, **41**:403.

Griffith, R. S., Boniece, W. S., McGuire, J. M., Wolfe, R. N., Joiner, M., Wick, W. E., and Holmes, D. H., 1957–58, *Antibiotics Ann.*, p. 370.

Guaolalupe Mayer Tanguma, M., 1959, *Acta Cient. Potosina*, **3**:137 (*Biol. Abstr.*).

Hall, I. C., 1930, *J. Bacteriol.*, **20**:407.

———, and Howitt, B., 1925, *Proc. Soc. Exp. Biol. Med.*, **22**:541.

———, and ———, 1925, *J. Inf. Dis.*, **37**:112.

Hancock, J. C., Jr., Dulaney, A. D., and Caldwell, M. G., 1959, *Southern Med. J.*, **52**:1525.

Harding, H. B., and Snyder, R. A., 1960, *A.M.A. Arch. Internal Med.*, **105**:217.

Hare, R., Wildy, P., Billett, F. S., and Twort, D. N., 1952, *J. Hyg.*, **50**:295.

Harley, J. D., 1957, *Med. J. Australia*, II, **44**:673.

Hart, D., 1960, *J. Am. Med. Assoc.*, **172**:1019.

Hassal, J. E., and Rountree, P. M., 1959, *Lancet*, **1**:213.

Hay, D. R., 1960, *Quart. J. Med.*, **29**:313.

Haynes, B. W., Jr., Jones, V., and Gibson, C. D., Jr., 1959–60, *Antibiotics Ann.*, p. 728.

Hehre, E. J., and Neill, J. M., 1946, *J. Exp. Med.*, **83**:147.

Highman, B., Altland, P. D., and Eagle, H., 1952, *Proc. Soc. Expt. Biol. Med.*, **81**:135.

Hinton, N. A., Maltman, J. R., and Orr, J. H., 1960, *Am. J. Hyg.*, **72**:343.

———, and Orr, J. H., 1957, *J. Lab. Clin. Med.*, **49**:566.

———, Taggart, J. G., and Orr, J. H., 1960, *Am. J. Clin. Pathol.*, **33**:505.

Hite, K. E., and Hesseltine, H. C., 1947, *J. Inf. Dis.*, **80**:105.

———, ———, and Goldstein, L., 1947, *Am. J. Obstet. Gynecol.*, **53**:233.

Hlava, 1902, *Zentr. Bakteriol., Parasitenk., I Orig.*, **32**:263.

Hobson, P. N., Mann, S. O., and Oxford, A. E., 1958, *J. Gen. Microbiol.*, **19**:462.

Hofstad, T., and Vogelsang, T. M., 1960, *Acta Pathol. Microbiol. Scand.*, **48**:140.

Holloway, W. J., and Scott, E. G., 1959, *Delaware Med. J.*, **31**:198.

Holman, W. L., and Krock, F. H., 1923, *Proc. Soc. Expt. Biol. Med.*, **20**:280.

———, and ———, 1923, *Am. J. Hyg.*, **3**:487.

Horsfall, F. L., 1951, *J. Exp. Med.*, **93**:229.

Hugh, R., 1959, *Can. J. Microbiol.*, **5**:351.

———, Klopp, C. T., and Ryschenkow, E., 1959, *Med. Ann. Dist. Columbia*, **28**:61.

Hurst, V., 1957a, *J. Hyg.*, **55**:299.
———, 1957b, *ibid.*, **55**:313.
———, and Grossman, M., 1958, *Calif. Med.*, **89**:107.
———, and ———, 1960, *New Engl. J. Med.*, **262**:951.
———, ———, Ingram, F. R., and Lowe, A. E., 1958, *J. Am. Med. Assoc.*, **167**:1223.
Innes, A. G., 1960, *J. Appl. Bacteriol.*, **23**:108.
Irwin, J., and Seeley, H. W., Jr., 1958, *J. Bacteriol.*, **76**:29.
James, R. C., and MacLeod, C. J., 1961, *Brit. J. Exp. Pathol.*, **42**:266.
Jeffrey, J. S., and Sklaroff, S. A., 1958, *Lancet*, **1**:365.
Johns, A. T., 1951, *J. Gen. Microbiol.*, **5**:317.
———, 1951, *Biochem. J.*, **49**:559.
———, 1951, *J. Gen. Microbiol.*, **5**:326.
Johnson, J. E., Cluff, L. E., and Goshi, K., 1961, *J. Exp. Med.*, **113**:235.
Jones, D., and Shattock, P. M. F., 1960, *J. Gen. Microbiol.*, **23**:335.
Jones, M., 1950, *Am. Heart J.*, **40**:106.
Jordan, H. V., Fitzgerald, R. J., and Faber, J. E., Jr., 1956, *J. Dental Research*, **35**:404.
Judicial Commission, 1954, *Internat. Bull. Bacteriol. Nomen. and Tax.*, **4**:151.
Kamen, M. D., and Vernon, L. P., 1954, *J. Bacteriol.*, **67**:617.
Kapral, F. A., and Shayegani, M. Gh., 1959, *J. Exp. Med.*, **110**:123.
Kenner, B. A., Clark, H. F., and Kabler, P. W., 1960, *Am. J. Public Health*, **50**:1553.
———, ———, and ———, 1961, *Appl. Microbiol.*, **9**:15.
Kjellander, J., 1960, *Acta Pathol. Microbiol. Scand. Suppl.*, 136.
Koch, M. L., Lepley, D., Jr., Schroeder, C. M., and Smith, M. B., 1959, *J. Am. Med. Assoc.*, **169**:99.
Koenig, M. G., and Kaye, D., 1961, *New Engl. J. Med.*, **264**:257.
Kraus, F. W., Casey, D. W., and Johnson, V., 1953, *J. Dental Research*, **32**:613.
———, and Gaston, C., 1956, *J. Bacteriol.*, **71**:703.
Lachowicz, T., 1959, *Arch. Immunol. Terap Doswiadczalnej*, **7**:687 (*Biol. Abstr.*).
———, 1959, *ibid.*, **7**:693 (*Biol. Abstr.*).
Lancefield, R. C., 1933, *J. Exp. Med.*, **57**:571.
Lang, W. R., Israel, S. L., and Fritz, M. A., 1958, *Obstet. Gynecol.*, **11**:352.
Langford, G. C., Jr., Faber, J. E., Jr., and Pelczar, M. J., Jr., 1950, *J. Bacteriol.*, **59**:349.
Langston, C. W., Gutierrez, J., and Bouma, C., 1960a, *ibid.*, **80**:693.
———, ———, and ———, 1960b, *ibid.*, **80**:714.
Larkin, E. P., Litsky, W., and Fuller, J. E., 1956, *Am. J. Public Health*, **46**:464.
Laurell, G., and Wallmark, G., 1953, *Acta Pathol. Microbiol. Scand.*, **32**:424.
Lederberg, J., and Lederberg, E. M., 1952, *J. Bacteriol.*, **63**:399.
Lefebre, M., and Côté, G., 1958, *Union Méd. Canada*, **87**:694.
Lemierre, A., 1936, *Lancet*, **1**:701.
———, Reilly, J., and Laporte, A., 1938, *Ann. de Méd.* (*Paris*), **44**:165.
Lepper, M. H., Dowling, H. F., Jackson, G. G., and Hirsch, M. M., 1953, *A.M.A. Arch. Internal Med.*, **92**:40.

————, Jackson, G. G., and Dowling, H. F., 1955, *J. Lab. Clin. Med.*, **45**: 935.

Lewkowicz, X., 1901, *Arch. Méd. Exp. et Anat. Pathol.*, **13**:633.

Live, I., and Nichols, A. C., 1961, *J. Inf. Dis.*, **108**:195

Lowbury, E. J. L., 1960, *Brit. Med. J.*, **1**:994.

Mackaness, G. B., 1960, *J. Exp. Med.*, **112**:35.

MacLennan, J. D., 1943, *Lancet*, **2**:63.

Magara, M., Go, K., So, K., and Akima, T., 1948, *Japan. J. Bacteriol.*, **1**:289.

Maltman, J. R., Orr, J. H., and Hinton, N. A., 1960, *Am. J. Hyg.*, **72**:335.

Manfield, P. A., Shooter, R. A., and Lidwell, O. M., 1960, *Brit. Med. J.*, **1**:1098.

Mann, S. O., Masson, F. M., and Oxford, A. E., 1954, *J. Gen. Microbiol.*, **10**:142.

Mattman, L. H., and Senos, G., 1957, *J. Bacteriol.*, **74**:830.

Mazzarella, M. A., and Shklair, I. L., 1960, *J. Dental Research*, **39**:685.

Meiklejohn, G., and Hanford, V. L., 1944, *Proc. Soc. Expt. Biol. Med.*, **57**:356.

Melly, M. A., Thomison, J. B., and Rogers, D. E., 1960, *J. Exp. Med.*, **112**:1121.

Menolasino, N. J., Grieves, B., and Payne, P., 1960, *J. Lab. Clin. Med.*, **56**:908.

Mergenhagen, S. E., 1960, *J. Dental Research*, **39**:267.

————, Hampp, E. G., and Scherp, H. W., 1961, *J. Inf. Dis.*, **108**:304.

————, and Scherp, H. W., 1957, *J. Bacteriol.*, **74**:749.

Miles, A. A., Williams, R. E. O., and Clayton-Cooper, B., 1940, *J. Pathol. Bacteriol.*, **56**:513.

Millian, S. J., Baldwin, J. N., Rheins, M. S., and Weiser, H. H., 1960, *Am. J. Public Health*, **50**:791.

Mirick, G. S., Thomas, L., Curnen, E. C., and Horsfall, F. L., Jr., 1944, *J. Exp. Med.*, **80**:391, 407, 431.

Monro, J. A., and Markham, N. P., 1958, *Lancet*, **2**:186.

Moore, B., 1960, *ibid.*, **2**:453.

Morris, E. O., 1954, *Brit. Dent. J.*, **96**:95, 259.

Moustardier, G., Dulong de Rosnay, C., Du Pasquier, P., and Latrille, J., 1960, *Ann. Inst. Pasteur*, **99**:444.

Mundt, J. O., and Johnson, A. H., 1959, *Food Research*, **24**:218.

Myers, D. M., 1959, *Am. J. Clin. Pathol.*, **31**:128.

Nestoresco, N., Popovici, M., and Alexanco, E., 1960, *Arch. Roumaines Pathol. Exp. Microbiol.*, **19**:69 (*Biol. Abstr.*).

Niven, C. F., Jr., Smiley, K. L., and Sherman, J. M., 1941, *J. Bacteriol.*, **41**:479.

Oeding, P., 1952, *Acta Pathol. Microbiol. Scand. Suppl.*, 93, 356.

————, 1953, *ibid.*, **33**:324.

————, and Sompolinsky, D., 1958, *J. Inf. Dis.*, **102**:23.

Osebold, J. W., and Gray, D. M., 1960, *ibid.*, **106**:91.

Osler, A. G., Buchbinder, L., and Steffen, G. I., 1948, *Proc. Soc. Expt. Biol. Med.*, **67**:456.

Oxford, A. E., 1958, *J. Gen. Microbiol.*, **19**:617.

Pagano, J. S., Farrer, S. M., Plotkin, S. A., Brachman, P. S., Fekety, F. R., and Pidcoe, V., 1960, *Science*, **131**:927.

Pakula, R., Hulanicka, E., and Walczak, W., 1958, *Bull. Acad. Polon. Sci. Classe II*, **6**:325 (*Biol. Abstr.*).

——, ——, and ——, 1959, *Schweiz. Z. allgem. Pathol. u Bakteriol.*, **22**:202 (*Biol. Abstr.*).

Parker, M. T., Tomlinson, A. J. H., and Williams, R. E. O., 1955, *J. Hyg.*, **53**:458.

Pelczar, M. J., Jr., 1953, *J. Bacteriol.*, **65**:744.

——, 1957, in Breed, R. S., Murray, E. G. D., and Smith, N. R., *Bergey's Manual of Determinative Bacteriology*, 7th ed., The Williams & Wilkins Company, Baltimore, p. 485.

——, Hajek, J. P., and Faber, J. E., Jr., 1949, *J. Inf. Dis.*, **85**:239.

Pereira, A. T., 1961, *J. Pathol. Bacteriol.*, **81**:151.

Perry, K. D., Newland, L. G. M., and Briggs, C. A. E., 1958, *ibid.*, **76**:589.

Petersdorf, R. G., Forsyth, B. R., and Bernanke, D., 1958, *New Engl. J. Med.*, **259**:1250.

Plueckhahn, V. D., and Banks, J., 1958, *Med. J. Australia*, I, **45**:664.

Porch, M. L., 1941, *J. Bacteriol.*, **41**:485.

Porterfield, J. S., 1950, *J. Gen. Microbiol.*, **4**:92.

Posada, H. V., and Pérez-Miravete, A., 1958, *Rev. Latinoamer. Microbiol.*, **1**:273 (*Biol. Abstr.*).

Prévot, A.-R., 1933, *Ann. Sci. Nat., Botan. et Biol. Végétale*, Ser. 10, **15**:23, cited by Foubert and Douglas (1948).

——, 1948, *Manuel de classification et de détermination des bactéries anaérobies*, 2d ed., Masson et Cie., Paris.

——, 1957, *ibid.*, 3d ed.

——, de Cadore, F., and Thouvenot, H., 1959, *Ann. Inst. Pasteur*, **97**:860.

——, and Taffanel, J., 1942, *Compt. Rend. Soc. Biol.*, **136**:451.

Prohaska, J. V., 1959, *A.M.A. Arch. Surg.*, **79**:197.

——, Long, E. T., and Nelson, T. S., 1956, *ibid.*, **72**:977.

Provost, P. J., and Doetsch, R. N., 1960, *J. Gen. Microbiol.*, **22**:259.

Rantasalo, I., 1959, *Ann. Chir. et Gynaec. Fenniae*, **48**:449 (abstr. 1959, *J. Am. Med. Assoc.*, **173**:99).

Rebell, G. C., 1947, *J. Invest. Dermatol.*, **8**:13.

Reimann, H. A., 1957, *Proc. Soc. Expt. Biol. Med.*, **96**:411.

Richardson, R. L., and Jones, M., 1958, *J. Dental Research*, **37**:697.

Ridley, M., 1959, *Brit. Med. J.*, **1**:270.

Rifkind, D., and Cole, R. M., 1961, *Bacteriol. Proc.*, p. 127.

Ritter, C., Shull, I. F. and Quinley, R. L., 1956, *Am. J. Public Health*, **46**:612.

Rodaniche, E. C., Palmer, W. L., and Kirsner, J. B., 1943, *J. Inf. Dis.*, **72**:222.

Rogers, D. E., 1956, *Ann. N.Y. Acad. Sci.*, **65**:57.

——, and Melly, M. A., 1960, *J. Exp. Med.*, **111**:533.

——, and Tompsett, R., 1952, *ibid.*, **95**:209.

Rogosa, M., 1956, *J. Bacteriol.*, **72**:533.

——, Fitzgerald, R. J., MacKintosh, M. E., and Beaman, A. J., 1958, *ibid.*, **76**:455.

——, Hampp, E. G., and MacKintosh, M. E., 1961, *Bacteriol. Proc.*, p. 127.

Roodyn, L., 1960a, *J. Hyg.*, **58**:1.

——, 1960b, *ibid.*, **58**:11.

Rosebury, T., 1944, *Medicine*, **23**:249.

—— and Sonnenwirth, A. C., 1958, in Dubos, R. J. (ed.), *Bacterial and Mycotic Infections of Man*, 3d ed., J. B. Lippincott Company, Philadelphia, p. 626.

Rosenberger, R. F., and Elsden, S. R., 1960, *J. Gen. Microbiol.*, **22**:726.
Rosenblum, E. D., and Jackson, J. L. W., 1960, *Texas Repts. Biol. and Med.*, **18**:654.
Rountree, P. M., 1959, *J. Gen. Microbiol.*, **20**:620.
Rozansky, R., Wellisch, G., Halevi, C., and Birnbaum, D., 1960, *Bull. Research Council Israel Sect. E., Exp. Med.*, **8E**:105 (*Biol. Abstr.*).
Runnels, J. L., and Wilson, J. B., 1960, *J. Bacteriol.*, **80**:727.
Sakurai, N., Updyke, E. L., Nahmias, A. J., and Gerhardt, M. R., 1961, *Am. J. Public Health*, **51**:566.
Sanchez-Torres, L. E., Barocio-Lozano, L., Bolaños-Castellanos, G., Bruggemann-Schmidt, Ch., and Velasco-Hernandez, N., 1959, *Rev. Latinoamer. Microbiol.*, **2**:63 (*Biol. Abstr.*).
Sanders, G. B., and Kinnaird, D. W., 1955, *Southern Med. J.*, **48**:1226.
Saslaw, M. S., Saul, M., Jenks, S. A., and Jablon, J. M., 1959, *J. Bacteriol.*, **77**:519.
Schaub, I. G., and Davis, J. E., 1945, *Bull. Johns Hopkins Hosp.*, **77**:372.
———, and Merritt, C. D., 1960, *ibid.*, **106**:25.
Schwarz, O. H., and Brown, T. K., 1936, *Am. J. Obstet. Gynecol.*, **31**:379.
———, and Dieckmann, W. S., 1926, *Southern Med. J.*, **19**:470.
Selbie, F. R., Simon, R. D., and Robinson, R. H. M., 1949, *Brit. Med. J.*, **2**:667.
Sharpe, M. E., 1952, *J. Gen. Microbiol.*, **7**:192.
———, 1952, *J. Hyg.*, **50**:209.
———, and Shattock, P. M. F., 1952, *J. Gen. Microbiol.*, **6**:150.
Shattock, P. M. F., 1949, *ibid.*, **3**:80.
———, 1955, *Ann. Inst. Pasteur Lille*, **7**:95.
Sherman, J. M., 1937, *Bacteriol. Rev.*, **1**:3.
Shiota, T., and Kunkel, M. F., Jr., 1958, *J. Dental Research*, **37**:780.
Shooter, R. A., Girling, J. A., Matthias, J. Q., and Williams, R. E. O., 1960, *Brit. Med. J.*, **1**:1923.
Skadhauge, K., 1950, *Studies on Enterococci with Special Reference to the Serological Properties*, Medical dissertation, University of Copenhagen, E. Munksgaard, Copenhagen (*Biol. Abstr.*).
Slanetz, L. W., and Bartley, C. H., 1957, *J. Bacteriol.*, **74**:591.
Smith, H. W., and Crabb, W. E., 1960, *Lancet*, **2**:515.
Smith, I. M., Beals, P. D., Kingsbury, K. R., and Hasenclever, H. F., 1958, *A.M.A. Arch. Internal Med.*, **102**:375.
———, Wilson, A. P., Hazard, E. Ch., Hummer, W. K., and Dewey, M. E., 1960, *J. Inf. Dis.*, **107**:369.
Soltau, D. H. K., and Hatcher, G. W., 1960, *Brit. Med. J.*, **1**:1603.
Spink, W. W., and Vivino, J. J., 1942, *J. Clin. Invest.*, **21**:353.
Stefanesco, V., and Manoliu, N., Brailoiu, A., and Bustea, C., 1959, *Arch. Roumaines Path. Exp. Microbiol.* **18**:77 (*Biol. Abstr.*).
Stenderup, A., Bach, A., Pedersen, G. T., and Rosendal, K., 1959, *Acta Pathol. Microbiol. Scand.*, **45**:95.
Stone, M. L., 1940, *J. Bacteriol.*, **39**:559.
Sword, C. P., Shikashio, T., Sword, M. G., and Martin, M. K., 1961, *Bacteriol. Proc.*, p. 110.
Szita, J., 1957, *Acta Microbiol. Acad. Sci. Hung.*, **4**:289 (*Biol. Abstr.*).
Taplin, J., and Goldworthy, N. E., 1958, *Australian J. Exp. Biol. Med. Sci.* **36**:289.

————, and ————, 1959, *Med. J. Australia*, **46**:259.

Taylor, A. L., 1929, *A System of Bacteriology in Relation to Medicine* (*London*), **2**:136.

Thjötta, T., and Böe, J., 1938, *Acta Pathol. Microbiol. Scand. Suppl.*, **37**: 527.

Thomas, L., Mirick, G. S., Curnen, E. C., Zeigler, J. E., Jr., and Horsfall, F. L., 1943, *Science*, **98**:566.

Thompson, R., 1940, *Arch. Pathol.*, **30**:1096.

Toh, C. C. S., and Ball, K. P., 1960, *Brit. Med. J.*, **2**:640.

Turnball, R. B., Jr., 1957, *J. Am. Med. Assoc.*, **164**:756.

Van Eseltine, W. P., 1955, *Internat. Bull. Bacteriol. Nomen. and Tax.*, **5**:53 (*Biol. Abstr.*).

Veillon, A., 1893, *Comp. Rend. Soc. Biol.*, **45**:807.

Veron, M., Thibault, P., and Second, L., 1959, *Ann. Inst. Pasteur*, **97**:497.

————, ————, and ————, 1961, *ibid.*, **100**:166.

Vogelsang, T. M., 1958, *Acta Pathol. Microbiol. Scand.*, **43**:196.

————, 1959, *Tidsskr. Norske Laegeforen.*, **79**:517 (abstr. 1959, *J. Am. Med. Assoc.*, **171**:1428).

————, and Haaland, H., 1959, *Acta Pathol. Microbiol. Scand.*, **45**:67, 77, 281, 295.

Waisbren, B. A., and Abboud, F., 1960, *Ann. Internal Med.* **52**:643.

Wallmark, G., and Finland, M., 1961*a*, *Proc. Soc. Exp. Biol. Med.*, **106**:73.

————, and ————, 1961*b*. *J. Am. Med. Assoc.*, **175**:886.

Warner, G. S., Faber, J. E., Jr., and Pelczar, M. J., Jr., 1952, *J. Inf. Dis.*, **90**:97.

Weichselbaum, A., and Ghon, A., 1905, *Wien. klin. Wochnschr.*, **18**:625.

Weinstein, H. J., 1959, *New Engl. J. Med.*, **260**:1303.

White, A., 1961, *J. Clin. Invest.*, **40**:23.

White, E., 1933, *J. Obstet. Gynecol.*, **40**:630.

White, J. C., and Niven, C. F., 1946, *J. Bacteriol.*, **51**:717.

Whiteley, H. R., and Ordal, E. J., 1955, *ibid.*, **70**:608.

Wilkinson, A. E., 1952, *Brit. J. Venereal Diseases*, **28**:24.

Williams, J. R. B., Talbot, E. C. S., and Maughan, E., 1959, *Brit. Med. J.* **1**:1374.

Williams, N. B., Forbes, M. A., Blau, E., and Eickenberg, C. F., 1950, *J. Dental Research*, **29**:563.

Williams, R. E. O., 1956, *J. Pathol. Bacteriol.*, **72**:15.

————, Jevons, M. P., Shooter, R. A., Hunter, C. J. W., Girling, J. A., Griffiths, J. D., and Taylor, G. W., 1959, *Brit. Med. J.*, **2**:658.

————, and Rippon, J. E., 1952, *J. Hyg.*, **50**:320.

Wills, M. R., and Reece, M. W., 1960, *Brit. Med. J.*, **2**:566.

Wilson, G. S., and Miles, A. A., 1946, *Topley and Wilson's Principles of Bacteriology and Immunity*. 3d ed., The Williams & Wilkins Company, Baltimore, vol. 1, p. 537.

———— and ————, 1955, *ibid.*, 4th ed., vol. 2, p. 2259.

Winblad, S., 1960, *Acta Pathol. Microbiol. Scand.*, **50**:64.

Wolf, H. W., Harris, M. M., and Dyer, W. R., 1959, *J. Am. Med. Assoc.*, **169**:1983.

Wolinsky, E., Lipsitz, P. J., Mortimer, E. A., and Rammelkam, C. H., 1960, *Lancet*, **2**:620.

Wood, M., 1959, *J. Gen. Microbiol.*, **21**:385.

CHAPTER 3

INDIGENOUS GRAM-POSITIVE BACILLI

Lactobacilli

The lactobacilli are associated in man with activities in the mouth, the lower intestine, and the vagina. Species to which importance is attributed include saprophytes as well as strict parasites, and roles assigned to the group or members of it range from participation in disease to activities that seem protective of the host.

The Genus *Lactobacillus*

The generic term *Lactobacillus* is limited here to microaerophilic forms. Anaerobes formerly classified as *Lactobacillus bifidus* are regrouped under *Actinomyces* (page 58). The true lactobacilli are characterized principally [Breed, Murray, and Smith (1957)] as a diverse group of nonmotile Gram-positive rods, often long and slender, dissimilating carbohydrates either homofermentatively to lactic acid or heterofermentatively to lactic acid and other products including CO_2. They do not liquefy gelatin and do not produce catalase. The group is widely distributed in natural fermentations. Species include *L. acidophilus*, a typical amphibiont. We are concerned here with this species and also with saprophytic forms, like *L. casei*, that are prominent in the indigenous biota. For a more complete treatment of the systematics of lactobacilli and guides to the literature see Rosebury (1944a); Rogosa et al. (1953); Pederson and Albury (1955); Davis (1955, 1959); and Rogosa and Sharpe (1959).

Historical

The lactobacilli have been widely studied in at least four largely separate contexts: (1) in connection with the fermentation industries; (2) as a group with complex nutritional requirements and curious biochemical activities, including their use for microbiological assays for vitamins; (3) as apparently beneficial to man, beginning with the view of Metchnikoff (1908) of a relationship between the use of certain fermented milks and longevity, and including well-recognized effects in the adult vagina; and (4) as harmful to man in curious ways: (*a*) being possibly the principal bacterial agency in dental caries; (*b*) as vitamin-requiring forms that may antagonize vitamin-synthesizing bacteria in the intestinal tract; and (*c*) rarely in pathogenic activities of a more conventional sort, in which, as will be seen, the lactobacilli are in no way distinguishable from certain other amphibionts.

Symbionts or Pathogens? The apparent conflict between the suggested beneficial and harmful effects, particularly between attempts to use a lactobacillus as a therapeutic agent, on the one hand, and a postulated role for putatively the same lactobacillus as the cause of dental caries, gave rise to controversy that has now been essentially resolved. Until recently the obviously saprophytic species described by workers in areas designated 1 and 2 in the foregoing paragraph were thought to be quite distinct from the presumed parasites of areas 3 and 4. The difficulty arose, indeed, out of the further (erroneous) assumption that aerobic lactobacilli found in a parasitic milieu could be included within the single specific name reserved for a parasite, *L. acidophilus*. This step seemed to be justified by the early findings of Herter and Kendall (1908) and Rahe (1915) that Metchnikoff's *L. bulgaricus* could not be implanted in the monkey or human intestine, i.e., was not parasitic for these hosts. As recently as 1937, Pederson underscored the taxonomic problem with a comment on gas-producing lactobacilli that seemed applicable throughout the genus: "There is little justification for the large number of species listed in the group at present." Such considerations led workers in the dental field, including the writer [see Rosebury (1944*a*)] to lump all the aerobic lactobacilli that seemed to be parasitic, despite their obvious heterogeneity [e.g., Rosebury, Linton, and Buchbinder (1929)] as *L. acidophilus*.

Resolution of the difficulty has come principally within the 1950s. Pederson (1947) noted that certain oral lactobacilli that had been called *L. acidophilus* were indistinguishable from the saprophytic *L. casei* of milk. More recently Sharpe and Mattick (1957) noted that 4 strains used for implantation in the human intestine, presumed to be *L. acidophilus*, were also *L. casei* or a variety of *L. casei*. Pederson's observation has been confirmed by many workers and developed into a basis for an adequate classification of lactobacilli derived from the mouth [Rogosa, Mitchell, and Fitzgerald (1950, 1953); Tilden and Svec (1950, 1952); Grubb and Crasse (1953); Davis, Bisset, and Hale (1955); Davis (1955); and others]. Pederson and Albury (1955) and Davis and Hayward (1955) have provided evidence for the stability of the distinguishing characters. It is now clear that the lactobacilli of the mouth include *L. acidophilus* usually as a minority member among a group most of which are saprophytes. While no comparable study has been reported for the intestinal lactobacilli, there is suggestive evidence that a similar distribution applies. The early apparent conflict between Morishita (1928, 1929) and Rosebury, Linton, and Buchbinder (1929) and their respective camps can now be resolved both in the light of the foregoing discussion—*L. acidophilus* is a distinctive species found in both areas—and more precisely; since Harrison and Opal (1944) found that the fecal lactobacilli resembled in distribution of varieties those found in the mouth of the corresponding individual subject.

Classification of the Oral Lactobacilli

Both homofermentative and heterofermentative lactobacilli have been recovered from the mouth, the latter being distinguished in practice by the production of gas from glucose [or from maltose; see Hayward (1957)]. The species found most frequently, and their distinguishing features, are given in Table 3-1, adapted from Davis (1955; see Fig. 3-1).

L. casei, usually the commonest *homofermentative* species, is characterized by a smooth colony, curved bacilli often in curling chains, and growth at 15° but variably at 45°. Mannite, salicin, and mannose are fermented; arabinose is not; esculin and sodium hippurate are hydrolyzed; and acetylmethylcarbinol is usually produced. Lactose is regularly fermented by most varieties, but a lactose nonfermenting *L. casei* variant has been described by Jensen et al. (1956). The homofermentative parasitic *L. acidophilus* has a small rough colony; its cells are variable, straight, and usually rather long. Growth occurs at 45° but not at 15°; ammonia is not produced. Typical strains ferment salicin, lactose, melibiose, and mannose but not mannite, sorbitol, rhamnose, or arabinose; 8 per cent NaCl is not tolerated; other characteristics are variable. A less frequent homofermentative species is *L. plantarum*, which differs from *L. casei* chiefly in showing short straight bacilli. It usually fails to grow at 45°, usually ferments arabinose, and is less variable in its other reactions. An additional homofermentative species defined by Rogosa et al. (1953) is *L. salivarius*, which differs from *L. acidophilus* principally in that the former ferments mannitol and sorbitol.

Among *heterofermentative* species, *L. fermenti* is found most commonly in the mouth. The colony is usually smooth and relatively large, the cells straight and short. This species grows at 45° but usually not at 15°. It forms ammonia, usually hydrolyzes esculin and hippurate, and tolerates 10 per cent bile but not 8 per cent sodium chloride. Reactions in the differential carbohydrates are nearly all negative; arabinose and mannose are fermented variably. *L. brevis*, another gas-forming species, has a rough or intermediate colony and is distinguished otherwise by

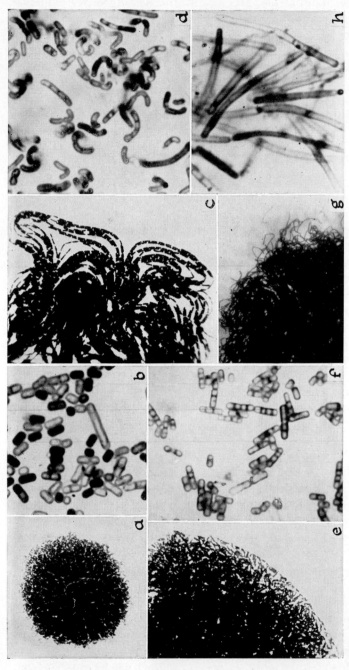

FIG. 3-1. Lactobacilli. *a, b, L. fermenti,* showing the characteristic morphology of heterofermentative oral strains: smooth colony, short bacilli. *c, d, L. casei;* "medusa-head" colony with bacilli in chains, curved bacilli; this morphology is also seen in certain strains of *L. acidophilus. e, f, L. brevis,* showing morphology of a minority of heterofermentative oral strains; smooth colony, septate bacilli longer than those of *L. fermenti. g, h, L. acidophilus;* rough colony, filamentous cells. Colony impression preparations by Bisset's method (1938, *I. Pathol. Bacteriol.,* **47:**223); stains for cell wall by Hale's phosphomolybdic acid method (1953, *Lab. Practice,* **2:**115). [*From Davis, Bisset, and Hale* (1955), *courtesy of Dr. G. H. G. Davis and I. Gen. Microbiol.*]

TABLE 3-1

PRINCIPAL SPECIES OF LACTOBACILLI IN THE HUMAN MOUTH
(COMPILED FROM THE DATA OF DAVIS, 1955)

	Homofermentative			Heterofermentative	
	Group I L. acidophilus and varieties	Group II L. casei and varieties	Group III L. plantarum	Group IV L. fermenti	Group V L. brevis
Colony	Medusa-head; flat, rough, irregular	Mucoid, smooth to intermediate	Smooth	Smooth to intermediate	Rough, irregular
Cell type	Long bacilli	Curling chains	Short single and paired bacilli	Short single and paired bacilli	Short to medium bacilli
Growth at 15°	−	+	+	−/W	−
Growth at 45°	+	+/W	−/W	+	+
NH₃ from arginine	−	−	−	+	−V
Esculin hydrolyzed	V	+	+	−	+
Hippurate hydrolyzed	−/W	+	+	−	+
Acetoin produced	−/W	W/+	+	−	−
Fermented:*					
Mannitol	−	+	+	−	−
Sorbitol	−	+V	+	−	−
Salicin	+V	+	+	−	+V
Rhamnose	−	+V	+	−	−
Arabinose	−	−	+V	−V	+
Mannose	+	+	+	−V	−
Tolerance of:					
10 % bile	+V	+V	+	+	−
8 % NaCl	−V	+V	+	−	−
Titratable acid from glucose (ml 0.1N NaOH in 10 ml)	1–6	4–6	4–6	2–4	1–3
Percentage frequency in the mouth	9.4	44.6	1.2	40.0	4.7

+, normally positive; −, normally negative; +V, variable, over 50 % positive; −V, over 50 % negative; W, weak (+/W, positive to weak; −/W, negative to weakly positive).

* Substrates given in the original having no differential value (e.g., raffinose, lactose) have been omitted; also omitted are other tests (e.g., tolerance of 0.3–0.4 % phenol) which gave positive or variable results throughout.

hydrolysis of esculin and sodium hippurate, by failure to grow in 10 per cent bile, and usually by failing to form NH₃. Two additional hetero-fermentative lactobacilli that have been described as occurring in the mouth are *L. buchneri*, closely related to *L. fermenti*; and *L. cellobiosus*, distinguished principally by fermentation of cellobiose [see Rogosa et al. (1953), Hayward, 1957)].

The homofermentative species, when they grow abundantly in vitro [see Rosebury (1932); Sullivan, Still, and Goldsworthy (1939)], are more active acid-producers than the heterofermentative forms, as would be expected. A rough correspondence between the foregoing classification and the older one of Hadley (1933) may be noted: Hadley's type I corresponds generally to *L. casei*, type II to *L. fermenti*, and type III to *L. acidophilus*.

Some Biochemical Characteristics. The metabolic characteristics of lactobacilli, like those of streptococci (of lactic acid bacteria in general), have been well characterized by Thiman (1955), who noted that "true lactic organisms do not produce large colonies on ordinary solid media" because of three peculiarities: (1) they are microaerophilic, having no cytochrome oxidase or catalase, and respire only by spontaneous oxidation of reduced flavoprotein, forming hydrogen peroxide; (2) they have little ability to synthesize amino acids, and hence tend to require them preformed in the medium [see Koser and Thomas (1955)]; and (3) they also require B-group vitamins. These requirements permit the use of certain strains of lactobacilli in the bioassay of the required amino acids or vitamins. It may be noted that catalase activity has occasionally been described among lactobacilli [Prévot and Raynaud (1955); Dacre and Sharpe (1956); but see the doubt mentioned by Rogosa and Sharpe (1959), and the comment by Gutakunst, Delwiche, and Seeley (1957)]. Strittmatter (1959) was unable to demonstrate iron-porphyrin enzymes in lactobacilli by spectrophotometric or chemical means and found that electron transport to oxygen by *L. casei* seemed to be mediated largely if not exclusively by flavoprotein enzyme systems. While lactobacilli as a group evidently depend principally on anaerobic carbohydrate breakdown for their energy, they may also metabolize amino acids [Lagerborg and Clapper (1952)]. *L. casei* has been found to deaminate serine, cysteine, and asparagine [Kristoffersen and Nelson (1955)], and this and other species of lactobacilli have been shown to have proteolytic activity of importance in the cheese industry [see Brandsaeter and Nelson (1956)].

Other Bases for Classification. Alternative bases for the classification of lactobacilli to replace the cumbersome group of criteria exemplified in Table 3-1 have been sought for many years. Among these may be mentioned attempts at an immunologic classification of the oral species [Harrison et al. (1939); Harrison (1942); Williams (1947, 1948); Orland (1950)] which has more recently been broadened to include the whole genus [Sharpe (1955); Sharpe and Wheater (1957); see also Princivalle et al. (1959)]. Other suggested procedures have made use of reduction of 2,3,5-triphenyltetrazolium chloride [Schmidt and Burnett (1956)], infrared absorption spectra [Goulden and Sharpe (1958)] or paper chromatography (Botazzi (1958); Botazzi and Sharpe (1958); Cheeseman (1960)]. Following the isolation of bacteriophages from cheese lactobacilli by Kiuru and Tybeck (1955) and the recovery of lactobacillus phages from millipore-filtered mouth washings by Meyers et al. (1958), data pointing to the usefulness of phage typing of lactobacilli were presented by Coetzee, deKlerk, and Sacks (1960).

Media

Media for selective isolation of lactobacilli from mucous membrane sources have been devised by Kulp and White (1932); Hadley (1933); Rogosa, Mitchell, and Wiseman (1951); and Emard and Vaughn (1952); see also Dewar and Parfitt (1951) and Charlton and Spies (1956). Ellis and Sarles (1958) have developed a procedure, using the medium of Rogosa et al. (1951) and the replica plating technique of Lederberg and Lederberg (1952), for isolation of antibiotic-resistant lactobacilli from human feces. A medium for cultivation and a base for fermentation tests, suitable for fastidious strains, has been devised by De Man, Rogosa, and Sharpe (1960). [See also Rogosa, Franklin, and Perry (1961) and Dawbarn, Forsyth, and Kilpatrick (1961).]

Distribution

Lactobacilli are found principally in the mouth, in the lower intestine, and in the vagina during the period of sexual activity.

Mouth. The presence and concentration of lactobacilli in the mouth are correlated with the activity of dental caries. Counts in mixed stimulated saliva, made as an index of caries activity, show concentrations per milliliter, when positive, up to 10^6 with a median of approximately 10^4 (see Charlton and Spies, 1956). In the "census" of saliva reported by Richardson and Jones (1958), the mean count for lactobacilli in 14 subjects was given as 3.5×10^4, the range as 0 to 2.5×10^5.

Representative data on the distribution of species of lactobacilli in the mouth are given in Table 3-2. Those reported from Britain and the United States are in good agreement, indicating that the homofermentative *L. casei* and the heterofermentative *L. fermenti* are most common, with *L. acidophilus* accounting for roughly 10 per cent of isolations and the other species occurring less frequently. The other data depart more or less widely from this pattern, perhaps as a reflection of the characteristic diet of the locality [see Baird-Parker, Bisset, and Pike (1958) and Featherstone (1960b)].

Intestine. In the intestine of adults lactobacilli may be sparse and difficult to isolate. Their numbers have been increased, e.g., by feeding high lactose diets [Kopeloff (1926); Rettger et al. (1935)]. Harrison and Opal (1944), in a study of 20 hospitalized children aged 8 to 17 over approximately 6 weeks, found lactobacilli in the mouths of 93 per cent and in the feces of 66 per cent. Five subjects who yielded lacto-

TABLE 3-2

PER CENT DISTRIBUTION OF *Lactobacillus* SPECIES IN THE MOUTH*

	British		U.S.	Italian urban	Australian aborigines	
					Semi-civilized	Primitive
Number of subjects	[a]	16[b]	130[c]	66[d]	22[e]	49[f]
Number of cultures	403	673	500	357	32	53
L. casei	45	41	39	32†	3	0
L. plantarum	1	3	2	4	9	0
L. salivarius		3	2	3	25	19
L. acidophilus	9	10	11	22	9	13
L. fermenti	40	30	31	28	34	53
L. brevis	5	6	6	7	16	8
L. buchneri		4	5	4		
L. cellobiosus			2			8
Other spp. or unidentified		2	2		3	

* Based on number of cultures except for column 5, where the base is "number of individuals in which species occur[red]."

† Includes 10% identified as *casei-plantarum* intermediates.

[a] Davis (1955)　　　　　　[d] Hayward and Davis (1956)
[b] Hayward (1957)　　　　　[e] Featherstone (1959)
[c] Rogosa et al. (1953)　　　[f] Featherstone (1960)

bacilli in only one-third of their saliva samples failed to reveal the organisms in their feces. Attempts to isolate lactobacilli from stool specimens were always unsuccessful when the specimens were obtained 24 to 40 hours after negative saliva samples had been collected. Three-fourths of the fecal samples yielded lactobacilli when the corresponding saliva count had been above 10^3 per ml, and only one-fifth gave positive cultures when the saliva count was lower. In paired samples, the varieties of lactobacilli, as determined by morphologic and biochemical tests without attempts to distinguish species, seemed to be the same in each individual in the two source materials. "*Lactobacilli were not found in any of 14 stool specimens from 5 children whose mouths were free from dental caries.*" As Harrison and Opal pointed out, it thus appears that the intestinal lactobacilli originate in the mouth, and that in both sites their frequency and numbers are probably correlated with dental caries activity.

Smith and Crabb (1961*a,b*) found lactobacilli, regarded as generally typical, in all of 10 samples of feces from human adults, in median concentration ($10^{8.8}$ per Gm) second only to bacteroides (see Chap. 10 and Table 10-4).

Vagina. It is generally accepted that the lactobacilli originally described in the vagina by Döderlein in 1892 are constant and perhaps dominant members of the biota in the interval between puberty and the menopause; that these organisms are responsible for the low pH of the vaginal secretion during this period, and that the acidity in turn serves a protective function by inhibiting the growth of many other bacteria, including pathogens [see Rosebury (1944); Laughton (1948); and Chap. 10]. The common assumption that Döderlein's bacillus is *L. acidophilus* is apparently no more tenable than the comparable assumptions made for oral and intestinal lactobacilli. Only 4 of 18 strains of lactobacilli from the vagina were found by Hayward (1957) to be *L. acidophilus;* 10 were *L. fermenti,* 3 were *L. salivarius,* and 1 was unidentified. Hunter, Long, and Schumacher (1959) have also found the vaginal lactobacilli to be heterogenous. Rogosa and Sharpe (1960) reported that some 25 per cent of 35 strains from the vagina of 21 normal nonpregnant women were heterofermentative, including *L. fermenti* and *L. cellobiosus;* 14 of 21 isolates were *L. acidophilus* and 2 were *L. casei.*

Weinstein (1938) found that the incidence of aerobic lactobacilli in the vagina increased during pregnancy to a maximum in the last two months. Hite et al. (1947) found "aciduric rods," presumably lactobacilli, in only 39 of 61, or 63 per cent, of instances in the normal prenatal vagina. Laughton (1950; see also page 78) has suggested that actively acidogenic corynebacteria may be even more frequent in the premenopausal vagina than Döderlein's bacillus, and may play a definite role in production of the high vaginal acidity characteristic of that time.

Animals. Lactobacilli are also found in the ovine and bovine rumina with a distribution of species not markedly different from that of the human mouth [see Jensen et al. (1956)], but species other than *L. acidophilus* and *L. casei* were present at concentrations of 10^6 per ml or higher. Wilssens and Buttiaux (1958) found both homofermentative and heterofermentative lactobacilli in the feces of healthy cattle.

Ecologic Relations

The significance attributed to lactobacilli in the indigenous biota, including their beneficial effects in the vagina as well as their harmful effects in dental caries, is customarily linked to their capacity to produce and withstand pH levels low enough either to inhibit other bacterial species or to decalcify teeth. Activities have been suggested, however, on the basis of other mechanisms. Guillot (1958), for instance, has reported that *L. acidophilus* produces a water-soluble substance other than acid which has a degree of inhibitory action against *Candida albicans* and may help to stabilize this fungus in the indigenous biota. It is noted elsewhere that *C. albicans* characteristically accompanies the lactobacilli in the so-called "aciduric biota" (Chap. 7). Johansson, Peterson, and Dick (1953) reported that in rats given chlortetracycline as a growth stimulant, increased growth was associated with a relative increase of coliform organisms and a decrease of lactobacilli in the intestine [see also Johansson and Sarles (1949)]:

Since coliform bacteria are able to synthesize most growth factors which they require . . . and lactobacilli demand a wide variety of preformed vitamins, amino acids and so forth, the shift in the relative numbers of these organisms in favor of the coliforms may reduce the total amounts of nutrilites bound within nutritionally fastidious cells and stimulate the synthesizing flora. . . . The decrease in lactobacilli was compensated for by a rise in enterococci, which require fewer growth factors. . . .

Rhodes et al. (1954) and Wiseman et al. (1956) have reported similar results in antibiotic-fed chicks. Veltre et al. (1953) suggested that antibiotic growth stimulation in chicks and turkey poults may also involve inhibition of the anaerobic *Actinomyces bifidus*.

Pathogenicity

Lactobacilli have been recovered from the blood in rare instances of bacterial endocarditis [Marschall (1938); Biocca and Seppilli (1944, 1947)]. Korttila (1953) isolated *L. acidophilus* as the apparently sole agent from a case of lung abscess; the isolated organism appeared to be pathogenic for mice, doubtfully so for guinea pigs, and innocuous for rabbits or rats.

Actinomyces

Two well-defined genera of actinomycetales—bacteria tending to form filaments and tending to branch—appear to be or to include indigenous forms: (1) the anaerobic or microaerophilic parasitic mycelial forms that constitute the genus *Actinomyces*, and (2) members of the genus *Mycobacterium* (see page 82).

Certain Properties of *Actinomycetales*

Fungi or Bacteria? All actinomycetales, including saprophytic mycelial genera (e.g., *Nocardia*, *Streptomyces*) are now unequivocally classed with the bacteria rather than with the higher fungi. Waksman (1957) has reviewed the bases for this taxonomic disposition. As distinguished from the fungi, the actinomycetes have the following characteristics: (1) they resemble bacteria in size (the diameter of mycelium and spores) and staining properties (Gram-positive; some are acid-fast); (2) some actinomycetes, notably species of *Actinomyces* and *Nocardia*, are closely related to such bacterial genera as *Lactobacillus* and *Corynebacterium*; (3) the actinomycetes, like the bacteria, do not seem to contain fully organized nuclei [Hagedorn (1955)]; (4) actinomyces are susceptible to phages; (5) actinomyces are sensitive to antibiotics which attack bacteria; and (6) unlike fungi but like bacteria, actinomycetes contain neither chitin nor cellulose in their cell walls [Avery and Blank (1954)]. Romano and Nickerson (1956) found the cell wall of the vegetative mycelium of a *Streptomyces* (*S. fradiae*) to be similar to that of bacteria in its content of mucopolysaccharides and amino acids. Cummins and Harris (1958) have reported comparable findings for *Actinomyces israelii*.

Generic Characteristics of *Actinomyces*. The genus *Actinomyces* consists of Gram-positive rods and filaments usually 1 μ or less in diameter, sometimes forming a true mycelium which fragments easily into bacillus-like elements or into irregular V- and Y-branched twiglike forms. Spores or conidia are not formed. The organisms are anaerobic or microaerophilic, not acid-fast, and nonmotile. They produce acid without gas in fermentation and are catalase-negative; gelatin is not liquefied.

Major Groupings. The definition of species within the genus *Actinomyces* has been a vexed question virtually from the outset and is only beginning to be clarified. An initial separation into 2 groups will be found justified by a growing consensus: (1) the *Bifidus* group, previously classed with the lactobacilli, and (2) the *Israelii* group, including or comprising the forms associated with actinomycosis in man.

The *Bifidus* Group (*Lactobacillus bifidus*)

Historical. At the turn of the century Tissier (1899, 1900, 1905) pointed out that neither colon bacilli nor aerobic lactobacilli are characteristically found in the intestines of breast-fed babies. Rather, anaerobic bacilli showing a single Y-branch (crooklike bifurcation) on one or both ends, which he called *Bacillus bifidus communis*, are found nearly exclusively in nurseling feces; whereas in bottle-fed infants similar organisms are present but scarce in a mixed biota. These findings have been confirmed repeatedly (see Chap. 10); and the bacteriologic differences between breast-fed and bottle-fed infants has come to be associated with differences in growth rate and in resistance to infection, respiratory as well as intestinal, favoring the use of human milk [see Cruickshank (1945); Robinson (1951); Robinson and Thompson (1952)]. Many efforts to elucidate the mechanism of this phenomenon have led to only partial success up to the present, as will be noted below. This organism came to be classed as a lactobacillus, but seemed to constitute a group entirely distinct from other species of this genus.

Actinomyces bifidus. Much of the confusion that has surrounded the taxonomy of this bacterium (see below) may be dispelled by its removal from the genus *Lactobacillus* and its placement in *Actinomyces.* The latter step has been suggested repeatedly [see Rosebury (1944b); Frank and Skinner (1954); Pine and Howell (1956)]; Rogosa and Sharpe (1959) have rejected it as a lactobacillus. Pine and Howell studied 4 strains of *A. bifidus* including 2 previously reported on by Norris et al. (1950; see below), and compared them with strains of the *A. israelii* group. Their bifidus cultures showed bifid morphology consistently and almost exclusively, with no tendency to mutation. One of three strains tested grew slightly under aerobic conditions in the presence of added CO_2; the other two grew only anaerobically with CO_2. None of the strains produced gas. All were catalase-negative; none liquefied gelatin. The bifidus strains were remarkably similar to the *israelii* forms in their biochemical characteristics, with two principal differences: (1) the latter reduced nitrates, the bifid strains did not; and (2) the *israelii* group produced larger quantities of acetic acid from glucose, apparently by utilizing a separate metabolic pathway. [See also Beerens, Gerard, and Guillaume (1957).] From morphologic studies of both of these groups and also of *Butyribacterium rettgeri*, *Propionibacterium* spp., *Corynebacterium acnes*, and *Lactobacillus* spp., Sundman, Björksten, and Gyllenberg (1959) confirmed a relationship of the *pennsylvanicus* variety of bifidus (see page 60) to *Actinomyces* and suggested that the others are related to *Butyribacterium.* They were agreed that the bifid bacteria do not belong in the genus *Lactobacillus.* On the other hand, Slack, Winger, and Moore (1961) observed no interaction between two strains of bifidus and fluorescein-labeled antibody to israelii-group actinomycetes.

Attempts at a Finer Classification of *A. bifidus.* Rettger and his co-workers [Weiss and Rettger (1934, 1938); Lewis and Rettger (1940); King and Rettger (1942)] suggested that there were 2 varieties of Tissier's bacillus which they distinguished as *L. bifidus*, the pleomorphic form showing branching—characterized as microaerophilic—and an unbranched form, *L. parabifidus*, strictly anaerobic; the 2 groups were reported to differ serologically and in other respects. On the other hand, Norris et al. (1950) held that unbranched strains are probably derived by mutation from the branched forms. These workers stated that the unbranched forms grow aerobically; although characterized as related to or identical with *L. acidophilus*, they were described as forming large amounts of molecular CO_2—i.e., as heterofermentative. The bifid forms, in the hands of these workers, required CO_2 for growth and tolerated up to 3 per cent of atmospheric oxygen when grown on solid media; in broth they grew in air without added CO_2. The names *L. bifidus* and *L. parabifidus* were then applied, with morphologic but not with biochemical consistency, to the bifid-micro-aerophilic and the straight-aerobic forms, respectively—neither, obviously, was strictly anaerobic. It is of interest that a later paper from the same group [Barbero (1952)], referring to the Norris study, spoke of "*L. bifidus* and its mutant (*L. acidophilus*)." Robinson and Thompson (1952), evidently guided by descriptions of American Type Culture Collection strains, referred to "*Lactobacillus acidophilus (bifidus).*" Williams, Norris, and György (1953), continued the use of *L. bifidus* and *L. parabifidus* as had their predecessors, noting that this usage reversed that of Weiss and Rettger (1934). They again characterized the former as homofermentative and *L. parabifidus* as heterofermentative, even though in some instances the latter had evidently been derived from *L. bifidus* cultures. Attempts at antigenic classification were inconclusive, but no cross-reactions were observed with three strains of *L. acidophilus*.

A. bifidus var. *pennsylvanicus*. György, Norris, and Rose (1954) [see also György and Rose (1955)] characterized a variety *pennsylvanicus* of *A. bifidus* as one with the special nutritional requirement of the blood-group mucoid or one of its lower molecular-weight oligo- or polysaccharide fractions (see below). This variety was held to be common in both breast-fed and bottle-fed infant stools [György (1953)], and apparently similar nutritionally exacting strains have been found by the same group of workers in the vagina of pregnant women [Harrison et al. (1953)]. Gyllenberg and Carlberg (1958), however, stated that a variety of *L. bifidus* with simpler nutritive requirements, as described by Hassinen et al. (1951) [see also Petuely (1956)]—growing with only biotin, pantothenic acid, and cysteine as specific growth factors—characterizes the intestinal biota of breast-fed infants, while most strains isolated from bottle-fed infants showed more complicated nutritional requirements.

A. bifidus **in the Nurseling Stool.** A tacit assumption that seems to underlie much of the research into the basis for the preponderance of *A. bifidus* in the nurseling stool is that a component of human milk selectively stimulates this species. The extensive studies of the Pennsylvania group seem to have this significance [György and collaborators (1953, 1954, 1955); Gauhe et al. (1954); Rose et al. (1954); Norris et al. (1954); Springer et al. (1954); György, Rose, and Springer (1954); György and Rose (1955); Glick, Zilliken, and György (1959)]. These workers found that a particular common variant of *A. bifidus* (var. *pennsylvanicus*) failed to grow in the usual bifidus media, but grew when a "growth factor" was provided. The growth factor was found to be a mucopolysaccharide (or some of its partially hydrolyzed fractions) made up of N-acetylglucosamine, fucose, and galactose, but no amino acids. Purified blood-group substances A and B were especially active, associated with B and H activity rather than with the A group. Activity was found to be very high in human colostrum, and much higher in human milk than in cow's milk. It is doubtful, however, that the occurrence of this "bifidus factor" in human milk can be an important part of the basis for either the predominance of *A. bifidus* in the nurseling stool or the correlated advantages of its presence to the infant. As noted previously (page 60), the *pennsylvanicus* variant of *A. bifidus* does not appear to be the characteristic organism of the nurseling's intestinal biota; the *A. bifidus* most commonly found there evidently does not require the bifidus factor. In another study [Barbero (1952)] from the Pennsylvania group, moreover, intubation at different levels of the intestinal tract of breast- and formula-fed infants revealed that the predominance of *A. bifidus* appeared only distal to the cecum, where a progressive fall in pH toward the rectum in nursing infants was associated with an increase in "lactobacilli" and a decrease in other bacterial types. There was marked proliferation of mixed bacterial types in the cecum, where the intestinal contents reached an alkaline peak; at this point and more proximally there were no differences in pH or bacterial composition between the breast- and bottle-fed groups. The whole question of the role of *A. bifidus* in the nurseling stool appears in a somewhat different light in view of the studies of Gyllenberg and Roine (1957), whose findings most relevant to this question are reproduced in Table 3-3. It is apparent from these data that the effect of human milk as compared with cow's milk is not to stimulate the growth of *A. bifidus* but rather to inhibit the growth of the other bacteria, and that the pH of the feces is not the principal determinant of its bacterial composition. Moreover, the characteristic ratio of *A. bifidus* to other bacteria in the nurseling group was abolished when boiled human milk was fed, despite the fact that the "bifidus factor," according to György, Norris, and Rose (1954), is not destroyed or altered in its activity by autoclaving. The mechanism of the relationship of *A. bifidus* in the intestines to the improved growth and resistance of nursing infants is evidently not so simple as it once seemed and is in need of further clarification.

A. bifidus **in Other Indigenous Loci.** The presence of *A. bifidus* was recorded in the mouth of 3-month-old infants by Lewkowicz (1901) and of children by Howe and Hatch (1917) and others. Beerens, Gerard, and Guillaume (1957) suggested that oral strains differ from Tissier's bacillus in that the former more constantly ferment mannitol.

TABLE 3-3

AVERAGE CONCENTRATIONS OF *Actinomyces bifidus*, ENTEROCOCCI,
AND *E. coli* IN FECES OF INFANTS FED DIFFERENT MILK
FORMULAS (ADAPTED FROM GYLLENBERG AND ROINE, 1957)

Milk formula	Number of samples	Geometric means of colony counts $N \times 10^6$ per Gm feces				pH§	A. bifidus, %
		A. bifidus*	Entero-cocci†	Coli-forms‡	Total		
Human milk	15	1,100	5	10	1,115	5.76	99
Boiled human milk, full-term infants	12	120	55	35	210	5.82	57
Boiled human milk, premature infants	25	600	300	440	1,340	5.92	49
⅔ cow's milk, extra sucrose	48	1,200	580	1,450	3,230	7.41	37
⅔ cow's milk, extra lactose and sodium hexameta-phosphate	57	3,600	500	2,000	6,100	7.18	59

* Counted on the medium of Petuely and Lynau (1954, *Biochem. Z.*, **326**:62), which the authors consider "the most selective among known media for '*L. bifidus*.'"

† Counted on the medium of Carey, Foster, and Frazier (1941, *J. Dairy Sci.*, **24**:1015) modified to prevent the growth of *A. bifidus*; about 90% of the count was considered to be enterococci, the remainder ordinary straight lactobacilli.

‡ Counted on E.M.B. plates.

§ Arithmetic means.

Blaurock (1940) recovered bifid bacteria from the vagina of normal women, and Montagna and Cataldi (1944) found them in this locus postpartum. Harrison and his coworkers (1953) confirmed these findings and observed a sudden marked increase of *A. bifidus* in the vagina immediately before delivery. The peak incidence at term was 72 per cent, as compared with 20 to 36 per cent in the nonpregnant vagina or during the second or third trimesters of pregnancy. Cataldi and Müller (1947) suggested that colostrum or the skin of the breast were more likely to be the sources of *A. bifidus*, especially in Cesarian infants. They found the organism in colostrum in 22 per cent and on the skin of the lactating breast in 14 per cent.

An organism that appears to have been *A. bifidus*, recovered from the bovine rumen, was found by Clarke (1959) to ferment the dextran of *Streptococcus bovis*. Bailey and Clarke (1959) found a dextranase as well in a human strain of *A. bifidus*, but not in species of *Lactobacillus*. Gibbons and Doetsch (1959) recovered from the bovine rumen an organism thought to be closely related to *A. bifidus*, distinguished by the ability to hydrolyze urea.

A study of the sensitivity to antibiotics of 20 strains of *A. bifidus* from nurseling stools has been reported by Lavergne et al. (1959).

The *Israelii* Group

The most characteristic members of the genus *Actinomyces* are the anaerobic mycelium-forming bacteria found in actinomycosis, especially of man. These microorganisms were first cultivated and clearly characterized by Wolff and Israel in 1891 and have come to be termed *Actinomyces israelii* with little disagreement. There is continuing controversy, however, on the specific status of organisms found in actinomycosis of animals, particularly of cattle, and on the identity or difference of some of the forms found in man apart from disease.

Classification. Specific distinction is widely given to the organism found in bovine actinomycosis, which is called *A. bovis*, whereas the form from disease in man is termed *A. israelii* [Erikson (1940); Thompson (1950); Garrod (1952)]. The 2 "species" are listed thus by Breed, Murray, and Smith (1957). Since the two principal bases for the distinction are habitat and characteristics associated with colony form [smoothness or roughness; see Erikson and Porteous (1955); Suter (1956); King and Meyer (1957)], both of which are unreliable, the writer has considered the distinction unconvincing. The so-called *A. bovis* usually appears as a smooth diphtheroid-like colony and grows diffusely in broth, whereas the *israelii* characters are colonial roughness and a tendency to grow as crumblike masses at the bottom of otherwise clear broth. But the smooth and rough forms intergrade among these organisms as they do generally. Both may be found in either host species, and rough strains may become smooth after cultivation [Rosebury, Epps, and Clark (1944)]. The aerial hyphae described by Erikson (1935, 1940b) as a distinguishing feature of *A. israelii* have not been seen by the writer and are not noted by other more recent workers [see Morris (1951)]. Slack et al. (1955), moreover, were unable to distinguish actinomyces from human and various animal sources by agglutination. Their 20 strains, derived from disease and from non-actinomycotic sources, fell into 2 antigenic groups, both of which included human, bovine, and equine strains. One strain from porcine actinomycosis, 1 from pyorrhea in man, and 4 from "human non-actinomycotic tonsils" all fell into a single group. Both rough and smooth *Actinomyces*, whether isolated from actinomycotic lesions or from mucous membranes, have been found capable of producing actinomycosis-like lesions in small experimental animals [Rosebury et al. (1944); Meyer and Verges (1950)]. In a more recent study based on fluorescent-antibody tests, Slack, Winger, and Moore (1961) found 4 serologic groups of anaerobic actinomycetes which, as before, were unrelated to source. It is of interest that *Corynebacterium acnes* and anaerobic diphtheroids cross-reacted with the actinomycetes, but that *"Lactobacillus bifidus,"* other lactobacilli, and aerobic corynebacteria did not.

On the other hand, Cummins and Harris (1958) have reported striking differences in cell-wall composition between actinomyces, the differences having been clearly related to source in man or cattle. All their strains seem to have come from disease. Eleven strains from man labeled as *A. israelii*, one human strain labeled as *A. bovis*, and another *A. bovis* strain of unknown origin constituted a homogeneous group in which the principal cell-wall components were galactose, glucosamine, muramic acid, alanine, glutamic acid, and lysine. These strains were all typically rough in broth. Ten strains labeled as *A. bovis* and derived from cattle were generally different from the preceding and among themselves. The cell-wall composition of 6 of these resembled that previously found for lactobacilli by the same workers [Cummins and Harris (1956)]; these were smooth strains. Two others of these ten appeared to be corynebacteria in terms of cell-wall composition; and the remaining 2 showed a distinctive cell-wall pattern. These workers pointed out that their findings not only confirmed the distinction between human and bovine strains suggested by others, but indicated that the bovine organisms should probably not be classed as *Actinomyces.*

Thompson and Lovestedt (1951) have suggested further that the actinomycetes found most commonly in the healthy mouth be specifically separated as *A. naeslundii.* This "species" was distinguished as being capable of aerobic growth and as nonpathogenic—the latter property being apparently assumed from a conventional view of pathogenicity, without experimental verification. That the actinomyces in question range in relation to oxygen from strict anaerobiosis to a limited ability to grow in air on an agar surface is well known [see Rosebury (1944b)]. Garrod (1952) and others seem to have accepted the term *A. naeslundii* with reservations. Howell et al. (1959), in a study of 200 strains of actinomyces from the mouth in the absence of actinomycosis and of 11 from actinomycosis in man, accepted the designation *A. naeslundii* for members of the former group, but failed to characterize it clearly. According to these workers, *A. naeslundii* differs from *A. israelii* in being more frequently isolated on aerobic blood plates, in showing usually rapid and diffuse or flaky growth in thioglycollate broth, and in having a "primitive" mycelium. In a later study, Pine, Howell, and Watson (1960) suggested that the three "species," *bovis, naeslundii,* and *israelii* could be distinguished not only on the basis of increasing roughness and tendency to form a true mycelium in the order named, but also on these grounds: *A. bovis* hydrolized starch rapidly and completely to acid products; it did not ferment xylose, raffinose, or mannite. *A. israelii* failed to ferment starch, produced acid from xylose and mannite, and occasionally fermented raffinose. *A. naeslundii* formed acid from raffinose but not from the other substrates. The last form, moreover, reduced nitrate to nitrite; *A. bovis* did not, and *A. israelii* was variable in this respect [but see Pine and Howell (1956) and page 59]. These findings support those of Cummins and Harris (1958) in pointing to differences between *A. israelii* and the organism called *A. bovis*, perhaps great enough to warrant placing them in separate genera, but their value in distinguishing the so-called *A. naeslundii* seems to the writer to need additional study.

Although Breed, Murray, and Smith (1957) did not include *A. naeslundii*, they listed as a third species, in addition to *A. bovis* and *A. israelli*, an organism termed *A. baudetii* after Brion (1942) [see also Brion et al. (1952)], said to be distinguished from *A. israelii* by being the "cause of actinomycosis in cats and dogs" and to form basophilic rather than acidophilic clubs in tissue granules. Little is known about the nature of such tissue clubs [see Morris (1951)]. They are usually assumed to involve a host reaction. Neither of the stated criteria, at all events, seems acceptable to distinguish a species. Prévot et al. (1951) were unable to find actinomyces in 9 cases of actinomycosis-like disease in cats, but isolated the motile anaerobe *Fusobacterium girans* (Chap. 5) from 7 of them. Still another "species" of *Actinomyces* has been designated by Batty (1958) as *A. odontolyticus*, said to occur universally in deep dental caries. This organism does not seem to have been compared directly with known cultures of actinomyces. It was reported to differ from the latter as described by Morris (1951) by a greater tolerance for oxygen (growing equally well under aerobic and anaerobic conditions) and the production of a reddish-brown pigment on blood agar. The heterogeneity of this group of microorganisms is hardly questionable, but it seems to the writer that the satisfactory definition of species within it requires more reliable criteria than are as yet available.

Cultivation and Cultural Characteristics. Actinomycetes of the *israelii* group are best isolated and maintained on enriched media containing a utilizable carbohydrate under anaerobic conditions, but neither enrichment nor anaerobiosis is obligatory for all strains or all transfers of a given strain. The writer has used Bacto brain-heart infusion medium with 2 per cent agar for isolation, and glucose infusion or glucose heart infusion broth alternating with similar media for maintenance. Growth of smooth strains is not characteristic. Rough strains, seen under a dissecting microscope at 5 to 10 diameters, produce dis-

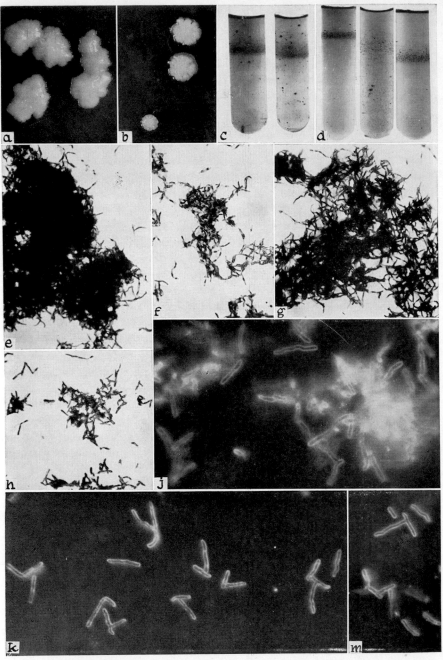

FIG. 3-2. *Actinomyces israelii. a, b,* typical rough "heaped-up" surface colonies on anaerobic brain-heart agar, ×12. *c, d,* shake cultures in glucose agar incubated aerobically, showing concentration of colonies in a layer below the surface. *e, f, g, h,* typical Gram-stained films, ×750. *j, k, m,* unstained wet film preparations, darkfield illumination, ×1,200 [*From Rosebury, Epps, and Clark* (1944), *courtesy of J. Infectious Diseases.*]

tinctive white, glistening "heaped-up" irregular colonies, sometimes molariform both in contour and in surface texture as noted by Sullivan and Goldsworthy (1940; see Fig. 3-2). Such colonies are homogeneous in texture to their edge. Similar colonies with a mucoid edge, seen on anaerobic plates, may be produced by streptococci. In broth, rough strains tend to grow as crumblike masses at the bottom, the supernatant being clear. Gale, in the writer's laboratory, obtained dispersed growth of rough strains in the Middlebrook-Dubos Tween albumin medium. Salvin and Hoyer (1951), using a fluid medium containing casitone (Difco), yeast extract, cysteine, and sodium thioglycollate, obtained abundant growth of rough strains either by seeding into medium within a Visking loop contained in a flask of the same medium, or by using a tube in which the sedimenting surface was increased with a series of ridges. Homogeneous suspensions were produced by shaking with glass beads for 20 minutes, giving a linear relation between nephelometer readings and nitrogen content.

Erikson and Porteous (1953) reported that growth could be obtained by "training" in a medium containing 99 volumes of 1 per cent casein hydrolysate and 1 volume of heart broth with 0.5 per cent glucose. Attempts to substitute a wide variety of amino acids, fatty acids, growth factors, and mineral salts for the heart broth were not successful. Howell and Pine (1956) found that either or both of two purified fluid media containing casein hydrolysate, glucose, amino acids, vitamins and, in òne, purified potato starch, supported growth of actinomyces strains as well as or better than a casitone–yeast extract medium. With most strains better growth resulted when the starting pH was 6.5 than when it was 7.0 or 7.5 [see also Pine and Watson (1959); Christie and Porteous (1959, 1960)].

Metabolism. There have been few studies of the metabolism of these actinomycetes. Erikson and Porteous (1953) found with rough strains that 30 to 60 per cent of the glucose utilized appeared as lactic acid. [See also Christie and Porteous (1959)]. In the studies of Pine and Howell (1956), 90 to 100 per cent of the carbon of the glucose fermented by A. israelii in a casein hydrolysate medium, or 80 to 93 per cent of the total glucose, was found to be lactic acid, but small amounts of formic and acetic acids and perhaps of ethanol were also produced. In a casitone–yeast extract medium, lactic acid accounted for 63 to 82 per cent of the glucose fermented, and succinic acid appeared among the products. This finding suggested that CO_2 was being fixed consistently with the Wood-Werkman scheme [see also Pine (1956), and correction (1960)]. Pine (1956) has pointed out that the production of succinic acid by both A. israelii and A. bifidus adds weight to the close relationship previously noted between these 2 microorganisms, and further supports their differentiation from the genus *Lactobacillus*, members of which do not form succinic acid, as well as from *Corynebacterium* and *Propionibacterium*, which form propionic acid.

Life Cycle. Morris (1951), working with 10 strains of actinomyces from cattle and 2 from human lesions of actinomycosis, including both rough and smooth forms, reported that all passed through a similar life cycle, beginning with a spherical or oval spore from which a germ tube grew and branched during 2 to 4 days of growth (a haploid phase), then forming clubs which separated as oval or pear-shaped cells. These cells were said to conjugate and begin a diploid phase, in which the fusion cell budded and the club-shaped buds formed wavy filaments, either single or multiple, which became bent and irregular and formed a radiating mass. Each tube, bud, and filament was said to contain at least one nucleus, the bent filaments many. Branching was found to occur adjacent to a nucleus which underwent division. The spore formed after 4 to 12 days of growth.

Distribution. The obligately indigenous character of these actinomycetes has come to be generally accepted. These organisms have been recovered repeatedly from the human mouth and throat [Lord (1910); for other references see Rosebury (1944*b*)]. They are evidently also indigenous to the mucous membranes of animals. They have not been found in nature apart from a parasitic habitat. The forms isolated by Hvid-Hansen (1951) from ground water, although called *A. israelii*, differ from the organisms in question in their colonial characteristics ("greyish-white or white, transparent"), and in being hemolytic, gelatin-liquefying, and catalase-positive. They also formed appreciable amounts of propionic acid from glucose. These properties suggest *Corynebacterium acnes* (see page 80). The frequency of occurrence of these actinomycetes in indigenous loci is not definitely known, nor is the question clearly answered of their presence in areas other than the mouth and throat—a presence to be suspected in view of the primary localization of actinomycosis. Information on these questions, as well as on the concentration of actinomycetes wherever they occur, requires a satisfactory selective medium for their isolation, which is not at present available. In the writer's experience, *A. israelii* occurs in the healthy mouth frequently but not constantly, and probably always in low concentrations. Emmons (1938) found actinomyces-like forms in smears from the crypts of 74 of 200 pairs of excised tonsils, and isolated *A. israelii* from 22. Ennever et al. (1949, 1951) recovered the organisms from all of 11 samples of tooth scrapings. Garrod (1952) observed them in "almost every specimen" of normal saliva and isolated them in 18 of 20 instances.

Pathogenicity. *A. israelii* is clearly implicated in actinomycosis in man. That this disease is of endogenous origin seems clear, but many aspects of its pathogenesis remain uncertain, including the possible role of auxiliary bacterial species in addition to *A. israelii*. [For details and references see Rosebury (1944*b*); Rosebury and Sonnenwirth (1958); Holm (1951); Lentze (1953, 1958); and Heinrich (1960)].

It has also been suggested that *A. israelii* may participate in the deposition of salivary and other calculi [see Rosebury (1944*b*); Rains et al. (1960)].

Leptotrichiae

Among a group of seemingly distinctive bacteria long associated with the human mouth and frequently classified in the genus *Leptotrichia*, certain peculiar questions confront us which are, again, reflections of our insecure knowledge of many of the indigenous microbes. Here, on the one hand, 2 evidently distinct bacteria have competed for a single specific name, *L. buccalis;* yet the generic term itself was considered invalid by Breed, Murray, and Hitchens in the sixth edition of *Bergey's Manual of Determinative Bacteriology* (1948) and was entirely omitted from the seventh (1957). It had in the meantime been conserved by the International Judicial Commission (1954). One of the two distinctive forms, now accepted as *L. buccalis*, has been confounded with *Fusobacterium* and perhaps with other Gram-negative genera; it is now known to be related to *Lactobacillus*. The other form, called *Leptotrichia buccalis* by Bibby [see Bibby and Berry (1939)], is a branching filamentous organism originally isolated anaerobically but growing well aerobically in subculture. The two forms differ in characteristic colony form, cell morphology, and other respects. Bibby's organism was renamed *Leptotrichia dentium* by Baird-Parker and Davis (1958) and has more recently been placed in a separate genus, *Bacterionema*, by a group of workers including Bibby himself [Gilmour, Howell, and Bibby (1961)]. The 2 species are considered in sequence in the following paragraphs.

Leptotrichia buccalis

The first claimant to the name *L. buccalis* can be identified as the organism called *Leptothrix buccalis* by Kligler (1915), *L. innominata* by Wherry and Oliver (1916), and *Leptotrichia buccalis* by Thjötta, Hartmann, and Böe (1939), and Böe and Thjötta (1944). It is the species to which the writer has in the past given this name [Rosebury (1944*b*); Rosebury, Macdonald and Clark (1950); Rosebury, Clark, Engel, and Tergis (1950); Rosebury and Sonnenwirth (1958)]; and it has been studied by Jackins and Barker (1951) and by Hamilton and Zahler (1957). It is characterized as a rather thick, unbranched Gram-positive form, occurring in loglike rods or filaments, straight, often with one blunt and one pointed end, in chains or in wavy filaments, or twisted rope-strands [Wherry and Oliver (1916); Rosebury,

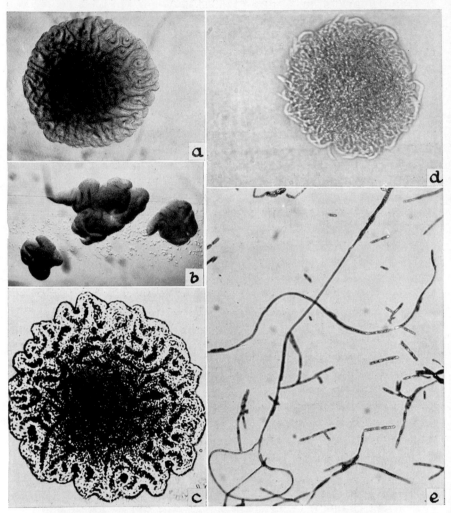

Fig. 3-3. *Leptotrichia buccalis. a, b,* colonies on the Hamilton-Zahler starch medium at 32 hours, ×16. *c,* 3-day colony, ×15. *d,* 48-hour microcolony, ×320. *e,* Gram-stain of 12-hour thioglycollate broth culture, ×2,000. [*a, b, from Hamilton and Zahler* (1957), *courtesy of Dr. Zahler and J. Bacteriol. c, from Baird-Parker and Davis* (1958), *courtesy of Dr. Davis and J. Gen. Microbiol. d, e, from Gilmour, Howell, and Bibby* (1961), *courtesy of the authors and Bacteriol. Revs.*]

Macdonald, and Clark (1950); see Figs. 3-3 to 3-5]. The organism is Gram-positive in young cultures but is easily decolorized; it may show Gram-positive granules in a Gram-negative ground. The surface colony is typically translucent with an irregular medusa-head shape, or round and coarsely convoluted. Kasai (1955) and Hamilton and Zahler (1957) have used soluble starch in the medium for isolation. We have found Mueller-Hinton agar satisfactory when enriched with 10 per cent serum or ascitic fluid.

The organism appears to be obligately saccharophilic; glucose, sucrose, maltose, and other carbohydrates are fermented with a final pH of 5 or slightly lower, and gas is not formed. Jackins and Barker (1951) found that the organism induced a simple lactic fermentation and did not attack amino acids. *L. buccalis* was grown by Thjötta, Hartmann, and Böe (1939) in an atmosphere of CO_2; most workers, including the writer, have found strictly anaerobic conditions with 5 per cent CO_2 indispensable for isolation and maintenance. Hamilton

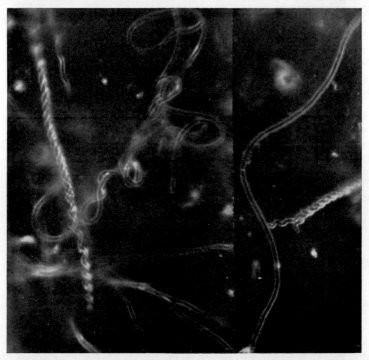

Fig. 3-4. *Leptotrichia buccalis*. Filaments, some tangled and some regularly intertwined—"rope strands." Fresh preparations from deep culture in ascitic fluid–guinea-pig kidney ("AFK") agar as used by the author for growth of spirochetes. Darkfield illumination, ×1,600. [*From Rosebury, Macdonald, and Clark* (1950), *courtesy of J. Dental Research.*]

and Zahler (1957) found that 2 of 9 strains were capable of limited aerobic growth after 300 or more daily transfers. There is general agreement that *L. buccalis* fails to liquefy gelatin or to form indole or ammonia. It is usually said not to form hydrogen sulfide, but traces of this compound were found by Hamilton and Zahler, while Davis and Baird-Parker (1959) reported H_2S " . . . usually positive from cysteine. Sometimes positive from peptone." Most strains have also been reported not to reduce nitrate, but reduction by certain strains was observed by Thjötta, Hartmann, and Böe (1939) and by Hamilton and Zahler (1957), who also noted that all strains induced the dis-

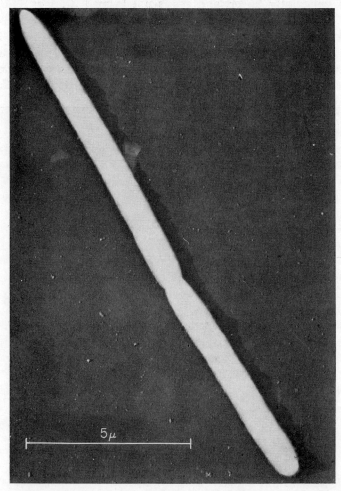

Fig. 3-5. *Leptotrichia buccalis*. Electron micrograph, palladium shadowed. [*From Hamilton and Zahler (1957), courtesy of Dr. Zahler and J. Bacteriol.*]

appearance of nitrite within 72 hours. The latter workers reported no catalase, and observed a reaction in starch interpreted as the production of a weak α-amylase; starch was hydrolyzed in the presence of fermentable sugar but not otherwise unless reinoculated with the same strain. Takazoe and Frostell (1960) have reported observations on *L. buccalis* generally consistent with the foregoing. Their strains were nonhemolytic, unbranched, and failed to form H_2S. These workers presented data on antibiotic sensitivity [see also Kasai (1961)].

L. *buccalis* Kligler has been confused with the genus *Fusobacterium*, as Thjötta et al. (1959) and Böe and Thjötta (1944) have pointed out in particular; see also Baird-Parker (1960). The *Fusobacterium plautvincenti* studied by Jackins and Barker (1951), recognized as the type II *Fusobacterium* of Spaulding and Rettger (1937), is clearly identifiable with the Kligler organism, while the *Fusiformis dentium* of Hine and Berry (1937), the type IV, and with less assurance the type III, fusiform bacillus of Slanetz and Rettger (1933) and perhaps the types III and IV fusiform organisms of Varney (1927) all seem to belong here rather than with the genus *Fusobacterium*. The rough *Fusiformis* of Morris (1953) also seems to be *L. buccalis*. Varney's type III organism did not react with serums prepared against more typical fusiforms; and Böe found *Leptotrichia* to be distinct from *Fusobacterium* in both agglutination and complement-fixation tests. Jackins and Barker (1951) confirmed this distinction by biochemical means and noted that the organism called *Fusobacterium plaut-vincenti* (which conformed with *L. buccalis* Kligler) was sometimes Gram-positive in young cultures; these workers remarked on the similarity of the Kligler organism to homofermentative lactobacilli. Hamilton and Zahler (1957) suggested that the name *Leptotrichia buccalis* be retained for this organism and that it be classified in the family *Lactobacteriaceae*, tribe *Lactobacilleae*. They also suggested that "no other described species clearly belongs to this genus." In a note by Howell and Rogosa (1958) describing the Bibby organism, the forms described by Hamilton and Zahler were said to "have all the characteristics of lactobacilli." They are distinct, however, both morphologically and as anaerobes from the lactobacilli described previously (see page 48). A more recent study by Davis and Baird-Parker (1959) substantiates the foregoing description of *L. buccalis* and distinguishes it from the organism considered below. For a discussion of other usages of the names *Leptotrichia* and *Leptothrix* see Rosebury (1944b).

Leptotrichia dentium (Bacterionema matruchotii)

The organism to which Bibby gave the name *Leptotrichia buccalis* [Bibby and Berry (1939)] was reconsidered briefly by Gilmour and

Hunter (1958) and Howell and Rogosa (1958), and was studied and well characterized by Baird-Parker and Davis (1958) and Davis and Baird-Parker (1959). These workers (1958) suggested the name *Leptotrichia dentium* for this distinctive organism. It seems to correspond with the *Leptothrix buccalis* of Bulleid (1924) and the *Leptotrichia* of Morris (1954). It is characterized by finely filamentous colonies and by the occurrence of branching filaments. A morphologic oddity that seems characteristic is a thin filament attached at one end to a somewhat thicker bacillus-like form (see Figs. 3-6 and 3-7). The organism is aerobic, although anaerobic methods have been used for its isolation. Howell and Rogosa (1958) stated that it prefers aerobic conditions; and all strains studied by these workers were strongly catalase-positive. Bulleid (1924) described the organism as growing more rapidly anaerobically in primary culture. It was Gram-positive, nonmotile, did not liquefy gelatin or form gas; it tended to sediment in broth, and its growth was favored by glucose. Bibby and Berry (1939) found that the organism fermented sugars with acid but no gas; 7 of 34 strains fermented starch; final pH values ranged from 4.8 to 5.1; gelatin was not liquefied; indole, ammonia, and hydrogen sulfide were not formed; and nitrates were reduced. Davis and Baird-Parker (1959) suggested a nocardia-like life cycle for this organism and compared it with *L. buccalis*. They confirmed the characteristics noted for *L. dentium* and added several others, among them consistent Gram-positivity, production of acetylmethylcarbinol, consistent absence of H_2S and hydrolysis of sodium hippurate—all of these being considered features distinguishing this organism from *L. buccalis*. The 2 organisms, as noted above, also differ morphologically. *L. dentium*, the branching form, is more aerobic, forms catalase and reduces nitrate more regularly. [See also Richardson and Schmidt (1959)]. Davis and Baird-Parker (1959*b*) reported that the cell-wall composition of both *L. dentium* and *L. buccalis* resembles that of *Nocardia* in containing DAP, which is not found in *Actinomyces israelii* [Cummins and Harris (1958)] or in *Fusobacterium*. The 2 leptotrichiae were also similar in the pattern of amino acids in their cell walls, as well as in the presence of glucose and the absence of galactose; arabinose appeared in the pattern of *L. dentium* but not in that of *L. buccalis*. These findings suggest a closer relationship between these 2 organisms than do their other properties which, as Bisset and Davis (1959) pointed out, make it doubtful that both belong in the same genus.

A more recent series of papers incorporates the suggestion that these microorganisms be separated from *L. buccalis*, the identity of which seems to have achieved a consensus. An organism conforming closely to the characteristics of *L. dentium* was described in 1919 by Mendel

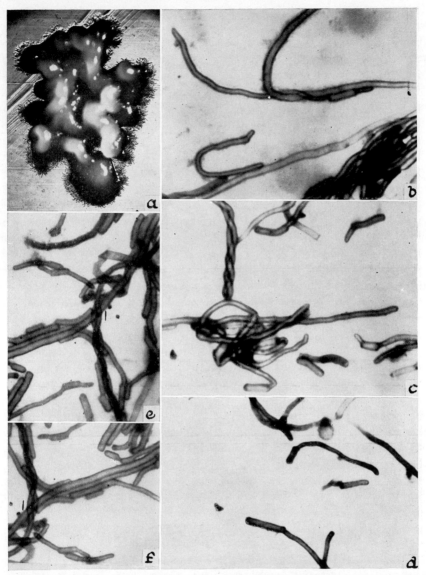

Fig. 3-6. *Leptotrichia dentium*, as shown by Baird-Parker and Davis (1958). *a*, aerobic surface colony, 2 days, ×14. Photomicrographs from broth cultures, stained by the phosphomolybdic acid–methyl green procedure of Hale (1953, *Lab. Practice*, 2:115), ×1,450. *b*, typical "whip-handle" forms showing variation in diameter of filaments. *c*, similar forms and twisting (compare Fig. 3-4). *d*, large body. These structures were described as stages in the development of L forms; other structures were considered "streptomyces-like" by these authors. *e*, *f*, previously unpublished. (*a, b, c, d, courtesy of J. Gen. Microbiol. e, f, courtesy of Dr. Davis.*)

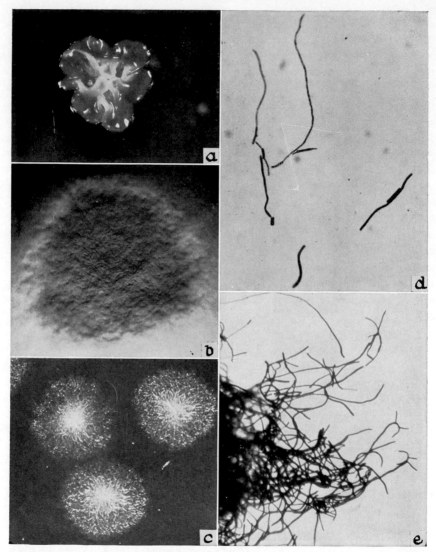

Fig. 3-7. *Leptotrichia dentium* (*Bacterionema matruchotii*) as shown by Gilmour et al. *a*, aerobic surface colony, 4 days, ×5. *b*, 2-day anaerobic surface colony on blood agar plus starch, ×70. *c*, anaerobic colonies, 3 days on blood agar, ×14. *d*, Gram stain ×700, showing variation in thickness. *e*, Gram stain, thioglycolate broth, 48 hours anaerobically, ×500, showing branching. [*a, b, d, e, from Gilmour, Howell, and Bibby* (1961), *courtesy of the authors and Bacteriol. Revs. c, from Gilmour and Hunter* (1958), *courtesy of J. Bacteriol.*]

as *Cladothrix matruchoti*. This specific name evidently has priority; and the suggestion has been put forward by Gilmour, Howell, and Bibby (1961) that this bacterium be placed in a new genus with the name *Bacterionema matruchotii*, considered to be related to the actinomycetes rather than to the lactobacilli but thought to be distinct from the genera *Actinomyces* and *Nocardia*. These authors regarded *B. matruchotii* as equivalent to the *L. buccalis* of Kligler (1915), apparently because of what may have been a misuse by the latter of the word "club" to describe the untapered end of the rod. As the preceding discussion indicated, Kliger's description is otherwise consistent with the *Leptotrichia buccalis* of other workers. In the other papers in the series on *B. matruchotii*, the mode of reproduction of the branching form was described as different from those of *Nocardia* and *Actinomyces* [Gilmour (1961)]; characteristics in general agreement with those of the British workers [Baird-Parker and Davis (1958); Davis and Baird-Parker (1959)] were detailed [Gilmour and Beck (1961)]; and a study was made by Howell and Pine (1961) of the relations of the organism to oxygen. The latter workers studied 43 strains, including 6 isolated by Gilmour. They were found predominantly aerobic, many strictly so; although most strains were found capable of limited anaerobic growth for at least one transfer—which would be true of nearly all aerobic bacteria. Heavy growth was obtained only with glucose, maltose, and sucrose among 16 carbohydrates tested, and with acetate, lactate, and pyruvate among 8 organic acids tried. Other metabolic characteristics of the organism were noted.

Further studies of this organism are needed to clarify its generic status, including comparisons with related genera by chemical and serologic means.

Organisms described as *Leptotrichia* are not known to be capable of pathogenic activity, although suggestions to this effect have been made repeatedly [see Mackenzie (1931); Patocka and Sebek (1948); Ludwig (1952); Henry (1953)].

Corynebacteria

Aerobic Diphtheroids

The aerobic corynebacteria of human mucous membranes are conventionally classified principally by fermentation of glucose and sucrose. The pathogenic *C. diphtheriae* ferments glucose but not sucrose; *C. hofmanni* (*C. pseudodiphtheriticum*), originally found in the throat, ferments neither; and *C. xerosis*, originally isolated from the conjunctiva, ferments both. This simple basis of classification is inadequate both for its original purpose of distinguishing pathogens or potential pathogens, and for our present purpose of defining the indigenous members of the group.

The Diphtheria-like Corynebacteria. It has become clear in recent years that corynebacteria with characteristics otherwise typical of *C. diphtheriae* may be nontoxigenic, hence presumably amphibiotic, unless they have been made lysogenic by specific phage infection [Freeman (1951); Groman (1953); Groman and Memmer (1958)]. The organism called *Corynebacterium belfanti,* found in ozena, was reported by Gunderson and Henriksen (1959) to be convertible to toxigenic *C. diphtheriae* by lysogenization [see also Henriksen and Gunderson (1959)]. Certain other diphtheria-like corynebacteria [so-called *C. ulcerans,* Saxholm (1951); Henriksen and Grelland (1952)], found both in sore throats and in healthy carriers, differ from *C. diphtheriae* biochemically and in their phage specificity, the latter being seemingly independent of toxigenicity [Howard and Jann (1955); Henriksen (1955)].

Indigenous Corynebacteria. Among corynebacteria that seem to be indigenous to man it is now clear that the three fermentation patterns mentioned, with variations in other respects that have not provided a basis for classification, occur without regard to source of the strains [see Laughton (1950)]. Hite, Hesseltine, and Goldstein (1947) had recorded the presence of diphtheroid rods in the healthy antepartum vagina in 44 per cent of 61 instances. The vaginal cultures studied by Laughton were principally xerosis-like in their fermentation reactions. Many of them resembled *C. hofmanni* or *C. diphtheriae* in their morphology and staining properties. Some of these xerosis-like strains were actively acidogenic, were said to occur in the premenopausal vagina even more commonly than Döderlein's lactobacillus (page 56), and were thought by Laughton to play a definite role in producing the low vaginal pH usually attributed to the lactobacillus. It may be noted that the animal pathogen, *C. pyogenes,* which differs from *C. xerosis* principally in that the former is hemolytic and liquefies gelatin, may lose these distinguishing features under cultivation [Ryff and Browne (1954)] and thus come to resemble the actively acidogenic variant of *C. xerosis.* On the other hand, Cummins and Harris (1956) found a consistent difference in cell-wall composition between *C. pyogenes* and a group of corynebacteria including those parasitic for man. *C. diphtheriae, C. ulcerans, C. xerosis,* and *C. hofmanni* (among other species) regularly yielded from their cell walls arabinose, galactose, glucosamine, an unknown "hexosamine," alanine, glutamic acid, and DAP. *C. pyogenes* and *C. haemolyticum,* by contrast, yielded rhamnose and lysine but no arabinose, galactose, or DAP.

This pattern of cell-wall composition in *C. pyogenes* and *C. haemoly-*

ticum was found to resemble closely that of a number of strains of streptococci of several Lancefield groups including group A. Maclean, Liebow, and Rosenberg (1946) had commented on the close resemblance of *C. haemolyticum* to *Streptococcus pyogenes*, and had observed that the growth of *C. pyogenes* on blood agar and in broth was closely similar to that of a β-hemolytic streptococcus. These 2 corynebacteria, moreover, resemble streptococci in being catalase-negative, while other corynebacteria are catalase-positive. Cummins and Harris accordingly suggested that *C. pyogenes* and *C. haemolyticum* be considered as streptococci rather than as corynebacteria. In a later paper, Barksdale, Cummins, and Harris (1957) reported that an organism showing all the properties of *C. haemolyticum* appeared on blood agar as a variant of *C. pyogenes*, and that a single mutation involving cell-wall structure could account for the change. For further details on *C. haemolyticum*, see Hermann (1961).

Diphtheroids in Blood Cultures. Aerobic diphtheroid-like bacteria have been rather widely reported as occurring in certain routine blood cultures under unusual conditions of cultivation—prolonged incubation, "blind" subculture, or incubation with 10 per cent CO_2. The literature on such bacteria up to 1952 was reviewed by Fleisher (1952). In many instances, positive cultures of this kind have been associated with disease of lymphoid tissue, including Hodgkin's disease, but the isolated organisms have not been found pathogenic. The 50 strains studied by Carpenter, Howard, and Lehman (1956) had minute colonies, were catalase-positive, and failed to produce acetylmethylcarbinol, but were variable in all other respects. Specific names have not been assigned to these organisms. The findings of Kassel and Rottino (1955) suggest that their occurrence in blood cultures may possibly depend on contamination from skin or air. Points of similarity between these organisms and the anaerobic diphtheroids described in the following section should be noted. [See Wittler et al. (1960)].

Anaerobic Diphtheroid-like Bacteria

Generic Position. Anaerobic or microaerophilic diphtheroid-like bacteria are common both on skin and on mucous membranes, but their taxonomic status is in doubt. Prévot and Tardieux (1953), Seeliger (1953), and Linzenmeier (1954) included anaerobes in the genus *Corynebacterium*. Prévot (1957) listed other Gram-positive nonmotile anaerobic indigenous bacilli under the generic names *Eubacterium*, *Catenabacterium*, and *Ramibacterium*; with many species noted as "assez rare," "rare," or "très rare" that were apparently based on descriptions of single strains. These names have seldom been used in this country and their apparently uncritical inclusion (as members of the family *Lactobacillaceae*) in the seventh edition of *Bergey's Manual of Determinative Bacteriology* [Breed, Murray, and Smith (1957)] does not help to disentangle this part of our subject. Prévot's *Corynebacterium anaerobium* has been reported by Beerens and Demont (1949) to have the same biochemical characteristics as *Actinomyces israelii*.

Beerens (1953–54) studied 25 strains of an organism termed *Ramibacterium pleuriticum* [see Prévot, et al. (1958)], including strains from Prévot and their own isolations, the latter from the mouth, from cervicofacial actinomycosis and from other purulent processes. The group of strains showed the following properties uniformly: they were Gram-positive, nonmotile, nonsporulating polymorphic rods with "false branching" and granular cytoplasm. They formed acid (valerianic, acetic, and lactic) and gas from glucose, fructose, and mannite; milk was not altered; catalase was negative, gelatin was not liquefied, nitrate was not reduced, and indole and hydrogen sulfide were not formed. The organisms were nonhemolytic, and attempts to demonstrate pathogenicity for mice or hamsters by the methods developed for *Actinomyces israelii* by Meyer and Verges (1950) and Hazen, Little, and Resnik (1952) were unsuccessful. On the other hand, 1 strain isolated from bovine actinomycosis injected intraperitoneally into a rabbit (5 ml of whole culture) induced a fatal peritonitis. Serologic studies showed 7 strains to be homogeneous and distinct from *Actinomyces bifidus* and other Gram-positive nonsporulating anaerobes (*Corynebacterium liquefaciens, Ramibacterium tortuosum*). A close relationship to *A. bifidis* is nevertheless suggested by the characteristics given, and deserves further exploration.

Corynebacterium acnes.   The most clearly identified of the anaerobic corynebacteria is *C. acnes*, an organism long known but comparatively little studied [see Eberson (1918)]. It appears to be the most numerous member of the biota of skin (see Chap. 10). In the writer's laboratory [Watson, et al. (1962)] it has been found in the nasal passages and is probably widespread in other indigenous loci. Douglas and Gunter (1946) found it to be "one of the principal contaminants" of human blood plasma destined for a blood bank, and suggested that it may enter the blood from skin via inadequate surface disinfection before venipuncture. Gutierrez (1953) recovered what is evidently the same organism from the rumina of sheep and cattle and also from hay and soil; it is thus a saprophytic amphibiont.

The anaerobic diphtheroids that have been confused with *Actinomyces israelii* [Meyer and Verges (1950); Frank and Skinner (1954); Erikson and Porteous (1955); Suter (1956)] have been shown by King and Meyer (1957) to be indistinguishable from *C. acnes* serologically and in other respects. Murray (1957) identified the *C. lique-faciens* of Prévot (1938) with *C. acnes*. Hazen and Little (1958) were able to distinguish sharply between catalase-positive "anaerobic diph-theroids"—presumably *C. acnes*—and *Actinomyces israelii* (*bovis*) on the basis of pathogenicity for young male hamsters. *Actinomyces israelii* produced purulent infection with club-bearing granules; the diphtheroids were not infective. In cross-hemagglutination tests, Caille and Toucas (1960) reported that rabbit antiserums prepared against strains of *C. acnes* reacted with other "species" of anaerobic coryne-bacteria, in some instances to titers as high as in the homologous reac-tions. Cross-reacting "species" included *C. anaerobium*, *C. granulosum*, and *C. liquefaciens*. With an antiserum prepared against an anaerobic diphtheroid and using as an antigen latex particles sensitized with washed bacterial suspensions, Florman and Scoma (1960) reported cross-reactions with *C. acnes* but not with aerobic corynebacteria, *A. israelii*, or other bacteria. Slack, Winger, and Moore (1961), on the other hand, found by the fluorescent-antibody technique that *C. acnes* and anaerobic diphtheroids cross-reacted with israelii-type actino-mycetes.

Corynebacterium acnes, as defined by Douglas and Gunter (1946) is variably anaerobic. Most strains prefer anaerobic conditions, but many grow in air with a heavy inoculum. Its morphology varies from uniform short plump rods, often in V-shaped pairs under anaerobic conditions, to diphtheroid clubbing and even rudimentary branching, the latter under aerobic conditions. The catalase test is consistently positive. Gelatin is slowly liquefied, and nitrate reduction and indole formation are usual. A rennet curd followed by digestion of casein was said to occur in litmus milk. These workers reported β-hemolysis on a buffered glucose agar containing 5 per cent of citrated human blood. Fermentation of glucose was found to be of the propionic type. Gutierrez (1953) found that both animal and saprophytic strains fermented lactate anaerobically, and stated that Douglas had also ob-served lactate utilization in strains from human sources. Variation in gelatin liquefaction, with some strains weak or negative, was re-ported for nasal strains by Watson et al. (1962), who also found 7 of 8 strains nonhemolytic and reported acid production in milk without clotting or digestion. Variation in gelatin was also reported by King and Meyer (1957) for anaerobic diphtheroids and *C. acnes*.

A stimulating effect of oleic acid on growth of *C. acnes*, suggesting a basis for the predilection of this organism toward a habitat in skin, was noted in 1909 by Fleming and was confirmed by Pollock, Wain-wright, and Manson (1949), who observed similar stimulation of aerobic diphtheroids from skin, but only in freshly isolated cultures.

Pochi and Strauss (1961) have studied the sensitivity of *C. acnes* to antibiotics.

Mycobacteria

The presence of certain mycobacteria in the indigenous biota of man has long been widely if tacitly accepted. It was directly reconsidered in 1959 (Edwards and Palmer) after a lapse—so far as the writer is aware—of nearly half a century. In the older literature, the most recent reference bearing immediately on the question seems to be that of Marchoux and Halphen (1912). Up to 1912, and, indeed, until more recently, it would have seemed appropriate to limit a discussion of indigenous mycobacteria to the organism commonly known as *M. smegmatis*. Coincident with the decline of tuberculous disease and the emergence in clinical experience of a new or newly recognized array of mycobacteria—some of which, quite apart from the smegma bacillus, look suspiciously like amphibionts—the subject has begun to take on a different aspect. Pending further development, the two aspects, old and new, are given separately in what follows.

Mycobacterium smegmatis

The smegma bacillus was first described by Alvarez and Tavel (1885) and was grown in pure culture by Laser (1897) and by Czapelewski (1897). The early literature on its distribution is summarized by Topley and Wilson (1936). *M. smegmatis* was found in varying numbers in human preputial and clitoral secretions, in the smegma of dogs, and was recovered from various other locations in man —from a gangrenous lung, from feces, tonsils, and nasal secretion, as well as from metal wind instruments and other environmental sources. The term "saprophyte" seems to be applicable to this organism in the strict sense rather than in the sense of "nonpathogen" usually implied in the jargon of mycobacteriologists [see Juhlin (1960)].

Organisms now regarded as members of this species [Gordon and Smith (1953)] include not only those originally identified as such, but also both environmental strains and degraded cultures of both human and bovine tubercle bacilli, among them Koch's strain! Gordon and Smith (1953) studied 56 strains of *M. smegmatis* received as 12 "species." They described it as acid-fast, slender, often filamentous, sometimes branched, curved, or beaded, and as producing dense colonies with smooth edges, or dense colonies fringed with filaments, or filamentous colonies. They distinguished it from *M. tuberculosis* mainly by its rapid and abundant growth on simple media at either 37° or at room temperature. Growth in 2 or 3 days on glycerol agar was spreading, finely wrinkled and creamy white, becoming more abundant, waxy, creamy yellow or beige to orange on this or other media in 2 weeks. *M. smegmatis* and other saprophytic mycobacteria were further distinguished from pathogens by growing as a pellicle on the surface of fluid media, failing to form serpentine cords, reacting negatively in the neutral red test of Middlebrook and Dubos (1948), and failing to produce progressive disease in guinea pigs or mice.

The question of pathogenicity is, however, not thus simply disposed of. Levaditi, Vaisman, and Levy (1949) observed that many so-called saprophytic mycobacteria had pathogenic capabilities. Linell and Norden (1954) noted that *M. smegmatis* was less pathogenic for guinea pigs than *M. balnei* (see page 85), which had little effect on this animal. Forbus et al. (1958) reported that nearly all of a long series of strains of mycobacteria from soil had demonstrable pathogenicity for mice, guinea pigs, rats or all three; a strain labeled *M. smegmatis* produced local abscesses in rats and granulomatous lesions in guinea pigs. (This matter is considered further on page 86.)

Magnusson (1961) found the tuberculin ("sensitin") prepared from a strain of *M. smegmatis*, as tested intradermally in guinea pigs, distinct from those of other acid-fast bacilli.

Atypical, Anonymous, or Unclassified Mycobacteria

During the 1950s, a group of mycobacteria have emerged in cultures from clinical sources, and a welter of literature has appeared on the questions especially of their classification and pathologic significance. These organisms differ from typical tubercle bacilli, in general, in being avirulent for guinea pigs, and in failing to form nicotinic acid. They are resistant to isoniazid, many are pigment-formers, most are slow growers like *M. tuberculosis* but some resemble *M. smegmatis* in growing rapidly on unenriched media; and, indeed, the smegma bacillus itself is evidently encompassed within the group. The general qualifying adjectives applied to these mycobacteria, "atypical," "anonymous," and "unclassified," reflect the difficulty of dealing with them as a group. While none of them are typical tubercle bacilli, they are not all anonymous—species names have achieved currency for certain members of the group—and the outline of a classification has been emerging and gaining wide acceptance.

Relationship to Tubercle Bacilli. The question remains in dispute whether the atypical mycobacteria have been derived from tubercle bacilli as a result of the widespread use of antituberculous drugs, or whether they are of independent origin and have merely been unmasked by the increasing use of cultures in clinical practice and by the coincident declining prevalence of *M. tuberculosis*. Tarshis (1958) has been able to produce resistant atypical forms after prolonged serial passage in media containing streptomycin and isoniazid. In a later note [Tarshis (1960)] these variants were described as chromogenic but non-acid-fast. This worker recognized the opinion of Runyon that they were not mycobacteria, but himself continued to advance the hypothesis of their derivation from tubercle bacilli [see also Xalabarder (1961)]. Among others, Atwell and Pratt (1960) considered these forms not to be variants or mutants of *M. tuberculosis.*

Distribution. The focal question from our present viewpoint is that of autochthony; available data permit only a tentative affirmative answer. The principal concern with these organisms in the literature has, of course, been their relationship to disease, and there is little doubt that many of them are important human pathogens capable of producing severe pulmonary tuberculosis-like disease in man as well as other clinical manifestations. Others, however, have been classed as "contaminants"—presumably meaning amphibionts, since the word saprophyte is recognizably inappropriate [Juhlin (1960)]. Direct evidence on this point has been provided by Edwards and Palmer (1959). These workers observed that more than two-thirds of a group of naval recruits in Georgia and Florida, with little recognized disease, reacted to a PPD made from one of the atypical mycobacteria (Battey, group III, see page 85), whereas only 6 per cent reacted to the standard preparation (PPD-S). They accordingly studied a group of approximately 375 persons—Negro plantation workers and their families—in Georgia in whom, also, there was little evidence of tuberculous infection or disease. Of 122 specimens of sputum often strenuously induced, and sometimes having the appearance of saliva, from all subjects aged over 14 years, 16 (13.3 per cent) yielded mycobacteria. None was a typical tubercle bacillus, and none fell into group I; 3 were classified in group II, 7 in group III, 5 in group IV (including 3 *M. fortuitum*), and 1 was a mixture of 2 strains of groups II and III. It was noted that "organisms were isolated almost as often from specimens that looked like saliva as from those that appeared to contain some sputum." Atwell and Pratt (1960) have found atypical mycobacteria, mainly group II with a few group III, in approximately 2 to 3 per cent of instances in gastric washings from healthy hospital employees, and in about the same proportion of patients with pulmonary disease. The suggestion that these organisms, whose demonstration in culture might well be difficult if their concentration at the source were low, may be indigenous to the mouth and upper respiratory tract seems worth further exploration.

Classification. Much of the large literature on the atypical mycobacteria is devoted to their classification as a matter of clinical importance. Our purpose will be met with a brief summary, based especially on the reports of Juhlin (1960) and Csillag (1961) which should be consulted for methods and additional literature [see also Tarshis (1961); Kubica et al. (1961)]. Juhlin (1960) summarized a consensus reached at the 15th International Conference on Tuberculosis at Istanbul in 1959, in which a classification originally proposed by Runyon (1955) was elaborated on the basis of more than 400 strains from 30 countries. Morphologic and other details contributed by Csillag are incorporated into the following abridged scheme. Groups I, II, and III are slow growers, requiring 1 to 2 weeks at 37°, 3 to 4 weeks at 22°.

Group I. Photochromogens. Forming yellow to yellow-orange pigment when grown in the light, or (in tests of fresh strains) when well-developed 8- to 10-day dark cultures on Löwenstein-Jensen slants are exposed to a 30-watt lamp at a distance of 45 cm for 1 hour and then reincubated for 24 hours ("photochromogenesis test"). Pathogenic for mice, slightly for guinea pigs, not for rabbits or hens. Common in disease of man, especially pulmonary; also in cervical adenopathies, sometimes in skin, bone, meninges, testicles. Long, beaded, strongly acid-fast; tendency to cord formation; periodic acid–Schiff test positive; catalase strongly positive. This group includes the "yellow bacilli" of Bühler and Pollak (1953) and was named *M. kansasii* by Hauduroy (1955). The *M. balnei* of Linell and Norden (1954), which grows within 10 days at 31° but fails to grow at 37°, belongs in this group according to Juhlin (1960), but it has been placed in the fast-growing group IV by Leach and Fenner (1954) and others [e.g., Bialkin, Pollak, and Weil (1961)].

Group II. Scotochromogens. Forming yellow to yellow-orange pigment in the dark, and orange to red in continuous light; photochromogenesis test negative. No growth at 45°. Not pathogenic for mice, guinea pigs, or rabbits. "Often isolated from skin, sputum, gastric washings and also from water"; may appear in disease but usually considered "contaminants" (Juhlin). Length variable; beaded, strongly acid-fast; no cords; catalase strongly positive; periodic acid–Schiff test positive. Includes the "orange bacilli" of Bühler and Pollak (1953).

Group III. Nonphotochromogens (Battey type). Forming no pigment in the dark and little or none (buff or yellow) in the light. Photochromogenesis test negative. Variably pathogenic for fowl; most strains are pathogenic for mice, some for rabbits, not for guinea pigs. Usually shorter than the H37Rv strain of human tubercle bacillus, or pleomorphic; usually no cords. Periodic acid–Schiff test negative; catalase variable. This group includes among other human pathogens *M. ulcerans* [MacCallum et al., (1948); Leach and Fenner (1954)] which, like

M. balnei of Group I, grows at 31° but not at 37°. *M. avium* is tentatively assigned to this group among fowl-pathogenic strains growing at 45°. Also included is the organism called *Nocardia intracellularis* by Cuttino and McCabe (1949) and renamed *Mycobacterium intracellularis* by Bojalil and Cerbon (1960).

Group IV. Fast Growers. These organisms grow in 2 to 3 days at either 22° or 37° and, unlike the preceding, grow on blood agar or nutrient agar and (within 6 weeks) in gelatin stab cultures. They do not grow at 45°. They are usually not pigmented and are negative in the chromogenesis test. Although usually nonpathogenic for laboratory animals, they may induce disease of skin, bones, or joints in mice, and sometimes appear in serious disease of man. In morphology and staining (including acid-fastness) they resemble human tubercle bacilli; the periodic acid–Schiff test is negative; they may form tight cords. This group includes *M. smegmatis, M. fortuitum,* and such true saprophytes as *M. phlei.*

The organism known as *Mycobacterium fortuitum,* listed above as a member of group IV, was distinguished as a species by Cruz (1938); [see also Wells, Agius, and Smith (1955); Gordon and Smith (1955)]. In a series of tests including acid-fastness, growth characteristics, and utilization of organic acids, McMillen and Kushner (1959) found this organism and *M. smegmatis* alike except for the following: *M. smegmatis* showed somewhat darker (buff) and drier growth on Löwenstein–Jensen medium and was able to utilize oxalate, tartrate, and benzoate. Cerbón and Bojalil (1961) have distinguished yellow- to orange-pigmented fast-growing mycobacteria (*M. smegmatis, M. phlei,* and others) from unpigmented, buff or pale straw-colored forms (*M. fortuitum* and others) by the Adansonian (computer) method of Sneath [see Sneath and Cowan (1958)]. In a further study by this method, Bojalil and Cerbón (1961) found *M. fortuitum* to be the only well-defined species among 43 nonpigmented strains.

Pathogenicity. As the foregoing discussion indicates, organisms belonging in groups I and III are the more pathogenic and are more often involved in serious illness in man, but members of the other groups cannot be dismissed as nonpathogens. Adachi (1959) found that 5 atypical mycobacteria isolated from disease in man, including 3 group I strains and 1 each of groups II and III, were all as virulent for mice as a human strain of *M. tuberculosis.* FitzPatrick (1960) reported that cortisone, which is known to increase the virulence for mice of the H37Rv strain, was also active, although less so, with 3 of 9 group I strains and 2 of 4 strains of group II; but 7 group III strains and one of *M. phlei* were nonpathogenic for mice with or without cortisone.

Shepard (1955, 1957) found that virulent mycobacteria grew intracellularly in HeLa cell cultures, whereas rapidly growing forms grew extracellularly and quickly killed the cells. When extracellular growth was suppressed by adding 2,000 μg per ml of streptomycin, which did not affect intracellular growth, and by breaking up clumps by paper filtration, *M. phlei* and *M. smegmatis* were phagocytized but failed to grow intracellularly, while *M. fortuitum* grew intracellularly and killed the infected cells. In a later paper, Shepard (1958) reported that mycobacteria could be arranged in the following order in terms of growth rate in tissue cultures of HeLa cells or of monkey kidney or human amnion cells: *M. fortuitum, M. balnei,* the "yellow bacillus" of Bühler and Pollak (1953), followed closely by *M. tuberculosis.*

Spore-bearing Bacilli

The genera of Gram-positive sporulating bacilli, *Bacillus* and *Clostridium*, are both so widely distributed in the soil that their frequent recovery in cultures from healthy human body surfaces is to be expected and of itself has no significance. This statement may be applied without further qualification to the aerobic genus, *Bacillus.* No information known to the writer suggests that the presence of this genus in the loci of the indigenous biota is ever to be attributed to anything but environmental contamination. With certain of the anaerobic spore-bearers—the clostridia—however, the direction of the evidence is less simple. That both genera consist primarily of soil saprophytes is unquestioned; but certain clostridia seem nevertheless to be classifiable among the normal flora because they (1) occur frequently, especially in the intestine; and (2) seem capable of proliferating in man without necessarily giving rise to disease.

The principal species thus involved is *Cl. perfringens,* as noted below. *Cl. tetani* is commonly found in the intestines of animals, but irregularly in man [Tenbroeck and Bauer (1922); Kerrin (1928); see also Prévot (1955)]. Prévot (1955) mentions the human intestinal tract as a habitat also of *Cl. bifermentans* and *Cl. sporogenes.* Clostridia have also been recovered from the human vagina and cervix [Patocka and Sebek (1947)]. Hite, Hesseltine, and Goldstein (1947) mentioned that earlier workers had recovered sporulating anaerobes from the female genital tract, but did not list clostridia among anaerobes they themselves found in this area. Unpublished studies from the writer's laboratory failed to reveal spore-formers in heat-shocked undiluted saliva streaked on blood agar and grown under both aerobic and anaerobic conditions.

Clostridium perfringens

Cl. perfringens is the most important spore-bearing anaerobe indigenous to man. It is said to occur uniformly in human feces [Wilson

TABLE 3-4

INCIDENCE OF *Clostridium perfringens* IN DIRECT PLATE CULTURES
OF FECES (ADAPTED FROM GOUDIE AND DUNCAN, 1956)

	Hospital patients with diarrhea			Hospital patients without diarrhea		Persons in normal health	
	After abdominal surgery	Non-surgical	Total	Without purgation	After purgation	Without purgation	After purgation
Number examined	33	29	62	24	23	4	3
Cl. perfringens:							
None	4	9	13	11	5	3	0
Few	2	11	13	6	12	1	1
Many	27	9	36	7	6	0	2

and Miles (1959); see also Chap. 10]. Goudie and Duncan (1956), although they presented no actual counts, found "large numbers" of *Cl.
perfringens* in feces of certain healthy subjects as well as of persons
with diarrhea ascribed to various antecedents. The relevant data are
summarized in Table 3-4. It may be observed that negative cultures
appeared in all categories except for the 3 normal persons after purgation. On the whole, diarrhea or purgation, "intestinal hurry" in the
words of these authors, seemed to bring larger numbers of clostridia to
the feces. The concentrations of these bacilli recovered indicated to
Goudie and Duncan that marked proliferation occurs somewhere in the
intestine. Williams (1926–27); Duncan et al. (1954); and Schwabacher, Salsbury, and Loosemore (1959) have provided evidence that
Cl. perfringens may proliferate in the stomach or small intestine under
pathologic conditions. Cregan and Hayward (1953) recovered the
organism once in 14 trials by aspiration from the healthy lower ileum.
Bishop and Allcock (1960) found it among other predominantly fecal
forms in the accumulated flora above an obstruction of the small intestine.

Borthwick and Gray (1937) found that the *Cl. perfringens* of the
human intestine is exclusively type A; and Goudie and Duncan (1956)
also reported that all their strains, whether from healthy or from pathologic intestines, were type A both serologically and toxigenically. Since
this is the organism most frequently associated with anaerobic cellulitis
and gas gangrene in man, its attributes have been adequately described
in standard texts and need not be repeated here. Nor are we concerned
with the more characteristic aspects of its pathogenicity. Beerens and

Delcourte (1958) reported that strains of *Cl. perfringens* from feces can be distinguished from those derived from soil by resistance of the latter but not the former to high concentrations of NaCl or other monovalent, highly dissociated mineral salts.

A variety of *Cl. perfringens* type A which is weakly toxigenic, non-hemolytic, and differs from most strains particularly in the greater heat resistance of its spores, has been implicated in a form of mild food poisoning. Hobbs et al. (1953), who reviewed the earlier literature, found this variety in the stool of 89.9 per cent of 129 cases of this type of food poisoning, in only 1 of 45 normal stools, and in from 2 to 15 per cent of 340 persons most of whom had diarrhea or food poisoning from other sources. The strain of *Cl. perfringens* isolated in 6 outbreaks of food poisoning, in 3 from both feces and implicated food (salt beef), and in 3 others from feces only, was serologically and toxigenically consistent in each instance. These findings, including the peculiarities of the organism and its low prevalence apart from the specific illness, bespeak exogenous infection [see also McKillop (1959)]. Attempts to produce the disease by feeding *Cl. perfringens* to human volunteers have yielded variable results; Dack et al. (1954) reported unsuccessful attempts and regarded previous positive findings as dubious. Goudie and Duncan (1956) were able to demonstrate α-toxin neutralizing substances in some specimens of feces, and suggested that these substances may have played a part in protecting the subjects of such feeding experiments, and that in general they may also participate in keeping this "potentially pathogenic organism," despite its ability to proliferate in the lower ileum, "a mere commensal in the normal, intact intestine." Even in instances of intestinal perforation this organism is evidently seldom pathogenic for man [see Silver (1961)].

A related but apparently not identical variety of *Cl. perfringens*, classified as type F, has been implicated by Zeissler and Rassfeld-Sternberg (1949) and others in an acute and sometimes rapidly fatal disease of man termed enteritis necroticans. The organism resembles the preceding, and differs from most type A strains, in that its spores are highly heat-resistant. It differs otherwise from type A in containing only traces of α-toxin, and in that its principal toxin is the β-toxin characteristic of animal pathogenic types of *Cl. perfringens*. *Cl. perfringens* type F was also isolated by this group both from the feces and from food incriminated in a fatal case of diarrhea. Similar organisms were recovered from 17.6 per cent of 108 fecal specimens in Hamburg, but these strains appeared less toxic for guinea pigs than those recovered from cases of enteritis necroticans. It has been suggested that this disease may be endogenous [see Patterson and Rosenbaum (1952)], but additional information is needed to decide the question.

Loh and Bagley (1956) have suggested that the modified Wilson–Blair medium for clostridia [Lockwood, et al. (1949)] is suitable for its enumeration. Lowbury and Lilly (1955) devised a selective plating medium for *Cl. perfringens* utilizing the Nagler reaction with human serum [Hayward (1943)] and the relative resistance of this species to neomycin. Willis and Hobbs (1959) compared several media for clostridia and described a lactose–egg yolk–milk agar containing neomycin sulfate for isolation of all types of *Cl. perfringens* and other common clostridia. Rapid methods applied to clostridia, for testing fermentation reactions and simultaneous tests for liquefaction of gelatin and production of indole, have been described by Kaufman and Weaver (1960).

References

Adachi, K., 1959, *Sci. Repts. Research Inst., Tohoku Univ. Ser. C. Med.*, **9**:25 (*Biol. Abstr.*).

Alvarez and Tavel, 1885, *Arch. Physiol. Norm. Pathol.*, **6**:303.

Atwell, R. J., and Pratt, P. C., 1960, *Am. Rev. Resp. Dis.*, **81**:888.

Avery, R. J., and Blank, F., 1954, *Can. J. Microbiol.*, **1**:140.

Bailey, R. W., and Clarke, R. T. J., 1959, *Biochem. J.*, **72**:49.

Baird-Parker, A. C., 1960, *J. Gen. Microbiol.*, **22**:458.

———, Bisset, K. A., and Pike, E. B., 1958, *Brit. Dental J.*, **105**:137.

———, and Davis, G. H. G., 1958, *ibid.*, **19**:446.

Barbero, G. J., Runge, G., Fischer, D., Crawford, M. N., Torres, F. E., and György, P., 1952, *J. Pediat.* **40**:152.

Barksdale, W. L., Cummins, C. S., and Harris, H., 1957, *J. Gen. Microbiol.*, **16**:749.

Batty, I., 1958, *J. Pathol. Bacteriol.*, **75**:455.

Beerens, H., 1953–54, *Ann. Inst. Pasteur Lille*, **6**:116.

———, and Delcourte, F., 1958, *Ann. Inst. Pasteur*, **95**:739, 740.

———, and Demont, F., 1949, *Compt. Rend. Soc. Biol.*, **143**:17.

———, Gerard, A., and Guillaume, J., 1957, *Ann. Inst. Pasteur Lille*, **9**:77.

Bialkin, G., Pollak, A., and Weil, A. J., 1961, *Am. J. Diseases Children*, **101**:739.

Bibby, B. G., and Berry, G. P., 1939, *J. Bacteriol.*, **38**:263.

Biocca, E., and Seppilli, A., 1944, *Arquiv. Biol.* (São Paulo), **28**:143.

———, and ———, 1947, *J. Inf. Dis.*, **81**:112.

Bishop, R. F., and Allcock, E. A., 1960, *Brit. Med. J.*, **1**:766.

Bisset, K. A., and Davis, G. H. G., 1959, *Arch. Oral Biol.*, **1**:80.

Blaurock, G., 1940, *Deut. med. Wochschr.*, **66**:1133.

Böe, J., and Thjötta, T., 1944, *Acta Pathol. Microbiol. Scand.*, **21**:441.

Bojalil, L. F., and Cerbón, J., 1960, *Am. Rev. Resp. Dis.*, **81**:382.

———, and ———, 1961, *J. Bacteriol.*, **81**:338.

Borthwick, G. R., and Gray, J. D. A., 1937, *Brit. J. Exp. Pathol.*, **18**:119.

Botazzi, V., 1958, *Ann. Microbiol.*, **8**:45 (*Biol. Abstr.*).

———, and Sharpe, M. E., 1958, *ibid.*, **8**:64 (*Biol. Abstr.*).

Brandsaeter, E., and Nelson, F. E., 1956, *J. Bacteriol.*, **72**:68, 73.

Breed, R. S., Murray, E. G. D., and Hitchens, A. P., 1948, *Bergey's Manual of Determinative Bacteriology*, 6th ed., The Williams & Wilkins Company, Baltimore.

———, ———, and Smith, N. R., 1957, *ibid.*, 7th ed.

Brion, A., 1942, *Rev. Med. Vet. y Parasitol.*, **91**:157, cited by Breed et al., 1957, p. 743.

———, Goret, P., and Joubert, L., 1952, *Proc. VI Congr. Internat. de Patol. Comp.*, Madrid, i, 48; cited by Breed et al., 1957, p. 743.

Bühler, V. P., and Pollak, A., 1953, *Am. J. Clin. Pathol.*, **23**:363.

Bulleid, A., 1924, *Guy's Hosp. Repts.*, **74**:444.

Caille, B., and Toucas, M., 1960, *Ann. Inst. Pasteur*, **98**:276.

Carpenter, C. M., Howard, D. H., and Lehman, E. L., 1956, *J. Lab. Clin. Med.*, **47**:194.

Cataldi, M. S., and Müller, A., 1947, *Dia. Med.*, **19**:473.

Cerbón, J., and Bojalil, L. F., 1961, *J. Gen. Microbiol.*, **25**:7.

Charlton, G., and Spies, H. C., 1956, *J. Dental Research*, **35**:800.

Cheeseman, G. C., 1960, *J. Appl. Bacteriol.*, **22**:341.

Christie, A. O., and Porteous, J. W., 1959, *Biochem. J.*, **73**:47.

———, and ———, 1960, *J. Gen. Microbiol.*, **23**:261.

Clarke, R. T. J., 1959, *ibid.*, **20**:549.

Coetzee, J. N., de Klerk, H. C., and Sacks, T. G., 1960, *Nature*, **187**:348.

Cregan, J., and Hayward, N. J., 1953, *Brit. Med. J.*, **1**:1356.

Cruickshank, R., 1945, *Arch. Disease Childhood*, **20**:145.

Cruz, J. C., 1938, *Acta Med. (Rio de Janiero)*, **1**:297.

Csillag, A., 1961, *J. Gen. Microbiol.*, **24**:261.

Cummins, C. S., and Harris, H., 1956, *ibid.*, **14**:583.

———, and ———, 1958, *ibid.*, **18**:173.

Cuttino, J. T., and McCabe, A. M., 1949, *Am. J. Pathol.*, **25**:1.

Czapelewski, E., 1897, *Münch. med. Wochschr.*, **44**:1192.

Dack, G. M., Sugiyama, H., Owens, F. J., and Kirsner, J. B., 1954, *J. Inf. Dis.*, **94**:34.

Dacre, J. C., and Sharpe, M. E., 1956, *Nature*, **178**:700.

Davis, G. H. G., 1955, *J. Gen. Microbiol.*, **13**:481.

———, 1959, *J. Appl. Bacteriol.*, **22**:350.

———, and Baird-Parker, A. C., 1959a, *Brit. Dent. J.*, **106**:70, 142.

———, and ———, 1959b, *J. Gen. Microbiol.*, **21**:612.

———, Bisset, K. A., and Hale, C. M. F., 1955, *ibid.*, **13**:68.

———, and Hayward, A. C., 1955, *ibid.*, **13**:533.

Dawbarn, M. B., Forsyth, H., and Kilpatrick, D., 1961, *Australian J. Exp. Biol. Med. Sci.*, **39**:305.

De Man, J. C., Rogosa, M., and Sharpe, M. E., 1960, *J. Appl. Bacteriol.*, **23**:130.

Dewar, M. F., and Parfitt, G. J., 1951, *Brit. Dent. J.*, **90**:150.

Döderlein, A., 1892, *Das Scheidensekret und seine Bedeutung für das Puerperalfieber*, E. Besold, Leipzig.

Douglas, H. C., and Gunter, S. E., 1946, *J. Bacteriol.*, **52**:15.

Duncan, I. B. R., Goudie, J. G., Mackie, L. M., and Howie, J. W., 1954, *J. Pathol. Bacteriol.*, **67**:282.

Eberson, F., 1918, *J. Inf. Dis.*, **23**:1.

Edwards, L. B., and Palmer, C. E., 1959, *Am. Rev. Resp. Dis.*, **80**:747.

Ellis, R. H., and Sarles, W. B, 1958, *J. Bacteriol.*, **75**:272.

Emard, L. O., and Vaughn, R. H., 1952, *ibid.*, **63**:487.

Emmons, C. W., 1938, *Public Health Repts.*, **53**:1967.

Ennever, J., Robinson, H. B. G., and Kitchin, P. C., 1949, *Science*, **110**:334.

———, ———, and ———, 1951, *J. Dental Research*, **27**:599.

Erikson, D., 1935, *Med. Research Council, Spec. Rep. Ser.*, No. 203.

———, 1940, *ibid.*, No. 240.

———, and Porteous, J. W., 1953, *J. Gen. Microbiol.*, **8**:464.

———, and ———, 1955, *ibid.*, **13**:261.

Featherstone, J. L., 1959, *Australian Dental J.*, **4**:39.

———, 1960*a*, *ibid.*, **5**:204.

———, 1960*b*, *ibid.*, **5**:149.

FitzPatrick, F. K., 1960, *Proc. Soc. Expt. Biol. Med.*, **104**:558.

Fleisher, M. S., 1952, *Am. J. Med. Sci.*, **224**:548.

Fleming, A., 1909, *Lancet*, **1**:1035.

Florman, A. L., and Scoma, J. L., 1960, *Proc. Soc. Expt. Biol. Med.*, **104**:683.

Forbus, W. D., Cuttino, J. T., Smith, A. G., Margolis, A. McC., and Reid, D. W., 1958, *A.M.A. Arch. Pathol.*, **66**:1.

Frank, H. A., and Skinner, C. E., 1954, *Mycologia*, **46**:728.

Freeman, V. J., 1951, *J. Bacteriol.*, **61**:675.

Gale, D., unpublished data.

Garrod, L. P., 1952, *Tubercle*, **33**:258.

Gauhe, A., György, P., Hoover, J. R. E., Kuhn, R., Rose, C. S., Ruelius, H. W., and Zilliken, F., 1954, *Arch. Biochem. Biophys.*, **48**:214.

Gibbons, R. J., and Doetsch, R. N., 1959, *J. Bacteriol.*, **77**:417.

Gilmour, M. N., 1961, *Bacteriol. Revs.*, **25**:142.

———, and Beck, P. H., 1961, *ibid.*, **25**:152.

———, Howell, A., Jr., and Bibby, B. G., 1961, *ibid.*, **25**:131.

———, and Hunter, P. A., 1958, *J. Bacteriol.*, **76**:294.

Glick, M. C., Zilliken, F., and György, P., 1959, *ibid.*, **77**:230.

Gordon, R. E., and Smith, M. M., 1953, *ibid.*, **66**:41.

———, and ———, 1955, *ibid.*, **69**:502.

Goudie, J. G., and Duncan, I. B. R., 1956, *J. Pathol. Bacteriol.*, **72**:281.

Goulden, J. D. S., and Sharpe, M. E., 1958, *J. Gen. Microbiol.*, **19**:76.

Groman, N. B., 1953, *J. Bacteriol.*, **66**:184.

———, and Memmer, R., 1958, *J. Gen. Microbiol.*, **19**:634.

Grubb, R., and Krasse, B., 1953, *Acta Pathol. Microbiol. Scand.*, **32**:539.

Guillot, N., 1958, *Ann. Inst. Pasteur*, **95**:194.

Gunderson, W. B., and Henriksen, S. D., 1959, *Acta Pathol. Microbiol. Scand.*, **47**:173.

Gutekunst, R. R., Delwiche, E. A., and Seeley, H. W., 1957, *J. Bacteriol.*, **74**:693.

Gutierrez, J., 1953, *ibid.*, **66**:123.

Gyllenberg, H., and Carlberg, G., 1958, *Acta Pathol. Microbiol. Scand.*, **42**:380.

———, and Roine, P., 1957, *ibid.*, **41**:144.

György, P., 1953, *Pediatrics*, **11**:98.

———Hoover, J. E., Kuhn, R., and Rose, C., 1954, *Arch. Biochem. Biophys.*, **48**:209.

———, Kuhn, R., Rose, C. S., and Zilliken, F., 1954, *ibid.*, **48**:202.

———, Norris, R. F., and Rose, C. S., 1954, *ibid.*, **48**:193.

———, and Rose, C. S., 1955, *J. Bacteriol.*, **69**:483.

———, ———, and Springer, G. F., 1954, *J. Lab. Clin. Med.*, **43**:543.

Hadley, F. P., 1933, *J. Dental Research*, **13**:415.

Hagedorn, H., 1955, *Zentr. Bakteriol. Parasitenk.*, *II*, **107**:353.

Hamilton, R. D., and Zahler, S. A., 1957, *J. Bacteriol.*, **73**:386.

Harrison, R. W., 1942, *J. Inf. Dis.*, **70**:69, 77.

——, and Opal, Z. Z., 1944, *J. Dental Research*, **23**:1.

——, Zidek, Z. C., and Hemmens, E. S., 1939, *J. Inf. Dis.*, **65**:255.

Harrison, W., Stahl, R. C., Magavran, J., Sanders, M., Norris, R. F., and György, P., 1953, *Am. J. Obstet. Gynecol.*, **65**:352.

Hassinen, J. B., Durbin, G. T., Tomarelli, R. M., and Bernhart, F. W., 1951, *J. Bacteriol.*, **62**:771.

Hauduroy, P., 1955, *Derniers aspects du monde des mycobactéries*, Masson et Cie, Paris, pp. 72–75; cited by Bialkin et al. (1961).

Hayward, A. C., 1957, *Brit. Dent. J.*, **102**:450.

——, and Davis, G. H. G., 1956, *ibid.*, **101**:43.

Hayward, N. J., 1943, *J. Pathol. Bacteriol.*, **55**:285.

Hazen, E. L., and Little, G. N., 1958, *J. Lab. Clin. Med.*, **51**:968.

——, ——, and Resnick, H., 1952, *ibid.*, **40**:914.

Heinrich, S., 1960, *Zentr. Bakteriol. Parasitenk.*, *I. Orig.*, **177**:255.

Henriksen, S. D., 1955, *Acta Pathol. Microbiol. Scand.*, **37**:65.

——, and Grelland, R., 1952, *J. Pathol. Bacteriol.*, **64**:503.

——, and Gunderson, W. B., 1959, *Acta Pathol. Microbiol. Scand.*, **47**: 380.

Henry, M., 1953, *Trans. Pacific Coast Oto-Ophth. Soc.*, **33**:173.

Hermann, G. I., 1961, *Am. J. Med. Technol.*, **27**:61.

Herter, C. A., and Kendall, A. I., 1908, *J. Biol. Chem.*, **5**:293.

Hine, M. K., and Berry, G. P., 1937, *J. Bacteriol.*, **34**:517.

Hite, K. E., Hesseltine, H. C., and Goldstein, L., 1947, *Am. J. Obstet. Gynecol.*, **53**:233.

Hobbs, B. C., Smith, M. E., Oakley, C. L., Warrack, G. H., and Cruickshank, J. C., 1953, *J. Hyg.*, **51**:75.

Holm, P., 1951, *Acta Pathol. Microbiol. Scand.*, **28**:391.

Howard, D. H., and Jann, G. J., 1955, *J. Bacteriol.*, **69**:108.

Howe, P. R., and Hatch, R. E., 1917, *Dental. Cosmos*, **59**:961.

Howell, A., Jr., and Pine, L., 1956, *J. Bacteriol.*, **71**:47.

——, and ——, 1961, *Bacteriol. Revs.*, **25**:162.

——, Murphy, W. C., III, Paul, F., and Stephan, R. M., 1959, *J. Bacteriol.* **78**:82.

——, and Rogosa, M., 1958, *ibid.*, **76**:330.

Hunter, C. A., Jr., Long, K. R., and Schumacher, R. D., 1959, *Ann. N.Y. Acad. Sci.*, **83**:217.

Hvid-Hansen, N., 1951, *Acta Pathol. Microbiol. Scand.*, **29**:335.

Jackins, H. C., and Barker, H. A., 1951, *J. Bacteriol.*, **61**:101.

Jensen, R. G., Smith, K. L., Edmondson, J. E., and Merilan, C. P., 1956, *ibid.*, **72**:253.

Johansson, K. R., Peterson, G. E., and Dick, E. C., 1953, *J. Nutrition*, **49**:135.

——, and Sarles, W. B., 1949, *Bacteriol., Revs.*, **13**:25.

Judicial Commission, 1954, *Internat. Bull. Bact. Nomen. Tax.*, **4**:151, (*Biol. Abstr.*).

Juhlin, I., 1960, *Acta Pathol. Microbiol. Scand.*, **50**:195.

Kasai, G. J., 1955, *J. Inf. Dis.*, **96**:279.

——, 1961, *J. Dental Research*, **40**:800.

Kassel, R., and Rottino, A., 1955, *A.M.A. Arch. Internal. Med.*, **96**:804.

Kaufman, L., and Weaver, R. H., 1960, *J. Bacteriol.*, **79**:119.

Kerrin, J. C., 1928, *Brit. J. Exp. Pathol.*, **9**:69.

King, J. W., and Rettger, L. F., 1942, *J. Bacteriol.*, **44**:301.

King, S., and Meyer, E., 1957, *ibid.*, **74**:234.

Kiuru, V. J. T., and Tybeck, E., 1955, *Suon. Kemistilehti*, B. 28:57; cited by Coetze, et al., 1960.

Kligler, I. J., 1915, *J. Allied Dental Soc.*, **10**:141, 282, 445.

Kopeloff, N., 1926, *Lactobacillus Acidophilus*, The Williams & Wilkins Company, Baltimore.

Korttila, K., 1953, *Ann. Med. Exptl. et Biol. Fenniae (Helsinki)*, **31**:22.

Koser, S. A., and Thomas, J. L., 1955, *J. Inf. Dis.*, **97**:287.

Kristoffersen, T., and Nelson, F. E., 1955, *Appl. Microbiol.*, **3**:268 (*Biol. Abstr.*).

Kubica, G. P., and Beam, R. E., 1961, *Am. Rev. Resp. Dis.*, **83**:733.

――――, and Rigdon, A. L., 1961, *ibid.*, **83**:737.

――――, and Vestal, A. L., 1961, *ibid.*, **83**:728.

Kulp, W. L., and White, V., 1932, *Science*, **76**:17.

Lagerborg, V. A., and Clapper, W. E., 1952, *J. Bacteriol.*, **63**:393.

Laser, H., 1897, *Münch. med. Wochschr.*, **44**:1191.

Laughton, N., 1948, *J. Obstet. Gynecol.*, **55**:608.

――――, 1950, *J. Hyg.*, **48**:346.

Lavergne, E. de, Burdin, J.-C., Schmitt, J., and Manciaux, M., 1959, *Ann. Inst. Pasteur*, **97**:104.

Leach, R. W., and Fenner, F., 1954, *Australian J. Exp. Biol. Med. Sci.*, **32**:835.

Lederburg, J., and Lederburg, E. M., 1952, *J. Bacteriol.*, **63**:399.

Lentze, F., 1953, *6th Congr. Internaz. Microb. Rome 5* (Sec. 14): 145.

――――, 1958, *Ärztliche Forsch.*, **12**:205.

Levaditi, C., Vaisman, A., and Levy, P., 1949, *Presse Méd.*, **57**:852.

Lewis, K., and Rettger, L. F., 1940, *J. Bacteriol.*, **40**:287.

Lewkowicz, X., 1901, *Arch. Méd. Exp. et Anat. Pathol.*, **13**:633.

Linell, F., and Norden, A., 1954, *Acta Turberc. Scand. Suppl.* 33, p. 5.

Linzenmeier, G., 1954, *Ann. Inst. Pasteur*, **87**:572.

Lockwood, J. S., Young, A. D., Bouchelle, McL., Bryant, T. R., Jr., and Stojowski, A. J., 1949, *Ann. Surg.*, **129**:14.

Loh, W.-P., and Bagley, E. P., 1956, *Am. J. Med. Technol.*, **22**:184.

Lord, F. T., 1910, *Boston Med. Surg. J.*, **163**:82.

――――, 1910, *J. Am. Med. Assoc*, **55**:1261.

Lowbury, E. J. L., and Lilly, H. A., 1955, *J. Pathol. Bacteriol.*, **70**:105.

Ludwig, T. G., 1952, *Dental J. Australia*, **24**:53.

MacCallum, P., Tolhurst, J. C., Buckle, G., and Sissons, H. A., 1948, *J. Pathol. Bacteriol.*, **60**:93.

Mackenzie, I., 1931, *A System of Bacteriology in Relation to Medicine (London)*, **8**:91.

Maclean, P. D., Liebow, A. A., and Rosenberg, A. A., 1946, *J. Inf. Dis.*, **79**:69.

Magnusson, M., 1961, *Am. Rev. Resp. Dis.*, **83**:57.

Marchoux, E., and Halphen, E., 1912, *Compt. Rend. Soc. Biol.*, **73**:249.

Marschall, F., 1938, *Zentr. Bakteriol. Parasitenk., I Orig.*, **141**:153.

McKillop, E. J., 1959, *J. Hyg.*, **57**:31.

McMillen, S., and Kushner, D. S., 1959, *Am. Rev. Resp. Dis.*, **80**:434.

Mendel, J., 1919, *Compt. Rend. Soc. Biol.*, **82**:583.

Metchnikoff, E., 1908, *Prolongation of Life*, G. P. Putnam's Sons, New York.
Meyer, E., and Verges, P., 1950, *J. Lab. Clin. Med.*, **36**:667.
Meyers, C. E., Walter E. L., and Green, L. B., 1958, *J. Dental Research*, **37**:175.
Middlebrook, G., and Dubos, R. J., 1948, *Am. Rev. Tuberc.*, **58**:698.
Montagna, C. P., and Cataldi, M. S., 1944, *Rev. Asoc. Arg. Dietol.*, **2**:47.
Morishita, T., 1928, *Proc. Soc. Exptl. Biol. Med.*, **25**:654.
———, 1929, *J. Bacteriol.*, **17**:7.
Morris, E. O., 1951, *J. Hyg.*, **49**:46.
———, 1953, *ibid.*, **51**:49.
———, 1954, *Brit. Dental J.*, **97**:29.
Murray, E. G. D., in Breed, Murray, and Smith, *Bergey's Manual of Determinative Bacteriology*, 1957, p. 595; footnote, p. 579.
Norris, R. F., De Sipin, M., Zilliken, F. W., Harvey, T. S., and György, P., 1954, *J. Bacteriol.*. **67**:159.
———, Flanders, R. M., Tomarelli, R. M., and György, P., 1950, *ibid.*, **60**:681.
Orland, F. J., 1950, *J. Inf. Dis.*, **86**:63.
Patočka, F., and Šebek, V., 1947, *Českoslov. Gynaekol.*, **12**:24, (*Biol. Abstr.*).
———, and ———, 1948, *Časopis lékáru českých.*, **87**:99 (*Biol. Abstr.*).
Patterson, M., and Rosenbaum, H. D., 1952, *Gastroenterologica*, **21**:110.
Pederson, C. S., 1937, *J. Bacteriol.*, **33**:90.
———, 1947, *ibid.*, **53**:407.
———, and Albury, M. N., 1955, *ibid.*, **70**:702.
Petuely, F., 1956, *Zentr. Bakteriol. Parasitenk.*, *I Orig.*, **166**:95.
Pine, L., 1956, *Proc. Soc. Expt. Biol. Med.*, **93**:468.
———, 1960, *ibid.*, **104**:702.
———, and Hardin, H., 1959, *J. Bacteriol.*, **78**:164.
———, and Howell, A., Jr., 1956, *J. Gen. Microbiol.*, **15**:428.
———, ———, and Watson, S. J., 1960, *ibid.*, **23**:403.
———, and Watson, S. J., 1959, *J. Lab. Clin. Med.*, **54**:107.
Pochi, P. E., and Strauss, J. S., 1961, *J. Invest. Dermatol.*, **36**:423.
Pollock, M. R., Wainwright, S. D., and Manson, E. E. D., 1949, *J. Pathol. Bacteriol.*, **61**:274.
Prévot, A.-R., 1938, *Ann. Inst. Pasteur*, **60**:304.
———, 1955, *Biologie des maladies dues aux anaérobies*, Editions Méd. Flammarion, Paris, p. 15.
———, 1957, *Manuel de classification et de détermination des bactéries anaérobies*, 3d ed., Masson et Cie, Paris.
———, Goret, P., Joubert, L., Tardieux, P., and Aladame, N., 1951, *Ann. Inst. Pasteur*, **81**:85.
———, Magnin, F., Levrel, J., Duby, D., and deCadore, F., 1958, *ibid.*, **95**:241.
———, and Raynaud, M., 1955, *ibid.*, **88**:229.
———, and Tardieux, P., 1953, *ibid.*, **84**:879.
Princivalle, M., DeFelip, G., VonLorch, L., and Alberti, S., 1959, *Rend. Inst. Super. Sanità*, **21**:989 (*Biol. Abstr.*).
Rahe, A. H., 1915, *J. Inf. Dis.*, **16**:210.
Rains, A. J. H., Barson, G. J., Crawford, N., and Shrewsbury, J. F. D., 1960, *Lancet*, **2**:614.
Rettger, L. F., Levy, M. N., Weinstein, L., and Weiss, J. E., 1935, *Lacto-*

bacillus Acidophilus and its Therapeutic Application, Yale University Press, New Haven.

Rhodes, R. A., Sarles, W. B., Monson, W. J., Harper, A. E., and Elvehjem, C. A., 1954, *J. Nutrition*, **53**:289.

Richardson, R. L., and Jones, M., 1958, *J. Dental Research*, **37**:697.

———, and Schmidt, J., 1959, *ibid.*, **38**:1016.

Robinson, E. L., and Thompson, W. L., 1952, *J. Pediat.*, **41**:395.

Robinson, M., 1951, *Lancet*, **1**:788.

Rogosa, M., Franklin, J. G., and Perry, J. D., 1961, *J. Gen. Microbiol.*, **25**:473.

———, Mitchell, J. A., and Fitzgerald, R. J., 1950, *J. Dental Research*, **29**:658.

———, ———, and Wiseman, R. F., 1951, *J. Bacteriol.*, **62**:132.

———, and Sharpe, M. E., 1959, *J. Appl. Bacteriol.*, **22**:329.

———, ———, 1960, *J. Gen. Microbiol.*, **23**:197.

———, Wiseman, R. F., Mitchell, J. A., Disraely, M. N., and Beaman, A. J., 1953, *J. Bacteriol.*, **65**:681.

Romano, A. H., and Nickerson, W. J., 1956, *ibid.*, **72**:478.

Rose, C. S., Kuhn, R., Zilliken, F., and György, P., 1954, *Arch. Biochem. Biophys.*, **49**:123.

Rosebury, T., 1932, *J. Bacteriol.*, **24**:321.

———, 1944a, *Arch. Pathol.*, **38**:413.

———, 1944b, *Bacteriol. Revs.*, **9**:189.

———, Clark, A. R., Engel, S. G., and Tergis, F., 1950, *J. Inf. Dis.*, **87**:217.

———, Epps, L. J., and Clark, A. R., 1944, *ibid.*, **74**:131.

———, Linton, R. W., and Buchbinder, L., 1929, *J. Bacteriol.*, **18**:395.

———, Macdonald, J. B., and Clark, A. R., 1950, *J. Dental Research*, **29**:718.

Runyon, E. H., 1955, *Am. Rev. Tuberc.*, **72**:866.

Ryff, J. F., and Browne, J., 1954, *Am. J. Vet. Res.*, **15**:617.

Salvin, S. B., and Hoyer, B. H., 1951, *Proc. Soc. Expt. Biol. Med.*, **78**:128.

Saxholm, R., 1951, *J. Pathol. Bacteriol.*, **63**:303.

Schmidt, E. G., and Burnett, G. W., 1956, *J. Dental Research*, **35**:370.

Schwabacher, H., Salsbury, A. J., and Loosemore, T. G. E., 1959, *J. Clin. Pathol.*, **12**:565.

Seeliger, H., 1953, *Arch. Hyg.*, **137**:1.

Sharpe, M. E., 1955, *J. Gen. Microbiol.*, **12**:107.

———, and Mattick, A. T. R., 1957, *Milchwissenschaft*, **12**:348 (*Biol. Abstr.*).

———, and Wheater, D. M. J., 1957, *J. Gen. Microbiol.*, **12**:676.

Shepard, C. C., 1955, *Proc. Soc. Exptl. Biol. Med.*, **90**:392.

———, 1957, *J. Bacteriol.*, **73**:722.

———, 1957, *J. Exptl. Med.*, **105**:39.

———, 1958, *ibid.*, **107**:237.

Silver, M. D., 1961, *Can. Med. Assoc. J.*, **84**:1418.

Slack, J. M., Spears, R. G., Snodgrass, W. G., and Kuchler, R. J., 1955, *J. Bacteriol.*, **70**:400.

———, Winger, A., and Moore, D. W., Jr., 1961, *ibid.*, **82**:54.

Slanetz, L. W., and Rettger, L. F., 1933, *ibid.*, **26**:599.

Smith, H. W., and Crabb, W. E., 1961a, *J. Pathol. Bacteriol.*, **82**:53.

———, and ———, 1961b, personal communication.

Sneath, P. H. A., and Cowan, S. T., 1958, *J. Gen. Microbiol.*, **19**:551.
Spaulding, E. H., and Rettger, L. F., 1938, *ibid.*, **34**:535, 549.
Springer, G. F., Rose, C. S., and György, P., 1954, *J. Lab. Clin. Med.*, **43**: 532.
Strittmatter, C. F., 1959, *J. Biol. Chem.*, **234**:2789, 2794.
Sullivan, H. R., and Goldsworthy, N. E., 1940, *J. Pathol. Bacteriol.*, **51**:253.
———, Still, J. L., and Goldsworthy, N. E., 1939, *J. Dental Research*, **18**: 513.
Sundman, V., Björksten, K. af, and Gyllenberg, H. G., 1959, *J. Gen. Microbiol.*, **21**:371.
Suter, L. S., 1956, *Mycopathol. et Mycol. Appl.*, **7**:220.
Takazoe, I., and Frostell, G., 1960, *Acta Odontol. Scand.*, **18**:365.
Tarshis, M. S., 1958, *Am. Rev. Tuberc.*, **78**:921.
———, 1960, *Am. Rev. Resp. Dis.*, **81**:426.
———, 1961, *J. Lab. Clin. Med.*, **57**:480.
———, 1961, *J. Clin. Pathol.*, **35**:461.
———, 1961, *Tubercle*, **42**:101.
Tenbroeck, C., and Bauer, J. H., 1922, *J. Exptl. Med.*, **36**:261.
Thiman, K. V., 1955, *The Life of Bacteria*, The Macmillan Company, New York, p. 421.
Thjötta, T., Hartmann, O. and Böe, J., 1939, *Avhandl. Norske Videnskaps-Akad.*, *Oslo I.*, *Mat.-Naturv. Kl.*, no. 3.
Thompson, L., 1950, *Proc. Staff Meetings Mayo Clinic*, **25**:81.
———, and Lovestedt, S. A., 1951, *ibid.*, **26**:169.
Tilden, E. B., and Svec, M., 1950, *J. Dental Research*, **29**:659.
Tissier, H., 1899, *Compt. Rend. Soc. Biol.*, **51**:943.
———, 1900, *Recherches sur la flore intestinale des nourissons (état normal et pathologique)*. Thèse, Faculté de Médecine de Paris, Carré, Paris.
———, 1905, *Ann. Inst. Pasteur*, **19**:109.
Topley, W. W. C., and Wilson, G. S., 1936, *The Principles of Bacteriology and Immunity*, 2d ed., The Williams & Wilkins Company, Baltimore, p. 288.
Varney, P., 1927, *J. Bacteriol.*, **13**:275.
Veltre, F. A., Shorb, M. S., and Pelczar, M. J., Jr., 1953, *Proc. Soc. Exptl. Biol.*, **83**:284.
Waksman, S. A., 1957, *Bacteriol. Revs.*, **21**:1.
Watson, E. D., Hoffman, N., Simmers, R., and Rosebury, T., 1962, *J. Bacteriol*, **83**:144.
Weinstein, L., 1938, *Yale J. Biol. Med.*, **10**:247.
Weiss, J. E., and Rettger, L. F., 1934, *J. Bacteriol.*, **28**:501.
———, and ———, 1938, *J. Inf. Dis.*, **62**:115.
Wells, A. Q., Agius, E., and Smith, N., 1955, *Am. Rev. Tuberc.*, **72**:53.
Wherry, W. B., and Oliver, W. W., 1916, *J. Inf. Dis.*, **19**:299.
Williams, B. W., 1926–27, *Brit. J. Surg.*, **14**:295.
Williams, N. B., 1947, *J. Bacteriol.*, **54**:14.
———, 1948, *J. Inf. Dis.*, **82**:31.
———, Norris, R. F., and György, P., 1953, *ibid.*, **92**:191.
Willis, A. T., and Hobbs, G., 1959, *J. Pathol. Bacteriol.*, **77**:511.
Wilson, G. S., and Miles, A. A., 1955, *Topley and Wilson's Principles of Bacteriology and Immunity*, 4th ed., The Williams & Wilkins Company, Baltimore, p. 977.

Wilssens, A., and Buttiaux, R., 1958, *Ann. Inst. Pasteur*, **94**:332.

Wiseman, R. F., Sarles, W. B., Benton, D. A., Harper, A. E., and Elvehjem, C. A, 1956, *J. Bacteriol.*, **72**:723.

Wittler, R. G., Malizia, W. F., Kramer, P. E., Tuckett, J. D., Pritchard, H. N., and Baker, H. J., 1960, *J. Gen. Microbiol.*, **23**:315.

Wolff, M., and Israel, J., 1891, *Virchow's Arch. pathol. Anat. u. Physiol.* **126**:11.

Xalabarder, C., 1961, *Am. Rev. Resp. Dis.*, **83**:1.

Zeissler, J., and Rassfeld-Sternberg, L., 1949, *Zentr. f. Bakteriol. Parasitenk, I Orig.*, **153**:304.

——, and ——, 1949, *Brit. Med. J.* **1**:267.

CHAPTER 4

INDIGENOUS AEROBIC GRAM-NEGATIVE BACILLI

Enterobacteria

The easily cultivated aerobic Gram-negative bacilli particularly characteristic of the intestinal tract are the best known indigenous microbes; and their leading member, the colon bacillus, is probably the most familiar of all bacteria. These microorganisms have been studied widely and intensively from many points of view, including their separation from the closely related pathogens, *Salmonella* and *Shigella;* their own proclivities as pathogens; and their use in morphologic, metabolic, immunologic, nutritional, and genetic research, and as hosts for the most widely studied bacteriophages. Any attempt to deal completely with them here would be impertinent. Indeed—on the plea that the available information on these organisms is readily accessible in other sources (the converse of which applies in most areas of our subject matter) they might be disposed of with bare mention. A position slightly to the left of the latter extreme may best suit our purposes. The following aspects of the subject seem most pertinent: (1) a brief characterization of the principal members of the group; (2) their distribution, principally on human body surfaces, as indigenous forms; (3) some features of their pathogenicity; and (4) certain aspects of their nonpathogenic significance as indigenous microorganisms (the last topic is considered in Chap. 11).

Differentiation of the Principal Indigenous Enterobacteria

The family of enteric bacteria as it is customarily defined comprises Gram-negative rods growing well on artificial media, forming acid, or acid and gas (including hydrogen) from glucose, nearly always reducing nitrate to nitrite (exceptions are found among the plant-pathogenic *Erwinia*); and, when motile, peritrichously flagellated.

The finer classification of the group has been given intensive and effective study. Its difficulties have been emphasized by workers who have contributed largely to it in terms that apply, in the writer's opinion, not only to this group but to the whole problem of bacterial taxonomy. Therefore they are worth quoting [Edwards and Ewing (1955)]:

The family is composed of a large number of interrelated types which display almost every conceivable combination of biochemical characteristics compatible with the definition of the family. These types form such a continuous series that they are not readily susceptible to division into distinct groups. . . . any attempt at grouping results in the exclusion of strains of intermediate character which do not conform to the properties established for each of the groups. However, our knowledge of the bacteria is so fragmentary and the types are so numerous that as a matter of expediency it is necessary to divide the family into groups which form the basis of practical work. Within the family are found dense centers of strains with similar biochemical properties and it is these centers which form the groups and genera which are generally recognized. . . . it should always be kept in mind that the groups are purely artificial and it must not be expected that all cultures which are studied will fall neatly into one or another of them.

The generic and other designations given by these workers, brought down to the date of their more recent work [Ewing and Edwards (1960)], are followed here. For the most part, they are based on usage and practical convenience and display a healthy disrespect for Linnaean rigidity, although even greater health might be found in moving further in the same direction; for instance, by abandoning the attempt to distinguish generically between *Klebsiella* and *Aerobacter*. But these terms are part of the technical language, and language grows by usage, not by logic. Ewing and Edwards (1960) speak now of "Citrobacter, formerly *Escherichia freundii*" in recognition of the disparity between this group and *E. coli*; but it may be wise to retain both names until usage chooses between them.

The distinguishing biochemical features of the major groups or "dense centers" among the indigenous enterobacteria are given in brief form in Table 4-1. Only such forms as are known or presumed to be members of the normal flora are included, and only definitely (rapid) positive or unambiguously negative reactions are given, these being sufficient to distinguish each listed "species." Lactose fermentation is not mentioned in the table, in line with the recommendation of Edwards and Ewing. Although in practice this disaccharide has obvious value, especially in plating media for the initial separation of "pathogens" from the first 3 groups listed (all of which normally acidify lactose), many strains are found that ferment it slowly or not at all but conform with the group in other respects. The same reasoning leads to abandonment of "paracolon" organisms and the so-called genus *Paracolobactrum*.

TABLE 4-1

BIOCHEMICAL REACTIONS OF THE PRINCIPAL IND ENTEROBACTERIA (BASED ON EWING AND EDWARDS, ADDITIONS FROM EDWARDS AND EWING, 19

	Shigella–Escherichia group		Salmonella–Arizona–Citrobacter group	Klebsiella–Aerobacter–Serratia group					Proteus–Providence group				
	Escherichia coli	Alcalescens–Dispar	Citrobacter (*Escherichia freundii*)	*Klebsiella pneumoniae*	*K. rhinoscleromatis*	*K. oxytoca*	*Aerobacter aerogenes*	*A. cloacae*	*Proteus vulgaris*	*P. mirabilis*	*P. morganii*	*P. rettgeri*	*Providence*
Indole	+	+	–	–	–	+	–	–	+	–	+	+	+
Methyl red	+	+	+						+	+	+	+	+
Voges-Proskauer	–	–	–	+	+	+	+	+	–		–		–
Simmons' citrate	–	–	+	+	+	+	+	+			–	+	+
H₂S (TSI agar)†	–	–	+						+	+	–	–	–
Urease	–	–	–						+	+	+	+	–
KCNᵃ	–	–	+	+		+	+	+	+	+	+	+	+
Phenylalanineᵇ	–	–	–	–	–	–	–	–	+	+	+	+	+
Gas from glucose	+	–	+	+	–		+						
Motility‡	+	–	+	–	–		+	+	+	+	+	*	+
Gas from inositol				+			+	–					
Gas from glycerol				+			+	–					
Lysine decarboxylaseᶜ				+			+	–					
Arginine decarboxylase				–			–	+					
Ornithine decarboxylase				–			+	+					
Gelatin	–	–	–	–	–	+			+	+	–	–	–

+, positive in 1 or 2 days; –, negative.
* Motile at 25°, usually not at 37°.
† In triple sugar iron agar (lead acetate paper gives more sensitive reactions).
‡ In semisolid agar.
ᵃ Growth in the KCN medium of Moeller (1954, *Acta Pathol. Microbiol. Scand.*, **34**:115).
ᵇ See Ewing, 1960, *Public Health Service Pub.* 734; Ewing et al., 1957, *Public Health Lab.*, **15**:153.
ᶜ See Ewing 1960, *loc. cit.* (note b).

Although omitted from the table, the Arizona group of enterobacteria requires mention, since Edwards, Fife, and Ramsey (1959) recovered 24 of 229 human strains from *feces in the absence of symptoms*. These organisms are typically pathogens of fowl, reptiles, and other animals as well as of man. They are closely related to *Salmonella*, but usually ferment lactose—so that they had been placed in the somewhat ubiquitous and now abandoned paracolon category. They are distinguished from salmonella by their ability to grow in a sodium malonate medium [Ewing (1960)], in addition to lactose fermentation, and from the Citrobacter group by the same test and also by the ability of the Arizona organisms to decarboxylate lysine. Edwards, Fife, and Ramsey (1959) recognized 32 groups based on O antigens as well as a series of H antigens, some of which crossed with salmonella.

It will be seen that the first 4 characters listed in Table 4-1 (constituting the IMViC set) serve to distinguish the first 3 groups, except for *Klebsiella oxytoca* [Lautrop (1956)], which departs from the generic pattern in forming indole and liquefying gelatin. The second quartet of characters distinguishes the Proteus–Providence group from the others and, together with the IMViC properties and gelatin liquefaction, from one another. The remaining characters are required to distinguish *E. coli* from the Alcalescens–Dispar group and to differentiate the members of the Klebsiella–Aerobacter group. The data for *K. rhinoscleromatis* are taken from the monograph by Edwards and Ewing (1955) while those for *A. cloacae* are from both earlier and later (1960) sources. The organism sometimes known as *K. ozaenae* is serologically a member of the *K. pneumoniae* group but biochemically related to *K. rhinoscleromatis*.

The distinction between the two principal members of the Klebsiella–Aerobacter group, *K. pneumoniae* and *A. aerogenes*, based on the latter's motility and decarboxylation of ornithine, is a particularly fine one. As recently as 1955 [see Edwards and Fife (1955)] these organisms had come to be considered essentially indistinguishable; indeed, even Breed, Murray, and Smith (1955) found it necessary to say that "until such time as the relationships of the two genera are clarified, it is inevitable that confusion will continue." Perhaps the needed means for clarification are at hand, but controversy persists. Epstein (1959) undertook a detailed biochemical study of 82 serotyped cultures designated "klebsiellae," including 34 strains of *K. pneumoniae* (8 types), 7 of *K. rhinoscleromatis*, 9 *K. ozaenae* (3 types), 7 *K. aerogenes* [sic] and 25 listed as untypable. Motility appeared only in 4 of the untypable strains, not in aerogenes. Ornithine decarboxylase tests were not recorded. None of the 7 aerogenes strains showed mucoid colonies; this property was not universal among the other groups.

Other differences seemed statistical rather than clearly differential. Epstein proposed that *K. pneumoniae* be renamed *K. friedlaenderi* following Cowan (1954) so as not to suggest an obligatory relationship to respiratory disease; he argued against the species designation *rhinoscleromatis;* and held that "no evidence for any other valid species was found." By contrast, Cowan, Steel, and Shaw (1960) not only spoke in favor of the Friedländer-aerogenes distinction but would name a new species and subspecies within the genus [see also Sedlak and Slajsova

(1959)]. If such distinctions will be practicable in the future, the literature is seldom explicit enough to permit making them retrospectively. In the following text the synthetic "species" name *Klebsiella aerogenes* will be used when necessary to refer to the group.

Further subdivision of the major groups of enterobacteria is dependent principally on serologic means. In the *E. coli* group, serotypes are based on the classical O (somatic) and H (flagellar) antigens and also on K antigens—somatic antigens in sheaths, envelopes or capsules which inhibit O agglutination. The K antigens are further subdivided into 3 or more varieties (L, A, B) based on physical behavior [see Kauffmann (1954); Edwards and Ewing (1955); Ewing et al. (1956); Davis and Ewing (1958); Sahab (1960, 1961)]. Coliform organisms have also been typed by their pattern of susceptibility to colicines [see Linton (1960); Parr, El Shawi, and Robbins (1960) and Chap. 11]. Encapsulated *Klebsiella* organisms are classified into serotypes principally via capsular polysaccharide antigens which are subject to a quellung reaction; unencapsulated forms react nonspecifically in somatic (O or R) agglutination. The Providence group is also distinguishable by K antigens.

Proteus is traditionally characterized by "swarming" or growth as a spreading film on moist agar. It is curious that although the designations H and O ("hauch" and "ohne hauch") were first applied in the study of proteus [Weil and Felix (1917)], the finer classification of this group has not advanced sufficiently as yet to permit routine serologic typing [see Namioka and Sakazaki (1959)]. A simple method has been suggested, however, by Krickler (1953) based on an observation by Dienes (1946) for determining whether 2 strains of swarming proteus are antigenically identical. If identical, the two merge when seeded so that their films meet on agar; if distinct, a clear line of demarcation separates them. The method has been applied for epidemiologic purposes by Story (1954) and by Edebo and Laurell (1958).

Distribution of Indigenous Enterobacteria

Although all these bacteria are found in the intestinal tract, the most characteristically indigenous form among them is *Escherichia coli*, the principal site of multiplication of which appears to be the lower intestine of man and animals. Even *E. coli*, however, is widely distributed in the environment, and all these forms must be thought of as true saprophytes.

Coliforms in Feces. The count of coliform organisms per gram of human feces in the absence of enteric disease averages roughly 10^7 to 10^8 with wide individual variations (see Chap. 10). Slanetz and Bartley (1957), using membrane filters, found the coliform count per gram in

20 samples of human feces to range from 1×10^4 to 2.6×10^8, with an arithmetic mean of 1.9×10^7 and a geometric mean of 2.1×10^6. It is of interest that the coliform counts of feces of 15 cows, 2 sheep, 1 horse, and 2 dogs ranged and averaged lower than those of human feces, the corresponding means for animals being 3.1×10^6 and 9.1×10^4 [see also Mansson (1957)]. In the rumen of calves, Mackay and Oxford (1954) reported the coliform count as not exceeding 10^6 per gram.

Coliforms in Other Areas. Coliform bacteria have also been recovered from the human vagina [Hite, Hesseltine, and Goldstein (1947)]. Members of the enteric family have been found, although uncommonly, in the urine of healthy adults [Philpot (1956)] and in the healthy external ear [Hardy et al. (1954)]. Coliform counts of saliva from healthy young adults were found in the writer's laboratory [Rosebury and Sonnenwirth (1958)] to range from 0 to less than 10^3 per ml, averaging roughly 10^2; similar results were reported by Richardson and Jones (1958). Of 22 cultures of coliforms isolated from the mouth by Chang and Foltz (1960), 3 were *E. coli* and 19 were klebsiellae by their IMViC patterns. Laurell (1952) recovered coliform organisms from nose and throat swabbings of hospitalized children frequently during the first year of life but only occasionally in older children. The strains recovered were biochemically and serologically heterogeneous and seemed to be disseminated in the hospital via air and dust. *K. aerogenes,* usually of capsular types uncommon in Friedländer pneumonia, has been observed occasionally in the healthy respiratory tract [Weiss et al. (1956)]. Jones (1960) reported that 82 of 511 strains of *E. coli* recovered from hospital specimens from nonintestinal sources were from throat swabs; 10 of the 82 were enteropathogenic serotypes.

Other Enterobacteria in Feces. The available data for enterobacteria other than *E. coli* in feces suggest lower concentrations [e.g., 10^4 to 10^5 for *K. aerogenes* and 10^2 to 10^4 for "paracolon" bacteria; Riddell et al. (1953); see also Orskov (1955a)]. Loh and Baker (1955) found *Proteus* in the feces of about 5 per cent of a small group of subjects, while Rustigan and Stuart (1945) reported a 10 per cent incidence of this group. Shidlovsky et al. (1957–58) reported the presence of *Proteus, K. aerogenes,* and "paracolon" organisms in the feces of a majority of their subjects. That the occurrence of these forms other than *E. coli* may be more nearly uniform in feces than the data from cultures suggest is perhaps implied by the emergence of some of them, notably *Proteus mirabilis,* following antibiotic therapy [see Loh and Baker (1955); Marmell, Shidlovsky, and Prigot (1955); Ruebner (1957)] and by the difficulty experienced in identifying 1 group in this family under pathologic conditions when it is greatly outnumbered by another [Thomson (1955a)].

Resident and Transient Forms. The availability of typing procedures of high sensitivity among members of the enteric family has made possible epidemiologic studies which must eventually extend beyond the immediate practical end of tracing hospital infections into the more basic realm of the mechanisms of origin and maintenance of the indigenous biota itself. A beginning along these lines has been made by Sears and his coworkers [Sears et al. (1949, 1956); Sears and Brownlee (1951)] with *E. coli*. These workers distinguished 2 kinds of strains found in the healthy intestine, resident and transient; the former, of which 1 or at times 2 may appear in a given subject, establish themselves and persist for periods of months or years, but eventually yield to other types. Transient strains persist for only a few days or weeks, and may come and go in considerable variety. In a middle-aged man and wife subject to intermittent diarrhea, no evidence of interchange of *E. coli* types could be found. The wife showed complete constancy of her resident strain over a 451-day period; the husband's resident strain changed twice in the same interval. Experiments with dogs showed a similar pattern; and attempts to establish new resident strains in the animals by feeding, even in enteric-coated capsules and after greatly reducing the bacterial population of the bowel by chemical means or by enema, neither displaced the resident strain nor established the intruder. Implantation via the rectum also failed. Postmortem studies of 1 dog showed the same *E. coli* strain in all parts of the intestinal tract. [See also Kauffmann and Perch (1943); Thomas and Baker (1955); Powers and Baker (1955).]

The findings of Gareau et al. (1959) on the concurrence of *E. coli* serotypes in feces of mothers and their newborn infants suggest that mother-to-child transmission occurs only occasionally. On the other hand, the occurrence of biochemically defined klebsiella-cloacae organisms in infant feces was apparently more dependent on environment (a 5-day stay in an old nursery, as compared with 3 days in a new one) than on the mother's fecal flora.

Coliforms in Disease. In the presence of disease, members of this family of bacteria have been recovered from a wide range of processes (other than gastrointestinal disease; see page 108), and their potential or actual pathogenicity is widely accepted. In urinary tract infections *E. coli*, *K. aerogenes* and *Proteus* species compete for prominence with staphylococci and pseudomonads, while other members of the enteric family, and other indigenous aerobes, occur less frequently [see Brisou et al. (1952); Ritts et al. (1957–58); Johnson, Perry, and Sokolski (1957–58); O'Sullivan et al. (1961)]. The emergence of antibiotic-resistant *E. coli* and their role in urinary tract infections have been considered by Kirby et al. (1956). The traditional occurrence of *K. pneumoniae* in respiratory disease is continued in more recent studies in which, however, emphasis has shifted away from the uncommon Friedländer pneumonia [see Hyde and Hyde (1943)] to the occurrence of this organism in the sputum from presumably nonspecific acute or chronic disease [Fulton and McKinlay (1954); Orskov (1955*b*), Eisenberg, Weiss, and Flippin (1958*a*); Zykin (1959)]. Both Orskov and Eisenberg et al. found the organisms they recovered from such processes serologically heterogeneous. The latter authors could find no evidence of emergence of klebsiella in the lower respiratory tract under the influence of penicillin, and suggested a nosocomial source. These organisms have also been found in a rare form of meningitis with poor prognosis, associated with lower serologic types of the organism and apparently derived from infection of middle ear, respiratory, or urinary tracts [Spivak et al. (1957)]. Purulent meningitis apparently due to *Aerobacter cloacae* has been described by Jessen (1958). Synergistic infections in mice have been described by Estrada-Parra and Perez-Miravete (1959) with either *E. coli* or klebsiella mixed with *Str. faecalis*, or with the former together with staphylococci or *P. mirabilis*.

Proteus **in Disease.** Eisenberg, Weiss, and Flippin (1958*b*) listed the frequency of isolation of *Proteus* species as follows (numbers of cases): from urine (292), pus (145), blood (36), and respiratory tract infections (18) in the order: *P. mirabilis* (383), *P. morganii* (59), *P. rettgeri* (28), and *P. vulgaris* (21). *Proteus* infections have increased in recent years and have been associated clearly with emergence under antibiotic stimulation. Omland (1960) reported a high incidence of urinary tract infections with antibiotic-resistant *P. rettgeri* in Oslo during 1958–59. Yow (1952), whose parallel findings with *P. aeruginosa* are noted on page 127, recovered *Proteus*, during or following antibiotic therapy for other diseases, from 15 urinary infections, 2 cases of bacteremia and 1 each of meningitis and peritonitis. No evidence of disease could be associated by Loh and Baker (1955) with a marked proliferation of *Proteus* in the intestine of normal subjects given chlortetracycline or oxytetracycline. Story (1954) isolated strains of *Proteus* from hospital cases, most frequently from urine, followed in order by infected wounds and ulcers, sputum, and ear, nose, and throat specimens. The findings of this worker suggest endogenous infection with *Proteus*, since 76 per cent of these patients revealed the organism in rectal swabs, and among these, 83 per cent of the rectal cultures were identical with the organism recovered in the same patient from the clinical specimen, as tested by the Dienes phenomenon. Edebo and Laurell (1958) also attempted to trace urinary tract infections in a hospital by means of the Dienes procedure. Their strains of *Proteus* fell into 4 groups by this means, with 64 per cent in one group and a few unclassifiable strains. Their epidemiologic findings suggested indirect contact via utensils contaminated with feces, including rectal thermometers, rather than autoinfection.

Pathogenicity

General. The mechanisms of pathogenicity among the enterobacteria —including the more overtly pathogenic *Salmonella* and *Shigella* as well as the indigenous varieties—has been left largely unresolved by a vast amount of research that cannot be reviewed here. Except for the exotoxic Shiga dysentery bacillus, all these forms seem to be similarly endowed biochemically in terms of pathogenic attributes which, so far as is known, center on their content of lipopolysaccharide endotoxins [reviewed by Rosen (1961)]. Despite their serologic specificity these substances are similar in their toxic effects throughout the family and, indeed, well beyond it, since they are found in unrelated Gram-negative organisms, including *Neisseria* and the pertussis bacillus. The presence of endotoxin is not correlated with known pathogenicity, nor is any other known attribute of these bacteria. For our present purposes it may suffice to suggest that disease in man in which indigenous enteric bacteria participate may cover a wide range from exogenous to endogenous, with factors of host resistance correspondingly less or more significant in pathogenesis. The findings for *Proteus* given in the preceding paragraph are an example of this range. For the most part experimental pathogenicity is difficult to demonstrate, requiring large doses or preparatory conditions such as cortisone injection or irradiation.

Experimental. The hemolysin of *Escherichia coli* has been studied in recent years by Robinson (1951) and by Bamforth and Dudgeon (1952).

Rowley (1954) studied 20 strains of *E. coli*, of which 7 were found virulent for mice when injected with gastric mucin. All 20 strains seemed similar in their toxicity, but a difference in resistance to the bactericidal power of complement was suggested as a determinant of virulence. Roantree and Rantz (1960) noted that enterobacteria isolated from blood were more often resistant to the heat-labile bactericidal action of human serum than strains from feces or urine. The bactericidal effect was found in rabbit as well as in human serum; and resistant *E. coli* and klebsiella strains reached higher concentrations in rabbit blood in vivo and were cleared from the blood somewhat more slowly than paired susceptible strains; but all strains were cleared within 48 hours [Roantree and Pappas (1960)]. The parallel sensitivity or resistance to human or guinea pig serum in vitro has also been found related to the ability of the strain to grow intraperitoneally in the guinea pig in capsules permeable to body fluids but not to bacteria [Roantree and Collis (1960)].

Moll and Ingalsbe (1955) found that 2 of 9 strains of *E. coli* were virulent for suckling mice when given orally, but none affected weaned mice or 1- to 4-day-old colostrum-fed calves. Braude et al. (1955) described a method for producing acute but nonfatal hematogenous pyelonephritis in rats by massaging the kidneys through the intact body wall after injecting *E. coli* intravenously. The data do not clearly establish the pathogenic role of the inoculated strain [see also Shapiro, Braude, and Siemienski (1956); Braude, Shapiro, and Siemienski (1959); Brumfitt and Heptinstall (1960); Heptinstall, Michaels, and Brumfitt (1960)].

Garber, Hackett, and Franklin (1952) studied the virulence of *Klebsiella* in relation to mutation of nutritional requirements; Ehrenworth and Baer (1956) and Hall and Humphries (1958) have reported on the virulence of these organisms in relation to encapsulation and susceptibility to phagocytosis. Epstein (1959*b*) has studied experimental klebsiella pneumonia in mice and reviewed the literature.

Miles (1951) found the LD_{50} for mice of 21 strains of *Proteus vulgaris* from human infections to range from 2.3×10^5 to 6×10^8 living bacilli. Virulence was not related to severity or site of infection in man from which the strain had been derived, nor was the high virulence of individual strains associated with the toxicity of their killed cell substance. Namioka and Sakazaki (1960) found proteus strains somewhat less active than salmonellae or pathogenic *E. coli* when inoculated into rabbit intestinal loops prepared by De's method (see page 109); they were able to produce severe gastrointestinal symptoms and systemic infection with proteus strains fed to puppies that had been pretreated 1 hour before by intravenous injection of formalin-killed *E. coli* strain O49. In the experiments of Braude, Shapiro, and Siemienski (1959) on hematogenous pyelonephritis in rats, proteus strains were said to establish the most severe lesions and to produce renal stones of magnesium ammonium phosphate. Wensinck (1961) reported that X-irradiation of mice with 700 r led to death with *P. mirabilis* bacteremia occurring commonly in animals previously found to have been carriers of this organism, but rarely in noncarriers. The bacteremia in these mice was derived from the respiratory rather than from the intestinal tract.

E. coli and Infantile Gastroenteritis

A matter of special interest in the area of enterobacterial pathogenicity is the participation of certain serotypes of *E. coli* in the severe and highly fatal gastroenteritis of infants that has long been a serious problem in hospitals. With the development in 1945 of an effective serologic classification of *E. coli* [Vahlne (1945); Knipschildt (1945); Kauffmann (1947)], the association of uncommon serotypes of the organism with this disease, first observed by Bray (1945), was soon established in many parts of the world [see Taylor and Charter (1952); Thomson (1955)]. Neter (1960) in a brief review of this problem, listed the following 11 enteropathogenic serotypes of *E. coli*, of which those marked (*) are particularly important and well studied: O26:B6(*), O55:B5(*), O86:B7, O111:B5(*), O112:B11, O119:B14, O124:B17, O125:B15, O126:B16, O127:B8(*), and O128:B12.

Feeding experiments with some of the implicated serotypes have induced disease in a 2-month-old infant with congenital defects [Neter and Shumway (1950)] and also in adults [Ferguson and June (1952); June, Ferguson, and Worfel (1953); Neter et al. (1953); Wentworth et al. (1956)]. The feeding of indigenous strains of *E. coli* induced neither symptoms nor a rise in agglutinins to the administered strain; but feeding the pathogenic strains tended to produce specific antibodies, especially in subjects that showed symptoms [see also Gillespie et al. (1950)]. In India, Bannerjea et al. (1956, 1958) found some of the same serotypes in gastroenteritis of adults as well as in the disease in infants. Using such adult strains, as well as the standard O26, O55 and O111 strains from infantile diarrhea, these workers [De et al. (1956)] demonstrated pathogenicity for an isolated loop of small intestine in the rabbit. *E. coli* from healthy intestines seldom showed such effects. The procedure used by these Indian workers has been confirmed and elaborated upon by Taylor, Maltby, and Payne (1958). De and his co-workers noted that the bowel changes produced by *E. coli* in the rabbit were similar to those elicited by cholera vibrios using the same technique; Thomson (1955b) has observed that infantile gastroenteritis resembles cholera. It is suggestive that Gillespie et al. (1950b) found agglutinins to human indigenous coliform bacteria in several animal serums, including that of a rabbit.

Thus far no difference between the serotypes involved in infantile disease and the ordinary *E. coli*, other than in the serologic specificity of their somatic and other surface antigens, has been brought forward to account for the pathogenic proclivities of the former—a difficulty which, as was noted above, applies throughout the enteric family of bacteria. Al'tgauzen (1959) reported highly type-specific agglutinins in children to pathogenic serotypes of *E. coli*, in titers between 200 and 3,200 increasing to a maximum between the second and third weeks after onset of illness.

On the other hand, Young and her associates (1960) found that normal *E. coli*, comprising 17 serotypes between O1 and O25, isolated from the feces of infants and young children with diarrhea, were also associated, in 12 of 30 instances, with a rise in hemagglutinin titer in convalescent as compared with acute phase serum. Taylor, Wilkins, and Payne (1961) in a further study along the lines mentioned previously, have described dilatation of ligated loops of rabbit gut as a reaction to smooth strains of *E. coli* from infantile enteritis, the reaction being not elicited by strains from urinary infections or by rough strains. Taylor and her coworkers, whose paper should be consulted for additional literature, also observed that rabbits could be protected partially by active, and completely by passive immunization, against the homologous serotype but not at all against different serotypes.

The epidemiologic evidence leaves no doubt that infantile gastroenteritis is an exogenous nosocomial process [see Anderson, Crockatt, and Ross (1954)].

Gamble and Rowson (1957) presented evidence suggesting that the epidemic serotypes of *E. coli*, which may be thought of as "transient" in the sense of Sears et al. (1956), are excreted by about 1 or 2 per cent of the adult population at any given time. They may enter the adult gastrointestinal tract frequently and be equally frequently and promptly rejected, but survive the experience. It would be of interest to test the hypothesis that the common serotypes of *E. coli* have become established in the intestinal tract everywhere by simple virtue of their ubiquity, with "squatters' rights" transmitted to the young via maternal antibody. The apparent susceptibility of adults in India to the pathogenic effects of the rarer serotypes may possibly be a matter of dosage, comparable with the susceptibility of the adult volunteers of Ferguson and June (1952) and June et al (1953).

Methods for the laboratory diagnosis and management and prevention of gastroenteritis due to *E. coli* have been presented by Rogers and Taylor (1961). J. D. Nelson and his coworkers (1961) have reported that the presence of *E. coli* O119:B14 could be detected in rectal smears both of infants and of an asymptomatic carrier more rapidly and more sensitively by a fluorescent antibody method than by culture, making possible the prompt control of an outbreak by removing the carrier and treating the infants.

The *Neisseria*-like Bacilli: *Moraxella, Mima*

A group of aerobic Gram-negative bacilli with certain consistent characteristics, recovered especially from the conjunctiva, the nose, and the genitourinary mucous membranes, apparently indigenous but with pathogenic propensities and suggestions of saprophytism, has emerged into modest prominence in the antibiotic era. Included are the well-established genus *Moraxella* [Lwoff (1939)] and the more doubtful group of "Mimeae" [DeBord (1939, 1942)], as well as organisms called by a confusing variety of other names. Unifying characteristics include neisseria-like attributes: (1) cells occurring frequently as short diplobacilli, but with longer rods and filaments as well; (2) Gram-negative, but tending to be Gram-variable; (3) some are oxidase-positive; (4) some are sensitive to penicillin; and (5) they appear frequently under pathologic conditions in spinal fluid or in genitourinary exudates, often within leukocytes, mimicking (hence "mimeae") meningococci or gonococci. But in another significant respect they resemble the *Pseudomonas-Alcaligenes* group (page 121)— they do not ferment glucose but either dissimilate it to acid products by an obligately aerobic process, like *Ps. aeruginosa*, or leave it apparently unchanged, like *A. faecalis* [Hugh and Leifson (1953)]. Some of them, like the latter, may utilize simpler carbohydrates. These characteristics, and the failure especially of the nonglucolytic group to reduce nitrate, distinguish these organisms from the enterobacteria.

Although there is as yet no agreement on the taxonomy of these bacteria, a review of the literature suggests to the writer that confusion may be resolved, or at least reduced, by two steps: (1) by considering these 2 groups together in consequence of their unifying features; and (2) by recognizing within the group a seemingly continuous gradient of distinguishing features such that the extremes seem far removed even though the distinctions are seldom if ever based on more than a single character. Some of these organisms have disappeared from the seventh edition of *Bergey's Manual of Determinative Bacteriology* [Breed, Murray, and Smith (1957)]; this fact, the apparently unresolved disagreement in the literature, and the scant treatment given these forms in current texts, warrant their consideration here in detail.

History. The Taxonomic Problem

The first member of the group was discovered independently by Morax (1896) and Axenfeld (1897) in angular conjunctivitis [see also Eyre (1900)]. This "Morax-Axenfeld bacillus" is commonly accepted as the causative agent of this disease, cultures having been found pathogenic experimentally in the human conjunctiva [Morax (1896)]. A similar bacterium was isolated by Petit (1900) from conjunctivitis with corneal ulceration; and closely related forms, characterized by their ability to liquefy serum or gelatin, have been recovered from keratitis in cattle [see Watt (1951); Barner (1952)]. A variant of Petit's bacillus, apparently identical but nonliquefying, was found commonly in sputum by Oliver and Wherry (1921) and has more recently been characterized as a common member of the indigenous biota of the nose [Henriksen (1958)]. In 1939, Lwoff separated these organisms from *Haemophilus* by their simpler growth requirements and suggested that they be grouped in the genus *Moraxella*, with the 2 species *lacunata* (Morax-Axenfeld) and *duplex* (Petit) distinguished by the former's requirement for animal protein in the medium. *M. duplex* was subdivided into 4 varieties, of which 2, *liquefaciens* and *non-liquefaciens* (liquefaction of gelatin or serum), were the more clearly defined. In 1940 Audureau distinguished *Moraxella lwoffi* by its capacity to grow in a synthetic medium containing citrate and ethyl alcohol. All the preceding forms were found inactive in glucose and other carbohydrates, but in 1951 Piéchaud et al. described a presumed variant of *M. lwoffi* which grew in Audureau's medium with glucose and formed acid from a limited range of carbohydrates. Prévot [Piéchaud et al. (1951)] applied the variant epithet *glucidolytica* to this form, and the term was then accorded specific status by Brisou and Morichau-Beauchant (1952).

Meanwhile, DeBord (1939), in a brief note, suggested the creation of a new tribe, *Mimeae*, for forms resembling the gonococcus, with 4 groups, of which only one was named at the time, with few details, as *Mima polymorpha*. DeBord subsequently (1942) defined 3 genera of *Mimeae*, each with a single species: *Mima polymorpha*, non-glucolytic forms with oxidase-positive and oxidase-negative variants otherwise identical; *Herellea vaginicola* (after D'Herelle), which formed acid from carbohydrates; and *Colloides anoxydana*, which Henriksen (1952) has characterized as biochemically identical with *Escherichia freundii*. Most writers on *Mimeae* have made no mention of *Moraxella*.

Concurrently with some of these studies, neisseria-like bacilli were described under other names. Schaub and Hauber (1948) applied the name *Bacterium anitratum* (not reducing nitrate) to an organism from urine and other sources which was found serologically unrelated to enterobacteria or to other common Gram-negative aerobic bacilli; while Stuart, Formal, and McGann (1949) described a clearly similar bacterium, thought to be a member of the enterobacteria, with the designation "B5W" (notebook code: a white colony from specimen B5). Ferguson and Roberts (1950) recognized the identity of "*B. anitratum*" and "B5W," as did Brooke (1951). Ewing (1949) had suggested that "*B. anitratum*" should be classed with *Mimeae*. Piéchaud, Piéchaud, and Second (1951) seem to have been the first to consider the relationship of these organisms to *Moraxella*; they studied 4 strains of the Schaub-Stuart organisms and found them identical with the glucolytic variety placed in that genus. Henriksen (1952), on the other hand, argued that the genus *Moraxella* should be limited to oxidase-positive organisms, thus excluding *M. lwoffi*, the oxidase-negative variant of *M. polymorpha*, and the glucolytic forms; he noted the similarity of *B. anitratum* to *Herellea*. Brisou and Morichau-Beauchant (1952) compared directly strains of *B. anitratum* with *Moraxella lwoffi* and *M. glucidolytica*, and found the first and last identical in all characteristics examined. These European studies seem to have attracted inadequate attention in this country.

Lutz et al. (1958) considered the glucolytic members of this group identical with the *Diplococcus mucosus* (*Neisseria mucosa*, see Chap. 2) of Von Lingelsheim; but Veron, Thibault, and Second (1959, 1961) have shown clearly that the latter organism is facultative, fermentative, reduces nitrate to nitrogen, and fails to cross-agglutinate with either the glucolytic or the nonglucolytic citrate-utilizing members of this group. The attempts of Billing (1955) and Brisou (1957) to classify these latter organisms in the pseudomonas-alcaligenes group (in the genera *Achromobacter* and *Acinetobacter*, respectively) have more merit; but such a step fails to recognize the neisseria-like morphology of these forms and implies, moreover, a clear distinction from *Moraxella*, which is assumed incorrectly to be obligately hemophilic or serophilic. *Moraxella* was originally defined as a genus by separation from *Haemophilus* [Lwoff (1939)], but evolutionary lines implied by such steps are of course entirely conjectural [see also Henriksen (1960)]. It is here suggested provisionally that the generic name *Mima* be retained for the less exacting members of this group, not as marking a sharp distinction—which in fact cannot be marked with available data—but as recognizing usage, and in an effort to abate the proliferation of synonyms to a working minimum. A similar suggestion for generic separation has been made by Courtieu, Chassignol, and Longeray (1961).

Serologic studies, thus far rudimentary in this group, suggest heterogeneity, a relationship within the members here classed as *Mima*, and the possibility of an antigenic bridge between the 2 subgroups via a mutual relationship with capsular antigens of *Klebsiella*. The last was reported by Henriksen (1948*b*) between a mucoid strain that appears to have been nonliquefying *M. duplex*, which cross-reacted with *Staph. aureus* as well as with klebsiella; and by Aiken, Ward, and King (1956) between glucolytic forms and klebsiella capsular antigens. The latter workers also reported cross-agglutination between glucolytic and nonglucolytic citrate-utilizing strains. In earlier studies, both Lwoff (1939) and Oag (1942) found *M. lacunata* and *M. duplex* distinct and heterogeneous by agglutination; Stuart, Formal, and McGann (1949) found the glucolytic organisms serologically heterogeneous. Ten capsular types based on quellung reactions were reported among these acid-forming organisms by Ferguson and Roberts (1950). Piéchaud and her coworkers (1951) also noted several serologic groups among the citrate-utilizing forms that failed to match the glucose-utilizing or nonutilizing varieties. Cary, Lindberg, and Faber (1956, 1958), who distinguished 19 serotypes in the nonglucolytic *Mima polymorpha,* also reported ambiguous relationships between these organisms and the glucolytic forms.

Matthiessen (1957) and Volkert and Matthiessen (1958) have found a soluble antigen in the nonglucolytic *M. vaginicola,* not found in a wide range of other Gram-negative bacteria, that reacted in a complement-fixation test with antibody in human serum to ornithosis virus.

Classification

The simplest scheme of classification appropriate for these organisms in the present state of knowledge comprises 3 groups or "species," each of which may be subdivided. Transitional forms, possibly subject to genetic alteration, appear in the first and especially in the second group. They are here defined, with respect for priority, in order as *Moraxella lacunata, Mima polymorpha,* and *Mima vaginicola.*

Group Characteristics. The unifying characteristics of the whole group, on which all authors seem to be agreed, are these: the *Moraxella-Mima* organisms are typically plump short rods or coccal forms occurring mainly in pairs or short chains, but with longer rods and filaments and often with swollen forms. They are Gram-negative but with a tendency to retain the violet dye. They are aerobic and do not produce gas. They do not produce indole or acetylmethyl carbinol. Other characteristics are subject to only occasional, perhaps doubtful, variation. These organisms are probably all nonmotile; but motility was suggested by Pike, Schultze, and McCullough (1951) for *Mima polymorpha* (var. *oxidans*) by growth in semisolid media; and ambiguously by Stuart et al. (1949) for 2 of 33 strains of *M. vaginicola* (B5W). The methyl red test is nearly always negative but has been reported as weakly positive for some glucolytic strains [Schaub and Hauber (1948); Brooke (1951); Brisou and Morichau-Beauchant (1952); Matthiessen (1957)]. Catalase is produced by the whole *Mima* group, whether oxidase is formed or not; it does not seem to have been looked for in *Moraxella.* Capsules are characteristic of many members of the group. Most strains have failed to produce H_2S, but exceptions have been noted by Oeding (1946a) for a proteolytic *M. duplex* and for occasional members of the mima group by Aiken and her coworkers (1956) and by Cetin and Toreci (1961). Failure to reduce nitrate is considered distinctive for mimae [King (1960)]; but Deacon (1945) mentioned that 2 of 8 mima-like cultures reduced it to nitrite. Henriksen, in 1947, reported that 5 of 9 strains of nonproteolytic inexacting moraxellae formed nitrite from nitrate, and noted such reduction for similar organisms again in 1948a. Aiken, Ward, and King (1956) studied one of Henriksen's strains and reported it nitrate-positive [see also Piéchaud (1961)].

Moraxella lacunata [Lwoff (1939)] is the name generally accepted for the Morax-Axenfeld bacillus, and is here applied with qualifications to Petit's bacillus (usually called *M. duplex*) as well and to subvarieties of both. The two have been distinguished by Lwoff (1939, 1959) and by Audureau (1940) by the single character that the first requires the addition of serum for growth in peptone water and the second does not. Both of these forms have been further subdivided on the basis of proteolytic activity, especially liquefaction of coagulated serum, correlated in *M. duplex* with action on gelatin, hence the "varieties" *liquefaciens* and *non-liquefaciens* [see also Piéchaud (1961)]. The last of these intergrades with *Mima polymorpha* (see below). These organisms did not grow on Audureau's (1940) synthetic medium, which contained a trace (0.001 per cent) of iron citrate with ethyl alcohol as the carbon and energy source. They do not attack glucose or other sugars. Their optimal growth temperature is 28 to 30° [Audureau (1940); Henriksen (1952)] and they may prefer or require a humid atmosphere when grown at 37° [Henriksen (1952)]. They are distinguished also by being oxidase-positive and sensitive to penicillin, characters augmenting their morphologic resemblance to neisseriae. This group reduces nitrate [Piéchaud (1961)].

Mima polymorpha [DeBord (1939, 1942)] is strikingly similar to the moraxellae in most of its characteristics, but also shows features that have led American workers to keep it apart from that genus and link it to *M. vaginicola*. Here included under this name are both oxidase-positive [var. *oxidans*, DeBord (1942)] and oxidase-negative forms, the latter being presumably identical with *Moraxella lwoffi* [Audureau (1940)]. Like *M. lacunata*, this organism fails to attack carbohydrates and grows well at 30° or slightly lower. Audureau's organisms grew in the synthetic medium mentioned above, and Brisou and Morichau-Beauchant (1952) found that a strain (of *M. lwoffi*) grew in citrate. Growth in Simmons' citrate has been found variable for strains called *M. polymorpha* [negative, DeBord (1942); Townsend, Hersey, and Wilson (1954); positive, Schuldberg (1943); variable, King (1960)].

In a study of 103 strains of *M. lwoffi*, Courtieu, Chassignol, and Longeray (1961) found 10 with proteolytic activity for casein, egg, coagulated serum, and gelatin, the others being negative with 1 exception for egg. All were inactive in carbohydrates, including 10 per cent lactose. The proteolytic strains all grew in citrate and 9 grew on SS agar; 11 of the nonproteolytic strains failed to grow in citrate, and only 28 of 92 tested strains of the latter group showed growth on SS medium. Of the 103 strains, only 1, a nonproteolytic form, produced urease. The whole group appears to have been oxidase-negative. These workers suggested that the oxidase-negative forms be separated in the genus *Mima* (or *Herellea*), with the specific names *lwoffi* for the nonproteolytic and *caseolytica* (*nov. sp.*) for the proteolytic varieties. The name *Mima polymorpha* is more in accord with American usage and is retained here provisionally for both varieties, considered transitional between moraxellae proper and the glucolytic forms.

In addition to oxidase production and citrate utilization, *M. polymorpha* is also transitional in relation to penicillin. Brooks (1954) and Fred et al. (1958) reported it as penicillin-sensitive; Schuldberg (1953), Olafsson, Lee, and Abernethy (1958), and Dexter et al. (1958) found it resistant. King (1960) observed variation from sensitivity to resistance among 35 strains.

Mima vaginicola [DeBord (1942) *emend.*]. The following appear to be synonyms: *Herellea vaginicola*, DeBord (1942); *Bacterium anitratum*, Schaub and Hauber (1948); B5W, Stuart, Formal, and McGann (1949); *Moraxella lwoffi* var. *glucidolytica*, Prévot [Piéchaud et al. (1951)]; *M. glucidolytica*, Brisou and Morichau-Beauchant (1952); *Neisseria winogradskyi*, Villecourt and Jacobelli (1954); *Achromobacter lwoffi* (*anitratum*), Brisou (1953), Brisou, Morichau-Beauchant, and Giminez (1953); Billing (1955); and *Acinetobacter anitratum*, Brisou (1957).

This organism resembles the oxidase-negative, penicillin-resistant variety of *Mima polymorpha*, but differs in being glucolytic under aerobic conditions only [see Hugh and Leifson (1953)]. It grew in Audureau's medium and has been found to utilize citrate. It appears to be uniformly unable to reduce nitrate and is oxidase-negative but positive for catalase [King (1960)]. It has also been found uniformly resistant to penicillin.

The study by Courtieu et al. (1961) referred to above included 111 glucolytic strains which, like the nonglucolytic forms, again fell into proteolytic and nonproteolytic groups; but in this instance the 2 were not sharply defined with any of the 4 substrates. Ten of these cultures were negative in citrate; 12 were urease-positive. These authors accepted the specific epithet *vaginicola* but preferred to limit it to the nonproteolytic forms.

The characteristics reviewed in the foregoing paragraphs are sum-

TABLE 4-2
PRINCIPAL DISTINGUISHING CHARACTERISTICS OF *Moraxella-Mima*

Neisseria-like short rods or coccal forms in pairs or short chains with some longer rods and filaments; Gram-negative to Gram-amphophile; aerobic, anaerogenic. Indole and Voges-Proskauer negative. Usually nonmotile, encapsulated, and methyl red negative.

	Serum required for growth	Growth in defined media	Liquefaction of serum or gelatin	Acid from glucose	H_2S formed	NO_3 reduced to NO_2	Oxidase	Sensitive to penicillin
Moraxella lacunata	V	0	V	0	0v	+	+	S
Mima polymorpha	0	V	V	0	V	0v	V	V
Mima vaginicola	0	+	V	+	V	0	0	R

+, positive; 0, negative; V, variable; 0v, usually negative; S, sensitive; R, resistant.

marized in Table 4-2. The indications in the table of gradients in characteristics of the 3 forms suggest the need for attempts to transform one into another. Suggestive evidence that such attempts may be fruitful is implied in the statement of King (1960) that acid production from carbohydrates by *Mima polymorpha* strains reported by Aiken et al. in 1956 could not be repeated with the same strains approximately 2 years later.[1]

Distribution

The distribution of the *Moraxella-Mima* group again shows indications of family uniformity with certain points of difference. Both major varieties of *Moraxella* were originally obtained from the inflamed conjunctiva of man and animals; both species of *Mima* have also been recovered from conjunctivitis [DeBord (1943); Brooke (1951); Piéchaud et al. (1951); Fedukowicz and Horwich (1953)]. According to Oeding (1946a), Petit's bacillus has been found in the normal conjunctival sac. All 3 species as defined here have been cultured from the respiratory tract [Oliver and Wherry (1921); Schaub and Hauber (1948); Ferguson and Roberts (1950); Piéchaud et al. (1951); Henriksen (1952); Cetin and Toreci (1961)]. Henriksen (1958) found the transitional moraxella-mima form (*M. duplex* var. *non-liquefaciens*) to be at times the predominant organism in cultures from the nose, mainly in noninfectious ailments; he regarded it as a common inhabitant and a member of the indigenous biota of that site. Lutz et al. (1958) found *M. vaginicola* in the nose. All 3 species have also been recovered from the genitourinary system [DeBord (1942,

[1] Miss King, commenting on this statement, suggested that the change may have been in the media rather than in the organisms themselves.

1943); Deacon (1945); Schaub and Hauber (1948); Ferguson and Roberts (1950); Brooke (1951); Henriksen (1952); Rocha and Guze (1957)]. DeBord (1942, 1943) and Lutz and his coworkers (1958) found *Mima vaginicola* in the normal vagina, while Philpot (1956) found the same organism in the urine of 2 out of 40 healthy men. No explicit record of the occurrence of these organisms in the mouth is known to the writer; Lutz et al. (1958) gave the source of 7 strains of *M. vaginicola* in a table as "gorge-bouche," 5 from infants and 2 from adults. Only oxidase-negative types have thus far been grown from feces [Ferguson and Roberts (1950); Piéchaud et al. (1951)]. Stuart et al. (1949) found *M. vaginicola* repeatedly in feces in diarrhea, but stated that they did not find it in several hundred fecal specimens from normal young adults.

Under pathologic conditions, either or both of the 2 species of *Mima* have also been cultured from war wounds [Deacon (1945)]; the blood [DeBord (1942); Schaub and Hauber (1948); Ferguson and Roberts (1950); Piéchaud et al. (1951); Peloux (1959)]; the ear [Brooke (1951); Piéchaud et al. (1951)]; and the skin [Dexter et al. (1958)]. Aside from their occurrence in conjunctivitis, pathologic significance in man has been attached to these organisms most strongly in relation to the presence in meningitis of *Mima polymorpha* [DeBord (1948); Schuldberg (1953); Olafsson et al. (1958); Fred et al. (1958)] and *M. vaginicola* [Opsahl (1961)]; and of both *Moraxella duplex* [Faust and Hood (1949)] and *Mima polymorpha* [Townsend et al. (1954)] in Waterhouse-Friderichsen syndrome. More recently Svihus et al. (1961) found members of this group, mainly penicillin-resistant but including both oxidase-reacting forms, in gonorrhea-like urethritis; and they have suggested that these organisms may be responsible for disease thought to be due to penicillin-resistant *N. gonorrheae*. Finally, both mimae have been recovered from saprophytic sites: *M. polymorpha* from river water [Kenner and Kabler (1956)] and from water or soil [Piéchaud et al. (1951)]. The organisms described by Villecourt and Jacobelli (1954) and by Billing (1955)— here considered to be *M. vaginicola*—were also saprophytes. A gradient from saprophytism in *Mima* to obligate parasitism in *Moraxella* is suggested by the requirement of some of the latter for serum in the growth medium.

Ellis (1961) has reported recovery of *M. vaginicola* from the tissues of chickens and a calf under pathologic conditions.

Pathogenicity

Demonstration of pathogenicity for experimental animals by members of this group has been variable and, when successful, has usually required inoculation of massive doses. After early reports of patho-genicity of *Moraxella lacunata* for man via the conjunctiva [Morax (1896)], this organism has been found nonpathogenic for man or ani-mals under experimental conditions [Audureau (1940); Oag (1942)]. *M. duplex* was reported as nonpathogenic by Oliver and Wherry (1921) when inoculated intrapleurally into a rabbit, and by Pike et al. (1951) when 0.5 ml of broth culture was given intraperitoneally to mice. However, Audureau (1940) reported feeble pathogenicity for this species when it was inoculated into the rabbit eye, and Deacon (1945) stated that it is pathogenic for guinea pigs. Henriksen (1948a, 1951) reported that mice were killed by intraperitoneal injection of 5×10^7 organisms but not by smaller doses. Oeding (1946a) found this organism, freshly isolated from a corneal ulcer, lethal to a mouse (probably intraperitoneally); but older cultures were avirulent. Audureau (1940) found *Mima polymorpha* nonpathogenic in all trials. Piéchaud et al. (1951) reported that 1 strain of this species killed mice intraperitoneally; and Schuldberg (1953), who tested *M. polymorpha* in mice, guinea pigs, and rabbits by intraperitoneal injection, and in rabbits intravenously, using as much as 2 ml of heavy suspensions, observed effects only in the guinea pigs, which died in 3 or 4 days with a florid purulent peritonitis and septicemia. Of the 5 strains of this organism recovered from pathologic sources by Cetin and Toreci (1961), 2 were inactive in mice by the intraperitoneal route, 2 others were irregularly lethal, and 1 killed all inoculated mice. None of these cultures was virulent for guinea pigs. Schaub and Hauber (1948) stated that mice were killed in less than 24 hours after intraperitoneal inoculation of 0.01 ml of a 24-hour broth culture of *Mima vaginicola:* the organism was recovered from the heart blood. Out of 11 strains of this species tested by Brooks (1951), who used 0.2 cc of an 18-hour culture in mice by the same route, 1 killed at a dilution of 1:100, 2 others at 1:10; the other 8 were ineffectual when given undiluted. In the experiments of Piéchaud et al. (1951) effects similar to those with *M. polymorpha* were obtained with 6 strains of *M. vaginicola* (1 iso-lated from soil); mice died with positive blood cultures the day after intraperitoneal inoculation of 0.5 ml of a whole broth culture. Waage (1953), however, found his strain of *M. vaginicola* nonpathogenic for mice or guinea pigs.

The sensitivity of these organisms to antibiotics and other anti-microbial drugs is summarized in Table 4-3. Sensitivity to penicillin tends to be associated with sensitivity to other agents. [See also Chab-bert and Courtieu (1961).]

The occurrence of lysogeny in *M. vaginicola*, suggesting possibili-ties of phage typing, has been described by Papavassiliou (1960).

TABLE 4-3

SENSITIVITY OF *Moraxella–Mima* TO ANTIMICROBIAL DRUGS

Number of strains

	Moraxella lacunata			*Mima polymorpha*						*M. vaginicola*		
	S	I	R	S	I	R	S	I	R	S	I	R
Penicillin		9[e]	9[e]									
Other agents												
Tetracycline	28[e]			21[g]	0[g]		10[g,k]	4[g]	5[g]	4[d,g]	17[d,g]	76[d,a,g]
Chlortetracycline				20[f,g]	2[g]	0[g]	5[g,h]	3[g]	8[g]	12[d,g]	25[d,g]	63[d,g]
Oxytetracycline	28[e]			22[f,g]	0[g]	0[g]	7[g,h]	9[g]	0[g]	6[a,d,g]	26[d,g]	68[d,g]
Chloramphenicol	28[e]			22[f,g]	1[b]	0[g]	11[c,g,h]	5[g]	3[g,j]	9[d,g]	78[d,j]	5[g,j]
Neomycin							6[c,k]			60[d]	7[d,j]	5[d]
Bacitracin	28[e]											
Polymyxin B				21[g]	0[g]	0[g]	14[g]	5[g,k]	2[h]	7[d,j]	0[g]	0[g]
Streptomycin	28[e]			16[f]	1[g]	4[g]	7[g]	2[g]	0[g]	12[d,g]	29[d,g]	68[a,d,g,j]
Dihydrostreptomycin	28[e]			1[f]			3[c,h]	9[a,k]	8[a,k]			
Erythromycin				22[f,g]	0[g]	0[g]	9[g]	9[a,k]	1[g]	2[d,g]	23[d,g]	54[d,g,j]
Novobiocin				1[f]					5[k]			
Magnamycin							5[k]			0[d]	3[d]	54[d]
Spiramycin							1[c]			0[d]	11[d]	47[d]
Oleandomycin												1[j]
Kanamycin							5[k]		5[k]			1[j]
Framycetin										65[d]	9[d]	4[d]
Nitrofurazone												
Furadantin												
Sulfonamides	10[e]	9[e]										1[j]

S, sensitive; I, intermediate or doubtful; R, resistant.

[a] Schuldberg (1953)
[b] Pike et al. (1951)
[c] Dexter et al. (1958)
[d] Lutz et al. (1958)
[e] Henriksen (1958)
[f] Fred et al. (1958)
[g] King (1960)
[h] Ino et al. (1959)
[j] Opsahl (1961)
[k] Cetin and Toreci (1961)

Pseudomonads and Alcaligenes

Two members in particular of a large group of saprophytic aerobic Gram-negative bacilli occur in man as amphibionts and in disease. The group, to which the term Pseudomonas-Achromobacter is applied [see Buttiaux and Gagnon (1958–59); Thornley (1960); Moore and Pickett (1960*a,b*)], consists of more than 100 species that are widespread in soil and water; included are plant pathogens and psychrophilic forms [see Alford (1960)] commonly implicated in spoilage of cold storage foods. The species that may be considered indigenous are *Pseudomonas aeruginosa* (syn. *Ps. pyocyanea*) and possibly other pseudomonads, and *Alcaligenes faecalis*. When the 2 named forms are typical, they can hardly be confused. The first produces extremely characteristic water-soluble pigments that give its colonies and the surrounding medium a fluorescent bluish-green color, and it is motile and acidifies glucose; the second is achromogenic, often nonmotile and without effect on carbohydrates. But pigment production may be lacking or lost in *Ps. aeruginosa*, and partially or totally achromogenic variants of these organisms have been isolated increasingly from clinical material [Gaby (1946); Haynes (1951); Gaby and Free (1953, 1958)]. When such variants fail to show appreciable acid in glucose and appear nonmotile, the diagnostic problem obviously becomes serious.

Differentiation of Indigenous Species

The principal distinguishing features of *Ps. aeruginosa, Alc. faecalis,* and related pseudomonads, other than pigment production, are given in Table 4-4. All the characteristics noted are to be considered as typical, not fixed or firmly diagnostic. As we saw in the preceding paragraph, motility, due to polar flagella, may not be demonstrable in pseudomonads, and acidogenesis may not be appreciable. Pseudomonads are strict aerobes, failing to grow in deep agar in the absence of nitrate [Veron (1961)]. The carbohydrate dissimilation induced by these forms is an obligately aerobic oxidation [Hugh and Leifson (1953)] similar to that of *Mima vaginicola*, which may not be demonstrable unless the usual carbohydrate-peptone ratio is increased; acid is not formed if free access of air is limited by covering the medium with a layer of melted petrolatum. *Ps. aeruginosa* may be hemolytic [Christie (1948)] but this attribute is not known to be distinctive [see also Liu (1957)]. Haynes (1951) suggested that this organism could be identified by 3 characteristics: (1) growth at 41 ± 1°; (2) oxidation of potassium gluconate; and (3) formation of slime in static cultures in a medium containing potassium gluconate.

In an attempt by Wetmore and Gochenour (1956) to distinguish *Pseudomonas* from the related pathogenic genus commonly called *Mal-*

TABLE 4-4

PRINCIPAL DISTINGUISHING CHARACTERISTICS OF ACHROMOGENIC AMPHIBIOTIC *Pseudomonas* SPECIES AND *Alcaligenes faecalis*

All are aerobic Gram-negative bacilli growing readily on simple media, forming a pellicle in broth; lactose is not fermented; ammonia is produced; indole is not formed

| | Motility | Action on carbohydrates | | | | | | | | | Litmus milk | Gluconate oxidized | Oxidase | Cytochrome oxidase | Odor, trimethylamine | H_2S | Urease | Nitrate reduced | Gelatin liquefied | Coagulated serum liquefied | Growth temperatures | | |
		Glucose	Fructose	Galactose	Sucrose	Arabinose	Trehalose	Xylose	Mannitol	Other "sugars"											Minimum	Optimum	Maximum
Pseudomonas aeruginosa	+	A	A	A	0	A	v	A	v	A	D, alk.	+	+	+	+	0	0v	+	+	+	21°	37°	42°
Intermediate species	+	A	0	v	0	v	0	Av	0v	0	alk.					0		*	+		10°	21–37°	42°
Ps. fluorescens	+	A	A	A	A	A	A	A	A	0	alk.		+			0	v	+	+	+		20–25°	
Alcaligenes faecalis	v	… None …									alk.	0	+	+s	0	0	0	v	0	0		25–37°	

+, positive; 0, negative; A, acid; v, variable; Av, usually acid; 0v, usually negative; D, digested; alk., alkaline; +s, positive, slow.
* Either not reduced (*Ps. ovalis*) or reduced beyond NO_2 after 4 hours (*P. stutzeri*); see Van Niel and Allen (1952) and Wetmore and Gochenour (1956).

leomyces, it was observed that *Ps. aeruginosa* differed from other members of the genus found in clinical sources particularly by its ability to grow well on a medium containing cetyltrimethylammonium bromide, which inhibited *Ps. fluorescens* in part and the other species (Table 4-4) completely. Gaby and Hadley (1957) noted that *Ps. aeruginosa* is predominantly proteolytic and only weakly saccharolytic; they considered its pigmentation, growth temperature relations, and pellicle formation unsatisfactory for positive identification and suggested that a test for cytochrome oxidase (based on development of indophenol blue after addition of α-naphthol and *p*-aminodimethylaniline oxalate, either to broth or to colonies on agar) was useful for distinguishing the genus. *Ps. aeruginosa* and 8 other species of *Pseudomonas* (unnamed) gave positive reactions in 15 to 30 seconds. *Alcaligenes faecalis* became blue much more slowly; other Gram-negative aerobes failed to react under the test conditions. In a later paper, Gaby and Free (1958) compared the cytochrome oxidase test in a group of clinical pseudomonad-like cultures with the gluconate oxidation test of Haynes and an oxidase test of increased sensitivity suggested for this purpose by Kovacs (1956). They found the Gaby and Haynes tests about equally reliable, the former technically simpler; the Kovacs test seemed too sensitive [see also Lutz, Schaeffer, and Hofferer (1958); Veron (1961)]. The rapid breakdown of arginine [Sherris et al. (1959)], often positive with pseudomonads, has been affirmed by Buttiaux (1961) as a means of distinguishing this genus from *Achromobacter*, enterobacteria, the moraxella-mima group, and other Gram-negative bacteria.

Pseudomonads Other than *Ps. aeruginosa*

Of the other species of *Pseudomonas* listed in Table 4-4, *Ps. fluorescens* produces only fluorescein (see page 124), and differs from *Ps. aeruginosa* principally in its lower optimum temperature; it fails to grow at $41 \pm 1°$ and grows poorly at $37°$. It has been regarded as a modified or degenerate form of *Ps. aeruginosa*, and is considered neither indigenous nor pathogenic. Pseudomonads with intermediate biochemical properties—forms that fail to reduce nitrate or reduce it rapidly to ammonia or free nitrogen, and grow at $10°$ as well as at $42°$—have been recovered from human source materials but are thought to be environmental contaminants. Wetmore and Gochenour (1956) reported that their strains of *Ps. ovalis* and *Ps. stutzeri* (the "intermediate species" of Table 4-4) were negative in the gluconate oxidation test of Haynes. The data of Gaby and Free (1958) indicate that the oxidase and cytochrome oxidase tests are nonspecific among pseudomonads, but exact information on the species of this genus listed in Table 4-4 other than *Ps. aeruginosa* is not available. See also Klinge (1960).

Pseudomonas aeruginosa

Ps. aeruginosa, the most important if not the only indigenous member of the genus, often considered the only one pathogenic for man, shares with a few other microorganisms—such as proteus, staphylococci and candida—the distinction of having greatly increased in pathogenic importance for man in the antibiotic era. Its importance becomes exaggerated, moreover, by its unusual resistance to antibiotics.

Pigments. Typical strains of *Ps. aeruginosa* are characterized by the production of 2 pigments, the blue-green pyocyanin, a phenazine derivative, soluble in water and in chloroform; and the greenish-yellow fluorescent fluorescein, soluble in water but not in chloroform. A pink or red pigment, pyorubin [Meader, Robinson, and Leonard (1925)], may be related to pyocyanin. Hellinger (1951), who reviewed the literature on pigment production, found that pyocyanin formation requires magnesium, phosphate, sulfate, and ammonium ions with a carbon source, preferably glucose, glycerol, or ethanol, supplemented with either glycine, L-tyrosine, DL-alanine, or L-leucine. Asparagine, used by earlier workers, was found unessential for pigment production, as were potassium and iron; ammonium salts could serve as the sole nitrogen source. The best medium for pyocyanin production contained DL-alanine, L-leucine, $MgSO_4$, K_2HPO_4, $FeSO_4$, glycerol, and chalk [see also Frank and DeMoss (1959)]. Friedheim (1931, 1934) suggested that pyocyanin may be a respiratory pigment, and Burton, Campbell, and Eagles (1948) demonstrated a relation of iron to fluorescein production. Totter and Moseley (1953) reported that production of fluorescein by *Ps. aeruginosa* was inversely proportional to the log of the concentration of iron in the medium. Good fluorescein production was obtained on a glycerol–ammonium sulfate medium. They suggested that removal of iron should stimulate fluorescein production, but oxine (8-hydroxyquinoline), an iron-chelating agent, did not have this effect. Paton (1959), on the other hand, has reported that pretreatment with oxine of a gluconate-salts medium greatly increased the fluorescence induced during subsequent growth of a pseudomonad. Pigment production by *Ps. aeruginosa* has been found to be inhibited by glucose at levels in nutrient agar of 1 to 10 per cent [Conroy (1960)], and also by chloramphenicol and erythromycin at concentrations that did not inhibit growth [Schneierson, Amsterdam, and Perlman (1960); see also Chabbert and Courtieu (1961)]. The chemistry of pseudomonad pigments has been studied by Takeda (1959).

Cultivation. *Ps. aeruginosa* grows well with ammonium salts as the nitrogen source and simple organic carbon. The medium used by Paton (1959) consisted per liter of $NH_4H_2PO_4$, 1 Gm; KCl, 0.2 Gm; $MgSO_4$. 0.2 Gm; and potassium or sodium gluconate, 5.0 Gm. A defined fluid medium with phenanthrene as the carbon and energy source described by Rogoff and Wender (1957) has been used effectively in the writer's laboratory, with sodium citrate substituted for phenanthrene, for growth of 3-liter lots of *Ps. aeruginosa* under continuous aeration. King, Raney, and Ward (1954) recommended 2 peptone-glycerol media whose combined use permitted identification of all of 107 strains of *Ps. aeruginosa*. Davis et al. (1960) have suggested the use of Sabouraud's maltose agar for routine clinical cultures.

Certain Biochemical Properties of *Ps. aeruginosa*. It was mentioned above that the carbohydrate metabolism of *Ps. aeruginosa* is oxidative and nonfermentative, normally proceeding only under aerobic conditions. The catabolic pathways, said to be unique, have been reviewed by Stern, Wang, and Gilmour (1960); see also DeLey (1960) and Veron (1961). Gluconate, α-ketogluconate, and pyruvate are important intermediates of glucose breakdown, and intermediates such as pyruvate or acetate may serve as secondary substrates. The pathway defined by Entner and Doudoroff (1952) seemed to be principally involved, with the pentose phosphate pathway functioning concurrently [see Wood (1955); Gunsalus and Schuster (1961)]. Collins (1960) has reported that glucose can be utilized by *Ps. aeruginosa* under anaerobic conditions in the presence of nitrate, which was reduced almost entirely to gaseous nitrogen or nitrous oxide, the glucose carbon going principally to CO_2 and bacterial cell substance. According to this worker, up to 11 per cent of the utilized glucose carbon was recovered as organic acids, including lactic and glycolic acids and smaller amounts of succinic, malic, fumaric, citric, α-ketoglutaric, and oxaloacetic acids. Volatile acids were formed in approximately the same quantity in both aerated and anaerobic cultures whether nitrate was present or not.

Antibiotic substances produced by *Ps. aeruginosa* are considered in Chap. 11.

Typing of *Ps. aeruginosa*. **Serology.** Both O and H antigens have been demonstrated in *Ps. aeruginosa*. The former is a lipopolysaccharide having the properties of endotoxin [Boivin and Mesrobeanu (1937)]. Munoz, Scherago, and Weaver (1949) were able to divide this species into 2 groups by flagellar and somatic agglutination; other species, including *Ps. fluorescens*, had species-specific antigens. Verder and Watt (1953), in a brief note,[2] reported that *Ps. aeruginosa* isolated from feces of 180 premature infants and of 50 older children and adults could be divided by the H and O antigens into serotypes belonging to 10 somatic groups. Kohler (1957) stated that the distribution of polysaccharide

---

[2] The results of a more extensive study of this organism, leading to recognition of 29 serotypes based on agglutination of O and H antigens, have been reported more recently by Verder and Evans (1961).

antigens demonstrated by a precipitin test was different in strains from the gastrointestinal tract as compared with a group from the external ear. Strains of *Ps. aeruginosa* from disease in animals were found by Sandvik (1960) to fall into 5 of 12 O groups previously established by Habs (1957) principally with strains of human origin. Liu (1961) has reported that all "pathogenic" species of *Pseudomonas*—a group into which this author places *Ps. aeruginosa* and the highly infective *Ps. (Malleomyces) pseudomallei* among others—produce extracellular antigenic toxic substances separable by centrifugation from cells grown on cellophane over agar plates [Liu (1957)]. Using a gel-diffusion procedure similar to the in vitro virulence test for diphtheria bacilli, *Ps. aeruginosa* was found species-specific when compared with 6 other cultures.

Phage Typing. Van den Ende (1952) classified 24 strains of *Ps. aeruginosa* into 6 types by precipitation of O antigens prepared by trichloracetic acid extraction; 4 of these types could be further subdivided by sensitivity to specific bacteriophages [see also Warner (1950); Dickinson and Codd (1952); van den Ende et al. (1952); Mead and van den Ende (1953)]. Detailed methods for the combined use in strain identification of agglutination and phage lysis have been given by Gould and McLeod (1960). The use in epidemiologic studies of both phages and pyocines (analogous to colicines, see Chap. 11) active against *Ps. aeruginosa* has been described by Holloway, Egan, and Monk (1960), and Holloway (1960).

Distribution: Indigenous. *Ps. aeruginosa* has been recovered from feces by many workers; from the skin, especially of hands, external ear, axilla and perineum; and occasionally from other sites in healthy persons. Hardy et al. (1954) found *Pseudomonas* in the ear in only approximately 1 per cent of 43 healthy young men. Horikawa et al. (1955) found it in about half of 33 excised tonsils and adenoids being used for virus isolation. Ringen and Drake (1952) recovered the organism from 11 per cent of fecal specimens, but Lowbury and Fox (1954) reported its presence in only about 3 per cent of stools of students, and in 3.2 per cent of a group consisting of patients without pseudomonad infections, and their contacts. Stools sometimes yielded large numbers of the organism.

These workers, whose studies were mainly concerned with the spread of *Ps. aeruginosa* in a hospital burns unit, failed to find *Ps. aeruginosa* among students in the nose, throat, or ear, or on the axillary or perineal skin, and also failed for the most part to recover it from sites other than feces in nurses and patients in wards not devoted to burns. The distribution of *Ps. aeruginosa* in the burn wards as found by these authors is given in the following paragraph. Loh and Baker (1955) were able to recover this organism from the feces of only 1 of 20 normal subjects given chlortetracycline for 5 days. In the one positive instance, the organism increased in numbers to 10^6 per Gm of wet feces for 2 days and then diminished, disappearing 5 days after cessation of treatment. These findings suggest a lower prevalence of *Ps. aeruginosa* in feces and on skin than is commonly assumed or implied by indirect evidence. For example, Biehl and Hamburger (1954) would explain the occurrence of *Ps. aeruginosa* meningitis following neurologic skin puncture —e.g., spinal tap—on the ground that the organism is ubiquitous on skin and difficult to destroy by routine procedures. The possibilities of environmental contamination of surgical materials, such as needles and catheters, with pseudomonads are suggested by Plotkin and Austrian (1958).

Distribution in Disease. Under pathologic conditions *Ps. aeruginosa* has been recovered from many sites, including the urinary tract, burns, wounds, or surgical infections, the feces in diarrheal disease, acute or chronic respiratory disease, septicemia and meningitis. Stanley (1947) reviewed this subject through 1945 and commented on the increasing number of infections with this organism following antibiotic therapy. He found an over-all mortality of 68 per cent in *Ps. aeruginosa* meningitis, higher when secondary to other infection than when primary (i.e., following lumbar puncture). Knight, Hardy, and Negrin (1952) suggested that mortality may be minimized in the literature because recoveries are more often reported [see also Schafter and Oppenheimer (1948)]. Pseudomonas septicemia in 23 persons, complicating other systemic disease—acute leukemia in 13—was described by Forkner et al. (1958).

Hardy et al. (1954) recovered pseudomonads from 65 to 81 per cent of cases of otitis externa, more frequently than any other microorganism. Wright, Potee, and Finland (1954) found this organism uncommon in severe systemic disease. In their experience, 51 of 110 strains were recovered from urine, 19 from wounds or other superficial infection, 16 from other purulent exudates, 14 from sputum, 8 from feces, and 2 from blood. Yow (1952) reported that among routine cultures in a large hospital laboratory in the period 1948–51 there was a distinct increase in the proportion of pseudomonas, proteus, and candida associated with a decreased recovery of *E. coli;* klebsiella remained roughly stationary. Yow found *Ps. aeruginosa* in 19 urinary tract infections, 4 pulmonary cases, 4 instances of empyema, 4 blood cultures, 3 cases of meningitis, and once each in arthritis and prostatitis. Hodges and de Alvarez (1960) have also recorded an increasing incidence of pseudomonas septicemia, with a mortality rate of over 50 per cent. Kneeland and Price (1960) have found the occurrence of pseudomonads second only to that of staphylococci in terminal pneumonia, nearly always in patients receiving antibiotics [see also Williams, Williams, and Hyams (1960)]. Serious *Ps. aeruginosa* infections of infants and children, usually secondary to other illness, have been described by Asay and Koch (1960) and by Burns and Rhodes (1961). See also Curtin, Petersdorf, and Bennett (1961).

Fox and Lowbury (1953) cited earlier literature which indicated that *Ps. aeruginosa* may be the agent of generalized infections and bronchopneumonia in burn cases, but that it is more often a simple contaminant of burns or wounds than an active pathogen. Such "silent infections," however, were thought to be responsible for failure of skin grafts and delay in healing. Lowbury and Fox (1954), in the paper referred to in preceding paragraphs, found *Ps. aeruginosa* occasionally, and nearly always in small numbers, in the nose or throat or on the skin of nurses in burn wards or patients in other than burn wards.

In contrast to these observations and to those among normal subjects mentioned above, were the principal findings of these workers in the burn wards themselves. Hand washings from nurses in these wards showed 11 of 29 (38 per cent) to be contaminated with *Ps. aeruginosa;* among the burned patients, cultures from uninjured parts were positive in from 1.4 to 19.1 per cent of instances when taken from nose, throat, nasopharynx, skin, and ear, and in 3 of 15 (20 per cent) of stool specimens. In the burns themselves, as many as 52 per cent became contaminated with *Ps. aeruginosa* in the hospital, often in large numbers, before the use of polymyxin ointment.

Cultures from many parts of the hospital environment incriminated contaminated wounds or burns as the principal sources of hospital infections, and air, dust, or contact as the chief transmitting media or means. Serologic typing suggested cross-infection rather than self-infection, except for transfer between burns of the same patient. A given strain tended to spread through a given ward but seldom from one ward to another—a finding that would seem to implicate contact transmission rather than the airborne route. The general subject of infection of burns has been reviewed by Lowbury (1960). An outbreak of wound infection with *Ps. aeruginosa* in an orthopedic unit was traced by Sussman and Stevens (1960) to cellulose wadding ("wood wool") used as padding under plaster casts.

Pathogenicity. The experimental pathogenicity of *Ps. aeruginosa* conforms to a pattern common to many amphibionts in being dependent either on massive dosage or on preceding tissue damage in the host. This pattern is in turn consistent with the behavior of the organism in disease in man. That viable cell concentrations of the order of 10^7 can be injected intravenously into adult rabbits without apparent effect has been shown by the live-vaccine immunization described by Millican and Rust (1960) and repeated successfully in the writer's laboratory. Rosenthal, Millican, and Rust (1957) found that 10^8 to 10^9 organisms were fatal to mice when given intraperitoneally. Pretreatment of the animals with cortisone permitted infection with smaller doses; under these conditions a factor present in human γ-globulin, not identified with antibody, was found to be protective. In further studies, these workers were able to protect mice against otherwise fatal *Ps. aeruginosa* infection by either prophylactic or therapeutic administration of specific rabbit antiserum, which was 250 to 800 times as protective as human γ-globulin [Millican and Rust (1960)]. Kibayashi (1958) has reported that mice could be infected with this bacterium if subjected 2 days before to 400 r of whole-body x radiation. Nelson and Becker (1959a) induced peritoneal exudation by injecting gelatin into irradiated mice and then inoculating them intraperitoneally with *Ps. aeruginosa* and enough polymyxin to inhibit extracellular growth. Under these conditions the numbers of bacteria surviving within phagocytes were found to be greatest in mice given the highest dose of radiation. Previously immunized mice destroyed intracellular pseudomonads more rapidly than others even thought they had been irradiated. The bacteria were found to survive and multiply within the spleen and liver of mice receiving 500 to 700 r, but were destroyed in the organs of unirradiated or immunized mice [Nelson and Becker (1959b)]. Liu, Abe, and Bates (1961) have studied the toxicity for mice of whole cells and various fractions, of which a slime fraction seemed most active. In the experiments of Braude, Shapiro, and Siemienski (1959) on experimental hematogenous pyelonephritis in rats (see page 108), renal destruction could be produced with *Ps. aeruginosa* among other species tested.

Indications in the preceding paragraph of protection against *Ps. aeruginosa* conferred by specific antibodies in experimental animals are adumbrated in scattered observations in man (see also Chap. 11). Lilley and Bearup (1928) and Gibson (1930) described the occurrence of agglutinins in man to *Ps. aeruginosa*. Sandiford (1937) reported serum agglutinins in urinary infections. Fox and Lowbury (1953) found agglutinins to saline antigens of *Ps. aeruginosa* in all of 12 normal subjects, at titers of 1:160 to 1:640. All of 39 patients with *Ps. aeruginosa*-contaminated burns showed agglutinins with titers ranging from 1:80 to 1:2,560; while 21 out of 23 patients with burns not contaminated with this organism showed titers similar to those of the normal subjects. A rise in specific titer was noted in serum samples taken several weeks after the appearance of *Ps. aeruginosa* in the burn. Gaines and Landy (1955) were unable to demonstrate agglutination of *Ps. aeruginosa* suspension by normal human serums; but, using human erythrocytes coated with lipopolysaccharide from this organism, they demonstrated agglutination increasing with age from 22 per cent at 0 to 1 year to 100 per cent at 4 to 15 years, with an occasional negative among a larger group in the 17 to 22 year age range. That the antibody found was specific for *Ps. aeruginosa* was indicated by its quantitative removal with 7 of 8 strains representing 8 somatic components of the 10 proposed by Verder and Watt (1953; see page 125) and by failure of absorption by any of a range of other Gram-negative bacteria. The absence of direct agglutination of the organism seemed to suggest that the antibody concerned may be incomplete, but attempts to demonstrate it by Coombs or blocking techniques were unsuccessful. If these findings are interpretable in terms of specific immunization—currently the most probable hypothesis—their apparent discordance with prevalence data for the organism itself, as noted above, calls for re-examination.

Sensitivity to Antibiotics. The resistance of *Ps. aeruginosa* to most antibiotics is a cardinal feature of the organism. Polymyxin B has been found most consistently active. Yow (1952), for example, noted by in vitro tests that neomycin was a poor second to polymyxin B, with oxytetracycline and streptomycin third and fourth; other antibiotics had little or no effect. This worker, whose particular concern was infections with *Proteus* or *Pseudomonas* arising during antibiotic therapy for other diseases, commented that the discontinuance of ineffective antibiotics was sometimes sufficient to control the disease by permitting restoration of the normal flora. Wright, Potee, and Finland (1954) found their strains sensitive in decreasing order to polymyxin B, oxytetracycline, tetracycline, and chlortetracycline (the last considerably less active than the others). Many strains were moderately sensitive to streptomycin and neomycin. Recently isolated strains were more often resistant to chlortetracycline, streptomycin, tetracycline, and neomycin than those isolated in or before 1949. Four completely achromogenic strains were the only ones found sensitive to 25 μg or less of erythromycin or to 200 μg or less of chloramphenicol, and were the most sensitive to the 3 tetracyclines. Koch (1959) found that the percentage of strains of *Ps. aeruginosa* resistant to chloramphenicol had risen from 59 in 1953 to 99 in 1955, and had then remained at 99 per cent during each year through 1958. On the other hand, Jolliff et al. (1960) reported continued sensitivity of most strains of *Ps. aeruginosa* to chloramphenicol during the years 1955 through 1958; in the hands of these workers nitrofurantoin was also effective against as high a percentage of strains (70 per cent) as was polymyxin B (69 per cent).

Mills and Kagan (1954) reported that oral polymyxin B is very effective in eliminating *Ps. aeruginosa* from the gastrointestinal tract.

They treated 24 ambulatory persons who were found to excrete the organism in the feces, and compared them with 8 untreated carriers. Half of the latter were spontaneously free of the organism after 25 or 39 days; the whole treated group was negative in 5 days and all but one were negative when examined 25 and 30 days later.

The polymyxin-like antibiotic, colistin, has been found active against *Ps. aeruginosa* both in vitro [Wright and Welch (1959–60); Graber, Tumbush, and Vogel (1959–60)] and in clinical trials [Hall (1960); see also Chabbert and Courtieu (1961)]. Demethylchlortetracycline was reported to be somewhat more frequently active against this organism than the other tetracyclines [Vineyard, Hogan, and Sanford (1959–60)].

Alcaligenes faecalis

The name *Alcaligenes faecalis* is applied to a somewhat hetero-geneous group of achromogenic aerobic nonglucolytic Gram-negative bacilli. They may be confused either with *Mima polymorpha* or with unpigmented *Pseudomonas aeruginosa*. They differ from the former in morphology and staining, being unequivocally bacillary and Gram-negative, in their somewhat simpler nutritive requirements, and in that many strains are motile. Unlike *Ps. aeruginosa* they fail to oxidize gluconate [Haynes (1951)] and react slowly in the cytochrome oxidase test of Gaby [Gaby and Hadley (1957); Gaby and Free (1958)]. Their characteristics are compared with those of *Pseudomonas* species in Table 4-4. An attempt to classify 40 strains resembling *Alc. faecalis* led Moore and Pickett (1960b) to question the validity of the generic name, in place of which they suggested *Achromobacter* [see also Conn (1942); Sarkar, Chowdhuri, and Tribedi (1959)]. Thibault (1961) studied 53 motile cultures with properties suggestive of *Alcaligenes;* only 6 of these, among 13 nonproteolytic peritrichous strains, seemed to be *Alc. faecalis;* he emphasized the need for further study of this group.

Like moraxella and *Mima polymorpha, Alc. faecalis* does not attack glucose or other test carbohydrates; the medium typically becomes alka-line. It can utilize lactate as the sole carbon and energy source [Braun and Cahn-Bronner (1921); see also Berthelot and Amoureux (1938); Conn (1942)]. Denault, Cleverdon, and Kulp (1953) reported that growth as good as in nutrient broth occurred in a medium containing sodium lactate, asparagine, and salts. Of many nitrogen compounds tried in place of asparagine only aspartic acid, histidine, or glutathione gave good growth of all strains tested; slight growth appeared with ammonium salts as the sole nitrogen source.

Hirst (1917) compared 9 strains of *Alc. faecalis* isolated from blood with descriptions of earlier workers. Motility was variable in both groups; Hirst found polar flagella, others had recorded either polar or peritrichous flagella (see page 133); his strains did not liquefy gelatin, while those of others were variable in this respect as well. All were nonfermenters, made litmus milk alkaline, and failed to form indole; pathogenicity for guinea pigs, mice, or rats was generally lacking. Oeding (1946b) has provided a good description of a hemolytic variant of *Alcaligenes* and notes on related strains isolated from clinical material. The hemolytic organism was nonmotile, unpigmented, strictly aerobic (failing to grow under petrolatum), negative in carbohydrates and citrate, and in the indole, methyl red, Voges-Proskauer, and H_2S tests. It slowly peptonized gelatin but did not liquefy coagulated serum. Mice were unaffected by 0.5 ml of a 24-hour broth culture given intraperitoneally. This organism had been derived from a bilateral conjunctivitis, in a 2½-week-old infant, which failed to respond to penicillin or sulfonamides. The organism had been found persistently in the eyes for a month after onset. King, Raney, and Ward (1954) observed no fluorescent pigment with alcaligenes-like organisms in media used to demonstrate chromogenicity of *Ps. aeruginosa*.

Distribution. The indigenous habitat of this organism appears to be feces [see Shidlovsky et al. (1957–58); Petruk (1959)]. Under pathologic conditions *Alc. faecalis* has been recovered from blood [Hirst (1917)], from the urinary tract, the conjunctiva, the nose and the lower respiratory tract [Oeding (1946b)], and from a number of infective processes including meningitis [see Weinstein and Wassermann (1951); Wynne, Old, and Cott (1952); LeNoc and Moustardier (1958)]. Hirst (1917) found agglutinin titers of 1:50 in the serum of patients from whose blood the organism had been isolated, and noted that earlier workers had recorded titers as high as 1:2,000. Weinstein and Wassermann (1951), who recovered the organism from the blood of a patient with infectious mononucleosis and fusospirochetal angina, also noted a rise in specific agglutinin titer during the illness.

Antibiotic Sensitivity. In a study of organisms isolated from the urinary tract, Ritts, Mao, and Favour (1957–58) found *Alc. faecalis* to be varyingly sensitive to most antimicrobial agents active against Gram-negative forms, but among the strains tested some were resistant to each agent. Nitrofurantoin, chloramphenicol, and furazolidine were among the most effective drugs for this organism.

Vibrios

Aerobic vibrios do not appear to be common or numerous in indigenous habitats. An organism named *Vibrio alcaligenes* [see Nyberg

(1935)] was described in the seventh edition of *Bergey's Manual of Determinative Bacteriology* [Breed, Murray, and Smith (1957)] as a variant of *V. percolans*, said to occur more frequently in the intestine than *Alcaligenes faecalis*. A strain labeled *Vibrio alcaligenes*, included among the 40 motile *Alc. faecalis*-like strains studied by Moore and Pickett (1960*b*) could not be distinguished from the latter biochemically, serologically, or in its pattern of phage lysis. Thibault (1961) found similar organisms in a collection of motile alcaligenes-like cultures and stressed the need for further study of the group. The results of computer analysis suggested to Liston (1960) that *V. percolans* and most other so-called *Vibrio* spp. tested belonged with *Pseudomonas* rather than with *Vibrio*.

Hemophili

The imaginary line that separates indigenous bacteria from overt pathogens is perhaps even more elusive in the instance of *Haemophilus influenzae* than it is for hemolytic streptococci, pneumococci, and meningococci, as well as for *Staphylococcus aureus*. A parallel with group A β-streptococci is suggested in the circumstance that the principal pathogens for man among influenza bacilli can be distinguished especially by the *b* capsular antigen of Pittman (1931) and by associated characters of smooth encapsulated strains; but the demonstration of pathogenicity in animals is reminiscent of amphibionts in its difficulty. Loss of smoothness in what is apparently the same organism is associated with a carrier rate in healthy persons distinctly high enough to warrant inclusion of organisms called *H. influenzae* as members of the normal flora. We include the organism as another borderline case; other species of the genus are also indigenous.

Classification. The genus *Haemophilus* consists of small aerobic Gram-negative bacilli, often pleomorphic, nonmotile, strictly parasitic, growing only in the presence of one or both of two growth accessories, the V factor (phosphopyridine nucleotide) or the X factor (hemin). Of the species found in the normal flora of man, both factors are required by *H. influenzae, H. haemolyticus* (distinguished as hemolytic), *H. aegyptius* (distinguished serologically), and doubtfully by *H. vaginalis*, said to require factors in addition to V and X (but see page 134). *H. parainfluenzae* and *H. parahaemolyticus* require only V factor, and are distinguished from each other by hemolytic activity of the latter.

H. parahaemolyticus was defined as a new species by Pittman (1953). It was described as larger than other hemophilic bacteria, occurring as long tangled threads, pleomorphic, with bigger, less translucent colonies; hemolytic, reducing nitrate, and usually not forming indole. Weak acidity is produced from glucose and usually from sucrose and maltose. The organism may be mistaken for hemolytic streptococci by its appearance on blood agar plates.

H. aegyptius, the so-called Koch-Weeks bacillus, was found by Pittman and Davis (1950) to resemble non-type-specific *H. influenzae.* It differed in having longer rods, growing somewhat more slowly, failing to form indole or to ferment xylose, and in being distinct by agglutination. Davis, Pittman and Griffits (1950) reported that 27 of 28 strains of this organism agglutinated human red blood cells, a property not shared by conjunctival and other strains of *H. influenzae* or by *H. parainfluenzae* or *H. haemolyticus.* Antigenic distinction between this organism and *H. influenzae* has been confirmed by Olitzki and Sulitzeanu (1960) by gel precipitation with sonically extracted antigens.

H. vaginalis is an organism of uncertain relationships. It is a small pleomorphic Gram-negative rod showing coccobacillary forms, isolated from urine under pathologic conditions by Leopold (1953) on blood agar as modified by Casman (1947). It is microaerophilic, growing in 48 hours at 37° in 10 per cent CO_2 as tiny hemolytic colonies. Subcultures were successful in fluid thioglycollate medium. The organism does not reduce nitrate or produce oxidase, forms acid without gas from glucose, maltose, and dextrin but not from sucrose, lactose, inulin, mannitol, or glycerin. Leopold found the organism nonpathogenic for small animals. According to Dukes (1956), see also Gardner and Dukes (1955), *H. vaginalis* requires both X and V factors and others in addition which are contained in blood or other tissue fluid. Edmunds (1960a,b), on the other hand, found that while the organism required blood or its constituents for aerobic growth, the factors needed were neither X nor V but seemed to reside chiefly in the red cell stromata. Edmunds found this organism Gram-variable, hemolytic, and tolerant of normal vaginal pH levels but inhibited by alkalinity; he noted that it ferments glycogen. Dukes and Gardner (1961) have distiguished *H. vaginalis* by agglutination from *H. influenzae, H. parainfluenzae,* and *H. aegyptius.*

Distribution. The influenza-like hemophili show a scattering incidence in the normal conjunctiva and nose, and have been found in the pharynx and mouth in as many as 90 to 100 per cent of cases in certain studies. Details will be found in Chap. 10. Huet (1957) reported a proportion of positive cultures for *Haemophilus* from healthy conjunctivas of 25 per cent; some of these were *H. aegyptius. H. vaginalis* has been considered a member of the vaginal flora by Heltai (1959, 1960).

The occurrence of typable *H. influenzae* in fulminating disease of the

upper respiratory tract and in meningitis of infants and children need
not be considered here [see Hara (1959); Vetto (1960)]. In adults the
pathologic effects of this organism seem nearly always secondary to
viral or other bacterial infections or to other agencies—emerging, for
example, after penicillin therapy [see Weinstein (1947)]. May (1954)
found *H. influenzae* in purulent or mucopurulent sputum from chronic
bronchitis in from 24 to 90 per cent of instances in different groups.
Allibone and coworkers (1956) recovered the organism from sputum
or bronchoscopic aspirations of all of 32 children with bronchiectasis
[see also Rogers, Zinnemann, and Foster (1960)]. *H. influenzae*
pyarthrosis was reviewed in 30 infants and reported in an adult by Dyer,
Romansky, and Holmes (1958); see also Crowell and Loube (1954).
Meningitis due to this organism is occasionally seen in adults [Holds-
worth (1960)].

   H. aegyptius is found principally in acute conjunctivitis [Pitttman
and Davis (1950); Huet (1957)]. *H. vaginalis* has been found in and
held responsible for genitourinary disease in both men [Leopold
(1953); Liebovitz (1954)] and women [Gardner and Dukes (1959)].

   Pathogenicity. It has long been known that pathogenicity of encapsulated type *b* strains of *H. influenzae* from disease, grown as 6-
hour cultures, can be demonstrated by intraperitoneal injection of mice
with suspensions in mucin. Pittman and Davis (1950) compared 6
strains of *H. influenzae* with 6 strains of *H. aegyptius* by this procedure and found the latter distinctly less infective. They were able to
confirm the findings of early workers that the Koch-Weeks bacillus
(and to a lower degree *H. influenzae*) was capable of producing conjunctivitis by inoculation of the eye of human volunteers. Pitman and
Davis reported negative results following instillation of either organism
into the eyes of monkeys, rabbits, guinea pigs, mice, rats, or chickens.

   Leopold (1953) found *H. vaginalis* nonpathogenic for small animals.

   Extensive studies of the antibiotic sensitivity of *H. influenzae* have
been reported by Hirsch and Finland (1960); see also Haggerty and
Ziai (1960).

References

Aiken, M. A., Ward, M. K., and King, E. O., 1956, *Public Health Lab.*,
    14:126.
Alford, J. A., 1960, *J. Bacteriol.*, **79**:591.
Allibone, E. C., Allison, P. R., and Zinnemann, K., 1956, *Brit. Med. J.*,
    2:1457.
Al'tgauzen, V. P., 1959, *Zhur. Mikrobiol. Epidemiol. Immunobiol.* (*transl.*)
    30:65.

Anderson, T., Crockatt, H., and Ross, C. A. C., 1954, *J. Pathol. Bacteriol.*, **48**:1.

Asay, L. D., and Koch, R., 1960, *New Engl. J. Med.*, **262**:1062.

Audureau, A., 1940, *Ann. Inst. Pasteur*, **64**:126.

Axenfeld, T., 1897, *Zentr. Bakteriol. Parasitenk. I Orig.*, **21**:1.

Bamforth, J., and Dudgeon, J. A., 1952, *J. Pathol. Bacteriol.*, **44**:751.

Bannerjea, A., Chatterji, D. N., and Mukherji, R. N., 1958, *Ann. Biochem. Exp. Med.*, **18**:121 (*Biol. Abstr.*).

———, ———, and Pramanick, K., 1956, *ibid.*, **16**:49 (*Biol. Abstr.*).

Barner, R. D., 1952, *Am. J. Vet. Research.* **13**:132.

Berthelot, A., and Amoureux, C., 1938. *Compt. Rend. Soc. Biol.*, **128**:980.

Biehl, J. P., and Hamburger, M., 1954, *A.M.A. Arch. Internal. Med.*, **93**:367.

Billing, E., 1955, *J. Gen. Microbiol.*, **13**:252.

Boivin, A., and Mesrobeanu, L., 1937, *Compt. Rend. Soc. Biol.*, **125**:273.

Braude, A. I., 1955, *J. Clin. Invest.*, **34**:1489.

———, Shapiro, A. P., and Siemienski, J., 1959, *J. Bacteriol.*, **77**:270.

Braun, H., and Cahn-Bronner, C. E., 1921, *Zentr. Bakteriol. Parasitenk. I Orig.*, **86**:196.

Bray, J., 1945, *J. Pathol. Bacteriol.*, **57**:239.

Breed, R. S., Murray, E. G. D., and Smith, N. R., 1957, *Bergey's Manual of Determinative Bacteriology*, 7th ed. The Williams & Wilkins Company, Baltimore.

Brisou, J., 1953, *Ann. Inst. Pasteur*, **84**:812.

———, 1957. *ibid.*, **92**:134.

———, and Morichau-Beauchant, J., 1952, *ibid.*, **82**:640.

———, ———, and Giminez, J., 1953, *ibid.*, **84**:814.

———, ———, ———, and Lenriot, A., 1952, *Bull. Soc. Pathol. Exotique*, **45**:439.

Brooke, M. S., 1951, *Acta Pathol. Microbiol. Scand.*, **28**:338.

Brooks, B. E., 1954, *U.S. Armed Forces Med. J.*, **5**:667.

Brumfitt, W., and Heptinstall, R. H., 1960, *Brit. J. Exp. Path.*, **41**:552.

Burns, R. P., and Rhodes, D. H., 1961, *Arch. Ophthalmol.*, **65**:517.

Burton, M. O., Campbell, J. J. R., and Eagles, B. A., 1948, *Can. J. Research*, 26C, 15, cited by Totter and Moseley (1953).

Buttiaux, R., 1961, *Ann. Inst. Pasteur*, No. 6, Suppl., p. 43.

———, and Gagnon, P., 1958–59, *Ann. Inst. Pasteur Lille*, **10**:121 (*Biol. Abstr.*).

Cary, S. G., Lindberg, R. B., and Faber, J. E., Jr., 1956, *J. Bacteriol.*, **72**:728.

———, 1958, *ibid.*, **75**:43.

Casman, E. P., 1947, *Am. J. Clin. Pathol.*, **17**:281.

Cetin, E. T., and Toreci, K., 1960, *Ann. Inst. Pasteur*, **100**:509.

Chabbert, Y., and Courtieu, A.-L., 1961, *ibid.*, No. 6, Suppl., p. 100.

Chang, J. C., and Foltz, V. D., 1960, *J. Dental Research*, **39**:1120.

Christie, R. 1948, *Australian J. Exptl. Biol. Med. Sci.*, **26**:425.

Collins, F. M., 1960, *ibid.*, *Sci.*, **38**:163.

Conn, H. J., 1942, *J. Bacteriol.*, **44**:353.

Conroy, D. A., 1960, *Rev. Latinoam. Microbiol.*, **3**:109 (*Biol. Abstr.*).

Courtieu, A.-L., Chassignol, S., and Longeray, C., 1961, *Ann. Inst. Pasteur*, No. 6, Suppl., p. 116.

Cowan, S. T., 1954, *Internat. Bull. Bact. Nomencl. Taxon.*, **4**:119.

———, Steel, K. J., and Shaw, C., 1960, *J. Gen. Microbiol.*, **23**:601.

Crowell, J., and Loube, S. D., 1954, *A.M.A. Arch. Internal Med.*, **93**:921.

Curtin, J. A., Petersdorf, R. G., and Bennett, I. L., Jr., 1961, *Ann. Internal Med.*, **54**:1077.

Davis, B. R., and Ewing, W. H., 1958, *Can. J. Microbiol.*, **4**:517.

Davis, D. J., Pittman, M., and Griffits, J. J., 1950, *J. Bacteriol.*, **59**:427.

Davis, I., Sellers, W., Orbach, H., and Waddington, G., 1960, *J. Lab. Clin. Med.*, **55**:139.

De, S. N., Bhattacharya, K., and Sarkar, J. K., 1956, *J. Pathol. Bacteriol.*, **71**:201.

Deacon, W. E., 1945, *J. Bacteriol.*, **49**:511.

DeBord, G. G., 1939, *ibid.*, **38**:119.

————, 1942, *Iowa State Coll. J. Sci.*, **16**:471.

————, 1943, *J. Lab. Clin. Med.*, **28**:710.

————, 1948, *J. Bacteriol.*, **55**:764.

DeLey, J., 1960, *J. Applied Bacteriol.*, **23**:400.

Denault, L. J., Cleverdon, R. C., and Kulp, W. L., 1953, *J. Bacteriol.*, **66**:465.

Dexter, H. L. T., Glacy, J., Leonard, J., Dexter, M. W., and Lawton, A., 1958, *A.M.A. Arch. Dermatol.*, **77**:109.

Dickinson, L., and Codd, S., 1952, *J. Gen. Microbiol.*, **61**:1.

Dienes, L., 1946, *Proc. Soc. Exptl. Biol. Med.*, **63**:265.

Dukes, C. D., 1956, *Bacteriol. Revs.* **20**:275.

————, and Gardner, H. L., 1961, *J. Bacteriol.*, **81**:277.

Dyer, R. F., Romansky, M. J., and Holmes, J. R., 1958, *A.M.A. Arch. Internal Med.*, **102**:580.

Edebo, L., and Laurell, G., 1958, *Acta Pathol. Microbiol. Scand.*, **43**:93.

Edmunds, P. N., 1960*a*, *J. Pathol. Bacteriol.*, **79**:273.

————, 1960*b*, *ibid.*, **79**:325.

Edwards, P. R., and Ewing, W. H., 1955, *Identification of Enterobacteriaceae*, Burgess Publishing Company, Minneapolis.

————, and Fife, M. A., 1955, *J. Bacteriol.*, **70**:382.

————, ————, and Ramsey, C. H., 1959, *Bacteriol. Revs.*, **23**:155.

Ehrenworth, L., and Baer, H., 1956, *J. Bacteriol.*, **72**:713.

Eisenberg, G. M., Weiss, W., and Flippin, H. F., 1958*a*, *Ann. Internal Med.*, **49**:310.

————, 1958*b*, *Am. J. Clin. Pathol.*, **30**:20.

Ellis, E. M., 1961, *Am. J. Vet. Research*, **22**:610.

Entner, N., and Doudoroff, M., 1952, *J. Biol. Chem.*, **196**:853.

Epstein, S. S., 1959*a*, *J. Clin. Pathol.*, **12**:52.

————, 1959*b*, *J. Pathol. Bacteriol.*, **78**:389.

Estrada-Para, S., and Perez-Miravete, A., 1959, *Rev. Latinoam. Microbiol.*, **2**:185 (*Biol. Abstr.*).

Ewing, W. H., 1949, *J. Bacteriol.*, **57**:659.

————, 1960, *Enterobacteriaceae. Biochemical Methods for Group Differentiation*, Public. Health Service Pub. 734.

————, and Edwards, P. R., 1960, *Internat. Bull. Bact. Nomencl. Taxon.*, **10**:1.

Eyre, J. W., 1900, *J. Pathol. Bacteriol.*, **6**:1.

Faust, J., and Hood, M., 1949, *Am. J. Clin. Pathol.*, **19**:1143.

Fedukowicz, H., and Horwich, H., 1953, *A.M.A. Arch. Ophthalmol.*, **49**:202.

Ferguson, W. W., and June, R. C., 1952, *Am. J. Hyg.*, **55**:155.

————, and Roberts, L. F., 1950, *J. Bacteriol.*, **59**:171.

Forkner, C. E., Jr., Frei, E., Edgecomb, J. H., and Utz, J. P., 1958, *Am. J. Med.*, **25**:877.

Fox, J. E., and Lowbury, E. J. L., 1953, *J. Pathol. Bacteriol.*, **65**:533.

Frank, L. H., and DeMoss, R. D., 1959, *J. Bacteriol.*, **77**:776.
Fred, H. L., Allen, T. D., Hessel, H. L., and Holtzman, C. F., 1958, *A.M.A. Arch. Internal Med.*, **102**:204.
Friedheim, E. A. H., 1931, *J. Exptl. Med.*, **54**:207.
———, 1934, *Biochem. J.*, **28**:173.
Fulton, J. K., and McKinlay, B. C., 1954, *Ann. Internal Med.*, **40**:245.
Gaby, W. L., 1946, *J. Bacteriol.*, **51**:217.
———, and Free, E. J., 1953, *ibid.*, **65**:746.
———, 1958, *ibid.*, **76**:442.
———, and Hadley, C., 1957, *ibid.*, **74**:356.
Gaines, S., and Landy, M., 1955, *ibid.*, **69**:628.
Gamble, D. R., and Rowson, K. E. K., 1957, *Lancet*, **2**:619.
Garber, E. D., Hackett, A. J., and Franklin, R., 1952, *Proc. Nat. Acad. Sci.*, **38**:693.
Gardner, H. L., and Dukes, C. D., 1955, *Am. J. Obstet. Gynecol.*, **69**:962.
———, ———, 1959, *Ann. N.Y. Acad. Sci.*, **83**:280.
Gareau, F. E., Mackel, D. C., Boring, J. R., and Payne, F. J., 1959, *J. Pediat.*, **54**:313.
Gibson, H. J., 1930, *J. Hyg.*, **30**:337.
Gillespie, H. B., Steber, M. S., Scott, E. N., and Christ, Y. S., 1950*a*, *J. Immunol.*, **65**:105.
———, ———, and Waugh, M. H., 1950*b*, *ibid.*, **65**:115.
Gould, J. C., and McLeod, J. W., 1960, *J. Pathol. Bacteriol.*, **79**:295.
Graber, C. D., Tumbusch, W. T., and Vogel, E. H., Jr., 1959–60, *Antibiotics Ann.*, p. 77.
Gunsalus, I. C., and Schuster, C. W., 1961, in Gunsalus, I. C., and Stanier, R. Y. (eds.), *The Bacteria*, Academic Press Inc., New York, **2**:16.
Habs, I., 1957, *Z. Hyg. Infektionskrankh.*, **144**:218.
Haggerty, R. J., and Ziai, M., 1960, *Pediatrics*, **25**:742.
Hall, H. E., and Humphries, J. C., 1958, *J. Inf. Dis.*, **103**:157.
Hall, J. W., 1960, *Am. J. Med. Sci.*, **240**:561.
Hara, H. J., 1959, *A.M.A. Arch. Otolaryngol.*, **70**:315.
Hardy, A. V., Mitchell, R. B., Schreiber, M., Hoffert, W. R., Yawn, E., and Young, F., 1954, *Laryngoscope*, **64**:1020.
Haynes, W. C., 1951, *J. Gen. Microbiol.*, **5**:939.
Hellinger, E., 1951, *ibid.*, **5**:633.
Heltai, A., 1959, *Ann. N.Y. Acad. Sci*, **83**:290.
———, 1960, *Gynaecologia*, 149 Suppl. 3/4:80 (*Biol. Abstr.*).
Henriksen, S. D., 1947, *Acta Pathol. Microbiol. Scand.*, **24**:184.
———, 1948*a*, *ibid.*, **25**:285.
———, 1948*b*, *ibid.*, **25**:493.
———, 1952, *J. Gen. Microbiol.*, **6**:318.
———, 1958, *Acta Pathol. Microbiol. Scand.*, **43**:157.
———, 1960, *Internat. Bull. Bact. Nomencl. Taxon.*, **10**:23, 231.
Heptinstall, R. H., Michaels, L. M., and Brumfitt, W., 1960, *J. Pathol. Bacteriol.*, **80**:249.
Hirsch, H. A., and Finland, M., 1960, *Am. J. Med. Sci.*, **239**:33.
Hirst, L. F., 1917, *J. Roy. Army Med. Corp*, **29**:476.
Hite, K. E., Hesseltine, H. C., and Goldstein, L., 1947, *Am. J. Obstet. Gynecol.*, **53**:233.
Hodges, R. M., and DeAlvarez, R. R., 1960, *J. Am. Med. Assoc.*, **173**:1081.
Holdsworth, D. E., 1960, *A.M.A. Arch. Internal Med.*, **106**:653.

Holloway, B. W., 1960, *J. Pathol. Bacteriol*, **80**:448.
―――, Egan, J. B., and Monk, M., 1960, *Australian J. Exptl. Biol. Med. Sci.*, **38**:321.
Horikawa, T., Suzuki, T., Fuzita, H., and Kitaziri, K., 1955, *Mie Med.*, **5**: 47 (*Biol. Abstr.*).
Huet, M., 1957, *Arch. Inst. Pasteur Tunis*, **35**:55 (*Biol. Abstr.*).
Hugh, R., and Leifson, E., 1953, *J. Bacteriol.*, **66**:24.
Hyde, L., and Hyde, B., 1943, *Am. J. Med. Sci.*, **205**:660.
Ino, J., Neugebauer, D. L., and Lucas, R. N., 1959, *Am. J. Clin. Pathol.*, **32**:364.
Jessen, O., 1958, *Acta Pathol. Microbiol. Scand.*, **43**:219.
Johnson, F. T., Perry, J. J., and Sokolski, W. T., 1957–58, *Antibiotics Ann.*, p. 27.
Jones, M., 1960, *J. Inf. Dis.*, **106**:304.
Joliff, C. R., Engelhard, W. E., Ohlsen, J. R., Heidrick, P. J., and Cain, J. A., 1960, *Antibiotics & Chemotherapy*, **10**:694.
June, R. C., Ferguson, W. W., and Worfel, M. T., 1953, *Am. J. Hyg.*, **57**:222.
Kauffmann, F., 1947, *J. Immunol.*, **57**:71.
―――, 1954, *Enterobacteriaceae*, 2d ed. Munsgaard, Copenhagen.
―――, and Perch, B., 1943, *Acta Pathol. Microbiol. Scand.*, **20**:201.
Kenner, B. A., and Kabler, P. W., 1956, *J. Bacteriol.*, **72**:879.
Kibayashi, Y., 1958, *Japan. J. Bacteriol.* **13**:127.
King, E. O., 1960, Personal communication.
―――, Raney, D. E., and Ward, M. K., 1954, *J. Lab. Clin. Med.*, **44**:301.
Kirby, W. M. M., Corpron, D. O., and Tanner, D. C., 1956, *J. Am. Med. Assoc.*, **162**:1.
Klinge, K., 1960, *J. Applied Bacteriol.*, **23**:442.
Kneeland, Y., and Price, K. M., 1960, *Am. J. Med.*, **29**:967.
Knight, V., Hardy, E. C., and Negrin, J., Jr., 1952, *J. Am. Med. Assoc.*, **149**: 1395.
Knipschildt, H. E., 1945, *Undersogeler over Coligruppens Serologi med Saerligt Henblik Paa Kapselformerne*, Nyt. nordiske Forlag, Copenhagen, chaps. 3–4, cited by Taylor and Charter (1952).
Koch, M. L., 1959, *Antibiotics & Chemotherapy*, **10**:364.
Kohler, W., 1957, *Z. Immunitätsforsch.*, **114**:282.
Kovacs, N., 1956, *Nature*, **178**:703.
Krickler, M. S., 1953, *The Serology of Proteus vulgaris*, Thesis, University of London, cited by Story (1954).
Lautrop, H., 1956, *Acta Pathol. Microbiol. Scand.*, **38**:481.
Laurell, G., 1952, *ibid.*, **31**:1.
LeNoc, P., and Moustardier, G., 1958, *Ann. Inst. Pasteur*, **94**:435.
Leopold, S., 1953, *U.S. Armed Forces Med. J.*, **4**:263.
Liebovitz, A., 1954, *Am. J. Syphilis*, **38**:203.
Lilley, A. B., and Bearup, A. J., 1928, *Med. J. Australia*, **1**:362.
Linton, K. B., 1960, *J. Clin. Pathol.*, **13**:168.
Liston, J., 1960, *J. Applied Bacteriol.*, **23**:391.
Liu, P. V., 1957, *J. Bacteriol.*, **74**:718.
―――, 1961, *ibid.*, **81**:28.
―――, Abe, Y., and Bates, J. L., 1961, *J. Inf. Dis.*, **108**:218.
Loh, W.-P., and Baker, E. E., 1955, *A.M.A. Arch. Internal Med.*, **95**:74.
Lowbury, E. J. L., 1960, *Brit. Med. J.*, **1**:994.
―――, and Fox, J., 1954, *J. Hyg.*, **52**:403.

Lwoff, A., 1939, *ibid.*, **62**:168.

――――, 1959, Personal communication.

Lutz, A., Grootten, O., Witz, M.-A., and Schaeffer, A., 1958, *Strasbourg. Med.*, **9**:204.

――――, Schaeffer, A., and Hofferer, M. J., 1958, *Ann. Inst. Pasteur*, **95**:49.

Mackay, E. S. M., and Oxford, A. E., 1954, *J. Gen. Microbiol.*, **11**:472.

Mansson, I., 1957, *Acta Pathol. Microbiol. Scand. Suppl.*, 119.

Marmell, N., Shidlovsky, B. A., and Prigot, A., 1955, *Harlem Hosp. Bull.*, **8**:24.

Matthiessen, M., 1957, *Acta Pathol. Microbiol. Scand.*, **41**:247.

May, J. R., 1954, *Lancet*, **2**:839.

Mead, T. H., and Van den Ende, M., 1953, *J. Hyg.*, **51**:108.

Meader, P. D., Robinson, G. H., and Leonard, V., 1925, *Am. J. Hyg.*, **5**:682.

Miles, A. A., 1951, *J. Gen. Microbiol.*, **5**:307.

Millican, R. C., and Rust, J. D., 1960, *J. Inf. Dis.*, **107**:389.

Mills, G. Y., and Kagen, B. M., 1954, *Ann. Internal Med.*, **40**:26.

Moll, T., and Ingalsbe, C. K., 1955, *Am. J. Vet. Research*, **16**:337.

Moore, H. B., and Pickett, M. J., 1960*a*, *Can. J. Microbiol.*, **6**:35.

――――, 1960*b*, *ibid.*, **6**:43.

Morax, V., 1896, *Ann. Inst. Pasteur*, **10**:337.

Munoz, J., Scherago, M., and Weaver, R. H., 1949, *J. Bacteriol.*, **57**:269.

Namioka, S., and Sakazaki, R., 1959, *J. Bacteriol.*, **78**:301.

――――, 1960, *Japan. J. Bacteriol.*, **15**:65.

Nelson, E. L., and Becker, J. R., 1959*a*, *J. Inf. Dis.*, **104**:13.

――――, ――――, 1959*b*, *ibid.*, **104**:20.

Nelson, J. D., Whitaker, J. A., Hempstead, B. A., and Harris, M., 1961, *J. Am. Med. Assoc.*, **176**:26.

Neter, E., 1960, *Pediat. Clinics of North Amer.*, **7**:1015.

――――, and Shumway, C. N., 1950, *Proc. Soc. Exptl. Biol. Med.*, **75**:504.

――――, Zalewski, N. J., and Ferguson, W. W., 1953, *ibid.*, **82**:215.

Nyberg, C., 1935, *Zentr. Bakteriol. Parasitenk.*, *I Orig.*, **133**:443.

Oag, R. K., 1942, *J. Pathol. Bacteriol.*, **54**:128.

Oeding, P., 1946*a*, *Acta Ophthalmol.*, **24**:159.

――――, 1946*b*, *Acta Pathol. Microbiol. Scand.*, **23**:271.

Olafsson, M., Lee, Y. C., and Abernethy, T. J., 1958, *New Engl. J. Med.*, **258**:465.

Olitzki, A. L., and Sulitzeanu, A., 1959, *J. Bacteriol.*, **77**:264.

Oliver, W. W., and Wherry, W. B., 1921, *J. Inf. Dis.*, **23**:341.

Omland, T., 1960, *Acta Pathol. Microbiol. Scand.*, **48**:221.

Opsahl, T., 1961, *ibid.*, **51**:72.

Orskov, I., 1955*a*, *ibid.*, **36**:461.

――――, 1955*b*, *ibid.*, **36**:454.

O'Sullivan, D. J., FitzGerald, M. G., Maynell, M. J., and Malins, J. M., 1961, *Brit. Med. J.*, **1**:786.

Papavassiliou, J., 1960, *J. Bacteriol.*, **80**:138.

Parr, L. W., El Shawi, N. N., and Robbins, M. L., 1960, *ibid.*, **80**:417.

Paton, A. M., 1959, *Nature*, **184**:1254.

Peloux, Y., 1959, *Bull. Soc. Pathol. Exotique*, **52**:166.

Petit, P., 1900, *Recherches cliniques et bactériologiques sur les infections aiguës de la cornée*, Thèse, Paris. (See also 1899, *Ann. Ocul.* **140**:166.)

Petruk, G. F., 1959, *J. Microbiol. Epidemiol. Immunobiol.* (transl.) **130**:132.

Philpot, V. B., Jr., 1956, *J. Urol.*, **75**:562.

Piéchaud, D., Piéchaud, M., and Second, L., 1951, *Ann. Inst. Pasteur*, **80**:97.

Piéchaud, M., 1961, *ibid.*, No. 6, Suppl., p. 74.

Pike, R. M., Schultze, M. L., and McCullough, M., 1951, *Am. J. Clin. Pathol.*, **21**:1094.

Pittman, M., 1931, *J. Exptl. Med.*, **53**:471.

———, 1953, *J. Bacteriol.*, **65**:750.

———, and Davis, D. J., 1950, *ibid.*, **59**:413.

Plotkin, S. A., and Austrian, R., 1958, *Am. J. Med. Sci.*, **235**:621.

Powers, D., and Baker, E. E., 1955, *Antibiotic Med.*, **1**:570.

Richardson, R. L., and Jones, M., 1958, *J. Dental Research*, **37**:697.

Riddell, M. I., Morton, H. S., and Murray, E. G. D., 1953, *Amer. J. Med. Sci.*, **225**:535.

Ringen, L. M., and Drake, C. H., 1952, *J. Bacteriol.*, **64**:841.

Ritts, R. E., Mao, F. N., and Favour, C. B., 1957–58, *Antibiotics Ann.*, p. 774.

Roantree, R. J., and Collis, L. R., 1960, *Nature*, **187**:1045.

———, and Pappas, N. C., 1960, *J. Clin. Invest.*, **39**:82.

———, and Rantz, L. A., 1960, *ibid.*, **39**:72.

Robinson, G. L., 1951, *J. Gen. Microbiol.*, **5**:788.

Rocha, H., and Guze, L. B., 1957, *A.M.A. Arch Internal Med.*, **100**:272.

Rogers, K. B., and Taylor, J., 1961, *Bull World Health Organization*, **24**:59.

———, Zinnemann, K., and Foster, W. P., 1960, *J. Clin. Pathol.*, **13**:519.

Rogoff, M. H., and Wender, I., 1957, *J. Bacteriol.*, **73**:264.

Rosebury, T., and Sonnenwirth, A. C., 1958, in Dubos, R. J. (ed.), *Bacterial and Mycotic Infections of Man*, 3d ed., J. B. Lippincott Company, Philadelphia, p. 626.

Rosen, F. S., 1961, *New Engl. J. Med.*, **264**:919, 980.

Rosenthal, S. M., Millican, R. C., and Rust, J., 1957, *Proc. Soc. Exptl. Biol. Med.*, **94**:214.

Rowley, D., 1954, *Brit. J. Exptl. Pathol.*, **35**:528.

Ruebner, B., 1957, *J. Pathol. Bacteriol.*, **73**:429.

Rustigan, R., and Stuart, C. A., 1945, *J. Bacteriol.*, **49**:419.

Sahab, K., 1960, *ibid.*, **79**:789.

———, 1961, *ibid.*, **81**:346.

Sandiford, B. R., 1937, *J. Pathol. Bacteriol.*, **44**:567.

Sandvik, O., 1960, *Acta Pathol. Microbiol. Scand.*, **48**:56.

Sarkar, J. K., Chowdhuri, B., and Tribedi, B. P., 1959, *Indian J. Med. Research*, **47**:1.

Schafter, A. J., and Oppenheimer, E. H., 1948, *Southern Med. J.*, **41**:460.

Schaub, I. G., and Hauber, F. D., 1948, *J. Bacteriol.*, **56**:379.

Schneierson, S. S., Amsterdam, D., and Perlman, E., 1960, *Antibiotics & Chemotherapy*, **10**:30.

Schuldberg, I. I., 1953, *Am. J. Clin. Pathol.*, **23**:1024.

Sears, H. J., 1949, *J. Bacteriol.*, **59**:293.

———, and Brownlee, I., 1951, *ibid.*, **63**:47.

———, Janes, H., Saloum, R., Brownlee, I., and Lamoreaux, L. F., 1956, *ibid.*, **71**:370.

Sedlak, J., and Slajsova, M., 1959, *Folia Microbiol.*, **4**:229 (*Biol. Abstr.*).

Shapiro, A. P., Braude, A. I., and Siemienski, J., 1956, *Proc. Soc. Exptl. Biol. Med.*, **91**:18.

Sherris, J. C., Shoesmith, J. G., Parker, M. T., and Breckon, D., 1959, *J. Gen. Microbiol.*, **21**:389.

Shidlovsky, B. A., Prigot, A., and Turell, R., 1957–58, *Antibiotics Ann.*, p. 651.

Slanetz, L. W., and Bartley, C. H., 1957, *J. Bacteriol.*, **74**:591.

Spivak, A. P., Eisenberg, G. M., Weiss, W., and Flippin, H. F., 1957, *Am. J. Med.*, **22**:865.
Stanley, M. M., 1947, *ibid.*, **2**:253.
Stern, I. J., Wang, C. H., and Gilmour, C. M., *J. Bacteriol.*, **79**:601.
Story, P., 1954, *J. Pathol. Bacteriol.*, **68**:55.
Stuart, C. A., Formal, S., and McGann, V., 1949, *J. Inf. Dis.*, **84**:235.
Sussman, M., and Stevens, J., 1960, *Lancet*, **2**:734.
Svihus, R. H., Lucero, E. M., Mikolajczyk, R. J., and Carter, E. E., 1961, *J. Am. Med. Assoc.*, **177**:121.
Takeda, R., 1959, *Bull. Agr. Chem. Soc. Japan*, **23**:165 (*Biol. Abstr.*).
Taylor, J., and Charter, R. E., 1952, *J. Pathol. Bacteriol.*, **64**:715.
———, Maltby, M. P., and Payne, J. M., 1958, *ibid.*, **76**:491.
———, Wilkins, M. P., and Payne, J. M., 1961, *Brit. J. Exptl. Pathol.*, **42**:43.
Thibault, P., 1961, *Ann. Inst. Pasteur*, No. 6, Suppl., p. 59.
Thomas, E. E., and Baker, E. E., 1955, *Antibiotic Med.*, **1**:545.
Thomson, S., 1955a, *J. Hyg.*, **53**:217.
———, 1955b, *ibid.*, **53**:357.
Thornley, M. J., 1960, *J. Appl. Bacteriol.*, **23**:37.
Totter, J. R., and Moseley, F. T., 1953, *J. Bacteriol.*, **65**:45.
Townsend, F. M., Hersey, D. F., and Wilson, F. W., 1954, *U.S. Armed Forces Med. J.*, **5**:673.
Vahlne, G., 1945, *Acta Pathol. Microbiol. Scand.*, Suppl. 62, p. 14.
Van den Ende, M., 1952, *J. Hyg.*, **50**:405.
———, Don, P. A., Elford, W. J., Challice, C. E., Dawson, I. M., and Hotchin, J. E., 1952, *ibid.*, **50**:12.
Van Niel, C. B., and Allen, M. B., 1952, *J. Bacteriol.*, **64**:413.
Verder, E., and Evans, J., 1961, *J. Inf. Dis.*, **109**:183.
———, and Watt, J., 1953, *Bacteriol. Proc.*, p. 58.
Veron, M., 1961, *Ann. Inst. Pasteur*, No. 6, Suppl., p. 16.
———, Thibault, P., and Second, L., 1959, *ibid.*, **97**:497.
———, ———, and ———, 1961, *ibid.*, **100**:166.
Vetto, R. R., 1960, *J. Am. Med. Assoc.* **173**:990.
Villecourt, P., and Jacobelli, G., 1954, *Ann. Inst. Pasteur*, **86**:493.
Vineyard, J. P., Hogan, J., and Sanford, J. P., 1959–60 *Antibiotics Ann.*, p. 401.
Volkert, M., and Matthiessen, M., 1958, *Acta Pathol. Microbiol. Scand.*, **44**:278.
Waage, R., 1953, *ibid.*, **33**:268.
Warner, P. T. J. C. P., 1950, *Brit. J. Exptl. Pathol.*, **31**:112.
Watt, J. A., 1951, *Vet. Record*, **63**:98.
Weil, E., and Felix, A., 1917, *Wein. klin. Wochschr.*, **30**:1509.
Weinstein, L., 1947, *Am. J. Med. Sci.*, **214**:56.
———, Wasserman, E. N., 1951, *New Engl. J. Med.*, **244**:662.
Weiss, W., Eisenberg, G. M., Spivak, A., Nadel, J., Kavser, L., Sathavara, S., and Flippin, H. F., 1956, *Ann. Internal Med.*, **45**:1010.
Wensinck, F., 1961, *J. Pathol. Bacteriol.*, **81**:395.
Wentworth, F. H., Brock, D. W., Stulberg, C. S., and Page, R. H., 1956, *Proc. Soc. Exptl. Biol. Med.*, **91**:586.
Wetmore, P. W., and Gochenour, W. S., Jr., 1956, *J. Bacteriol.*, **72**:79.
Williams, R., Williams, E. D., and Hyams, D. E., 1960, *Lancet*, **1**:376.

Wood, W. A., 1955, *Bacteriol. Revs.*, **19**:222.

Wright, S. S., Potee, K. G., and Finland, M., 1954, *Am. J. Clin. Pathol.*, **24**:1121.

Wright, W. W., and Welch, H., 1959–1960, *Antibiotics Ann.*, p. 61.

Wynne, E. S., Old, J. W., and Cott, C. L., 1952, *Am. J. Clin. Pathol.*, **22**:267.

Young, V. M., Sochard, M. R., Gillem, H. C., and Ross, S., 1960, *Proc. Soc. Exptl. Biol. Med.*, **105**:638.

Yow, E. M., 1952, *J. Am. Med. Assoc.*, **149**:1184.

Zykin, L. F., 1959, *Zhur. Mikrobiol. Epidemiol. Immunobiol.*, (transl.), **30**:71.

CHAPTER 5

BACTEROIDES, FUSOBACTERIUM, AND THE MOTILE ANAEROBES

This chapter is concerned with a group of amphibiotic bacteria that appear to be obligately indigenous to the mucous membranes of man and animals. Included are the numerically predominant members of the human intestinal biota. Among the particularly noteworthy features of some of these forms, in the context of this book, is a subtle pathogenicity which usually requires, in addition to host factors, the participation of more than one bacterial species in characteristic mixed infections. These bacteria are strict anaerobes with doubtful exceptions. None form spores. They are typically Gram-negative, but variation in Gram staining has been reported for some varieties.

The literature on these microorganisms extends back to the youthful period of bacteriology in a thin but remarkably steady trickle, unbroken up to the present by drought or flood. Interest in these nonsporulating anaerobes has persisted apart from the main current of bacteriology; their students consider it notorious that most medical bacteriologists have often seemed to equate "anaerobes" with "clostridia" as though nothing else existed. Hence, despite a considerable accumulated literature over the years, the subject has shown the usual consequences of neglect, among them a forbidding nomenclature. The taxonomists have not always been helpful, and it is significant that practical bacteriologists, in some instances after heroic efforts to conform, have generally rejected their suggestions. A simplified grouping is attempted here, but a note of caution may be urged. The literature contains at least one Linnaean name for nearly every conceivable variant within this group, even though additional varieties, probably still uncultivated, may well remain to be properly characterized. The listing given below does not pretend to be complete on either count. Students of this book who find a bacterium that differs in one or more respects from the forms listed should consult the older literature and count slowly to ten before they add another name to the overburdened literature.

Historical

The history of these bacteria can be traced back with confidence to Leeuwenhoek, who described and depicted microorganisms from his tooth scrapings, in his thirty-ninth letter to the Royal Society on September 16, 1683 [Dobell (1932); Schierbeek (1959)] among which the form we call *Spirillum sputigenum* can be clearly recognized. The thread of the subject was picked up again some two centuries later, when Ogston, in 1880 and 1881 [Bulloch (1938)] "figured spirilla and fusiform bacilli in alveolar abscesses." In 1884, Miller described and named *Sp. sputigenum*, and a year later Loeffler (1884) described in calf diphtheria the pleomorphic species of bacteroides. Fusiform organisms, not clearly identifiable with the *Fusobacterium* of today, as well as accompanying spirochetes, were described in 1888 by Lingard in noma-like disease in animals, and in the next few years by Verneuil and Clado (1889), Frühwald (1889), and Rauchfus (1893), respectively, in a sublingual abscess, in ulcerative stomatitis, and in pharyngitis. In 1893 Babes noted a curved and pointed bacillus in scurvy and attributed to it the gingivitis and hemorrhage of the characteristic oral lesions. In another paper in the same year, Babes (1893*b*) found fusiform organisms in healthy mouths as well as in gingivitis. Plaut (1894) distinguished fusospirochetal angina from diphtheria and redescribed "Miller's bacillus," while Vincent, whose name is linked with that of Plaut in the history of fusospirochetal disease, saw what was probably true *Fusobacterium fusiforme* in hospital gangrene (1896) and later in the angina to which his name is attached (1899), in ulceromembranous stomatitis (1904), in the healthy mouth and intestine (1905*a*), and in mercurial and scorbutic stomatitis (1905*b*).[1]

Meanwhile, Bang (1890–91) observed pleomorphic bacteroides in necrotic disease of cattle, horses, swine, and other animals and in the intestines of healthy swine, and seems to have been the first to cultivate them, using deep cultures in meat infusion agar containing peptone and gelatin. In a subsequent report, according to Lahelle (1947), Bang and Stribolt obtained better growth by adding serum to this medium. They called the organism "necrosis bacillus." Schmorl, in 1891, isolated Bang's bacillus from an epizootic in rabbits of a noma-like oral and pulmonary disease. He cultivated it in deep inspissated sheep serum and on serum agar plates in a hydrogen atmosphere, demonstrated its pathogenicity for rabbits and mice, and described finger abscesses as laboratory infections in himself and an assistant; a similar mouse-pathogenic organism was recovered from the abscesses together with pyogenic cocci.

[1] For a scholarly review of the history of Vincent's infection see Hirschfeld, Beube, and Siegel (1940).

Pleomorphic bacteroides were first recovered from naturally occurring disease in man by Veillon and Zuber in 1897, and were further described and given the specific name *funduliformis* by Hallé in 1898. In the same year, Veillon and Zuber presented their procedures for isolating and cultivating the nonsporulating anaerobes and gave details of species recovered from otitis, mastoiditis, brain abscess, lung gangrene, dental caries, appendicitis, peritonitis, and bartholinitis. These included, with the specific names applied by these workers, *Bacteroides fragilis*, *B. serpens*, and typical fusobacteria (*Bacillus fusiformis*). The dilution shake-culture technique used by Veillon and Zuber was applied in the years immediately following by other workers, who confirmed their findings. Harris (1901) isolated a serophilic, gasforming variant of *B. funduliformis* from a liver abscess in man, and Lewkowicz (1901) found what was probably the same organism in the mouth of a healthy nurseling.

In a series of studies, Gilbert and Lippmann (1902, 1904) reported the recovery of bacteroides and other anaerobes, by the Veillon-Zuber procedure, in the extrahepatic bile ducts, pancreatic ducts, and Stenson ducts of dogs, and in cholecystitis in man. They suggested that these organisms may occur in groups as normal inhabitants of the biliary system and that cholecystitis may be due either to autochthonous organisms or to primary, or more probably secondary, ascending intestinal infection. Among other studies published during the first decade of the century were those of Guillemot, Hallé, and Rist (1904) on putrid pleurisy, including detailed descriptions of bacteroides as well as of anaerobic diphtheroids, streptococci, and veillonellae. These workers remarked the occurrence of such anaerobes on healthy mucous membranes and their presence, usually in groups of species, in all putrid gangrenous suppurations originating from the digestive, respiratory, or genitourinary tracts.

The historical thread of the motile anaerobes other than *B. serpens* is partly intertwined with those of the nonmotile forms and partly separate. Their motility sometimes went unrecognized when studies were based on fixed films; the organisms were evidently confused on the one hand with the common nonmotile fusiform bacilli and on the other with spirochetes—confusion not completely resolved even today! It seems worthy of emphasis that Leeuwenhoek saw and described motility. Dobell (1932) has suggested that he used a primitive darkfield device, a method otherwise unavailable in practice until the modern form was introduced by Landsteiner and Mucha in 1906. Many observers at the turn of the century nevertheless saw and described motile organisms, principally in the mouth [see Repaci (1912); Prévot (1940b)]. W. D. Miller is credited with some of the earliest observations, not only of *Spirillum sputigenum* (1884) as noted above, but also of vibrios (1890).[2]

"Spirilla"—the word remains ambiguous—were seen by Guillemot in 1898 in pulmonary gangrene and putrid pleurisy. The earliest clear records of cultivation of these forms seem to be those of Mühlens and of Repaci, both in 1909. The former worker described cultures of *Spirillum sputigenum* and also of vibrios of the mouth in the lower layers of horse serum agar. Using Veillon's medium, Repaci cultivated from the mouth a vibrio that produced no gas or odor, and in later studies (1911, 1912), a series of microorganisms described as flagellated spirochetes. These seem to have included *Spirillum sputigenum* and may possibly have consisted of variants of the one species; but, as will be noted, much remains to be learned about these organisms today.

Much later, Seguin (1928) recovered from the mouth a strict anaerobe which he identified with that of Repaci (1911) and regarded as the *Spirillum sputigenum* of Plaut and the other early workers. It grew in Veillon agar in 5 to 6 days, on serum agar in 24 to 48 hours, was peritrichously flagellated and failed to liquefy gelatin. Curtis (1913) isolated from uterine discharges on blood agar a motile curved anaerobic organism which appears to have been the same as the *Vibrio sputorum* of Macdonald (1953) and the vaginal vibrios of Moore (1954) discussed below. Similar organisms were described by Tunnicliff (1914) from sputum and by Olitsky and Gates (1922), Olitsky and McCartney (1923), and Mills et al. (1928) from naso-pharyngeal secretions. On the other hand, the motile organism isolated from tonsillar granules which formed rosettes and "test-tube brush" groupings as described by Tunnicliff (1926), who found it weakly Gram-positive, and by Tunnicliff and Jackson (1930), who called it Gram-negative, corresponds with forms seen by the writer and others in gingival scrapings but not with other cultivated organisms.

It is probable that this and other true varieties or species of anerobes, including some of those described from the older literature by Prévot (1940) remain to be rediscovered and adequately characterized. The motile fusiform bacillus defined below as *Fusobacterium girans* was clearly characterized by Prévot in 1940 and has been established by the studies of Macdonald (1953).

The distinctive black-pigmented organisms here termed *Bacteroides nigrescens* were first cultivated and described by Oliver and Wherry in 1921 and have since been fully established as a distinctive form. The

[2] Prévot (1940*b*) mentioned without giving the reference that Miller, in 1892, described a (presumably anaerobic) vibrio. A second edition of *Die Mikroorganismen der Mundhöhle*, published by G. Thieme in Leipzig in 1892, has not been accessible to the writer. In the first English edition (1890), curved oral bacteria mentioned, other than *Sp. sputigenum*, all seem to have been easily cultivated aerobes.

more ambiguous small filter-passing anaerobes recovered from naso-
pharyngeal secretions by Olitsky and Gates (1921) and called by them
Bacterium pneumosintes also appear to belong in the genus *Bacteroides*.

Bacteroides

The generic name *Bacteroides* was proposed in 1919 by Castellani
and Chalmers for nonsporulating anaerobic bacilli, and was restricted
to Gram-negative bacilli by Weiss and Rettger in 1938. Included
within this term as it is used here are a variety of other generic names,
among them Prévot's *Ristella, Capsularis, Zuberella,* and *Sphaerophorus*
[Prévot (1957); see also Breed, Murray, and Smith (1957)]; the
Necrobacterium of Lahelle (1947); and many others [see Dack
(1940)]. The closely related genus *Fusobacterium* is separated in accord with common usage. Bacteroides occur on all the inhabited mucous
surfaces but are most common and conspicuous in the lower intestine.
They were shown to be the predominant organisms of feces by Eggerth
and Gagnon (1933); see also Weiss and Rettger (1937); Misra (1938);
Lewis and Rettger (1940); Hehre and Sery (1952). Their concentration
in feces has been found by several workers [Riddell et al. (1953);
Ruebner (1957)] to average 10^9 or more per Gm, wet weight, often
outnumbering coliforms by 100 to 1.

Cultivation

Many cultures of bacteroides grow in simple media such as peptone
water after isolation, but wide variation in apparent growth requirements is found, and failure of subcultures is a common experience.
Strict anaerobiosis is essential. Isolation is most successful in enriched
media. Infusion agar containing 10 per cent sheep blood has been used
effectively by the writer. Finegold et al. (1957) recommended a combination of neomycin (200 μg per ml) and vancomycin (7.5 μg per ml)
in blood agar as a selective medium. Sevin, Beerens, and Spy (1948)
found that incorporation of tyrothricin, 2 mg per liter, in a gelatin-
containing medium permitted selective isolation of Gram-negative
anaerobes from heavily contaminated sources. Isolation from feces is
easily made by plating high dilutions. For isolation of bacteroides
from pathologic material, Beerens (1957) has used the Veillon-Zuber
deep culture technique, with a beef-liver (V.F.) medium containing
0.2 per cent glucose, 0.8 per cent agar and either 20 per cent bile or
1:140,000 brilliant green. Addition of sodium azide was used to inhibit enterobacteria. Preliminary enrichment in Rosenow's cysteine
medium [Beerens (1953–54)] was often effective. Many strains grow
well in fluid thioglycollate medium, preferably heated to expel dis-

solved oxygen and cooled rapidly before inoculation, then sealed with solid petrolatum. Initial cultures should be incubated anaerobically at 37° for 5 to 8 days, but after isolation many strains grow well in 24 to 48 hours. These and other sensitive anaerobes have been maintained in dry ice without subculture for many years in the author's laboratory [see Rosebury and Francis (1950)]. Moureau (1952) has lyophilized them successfully. For other media and methods see Smith and Ropes (1945); Lahelle (1947); Sevin and Beerens (1949); Lodenkämper and Stienen (1955); and Beerens, Castel, and Abraham (1960).

Classification

The bacteroides found in feces by Eggerth and Gagnon (1933) and by Weiss and Rettger (1937) were tacitly assumed by earlier workers to be distinct from those recovered from disease processes (and also, as previously noted, from healthy mucous surfaces), the distinction being presumably made by analogy with "pathogens" among better known groups of bacteria. Lewis and Rettger (1940) observed that 4 of their intestinal strains seemed to conform to the B. funduliformis of Henthorne, Thompson, and Beaver (1936). Strains from healthy subjects have not been shown to be pathogenic, while those from disease have often, although by no means consistently, been found so (see page 157). The difference is not clear enough to be given taxonomic value. There has been no adequate comparative study of cultures from healthy versus diseased sources, nor are methods of typing available to label individual strains. In the absence of evidence to the contrary, it may be assumed provisionally that the forms found in the intestine and on other healthy mucous surfaces are the same as those recovered from pathologic source materials.

The elaborate classification proposed by Eggerth and Gagnon (1933) on the opposite assumption was soon criticized by Weiss and Rettger (1937); and, indeed, Lewis and Rettger (1940) seemed to be moving toward the simpler classification that has since been implied in the practice especially of American and British medical workers, although seemingly by default rather than on logical grounds. A careful reexamination of the question leads here to a similar conclusion. The "species" listed are to be considered as a minimal array, with each probably a group rather than a precise category.

Bacteroides fragilis

The species designation B. fragilis is used here and in common American and British practice to cover nonpleomorphic nonmotile organisms that are distinctly saccharolytic and comparatively acido-

TABLE

BIOCHEMICAL PROPERTIES OF *Bacteroides, Fusobacterium,* AND MOTILE

	Motility	Hemolysis	Capsule	Odor	Gelatin liquefied	Indole formed	H_2S produced	Nitrate reduced	NH_3 formed	Growth in peptone water	Final pH in glucose	Milk
Bacteroides fragilis[a-h]	0	0	V	V	V	V	V	0		0_v	4.6–5.4	AC_v
B. pneumosintes[*,h]	0				0	0	±	0			5.5	
B. putidus[e,f]	0		0	f	V	+	+					P_v
B. funduliformis[b,d-j]	0	$+_v$	0_v	fx	0	$+_v$	+	0_v	+	+	5.6–6.5	A_v
B. serpens[e,k,l]	+	0	0	f_v	+	$+_v$	$+_v$		+			AC
B. nigrescens[g,h,m,n]	0	+	0_v	f	$+_v$	+	+	0		0	6.7	A_v
Fusobacterium fusiforme[f-h,p-r]	0	0_v	0	f	0	+	+	0_v	$+_v$	0	6.0–6.9	0
F. girans[f,k,t]	+			x	0	0	0_v	0_v	+	0	6.2–6.9	AC
Vibrio sputorum[r,t,u]	+	α		0	0	0	$+_v$	V	+			0
Spirillum sputigenum[r,t,v]	+			0	0	0	0	0	+		5.1–5.4	AC

V, variable; A, acid; C, clot; P, peptonized; f, foul; x, acrid; α, greening; R, resistant; S, sensitive; 0, negative.

* Based on 1 strain, reference *h*.

[a] Eggerth and Gagnon (1933)	[e] Prévot (1957)	[i] Lahelle (1947)
[b] Henthorne et al. (1936)	[f] Beerens (1953–54)	[j] Dack et al. (1937, 1938)
[c] Weiss and Rettger (1937)	[g] Garrod (1955)	[k] Prévot (1938)
[d] Smith and Ropes (1947)	[h] Sonnenwirth (1960)	[l] Steen and Thjötta (1950)

genic, with wide variations in other biochemical characteristics as shown in Table 5-1. Morphologically they are not distinctive, appearing as thin Gram-negative rods with rounded ends, singly or in pairs; some are slightly curved. Long forms may be found in cultures, but the filaments and bizarre elements characteristic of *B. funduliformis* are absent. Veillon and Zuber (1898) noted a tendency of colonies to autolyze like the pneumococcus and hence called the organism *fragilis.* Among the forms described by Eggerth and Gagnon (1933) that fall into this group, some were oval, some polar staining, and some encapsulated. Capsules on *B. fragilis* have been noted by Smith and Ropes (1945). Strains described by Weiss and Rettger (1937) and by Weinberg, Nativelle, and Prévot (1937) resembled small fusiform bacilli. Sevin and Beerens (1950) gave the following characteristics of 5 cultures that fit into this group: they showed growth as smooth colonies on a maintenance medium consisting of brain extract agar with salts, sodium pyruvate, and calcium pantothenate; little tendency to pleomorphism in poorer media; acidification of the maintenance medium; no growth in a citrate-tartrate-cysteine medium that supported growth of *B. funduliformis;* the requirement of a fermentable

5-1

ANAEROBES MOST CLEARLY IDENTIFIED AS INDIGENOUS TO MAN

Fermentation reactions

Gas formed	Glucose	Sucrose	Mannitol	Glycerol	Maltose	Lactose	Salicin	Arabinose	Xylose	Fructose	Galactose	Rhamnose	Sorbitol	Inulin	Dextrin	Inositol	Raffinose	Dulcitol	Trehalose	Glycogen	Penicillin
±	A	A	V	0v	A	Av	0v	0v	Av	A	A	0v	0v	V	A	0	A	0	0v	Av	R
0	A		0	0	A	A	0	0	A	A	A	0	0	A		0		0	0	0	
0	0	0			0						0										
+	A	Av	0v	0v	A	Av	V	0v	V	A	Av	0v	0	0	V	0	V	0	0v	0v	V
+	A	0	0	0	A	A	0		A	A	A			0	A		0				S
+	Av	Av	Av	0*	Av	Av	0		A*	Av	0v		0	A*	A*	0*	0*	0*	0*	0*	S
V	A	0v	0	0	0v	0	0		0	A	0v	0	0	0	0	0	0	0	0	0	S
+	A	A	V	V	A	A	A	A	A	A	A										
0	0	0	0			0	0												0		S
0	A	A	Av			A															

m Oliver and Wherry (1921)	*q* Berger (1956)	*t* Macdonald (1953)
n Schwabacher et al. (1947)	*r* Rosebury et al. (1950)	*u* Moore (1954)
o Burdon (1932)	*s* Prévot (1940)	*v* Macdonald et al. (1959)
p Böe (1941)		

carbon source; strong saccharolytic activity; and growth in the presence of 40 per cent bile.

Guillaume, Beerens, and Osteux (1956) reported that 42 strains of *Ristella* species that belong in this group formed as products of glucose fermentation, tested by paper chromatography, mainly acetic acid (per cent), 50 to 80, average 67; with smaller amounts of propionic, 11 to 45, average 28; formic, 0 to 12, average 5. Total volatile acids, estimated as micromols per liter, were 7.3 to 38.6, average 21.1. The findings were consistent except for 1 strain that produced butyric but not formic acid. Beerens, Castel, and Abraham (1960) found in studies of 180 strains that 10 per cent beef bile in a proteose peptone–yeast extract–glucose medium stimulated the growth of *B. fragilis*, had no effect on *B. funduliformis*, and inhibited *Fusobacterium*. These 3 groups were also distinguished by Beerens, Guillaume, and Petit (1959) by the products of their action on L(-)threonine: *F. fusiforme* produced both propionic and α-acetobutyric acids, *B. funduliformis* only propionic acid, and *B. fragilis* neither. Sonnenwirth (1960) [see Rosebury and Sonnenwirth (1960)] whose biochemical findings are incorporated in Table 5-1, found 6 strains of *B. fragilis* interrelated in hemagglutination and gel-diffusion studies; a seventh strain was serologically distinctive.

B. fragilis as here defined is probably synonymous with the *B. vulgatus* of Lewis and Rettger (1940), as Smith and Ropes (1945) have suggested, as well as with nearly all the other "species" defined by Eggerth and Gagnon (1933) and the *Ristella* and *Capsularis* of Prévot (1957). *B. fragilis* thus defined would be the predominant member of the genus, hence presumably the predominant bacterium, in the lower intestinal tract of man. Henthorne et al. (1936) found *B. fragilis* distinct from *B. funduliformis* in agglutination and agglutinin-absorption tests. Sonnenwirth (1960) also found pleomorphic and nonpleomorphic bacteroides distinct in hemagglutination and gel-diffusion tests. Katz and Hanke (1941) reported that growth of a strain of *B. vulgatus* at low O-R potentials in the presence of 3 to 8 per cent oxygen was associated with measurable oxygen consumption. Bacteroides in feces, presumably *B. fragilis*, were observed by Hehre and Sery (1952) to be capable of splitting dextran; these "anaerobic dextran splitters . . . outnumbered all the viable aerobic bacteria, including *Escherichia coli*, in 11 of the 12 specimens [of feces] examined." (See also heparinase, page 156.)

Bacteroides putidus

The specific name *B. putidus*, attributed by Prévot (1957) as a variety name to Tissier and Martelly in 1902 [see Weinberg et al. (1937)], is taken here to represent an apparently uncommon group of nonpleomorphic nonmotile bacteroides that fails to ferment carbohydrates but shows putrefactive attributes. Only 1 such strain was recovered from feces by Eggerth and Gagnon (1933), while Prévot (1957) listed 2 "species" with these properties. Prévot's species were studied by Beerens (1953), who found them identical except for the 2 characteristics (gelatin liquefaction and action on milk) shown as variable in Table 5-1. Bacteroides described as biochemically inactive by other workers [Henriksen (1948); Rosebury et al. (1950c)] do not belong in this group and are equivocal. Macdonald (1959) has suggested that these organisms may have been *B. nigrescens* unidentified because they were incubated too briefly. The exacting growth requirements of Henriksen's cultures are in line with this view.

Bacteroides funduliformis

B. funduliformis is the most widely studied member of this genus, having been most frequently implicated in disease. Under this species name we now include all pleomorphic nonmotile bacteroides, among them the *B. necrophorus* of the veterinarians—the "necrosis bacillus" of Bang and Schmorl—careful reconsideration having failed to lend substantial support to our earlier practice [Rosebury and Sonnenwirth (1958)] of listing the two as closely related species. Comparative studies of strains from naturally occurring pathologic sources in animals and man have shown that they cannot be distinguished morphologically, biochemically, or serologically [Dack et al. (1937, 1938); Kirchheiner (1939); Prévot and Kirchheiner (1939); Jonsen and Thjötta (1950); Beerens (1953)].

Animal strains have often been found somewhat less pleomorphic, but all the bizarre forms in each group have been observed in the other. Strains from veterinary practice have more often been pathogenic for laboratory animals, but pathogenicity is too ambiguous among these organisms to be used as a taxonomic criterion. To morphologic and pathologic differences Prévot (1945) adds the matter of habitat, which is again inadmissible as a criterion from the viewpoint of this book. The exotoxin described in *B. necrophorus* by Cesari [(1912, 1913); Cesari and Alleaux (1912)] found in the supernatant of 24-hour broth cultures, said to produce a "humid eschar" in guinea pigs, was also reported by Orcutt (1930). However, it has not been found by other workers [Christiansen (1921, 1922); Vedel (1929); Lahelle (1947)]. On the other hand, the evidence of endotoxic activity in the veterinary cultures described by Cesari (1912) has been supported by the finding of Kirchheiner (1939) [see also Prévot and Kirchheiner (1939)], who reported that a lipopolysaccharide antigen toxic for mice could be extracted by Boivin's trichloracetic acid method from both *B. funduliformis* and *B. necrophorus* so-called, using 1 strain of each. The antigen extract from each strain was totally precipitated by rabbit antiserum prepared against the heterologous strain. More abundant antigen was present in the *funduliformis* organism. The 2 cultures nevertheless cross-agglutinated completely. Laporte and Brocard (1939) also reported that *B. funduliformis* and *B. necrophorus* could be distinguished, in this instance by the precipitin reaction.

Walker and Dack (1939) found that 12 strains fell into 4 antigenic groups not correlated with source in man or animals or with pathogenicity for rabbits, and the data of Lahelle (1947) obtained with agglutination and complement-fixation suggest a diversity of subgroups or types. Of 3 strains studied by Sonnenwirth (1960) by hemagglutination and gel diffusion, 2 were related but not identical; the third was distinct from these two but showed curious relationships with a serologically aberrant strain of *B. fragilis* as well as with *F. fusiforme* and *B. pneunosintes* (see also page 165). Beerens (1953–54, 1954) has reported that *B. funduliformis* and *B. necrophorus*, otherwise identical, could be distinguished on the basis that the latter agglutinates chicken and sheep red blood cells while the former fails to do so. The economical hypothesis of identity seems indicated pending more definitive study of this question.

Among organisms described as distinct species or variants of *B. funduliformis* which seem to fit within the group here designated by that name are the *B. mortiferus* of N. McL. Harris (1901), said to have been serophilic; the *Leptothrix anaerobius tenuis* of Lewkowicz (1901) and the *Leptothrix asteroide* of Mendel (1918), as well as the *Actinomyces pseudonecrophorus* of J. W. Harris and Brown (1927). Branching, reported by early workers and responsible for the designation *Actinomyces*—a generic misnomer in any event—was found to be an artefact by Henthorne et al. (1936) and is denied or not mentioned in more recent reports [see Hülphers and Henricson (1942)].

Morphology. *B. funduliformis* is characterized by pleomorphism appearing more often in cultures than in material taken directly from natural sources, more frequently in fluid media than in or on agar, and more markedly with certain strains than with others. In natural materials the organism may be morphologically no more varied than *Haemophilus influenzae*, which it may resemble in Gram strains under these circumstances [Alston (1955)]. It is consistently Gram-negative and nonmotile. It may show small, thin, straight, or slightly curved forms, uniformly stained or bipolar, or may appear as typical fusiform

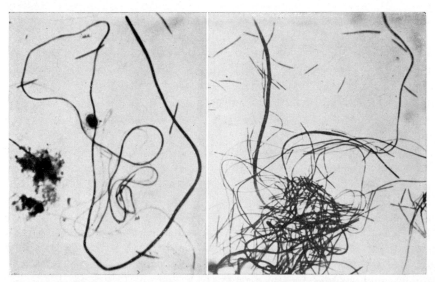

Fig. 5-1. *Bacteroides funduliformis.* Gram-stained preparations ×650. Left, a single very long filament of varying thickness, apparently originating in the tight coil or avoid body shown near the center. Right, tangled filaments and shorter forms.

elements or highly variable filaments. Often all 3 structures—rods, fusiform elements, and filaments—are present in a single preparation. The filaments may again be uniform or granular, with granules irregularly disposed or spaced with remarkable regularity; they range in length over extraordinary limits, 100 μ being common and as much as 700 μ having been recorded [Lahelle and Thjötta (1945)]; they may be straight but are usually bent or coiled, and a single filament may vary in thickness in different parts of its length from approximately 0.5 μ to more than 2 μ (Fig. 5-1). The characteristic swelling or spheroid bodies, with a diameter ranging up to about 4 μ, may occur at the end or in the middle of a rod ("funduliform") or filament, or detached as spheroplast-like bodies. This morphology has been compared with that of *Streptobacillus moniliformis;* and as with that organism, *B. funduliformis* has been used by several workers for the study of L-type variation (see Chap. 9). Electron micrographs of some of the structures found in *B. funduliformis* have been published by Smith et al. (1948) and by Jonsen and Thjötta (1950).

Dack and his coworkers (1937, 1938) reported that bizarre morphology could be induced irregularly by adding ascorbic acid, 1 mg per ml, to the blood agar on which the organism was grown. Filament formation (but not the development of spheroplast-like structures) was said to be induced with penicillin by Lahelle (1947) and with penicillin and tetracyclines by Fisher and McKusick (1952). Sevin and Beerens (1949) reported that spheroid forms could be produced by lowering the concentration of or omitting some of the constituents of a partially defined culture medium containing peptone, brain extract, glucose, citrate, pyruvate, pantothenate, and salts.

B. funduliformis has not been found to show capsules by most workers; but Shaw and Bigger (1934) observed encapsulation in smears of pus from human disease from which the organism was isolated, and Suter, Ulrich, and Vaughn (1955) reported the presence of capsules in smears from experimental liver abscesses in mice.

Biochemical Characteristics. The biochemical characteristics of *B. funduliformis* are shown in Table 5-1, with variations as reported in the literature. *Hemolysis* has been noted by most workers, usually complete and marked; but greening has also been observed. Dack, Dragstedt, and Heinz (1936) described greening in strains from human sources. In a later paper (1937), greening was said by these workers to occur only after removal of plates from anaerobic jars, changing to true hemolysis on refrigeration. Still later [Dack et al. (1938)], cultures from both human and animal sources were found to show greening, often changing to clear hemolysis after exposure to air for several hours [see also Chandler and Breaks (1941)]. Ruys (1947) has also reported

greening (on glucose blood agar), said to recede in successive subcultures. Lahelle (1947) stated that his animal strains showed true
hemolysis on human or rabbit blood and greening on sheep, goat, and
horse blood; but Jonsen and Thjötta (1948), working in the same
laboratory with Prévot's strains from human sources, which they regarded as identical with Lahelle's cultures, nevertheless stated that their
strains showed hemolysis on human, sheep, horse, and cow blood!
Lahelle (1947) reported the presence of a soluble antigenic hemotoxin;
but Sevin and Beerens (1950), whose strains were strongly hemolytic
on agar, observed no soluble hemotoxin in broth. Gesner and Jenkin
(1961) have found that a strain of pleomorphic bacteroides isolated
from human feces produced heparinase and could also degrade related
mucopolysaccharides (see also dextran, page 152).

Fermentation of glucose, maltose, and fructose has been reported
regularly but other test carbohydrates have been variable or negative.
B. funduliformis is distinctly less acidogenic than *B. fragilis*, but more so
than *Fusobacterium fusiforme*. Indole production was reported by most
workers. H_2S is regularly produced and most strains have a foul odor,
but an acrid or butyric odor has also been noted [Dack et al. (1938);
Chandler and Breaks (1941)]. Kirchheiner (1939) found that 1 strain
from bovine and 1 from human disease formed succinic as well as acetic
and butyric acids, and a trace of tartaric acid. Sevin and Beerens (1950)
reported the production of acetic, butyric, and lactic acids in fermentation; and Guillaume et al. (1956) found with 14 strains that butyric
acid was the principal product of glucose dissimilation, accounting for
31 to 56 per cent of the acids (average 45.5 per cent), and accompanied by propionic (24 to 45 per cent, average 37), acetic (6 to 29,
average 17), and sometimes by formic (0 to 4, average 0.5) acids.

Dack et al. (1938) stated that some strains produced acid (pH 6.6 to
6.9) or gas or both in the basal medium without addition of a test
carbohydrate; but the "group II spheropheraceae" of Sevin and Beerens
(1950) which appear to have been *B. funduliformis* (although these
workers suggested that inhomogeneity prevented final classification)
were distinguished from fragilis-like forms in failing to acidify the
maintenance medium, among other characteristics. According to these
workers the former organisms were polymorphic, growing as rough,
intermediate, or smooth colonies; they grew in a citrate-tartrate-cysteine
medium with the production of gas and a black sediment, and in 20 per
cent bile, but poorly in 40 per cent bile [Beerens (1955)]; they
formed aldehydes as well as indole and H_2S, were weakly saccharolytic and failed to coagulate milk [see also Disraely and Rogosa (1957)].
As noted previously, this organism was distinguished by Beerens,
Guillaume, and Petit (1959) by producing only propionic acid from

threonine, and by Beerens, Castel, and Abraham (1960) by showing growth unaffected by 10 per cent bile.

Pathogenicity. It was noted above that *B. funduliformis* is the member of this genus most frequently associated with disease. Veterinarians in many instances seem to look upon it without question as a pathogen, although failure to demonstrate pathogenicity with pure cultures [e.g., Hülphers and Henricson (1942); Ryff and Lee (1946)] has sometimes modified this view. The pathogenicity of pure cultures was demonstrated regularly for strains from both animal and human sources by the early workers, but results have been less consistent in more recent times.

McCullough (1938) successfully infected guinea pigs fed a vitamin C-deficient diet; and Dack (1940) considered that the success of early investigators in producing lesions in laboratory animals may have been due to presumably unsuspected dietary deficiency. On the other hand, Jensen, Flint, and Griner (1954), within more recent years, reported the experimental reproduction of liver abscesses in cattle by inoculating pure cultures into the portal vein.

While *B. funduliformis* is sometimes recovered in apparently pure culture from the blood in disease in man, and is often thought of as an agent of a "monobacterial" infection, its principal association with human disease is as a component of mixed infections. Both the clinical and the experimental aspects of such infections have been reviewed briefly [Rosebury and Sonnenwirth (1958); see also Weinstein (1960); Wills and Reece (1960); Tynes and Utz (1960); McHenry, Wellman, and Martin (1961)].

Serology. Antibodies have been found to *B. funduliformis* in agglutination and complement-fixation tests, in normal serum as well as in the serum of several healthy animal species [Feldman, Hester, and Wherry (1936); Dack et al. (1936, 1939)]. The titers have generally been low and seem not to have been increased in the presence of disease attributed to these organisms, although demonstrable antibodies have been reported to occur more frequently in disease [Dack et al.; see also Dragstedt et al. (1941)]. These findings should be repeated with more sensitive modern procedures, and the early report checked of Laporte and Brocard (1939)—of a complement-fixation test using as antigen an alcoholic extract of *B. funduliformis*, said to be useful diagnostically or for retrospective diagnosis. Naturally occurring antibodies to organisms of the fragilis type do not seem to have looked for. The report of Henthorne, Thompson, and Beaver (1913) that *B. fragilis* is serologically distinct from *B. funduliformis* has been supported by the studies of Sonnenwirth (1960) which suggest that *B. funduliformis* is serologically heterogeneous.

TABLE 5-2

IN VITRO SENSITIVITIES OF *Bacteroides* AND *F. fusiforme* TO THE COMMON ANTIBIOTICS*

Penicillin, units/ml	Tetracyclines, μg/ml	Chloramphenicol, μg/ml	Streptomycin, μg/ml	B. fragilis c	B. fragilis e	B. funduliformis c	B. funduliformis d	B. funduliformis e	B. nigrescens e	"Bacteroides" b	"Bacteroides" f	F. fusiforme a	F. fusiforme e
Reference / Not inhibited at higher concentrations				S	P[23]		S[3]P[6]			S[2]P[4]			
6.4	32	96	224										
3.2	16	48	112				S[5], STT			P			
1.6	8	24	56		C			S[3]	S[14], C[3], S[6]	S	T[11,3,2]†, C[9], P[45], S[53]		
0.8	4	12	28		S[23], C[19]	T	T[2], STP[4], ST[3], T[2]	S		P, P, S[2]	T[47,18,5]†, C[34], P[16]		P
0.4	2	6	14	C	T[9]			C	C[6], S[2]	C, T[2]	S[18], T[30,67,14]†, C[45]		
0.2	1	3	7	T	C[3], T[2]			C, P, T[2]	C[8]	P, C, S, T, C, T, P	P[27], S[17]		C, P, S[2]
0.1	0.5	1.5	3.5		T[12]								C[2], S[2], P[2], T[2]
Inhibited at lower concentrations								C[2]T[2]P[3]	C[5]T[22]P[22]	·C[2]T[7]P		P[15]	C[3]T[4]P[2]

S, streptomycin; C, chloramphenicol; T, tetracyclines; P, penicillin; **P**, etc., inhibited; P, etc., not inhibited.

* Each symbol = 1 strain; P[s], etc., = 15 strains.

† Chlortetracycline, oxytetracycline, and tetracycline in order.

[a] Lahelle (1947) [b] Fisher and McKusick (1952) [c] King et al. (1952) [d] McVay and Sprunt (1952) [e] Garrod (1955) [f] Lodenkämper and Stüenen (1955)

158

Antibiotic Sensitivity of the Group. Studies of in vitro sensitivity to antibiotics have seldom singled out *B. funduliformis*, and it is convenient to consider these data comparatively. The findings given in terms of antibiotic concentration by 6 groups of workers for the commoner antibiotics are assembled in Table 5-2, in which *B. fragilis*, *B. nigrescens*, *F. fusiforme* and undifferentiated "bacteroides" are listed together with *B. funduliformis* as such. The different antibiotic groups are shown in separate but superimposed scales which correspond only roughly with one another in terms of sensitivity but afford a basis for comparison. On this basis it is apparent from the findings that (1) strain variation is marked, particularly among bacteroides associated with disease (principally *B. fragilis* and *B. funduliformis*); and (2) *B. fragilis* is generally more resistant than *B. funduliformis*, especially to penicillin and streptomycin; while *F. fusiforme* is much the most sensitive to these and other drugs, and *B. nigrescens* somewhat less sensitive, especially to streptomycin. It seems suggestive of the strain variation, which forbids generalizing about the sensitivity or resistance of species as such, that although streptomycin is generally inactive in this group, instances of strain sensitivity to this antibiotic are evident. It may be noted that streptomycin has occasionally been used therapeutically with apparent good effects in disease attributed to bacteroides [Cressy et al. (1948); Wallach and Pomeranz (1949)].

The wide variation found within the group of undifferentiated bacteroides tested by Fisher and McKusick (1952) and by Lodenkämper and Stienen (1955) would be consistent with a finding that only *B. fragilis* and *B. funduliformis* were involved, and underscores the desirability of species identification. Beyond this, however, the need is apparent to test the strain isolated in the individual clinical case. For additional data on these antibiotics in in vitro tests with bacteroides, see Foley (1947); Ruys (1947); Schwabacher, Lucas, and Rimington (1947); Velu and Bouffanais (1948); Heck and McNaught (1952); Prévot, Pouliquen, and Tardieux (1954); and Stevens and Harrison (1958).

Garrod (1955) found that erythromycin was active against all 22 of his strains of *B. nigrescens* in the concentration range 0.015 to 0.5 μg per ml; the 4 tested strains of *B. funduliformis* were sensitive to 4 μg per ml; 8 of 23 strains of *B. fragilis* were inhibited by 2 or 4 μg per ml; and 2 of 5 strains of *F. fusiforme* were inhibited by 2 or 8 μg per ml. With polymyxin, Garrod reported sensitivity of *B. funduliformis* and *F. fusiforme*, some sensitivity of *B. nigrescens*, but complete resistance of *B. fragilis* at the concentrations tested. Bacitracin inhibited 21 of 22 strains of *B. nigrescens* at concentrations of 2 to 16 μg per ml but failed to affect the other 3 species. Berger (1956) reported that

F. fusiforme, of which he studied 6 strains, was sensitive to 10 to 20 μg per ml of nitrofurans but resistant to clinically applicable concentrations of neomycin, bacitracin, erythromycin, carbomycin, and polymyxin B. In a later paper, this worker [Berger (1958)] found 2 strains of bacteroides resistant to more than 100 μg per ml of oleandomycin. Berger (1959) found fusobacteria resistant to more than 100 μg per ml of vancomycin. Stevens and Harrison (1958), reporting on "bacteroides and similar forms" which were inadequately identified, observed among 13 strains that 3 were "very sensitive" to polymyxin B while 9 showed varying sensitivities to bacitracin. The latter finding, and the note that some of the strains were "irregular staining," suggests that Gram-positive organisms may have been included. Joliff and his coworkers (1960) included 2 strains of "bacteroides" in an extensive chemotherapeutic study and reported both strains sensitive to nitrofurantoin, chloramphenicol, oleandomycin, polymyxin B, and a mixture of novobiocin and penicillin. As noted earlier the relative resistance of bacteroides to tyrothricin [Sevin, Beerens, and Spy (1947, 1948)] and to neomycin and vancomycin [Finegold et al. (1957)] has led to the suggested use of these drugs in selective plating media.

Bacteroides pneumosintes

In 1921 Olitsky and Gates reported finding in Berkefeld-filtered nasopharyngeal washings taken during the first 36 hours of uncomplicated epidemic influenza, a minute anaerobic Gram-negative bacillus, growing in ascitic fluid–rabbit kidney media such as were used by Noguchi for spirochetes, and passing through Berkefeld V and N filters. They called this organism *Bacterium pneumosintes*. In subsequent years the Rockefeller Institute group published a series of papers on this and other Gram-negative anaerobes of the nasopharynx [Olitsky and Gates (1922, 1923); Olitsky and McCartney (1923); Mills, Shibley, and Dochez (1928)]. The early literature was reviewed in detail by Thomson and Thomson (1924–25).

Except for the property of filterability, which was part of the isolation technique used and was subsequently found feasible for the group, most if not all of these organisms clearly belong with the forms described in this chapter, and need no further mention at this point. The organism called *B. pneumosintes* is itself accepted as a member of this group but under the separate generic name *Dialister* [Breed, Murray, and Smith (1957)]. It is evident in the present context that the basis for such separation is dubious. The organism does not seem to have been reisolated or studied for more than three decades. It would have seemed worth no more than passing mention but for the fact that by chance a strain with this name, said to have come from

Prévot, was added to the writer's collection in 1958 and turned over to Sonnenwirth, who included it in his studies (1960). The results suggested an aberrant strain of *B. fragilis;* but aberrancy augmented the writer's suspicion voiced above that our catalogue of indigenous microorganisms may be incomplete. Hence this organism is treated separately. It is only for this reason and despite the failure of the evidence to establish a separate identity for *B. pneumosintes* that it is included in Table 5-1 and given the following space. It may be listed as a provisional species, *Bacteroides pneumosintes.*

According to Olitsky and Gates (1922*a*), *B. pneumosintes* on isolation grew only in media of the Noguchi type (see Chap. 6); but during cultivation for 1 to 3 years, 3 strains grew anaerobically in or on standard broth or agar media containing blood or other animal or vegetable supplements. It produced acid from glucose and showed variable morphology including spindle-shaped forms. The organism produced transmissible disease in rabbits [Oltisky and Gates (1923); see also Hall (1926)]. According to Mills et al. (1928), some of these forms, although recovered from filtrates of nasal washings, could generally not be filtered after cultivation, but in 2 of 3 attempts filterability was restored by passage through chick embryos. Similar organisms were isolated by Garrod (1928) by the methods of Mills and her coworkers. The writer has seen nothing in this record to separate these organisms fundamentally from the more fastidious bacteroides, such as *B. nigrescens,* except the matter of filterability which, having rarely been tested among known bacteroides, permits no resolution of the difficulty. Passage through Seitz and ultrafine sintered filters was noted by Huhtanen and Gall (1953) for a motile anaerobe from the rumen.

The pattern of biochemical reactions recorded in Table 5-1 for the strain of *B. pneumosintes* studied by Sonnenwirth (1960) is clearly admissible within the more varied pattern of *B. fragilis.* Soluble antigens prepared from this strain were, however, almost completely nonreactive with antiserums against *B. fragilis* or *B. funduliformis.* They were completely negative in hemagglutination tests, and negative in Ouchterlony plates except for a single band with the antiserum to 1 strain of *B. funduliformis.*

Bacteroides serpens

Bacteroides serpens, distinguished as a motile bacterium with regular morphology, growing in and liquefying gelatin, was described and named by Veillon and Zuber (1898) and noted by other early workers [Guillemot et al. (1904); Rist et al. (1907); Lewis (1911)]. This and other motile anaerobes found in habitats similar to those of other bacteroides have been grouped by Prévot (1957) into 2 genera, *Zuberella* and *Spherocillus*. Such forms, like *B. pneumosintes*, have all but disappeared from the literature of recent years. Patocka and Sebek (1947) mentioned *B. serpens* as a member of the anaerobic vaginal biota, and Steen and Thjötta (1950) published an extended description of a single strain of the same organism recovered from a cerebral abscess. The characteristics listed for this species in Table 5-1 are based on the last report and the early sources. The Steen-Thjötta organism occurred as uniform bacilli in cultures but appeared in lesion exudates in bizarre guise—as filaments and coarse spirochete-like forms—apparently in response to penicillin-streptomycin therapy. The strain was described as sensitive to penicillin. It showed peritrichous flagella and grew on "ordinary" blood agar, forming 1.5-mm smooth colonies in 96 hours under anaerobic conditions. Hoffman (1955) described a motile "fusiform bacillus" which resembled *B. serpens* in most respects other than morphology, but did not manifest flagella. A motile bacteroides-like organism briefly described by Macdonald and Sutton (1957) is evidently distinct.

Bacteroides nigrescens

B. nigrescens, distinguished principally by exacting nutritive requirements and the formation of a black pigment from hemoglobin, was first grown and described by Oliver and Wherry in 1921, who called it *Bacterium melaninogenicum*. The specific name *nigrescens* was suggested by Schwabacher, Lucas, and Rimington (1947), who showed the pigment to be hematin, not melanin. A persistent tendency to use the earlier term should be discouraged; priority is hardly more important here unless rules are to prevail over common sense (or age over beauty). The brief literature on this organism (in which, moreover, both terms appear) has in aggregate hardly enough mass to obstruct the substitution of a short precise term for a sesquipedalian misnomer.

B. nigrescens has been found in all the mucous membrane biotas: mouth, throat, male and female genitalia, and feces; and, as would be expected, has also been recovered from pathologic sources in these or associated areas [see Burdon (1928); Varney (1929); Patocka and Sebek (1947)]. Perez et al. (1956) found it in 10 per cent of cases of foot rot in sheep. It has sometimes been singled out as a putative pathogen, presumably because of its distinctive pigment; experimental studies [see Rosebury and Sonnenwirth (1958)] suggest a significant role in anaerobic mixed infections. The organism is pleomorphic, appearing as coccal or bacillary forms, with rods sometimes vacuolated or bipolar, and occasionally showing long forms or filaments [Burdon

(1932)]. It may show pointed ends [Cohen (1932)]. Shevky et al.
(1933) and Weiss (1937) described a capsule in exudates, but most
workers have found the organism uncapsulated. Spontaneous autolysis
may occur, especially in liquid media [Burdon (1932); Senos and Mattman (1955)]. On suitable media, preferably containing blood, e.g.,
hormone blood agar [Burdon (1932)], Bordet-Gengou agar [Shevky
et al. (1933)], or 5 per cent laked blood–tryptose–blood agar base
[Senos and Mattman (1955)] under anaerobic conditions, small,
smooth colonies appear in as little as 42 to 48 hours, becoming brown
and then jet black after 4 days or more, sometimes requiring 1 or 2
weeks for full pigmentation. Hemolysis appears as the pigment develops, and complete clearing of hemoglobin is seen after 14 days.

According to Burdon (1932) pigment formation is associated with
the decline phase of growth, and transfers are most successful when
made earlier, at about the fourth day. Schwabacher, Lucas, and Rimington (1947) extracted the pigment and identified it as hematin by
crystallization, coupling it with ox globulin to reconstitute methemo-
globin, oxyhemoglobin, and carboxyhemoglobin. They presented sup-
porting spectroscopic data. The hematin appeared to be united in the
cells with a bacterial protein.

Cultivation and maintenance of *B. nigrescens* are difficult. The organism has often been described as growing in association with a
streptococcus [Burdon (1932); Cohen (1932)]. Schwabacher and coworkers reported a requirement for CO_2 and noted that growth was improved by addition of either X or V factors, more markedly by X; but
all 7 strains studied showed small colonies on nutrient agar containing
peptone. Macdonald et al. (1954, 1956) were able to grow *B. nigrescens*
in Difco thioglycollate broth enriched with 20 per cent of a Seitz
filtrate of a broth culture either of a streptococcus or of a hemolytic
Staphylococcus aureus. *B. nigrescens* also grew in association with an
aerobic diphtheroid. A tendency of this organism to die out after
successive transfers, and failure to grow in enriched media [e.g., serum
brain-heart broth, Shevky et al. (1933)] suggest exacting nutritive
requirements.

In 1958 Lev reported that *B. nigrescens* isolated from the bovine
rumen required vitamin K. In a later paper this worker [Lev (1959)]
observed that compounds of the vitamin K group differed somewhat
in their activity toward a strain of this bacterium as compared with
their effects on animals: 1:4 naphthoquinone, inactive for animals,
was found active for *B. nigrescens*, while the reverse was true of
phthiocol, which acted as an antivitamin K for the bacterium. Many
of the synthetic vitamin K compounds showed unusual toxicity for the
microorganism. Gibbons and Macdonald (1960) found that the vita-

min K requirement of a strain of *B. nigrescens* could be satisfied by synthetic compounds having a naphthalene ring structure with an O, OH or COOH group in the α-position. They also reported that 12 of 14 strains from the mouth required hemin for growth. This finding suggests a link between this organism and *Haemophilus*, and perhaps further study will justify giving it separate generic status within the bacteroides-fusobacterium group.

The biochemical characteristics of *B. nigrescens*, as shown in Table 5-1, are subject to considerable variation, which may in part reflect difficulty in obtaining adequate growth in the usual test media. There is general agreement that the organism produces a foul odor and forms indole, H_2S and gas in sugar-free media. The fermentation reactions listed in Table 5-1 are those given by Oliver and Wherry (1921) supplemented by the findings of Sonnenwirth (1960). Burdon (1932) stated that carbohydrates were not fermented, while Schwabacher et al. (1947) found fermentation reactions impracticable because of acid formation in the basal media. Data reported briefly by Sawyer, Gibbons, and Macdonald (1961) suggest that variation in metabolism shown by organisms grouped under this head may justify dividing them into more than one species.

Cohen (1933) recorded the use of filtrates of *B. nigrescens*, apparently mixed with an anhemolytic streptococcus, for cutaneous preparation of the Shwartzman reaction in rabbits. Macdonald and Gibbons (1960) reported that this organism was able to liberate hydroxyproline by hydrolysis of collagen from guinea pig skin; the activity was present but not increased in unheated lysed bacterial cells. More recently, these workers [Gibbons and Macdonald (1961)] reported proteolytic activity of *B. nigrescens* for native collagen, gelatin, azocoll, casein, egg albumin, and plasma protein. Collagenolytic activity was found to be much weaker than that of *Clostridium histolyticum* and was associated with the bacterial cells rather than with the extracellular fluid.

Shevky, Kohl, and Marshall (1934) produced high-titered rabbit antiserums and found their strains homogeneous in agglutination tests. Weiss (1937) prepared nontoxic protein antigens from 2 strains by the methods used by Heidelberger and Kendall (1931) for hemolytic streptococci; the 2 *B. nigrescens* proteins were distinct by precipitin-absorption tests, but cross-reacted with an antiserum to group A streptococci. All 7 of the strains studied by Schwabacher, Lucas, and Rimington (1947) reacted in precipitin and complement-fixation tests with a rabbit antiserum prepared against one of the cultures. Soluble antigens prepared by Sonnenwirth (1960) from a single strain of *B. nigrescens* failed to react in hemagglutination and gel-diffusion tests with any of 5 *B. fragilis* or 3 *B. funduliformis* antiserums—a further suggestion, augmenting nutritional exactingness, of the distinctiveness of this microorganism.

Bacteroides of the Rumen

It is of interest that several species of bacteroides, similar to but evidently not identical with those of man, have been recovered from the rumen of sheep and cattle. Among them are organisms numerically prominent in rumen contents under certain conditions of feeding. In a review of rumen bacteriology, Bryant (1959) mentions 5 species:

B. succinogenes [Hungate (1950)], isolated from a 10^{-8} dilution of rumen contents, closely resembles the polysaccharide-fermenting strains of *B. fragilis;* it is actively cellulolytic and differs from *B. fragilis* especially in producing succinic acid from glucose. Bryant and Doetsch (1954*a*) reported that the organism would not grow without a factor in rumen fluid which they subsequently [Bryant and Doetsch (1954*b*, 1955)] identified as a combination of a C_5 to C_8 straight chain volatile fatty acid with isobutyric, isovaleric, or DL-α-methyl-*n*-butyric acid [see also Wegner and Foster (1960)]. Bryant, Robinson, and Chu (1959) in a study of the growth requirements of *B. succinogenes*, found biotin essential or stimulatory and PAB stimulatory for 2 of 5 strains. A strain of this organism obtained from Bryant was found by Sonnenwirth (1960) to react in hemagglutination tests, at low serum titers (1:20 to 1:80) with 4 of 5 anti-fragilis serums and with 2 of 3 anti-funduliformis serums. Two of the former serums showed single precipitin lines in Ouchterlony plates.

B. amylophilus [Hamlin and Hungate (1956)] was distinguished from other rumen bacteroides and from other species of the genus as a whole in that it ferments only starch and maltose. It was said to be similar otherwise to *B. ruminicola*, but has not been found encapsulated [Bryant et al. (1958)].

B. amylogenes [Doetsch et al. (1957)] was described as a slender curved rod that differs from other rumen bacteroides in producing large amounts of butyric acid, as well as acetic acid and small amounts of propionic and lactic acid, all from xylose, but does not produce succinic acid. These products resemble but are not identical with those obtained with 1 strain of *B. fragilis* by Guillaume et al. (1956; see page 151).

B. ruminicola [Bryant et al. (1958)] is another fragilis-like form which, however, like *B. succinogenes*, again produces succinic acid. This organism was said by Bryant (1959) to be among the predominant rumen bacteria in young calves. It was described as being often encapsulated, and tending to form round bodies in old cultures. It ferments glucose and many other carbohydrates with a final pH in glucose of 5.5, and liquefies gelatin but does not form H_2S or indole. The products of glucose fermentation include succinic, formic, and acetic acids. A subspecies *brevis* was defined by Bryant and his coworkers principally on the basis of ability to grow with trypticase and yeast extract substituted for rumen fluid. Bladen, Bryant, and Doetsch (1961) reported that a strain of *B. ruminicola* produces one or more of the branched-chain volatile acids required for growth by other rumen bacteria. Sonnenwirth (1960) tested soluble antigens prepared from 1 strain of each subdivision of this species and observed no interaction with either *B. fragilis* or *B. funduliformis* antiserums in hemagglutination and gel-diffusion tests.

A fifth variety or species of rumen bacteroides, a pleomorphic form apparently not given a specific name, was described by Bryant et al. (1958*b*) as a lactate-fermenting form producing gas, including hydrogen, and forming butyric and acetic acids and a small amount of propionic acid from glucose.

As noted above, *B. nigrescens* has also been isolated from the bovine rumen [Lev (1958)].

Fusobacteria

Generic Status

There is no more confused chapter in microbiology than that which deals with indigenous bacteria that are spindle-shaped or fusiform, yet all that is needed to dispel much of the confusion is to recognize that this description is not taxonomic—that all that is fusiform is not *Fusobacterium*. Here as elsewhere in the taxonomic hinterland of our science it is sometimes necessary to accept generic designations on grounds of convenience and usage rather than of logic. The genus *Fusobacterium* contains at present only 2 clearly recognizable species, *F. fusiforme* and *F. girans*. The two are as different as *E. coli* is from *E. freundii;* the first has close bonds with *Bacteroides* and probably belongs with that genus logically; but a long tradition and a short list of distinguishing features justify its separation. *Fusobacterium fusiforme*, the principal member of the genus and the organism that is (or ought to be) intended by the term "fusiform bacillus" in indigenous microbiology, has been confused with at least 4 other indigenous bacteria or groups of bacteria. These are (1) *Spirillum sputigenum*, the large, motile, flagellated organism of Miller and Plaut—still frequently identified as a "fusiform bacillus" in routine hospital smears; (2) certain spirochetes, which have also been confused with the preceding but have no relation to either; (3) *Leptotrichia buccalis*, a Gram-positive organism (see Chap. 3); and (4) several members of the genus *Bacteroides* which may assume the fusiform shape as noted previously. The generic term *Fusobacterium* [Lehmann; see Knorr (1923)] is preferred to *Fusiformis*, which was applied by Hoelling in 1910 to a group of aerobic bacteria found in termites.

Fusobacterium fusiforme

F. fusiforme is the fusiform bacillus of Veillon and Zuber (1898), whose description is compatible with the species here defined, and who applied the specific epithet *fusiformis*. This is the *F. nucleatum* of Knorr (1923) and of Hine and Berry (1937), and corresponds also with the *F. plaut-vincenti* of Böe (1941) and Berger (1956b).[3] It has been most completely studied and described by Böe (1941).

F. fusiforme is a small or medium-sized organism, usually less than 1 μ, sometimes less than 0.5 μ in widest diameter, varying in length over wide limits from approximately 4 μ to long filaments. It may be clear or granular, and the filaments may show regularly disposed granules. Its morphology closely simulates that of *B. funduliformis*, but funduliform elements, spheroid bodies, and the more bizarre filaments of the latter are rare or absent: *F. fusiforme* is less pleomorphic. Smooth colonies may show only uniform bacilli with tapering pointed ends, appearing singly, in tandem pairs, or often in bundles or sheaves of roughly parallel bacilli, especially when derived from a smooth droplet-clear colony in which internal crystal like masses or flecks appear (Fig. 5-2). Such colonies alternate with others that are rough or fimbriate and in which filaments are prominent. The organism is consistently Gram-negative, unencapsulated and nonmotile. Most workers have found it strictly anaerobic, but several reports suggest a capacity for limited microaerophilic growth after cultivation [Larson and Barron (1913); Slanetz and Rettger (1933); Bachmann and Gregor (1936); Spaulding and Rettger (1937); Malek and Malkova (1938); Illenyi (1939)].

Distinctive Characteristics

Fusobacterium fusiforme differs from *Leptotrichia buccalis* (see Table 5-1 and Chap. 3) in the following principal respects: *F. fusi-*

---

[3] Baird-Parker (1960) has suggested independently that this organism be called *Fusobacterium*, but perhaps because he failed to consult Veillon and Zuber (1898) in the original he used Knorr's specific names *nucleatum* and *polymorphum;* the distinction between the two is morphologic. It may be suggested that even if the species *F. fusiforme* as defined above should require to be split by future developments, the specific name *fusiforme* is valid for the type species. Omata and Braunberg (1960) also used the specific names *nucleatum* and *polymorphum*, but considered their morphologic differences minor and suggested that they be combined as 1 species.

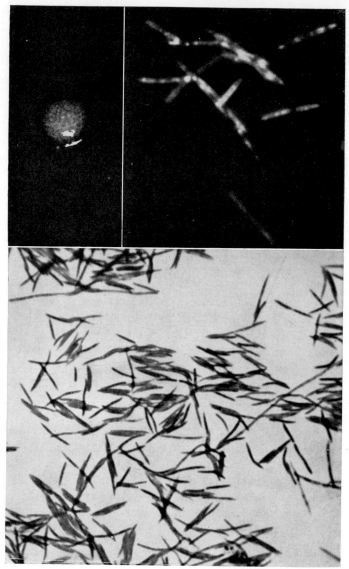

FIG. 5-2. *Fusobacterium fusiforme.* Upper left, typical smooth clear colony on anaerobic blood agar, showing internal flecked structure, ×6. Upper right, fresh preparation, darkfield illumination, ×1,200, showing paired forms and granular cytoplasm. Lower figure, Gram stain, ×1,000, showing "sheaves."

forme is consistently Gram-negative; produces indole, H_2S, and a foul odor; and fails to lower the pH of glucose broth below 6.0. The suggestion of a relationship between fusiform bacilli and spirochetes was advanced by Tunnicliff in 1906 and maintained by her for many years [e.g., Tunnicliff (1923, 1933)]. It was then withdrawn by implication [Tunnicliff (1938)]; but the idea is still occasionally repeated in textbooks. It was probably based on the occurrence of coiled or wavy filaments in cultures, some of which may have been *Leptotrichia buccalis*, and perhaps on confusion with *Spirillum sputigenum* or other motile forms. *F. fusiforme* seldom if ever shows helical forms and never shows motility.

F. fusiforme is less easily distinguished from *Bacteroides funduliformis*; the following points may be noted in addition to the lesser pleomorphism mentioned above:

1. *F. fusiforme* is less saccharolytic. It ferments only glucose consistently and does not lower the pH below 6.0 [Slanetz and Rettger (1933); Dicker (1938); Böe (1941); Lahelle (1947); Rosebury et al. (1950c); Berger (1956b)]. The strains studied by Jackins and Barker (1951), which were typical in other respects, fermented sucrose as well as glucose; while those of Beerens (1953–54) fermented glucose, maltose, and galactose weakly (as did their strains of *B. funduliformis*).

2. *F. fusiforme* fails to grow in peptone water [Lahelle and Thjötta (1945); Lahelle (1947)] or in 40 per cent bile [Beerens (1953–54); see also Sevin and Beerens (1950)].

3. Guillaume, Beerens, and Osteux (1956) reported that 32 strains of *F. fusiforme* produced from glucose more butyric acid and formic acid and much less propionic acid than *B. funduliformis*. The values for *F. fusiforme* were, in per cent: butyric acid, 47 to 85, average 67; acetic acid, 11 to 32, average 22; formic acid, 5 to 19, average 10; and propionic acid, 0 to 7, average 1; 24 to 43 μm per liter of volatile acids were produced, averaging 32.1. Omata and Braunberg (1960) identified lactic, acetic, and butyric acids as the products of glucose fermentation by this organism.

4. *F. fusiforme*, as noted on page 159, is consistently sensitive to penicillin, whereas *B. funduliformis* varies widely and is often markedly resistant.

5. A direct serologic comparison of the 2 forms was made by Lahelle (1947), who found evidence of an antigenic relationship short of identity. In both agglutination and complement-fixation tests, antiserums prepared against several strains of each species reacted with most strains of the other, but the titers of such cross-reactions were always distinctly lower than either the homologous titers or those obtained with heterologous strains within the same species. Sonnenwirth

(1960) observed hemagglutination with a soluble *F. fusiforme* antigen in only the lowest dilution (1:20) of one of 3 antiserums to *B. funduliformis*, and a single gel-precipitin band with a serologically atypical *B. fragilis* antiserum.

Hampp, Scott, and Wyckoff (1960) have reported an electron micrographic study of fusobacteria.

Cultivation. Isolation of *F. fusiforme* demands enriched media including serum or ascitic fluid. Slanetz and Rettger (1933) recommended the use of potato or other vegetable extracts and of crystal violet in isolation media; the dye in concentrations of 0.01 or 0.02 per cent greatly facilitates recovery of the organism from heavily mixed sources. Omata and Disraely (1956) have devised a useful although not highly selective medium for this purpose. Böe (1941) found growth to be favored by glucose (2 per cent), cysteine (0.05 per cent), or potato extract (15 to 25 per cent). Two to five days are required for initial cultivation; but after isolation many strains grow in 24 hours, and most of them grow well in fluid thioglycollate medium without enrichment. Jackins and Barker (1951) made use of a meat extract–peptone agar containing yeast extract, 0.1 per cent glucose, sodium thioglycollate, and crystal violet. Omata (1953) reported that an effective medium contained trypticase, yeast extract, sodium thioglycollate, and agar; and later [Omata (1959)] was able to grow the organisms in a basal medium containing acid-hydrolyzed, vitamin-free casein, glucose, and salts with calcium pantothenate, adenine, hypoxanthine, and 4-amino-5-imidazole carboxamide. In the presence of tryptophane, which was required for active growth, cystine had no effect.

Occurrence. *F. fusiforme* is often mistakenly assumed to be peculiar to or most characteristic of the mouth; it has merely been studied there most frequently. Vincent saw it in hospital gangrene in 1896 and in the mouth in 1899; Veillon and Zuber (1898) found it in appendicitis; and other workers have since recovered it from the healthy intestine [Vincent (1905)], the throat [Pilot and Brams (1923); Pratt (1927)], the genitalia [Pilot and Kanter (1923); Spaulding and Rettger (1937)] and under pathologic conditions from these and contiguous areas and others including the blood [Larson and Barron (1913); Grumbach and Verdan (1935)]. Unpublished studies show that the concentrations found in saliva in the writer's laboratory have averaged approximately 10^5 per ml, and there is no evidence of higher concentrations elsewhere in the healthy state. This organism is found in the so-called fusospirochetal complex; but even under pathologic conditions its concentration is lower than that of several accompanying organisms. In an analysis of an experimental fusospirochetal exudate from passage guinea pigs [Rosebury et al. (1950*b*)], fusiform bacilli [not all of which were *F. fusiforme*, see Rosebury et al. (1950*c*)] were estimated at the level of 2.3×10^9 organisms per ml in a total bacterial content per ml of approximately 8×10^{10} organisms. In other words, fusiform bacilli accounted for less than 5 per cent of the total; spirochetes were roughly seven times as numerous and streptococci outnumbered the fusiform organisms more than twentyfold.

Serology. Serologic studies other than those of Lahelle, mentioned above, have yielded little useful information about *F. fusiforme*. Some furnish evidence, not recognized by the authors concerned, of the distinction between this organism and *L. buccalis* [e.g., Varney (1927); Spaulding and Rettger (1937)]; others point to serologic heterogeneity within the species [e.g., Pratt (1927); Bachmann and Gregor (1936); Weiss and Mercado (1939)]. Antibodies do not seem to have been found in the serum of healthy subjects—perhaps a reflection of low concentrations of the organism on healthy mucous surfaces, or of insufficiently sensitive serologic methods; but antibodies have been found in serum under diverse pathologic conditions, including pleural empyema [Dicker (1938)], oral infections, and a finger infection [Lahelle (1945)]. Böe (1941) presented suggestive evidence of the presence of endotoxin in *F. fusiforme* capable of preparing rabbits for and of eliciting the Shwartzman reaction. Mergenhagen (1960) [see also Mergenhagen, Hampp, and Scherp (1961)] has also reported that fusobacteria contain soluble Shwartzman-reactive endotoxins.

Berger (1957) found 2 of 6 strains of *F. fusiforme* hemolytic, in contrast to the usual finding of inactivity on blood. Berger reported true hemolysis on agar made with rabbit but not with sheep blood, and of both rabbit and sheep erythrocytes in broth. Hemotoxin could not be demonstrated in culture filtrates. The organism did not produce leukocidin, fibrinolysin, plasma coagulase, or collagenase, and showed slight or doubtful hyaluronidase activity in whole cultures.

Other Species of Fusobacterium. Organisms described as fusiform bacilli under a variety of specific names include many that evidently do not fit within this species designation but cannot be assigned elsewhere with confidence. Among those described within relatively recent years with enough detail to make their distinction from *F. fusiforme* clear are the actively saccharolytic *F. biacutum* of Weinberg and Prévot (1926) see also Prévot and Kirchheiner (1938); Beerens et al. (1959, 1960); the *F. fusiformis* of Prévot and Taffanel (1942), which fermented a long list of substrates with a final pH of 5 to 5.5 in glucose and formed lactic as well as butyric and acetic acids; the 2 strains F41 and F47 recovered from a fusospirochetal exudate in guinea pigs by Rosebury et al. (1950*c*), which failed to ferment glucose or to form indole; the *F. hemolyticus* described as a natural pathogen of rabbits by Beerens and Gaumont (1952–53), and which was also included in the survey of fermentation products, using paper chromatography, reported by Guillaume et al. (1956); the indole negative fusiform bacillus of Brocard, Choffel, and Bouvier (1953) which fermented glucose, sucrose, maltose, and fructose but not mannite or lactose; and the fusiform organism RO-PR from the rumen described by Huhtanen and Gall (1953), which fermented maltose and fructose and gave a pH of 5.7 in glucose. Whether such organisms can be placed in other recognized categories or require separate status, in or out of the genus *Fusobacterium*, can be determined only by further study.

Fusobacterium girans

F. girans is a Gram-negative, strictly anaerobic, slender, variable bacillus, usually showing pointed ends, sometimes appearing as filaments, characterized particularly by a peculiar, elusive, gyratory motility, sometimes with slow translation, with no flagella demonstrable by any method used, including electron microscopy. An unflagellated motile fusiform bacillus was described by Shmamine in 1912; but the first full description of this organism was provided by Prévot (1940a), who cultivated 5 strains, 3 from feces and 2 from intestinal infections, and applied the specific name *girans*. Prévot was able to grow *F. girans* by Veillon's method and in glucose broth; he noted the occasional presence of spheroid bodies up to 3 μ in diameter, the formation of abundant gas including CO_2 and hydrogen, a strong, acrid, slightly aromatic odor like that of hawthorn leaves, and biochemical findings included in Table 5-1. The cultures appeared to be heterogeneous by agglutination. Prévot and Veillon (1940) recorded final pH values of 6.2 to 6.9 after 4 to 6 days' growth in glucose broth, and the fermentation products acetic and formic acids, ethyl alcohol, ammonia, methylamine, and traces of aldehydes and ketones. No lactic or succinic acid was found and acetylmethylcarbinol was absent. These observations suggest a metabolic pattern distinct from that of the other organisms considered in this chapter. Macdonald (1953) studied 5 strains of this bacterium, which he isolated from the mouth, and proposed that it be placed in the genus *Fusobacterium*. He described the motility as whiplike with slow gliding, and noted that many preparations failed to show motility at all. He also observed colonies on blood agar in 3 days that appeared as *depressions* in the agar surface, alternating with more typical small, raised, smooth or rough colonies.[4] Macdonald's strains, like Prévot's, were heterogeneous in

[4] Such depressed colonies were described previously among Gram-negative indigenous anaerobes of uncertain status by Henriksen (1948) and by Rosebury et al. (1950a, strain B13).

agglutination tests. They showed general biochemical agreement with Prévot's cultures, with variations indicated in Table 5-1. The organism studied by Beerens (1953–54) is also consistent with *F. girans*, but unlike the preceding, formed H₂S. Beerens listed *F. girans* as showing slight growth in 40 per cent bile (1+, as compared with 2+ for *B. funduliformis*, 3+ for *B. putidus*, 4+ for various "Ristella" here regarded as *B. fragilis*, and 0 for *F. fusiforme*). Berger (1956*b*) mentioned *F. girans* as saccharolytic and as motile without flagella; he and Macdonald et al. (1953) have published electron micrographs of this organism.

Anaerobic Spirilla and Vibrios

Classification

The curved, S-shaped or helicoidal flagellated bacteria of the indigenous biota are especially conspicuous in gingival material, both in health and particularly under pathologic conditions, when they appear among the so-called fusospirochetal biota. Their prominence depends more on their peculiar morphology and active motility than on their numbers, which are seldom if ever high compared with accompanying bacteria, including spirochetes; but actual counts of the present group have not been made. The existence of these motile bacteria, as was noted above, is traceable back to Leeuwenhoek, yet they remain among the least known of indigenous bacteria. Until relatively recent years, in fact, although several workers had evidently grown members of this group, the published information about them was almost all morphologic, with insufficient data to permit their classification. Indeed, the organisms described in these reports cannot be identified clearly today in retrospect [see Prévot (1940*b*); Gins (1942); Seguin and Boisvert (1942)]. In 1950 the writer and his coworkers [Rosebury et al. (1950*a,b,c*)], as part of a study of fusospirochetal infection, described 10 cultures of anaerobic curved bacteria, 6 of which had been isolated from a single "strain" of the experimental infection maintained in guinea pigs by transfer of whole exudates. The data given for 5 of these are sufficient to identify them retrospectively, 3 as *Vibrio sputorum* and 2 as *Spirillum sputigenum;* the latter identification was suggested at the time for the larger of the strains. Macdonald (1953), who continued this research, worked with 7 of these strains and a variant of one of them, to which he added 6 strains of *V. sputorum* and the group of cultures of *Fusobacterium girans* described above. Macdonald provided the classification that is followed here. These studies form the basis of our present knowledge of this subject, expanded by a few additional studies from Macdonald's laboratory and others as will be noted. The whole can hardly be said to constitute more than a start toward an understanding of these bacteria. Only the 2 species named can as yet be defined as indigenous to man, although many more are mentioned in the early literature. Distinct forms almost certainly remain to be discovered or rediscovered.

Spirillum sputigenum

Sp. sputigenum is a variable comma- or S-shaped crescentic or helicoidal organism, the smaller forms of which are characterized by a curious tumbling motility. Variation in size extends over wide limits, from organisms resembling the cholera vibrio to much larger single crescents and helices more than 1 μ thick, the helices having multiple (usually only 2 or 3) widely spaced coils. The ends are rounded and may or may not be tapered; they are never pointed. The Gram reaction is usually negative but residual positivity has been seen by the writer [Rosebury et al. (1950a)] and described for related rumen organisms (see below) by Huhtanen and Gall (1953) and by Bryant (1956).[5] Multiple flagella are present; their position has been a matter of controversy. The early literature [e.g., Repaci (1912); Seguin (1928)] speaks of peritrichous flagella; and the writer has seen and photographed peritrichous flagella [Rosebury (1942)] on the large crescentic mouth organism that is assumed to be the *Sp. sputigenum* of Miller and Plaut. Madlener (1958) has more recently described clearly identified cultures of this organism as having peritrichous flagella. Smaller forms and helicoidal forms, on the other hand, often show only a few flagella, which may appear at any one or at several points on the perimeter. In fresh preparations observed by the writer under darkfield they may, in fact, be seen to appear and disappear in turn in different positions, presumably as individual flagella combine and separate in and out of optical resolvability. Lessel and Breed (1954), noting that several workers had described flagella as attached on the concave side of crescentic organisms, related this species on that basis to an uncultivated organism found in the intestines of guinea pigs and other animals, called *Selenomonas palpitans*. Photomicrographs in an addendum to this paper prepared by Robinow [Lessel and Breed (1954)] clearly show the peculiar flagellation of *S. palpitans* from the guinea pig cecum. Lessel and Breed suggested that the bacterium of the mouth be termed *Selenomonas sputigena*, and that another organism, found in the herbivore rumen, be called *Selenomonas ruminantium*. Bryant

---

[5] See the suggestion of Bisset (1959) that anaerobiosis in obligate parasites may be incompatible with a "truly Gram-negative" status; Bisset and Davis (1959, 1960) would have placed *Fusobacterium* and *Bacteroides* with actinomycetes, and considered both anaerobic vibrios and spirilla as *Selenomonas*, i.e., protozoa.

(1956) adopted this name for the rumen organism, and we also accepted the generic name, albeit with reservations [Rosebury and Sonnenwirth (1958)]. The name *Selenomonas sputigena* has since been accepted for the oral organism by the Judicial Commission (1958). Macdonald, Madlener, and Socransky (1959) subsequently reexamined the flagellation of both mouth and rumen organisms in cultures and compared them with *Selenomonas palpitans* from guinea pigs, which could not be grown by methods used for the other species. In both cultivated forms the flagella were found to appear singly or as tufts at any point on the surface and not characteristically or exclusively at the concavity. These workers recommended that the generic name *Spirillum* be retained for the cultivated forms. Their findings are in accord with the writer's observations of these forms under critical darkfield illumination, which incline him to the view that they are bacteria rather than protozoa and should continue to be called *Spirillum*, as is done here. Park and Jeynes (1959), on the other hand, suggested from their morphologic studies of mouth material (which included electron micrography) that forms with "compound" flagella arising from the concave side comprise more than 70 per cent of flagellated organisms in such material, and that polar flagellated bacteria—true vibrios—are absent. Resolution of the controversy will perhaps require further study of the biochemical and serologic properties of isolated cultures.

The differential features of *Sp. sputigenum* are given in Table 5-1,

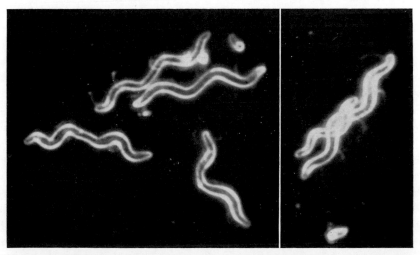

Fig. 5-3. *Spirillum sputigenum*, from a 24-hour culture in thioglycollate broth incubated under petrolatum; unstained, formalin-fixed in a gelatin mount, darkfield illumination, ×2,000, showing helical forms with blunt tapering ends and peritrichous flagella.

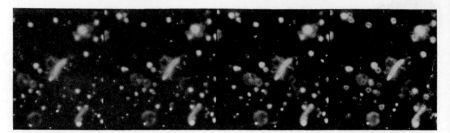

FIG. 5-4. Presumptive *Spirillum sputigenum* in gingival scrapings, from the writer's motion picture, "A Lecture on the Spirochetes" (1942), showing peritrichous flagella. × c. 700.

based on the studies of Rosebury et al. (1950*b*,*c*), Macdonald (1953), Macdonald and Madlener (1957), Madlener (1958), and Macdonald, Madlener, and Socransky (1959). These organisms have been found difficult to cultivate on agar surfaces, but once isolated they grow well in heated-cooled thioglycollate broth under seal. Macdonald and Madlener (1957) were able to isolate these organisms from the mouth in 16 out of 21 trials on a medium containing veal heart infusion [Proske and Sayers (1934); see Rosebury et al. (1951)], sodium lauryl sulfate [0.01 per cent; given by Madlener (1958), as 0.001 per cent], and sheep serum, 10 per cent. The second ingredient inhibited other bacteria, while serum was found effective in bringing about a rapid fall in oxidation-reduction potential at the agar surface within anaerobic jars, a condition evidently required for successful cultivation of the organism—it appears to be a more than ordinarily fastidious anaerobe. Macdonald (1953) found the 2 original strains to have identical somatic antigens by agglutinin absorption; their flagellar antigens were related but not identical. Madlener (1958) also reported strain differences in formalinized antigens.

Spirillum (Selenomonas) ruminantium

The organism called *Selenomonas ruminantium* as studied from the rumen by Huhtanen and Gall (1953; their "RO-HD" types) and more extensively by Bryant (1956) [see also Bryant and Burkey (1953); Bryant and Small (1956)] is evidently closely related to *Sp. sputigenum*. The RO-HD forms differed in producing abundant gas [noted as absent from *Sp. sputigenum* by Rosebury et al. (1950*c*)] and in their lower final pH (4.9) in glucose. In addition, the RO-HD forms fermented maltose and fructose and, in some instances, sucrose, dextrin, and starch; lactose was also variable; litmus milk was reduced and variably acidified and clotted. Bryant (1956) expressed the opinion that *S. ruminantium* differed from *Sp. sputigenum* only in that the former produced H_2S; but this worker, who studied 11 strains including 3 from Gall, provided far more information on them than is available for the oral organisms. Ten of the rumen strains, in addition to producing H_2S, gave minimum pH values in a poorly buffered glucose medium of 4.3 or 4.4; all 11 fermented xylose, arabinose, galactose, fructose, lactose, maltose, and cellobiose as well as glucose. Fermentation was variable in sucrose, trehalose, glycerol, mannite, dextrin, inulin, salicin, and esculin; a few strains hydrolyzed starch. Of the 10 principal strains none fermented xylan, and none of the 11 produced catalase or indole, liquefied gelatin, produced acid from gum arabic or pectin, or hydrolyzed cellulose.

The products of glucose fermentation as tested for 9 strains showed considerable variation. Lactic acid was conspicuous in 7 but absent in 1; varying amounts of acetic, propionic, succinic, butyric, and formic acids were produced, with CO_2 but no hydrogen. Three of the ten strains fermented lactate with the production of propionic and acetic acids, a fermentation similar to that of *Propionibacterium*. The eleventh strain failed to form H_2S, gave a terminal pH level in glucose of 5.2, fermented xylan, did not ferment lactate, and produced mainly butyric, lactic, and formic acids from glucose. Except for failure to reduce nitrate (a property found with three HD strains of Gall but not with the others), this exceptional culture seems to resemble *Sp. sputigenum* closely [see also Bryant (1959); Hobson and Mann (1961)].

Vibrio sputorum

V. sputorum is the name given by Prévot (1940*b*) to 1 of 2 vibrios that failed to ferment glucose—the one recovered from bronchial secretions by Tunnicliff in 1914. Prévot applied the name *V. mulieris* to the other form, which had been isolated from the vagina by Curtis in 1913. The two organisms seemed to differ in flagellation—that of Tunnicliff being described as monotrichate, that of Curtis as having 2 to 6 flagella. Similar vibrios, as noted above, were isolated from the mouth and described, but not named, by Rosebury et al. (1950), and the same cultures with additional oral isolations were restudied by Macdonald (1953), who adopted for them the name *V. sputorum*. Moore (1954), who studied 10 strains of what was clearly the same organism isolated from the vagina, has provided the most complete description thus far available; he related the organism to that of Curtis and considered, from the evidence in his paper, " . . . that Curtis' vibrio may have been monotrichate in spite of his statement to the contrary." To avoid confusion, the name *V. sputorum* is retained here tentatively and without prejudice.

V. sputorum is a small organism, straight or curved, often strongly crescentic, with pointed ends, occurring singly or in pairs or short chains, sometimes in clusters. It is usually Gram-negative, but Moore noted a dense central area, usually Gram-positive, both in direct vaginal smears and in cultures on 5 per cent blood agar; on 20 per cent serum agar the organism showed faint even Gram positivity. This worker described the motility of the organism as follows: "Single organisms in wet preparations show a very rapid corkscrew motion, the axis of progression being usually elliptical, so that a single vibrio may, although rapidly motile, remain for some considerable time within one microscopic field. This rapid movement is punctuated by sudden halts, followed by resumption of the previous trajectory or sometimes by a reversal of direction."

The organism has a single flagellum usually attached at or near the pole, sometimes in the concavity. Motility is lost rapidly on exposure to air. $V.$ $sputorum$ is strictly anaerobic. It requires CO_2 for primary isolation but not for later subculture. It is distinguished especially by its failure to form acid from glucose or other substrates, and by the other characteristics listed in Table 5-1. Moore's cultures grew well on veal-extract agar with horse, human, sheep, or guinea pig blood, better with 15 per cent than with 5 per cent blood. When grown in 10 per cent CO_2 they formed colonies surrounded by an olive-green zone 4 mm in diameter. In 4 to 6 days small colonies, either smooth or rough (effuse, matt) appeared, the latter consisting of more pleomorphic vibrios. Good growth developed in 2 days in thioglycollate medium containing 10 per cent serum, and in the Tween albumin fluid medium of Dubos and Middlebrook (1947), especially when the albumin concentration was doubled. No growth was obtained in nutrient broth without serum. The strains studied by the writer and by Macdonald (1953) grew poorly in fluid media, including thioglycollate, even when enriched with ascitic fluid and sterile extract of guinea pig kidney. Serologic studies reported by Macdonald (1953) and by Moore (1954) suggest heterogeneity of flagellar antigens. Moore found that 6 strains tested were sensitive to penicillin, streptomycin, chlortetracycline, and chloramphenicol.

Mashimo and Ellison (1959) have described a method which they found useful for isolation of both $Sp.$ $sputigenum$ and $V.$ $sputorum$, consisting of stab inoculation into tubes of 0.3 per cent agar in trypticase soy medium with anaerobic incubation, and isolation by breaking the tube and removing colonies with a capillary pipet.

Vibrios of the Rumen

Anaerobic vibrios distinct from the preceding by virtue especially of active fermentative capacity have been isolated from the rumen of cattle and sheep and well characterized [see Hungate (1950); Huhtanen, Rogers, and Gall (1952); Bryant and Burkey (1953); Huhtanen and Gall (1953); Bryant and Small (1956); see also Bryant (1959)]. It is of interest that saccharolytic vibrios (or spirilla) were described as indigenous to man in the early literature [summarized by Prévot (1948, 1957)] but not in recent years with an exception to be noted. The following abbreviated descriptions are taken principally from the two papers by Bryant and Small (1956).

Butyrivibrio fibrosolvens (perhaps the same as the filter-passing RO-H organisms of Huhtanen and Gall (1953) mentioned on page 161 and *Succinivibrio dextrinosolvens* are Gram-negative anaerobes similar in morphology to *V. sputorum*; both are active fermenters of a wide range of substrates. The 2 species differ in several respects, among them in the products of their fermentation, as the names imply. The former produces large amounts of butyric acid and is considered responsible for much of the concentration of that acid found in the rumen; the latter forms large amounts of succinic and acetic acids. The fermentation of *Butyrivibrio* has been studied by Lee and Moore (1959). Of particular interest is a report from members of this group [Brown and Moore (1960)] of the isolation of *B. fibrosolvens* from human feces. These vibrios were isolated in 2 of 7 trials from 10^{-6} dilutions of fecal material by anaerobic techniques used by Hungate (1950) for isolation of rumen organisms. They were also isolated from 10^{-6} dilutions of rabbit and horse feces. A comparison of concentrations of butyric and other fatty acids produced by these vibrios in rumen fluid glucose medium with concentrations of the same acids in human feces suggested that this vibrio may contribute materially to fermentative activity in the human intestinal tract. These observations call for confirmation and extension.

Lachnospira multiparus is another anaerobic vibrio, morphologically similar to the preceding, but showing many Gram-positive cells in young cultures, rapidly becoming Gram-negative. The fermentation products of this species include ethyl alcohol, lactic, formic, and acetic acids and CO_2, with a small amount of hydrogen [Bryant and Small (1956*b*)].

References

Alston, J. M., 1955, *Brit. Med. J.*, **2**:1524.
Babes, V., 1893*a*, *Deut. Med. Wochschr.*, No. 43, 1035.
———, 1893*b*, *Arch. Méd. Expér. et. Anat. Pathol.*, **5**:607.
Bachmann, W., and Gregor, H., 1936, Z. *Immunitätsforsch.*, **87**:238.
Baird-Parker, A. C., 1960, *J. Gen. Microbiol.*, **22**:458.
Bang, B., 1890–91, *Maanedskr. Dyrlaeger*, **2**:235, cited by Lahelle (1947).

Bang and Stribolt, cited by Lahelle (1947).

Beerens, H., 1953–54, *Ann. Inst. Pasteur Lille*, **6**:36.

———, 1954, *Ann. Inst. Pasteur*, **86**:384.

———, 1957, *Ann. Inst. Pasteur Lille*, **9**:86.

———, Castel, M. M., and Abraham, R., 1960, *Ann. Inst. Pasteur*, **99**:454.

———, and Gaumont, R., 1952–53, *Ann. Inst. Pasteur Lille*, **5**:113.

———, Guillaume, J., and Petit, H., 1959, *Ann. Inst. Pasteur*, **96**:211.

Berger, U., 1956a, *Arch. Hyg. u. Bakteriol.*, **140**:288.

———, 1956b, *Zentr. Bakteriol. Parasitenk.*, *I Orig.*, **166**:484.

———, 1957, *ibid.*, **167**:372.

———, 1958, *Z. Hyg. Infektionskrankh.*, **145**:1.

———, 1959, *Arch. Hyg., u. Bakteriol.*, **143**:316.

Bisset, K. A., 1959, *Nature*, **183**:29.

———, and Davis, G. H. G., 1959, *Arch. Oral Biol.*, **1**:80.

———, and ———, 1960, *The Microbial Flora of the Mouth*, Heywood & Company, Ltd., London.

Bladen, H. A., Bryant, M. P., and Doetsch, R. N., 1961, *J. Dairy Sci.*, **44**:173.

Böe, J., 1941, *Fusobacterium: Studies on Its Bacteriology, Serology and Pathogenicity, Skrifter Norske Videnskaps-Akad. Oslo, I., Mat.-Naturv. Kl.*, no. 9.

Breed, R. S., Murray, E. G. D., and Smith, N. R., 1957, *Bergey's Manual of Determinative Bacteriology*, 7th ed., The Williams & Wilkins Company, Baltimore.

Brocard, H., Choffel, C., and Bouvier, M., 1954, *J. Franc. Méd. et Chir. Thorac.*, **8**:1.

Brown, D. W., and Moore, W. E. C., 1960, *J. Dairy Sci.*, **43**:1570.

Bryant, M. P., 1956, *J. Bacteriol.*, **72**:162.

———, 1959, *Bacteriol. Revs.*, **23**:125.

———, and Burkey, L. A., 1953, *J. Dairy Sci.*, **36**:205.

———, and Doetsch, R. N., 1954a, *ibid.*, **37**:1176.

———, and ———, 1954b, *Science*, **120**:3127.

———, and ———, 1955, *J. Dairy Sci.*, **38**:340.

———, Robinson, I. M., and Chu, H., 1959, *ibid.*, **42**:1831.

———, and Small, N., 1956a, *J. Bacteriol.*, **72**:16.

———, and ———, 1956b, *ibid.*, **72**:22.

———, ———, Bouma, C., and Chu, H., 1958, *ibid.*, **76**:15.

———, ———, ———, and Robinson, I. M., 1958b, *J. Dairy Sci.*, **41**:1747.

Bulloch, W., 1938, *The History of Bacteriology*, Oxford University Press, New York.

Burdon, K. L., 1928, *J. Inf. Dis.*, **42**:161.

———, 1932, *Proc. Soc. Exptl. Biol. Med.*, **29**:1144.

Castellani, A., and Chalmers, A. J., 1919, *Manual of Tropical Medicine*, 3d ed., William Wood & Company, Baltimore.

Cesari, E., 1912, *Ann. Inst. Pasteur*, **26**:802.

———, 1913, *ibid.*, **27**:230.

———, and Alleaux, V., 1912, *ibid.*, **26**:652.

Chandler, F. A., and Breaks, V. M., 1941, *J. Am. Med. Assoc.*, **116**:2390.

Christiansen, M., 1921–22, *Maanedskr. Dyrlaeger*, **33**:557, cited by Lahelle (1947).

———, 1921, *Compt. Rend. Soc. Biol.*, **84**:643.

Cohen, J., 1932, *A.M.A. Arch. Surg.*, **24**:171.

————, 1933, *J. Inf. Dis.*, **52**:185.

Cressy, N. L., Lahey, W. J., and Kunkel, P., 1948, *New Engl. J. Med.*, **239**: 497.

Curtis, A. H., 1913, *J. Inf. Dis.*, **12**:165.

Dack, G. M., 1940, *Bacteriol. Revs.*, **4**:227.

————, Dragstedt, L. R., and Heinz, T. E., 1936, *J. Am. Med. Assoc.*, **106**:7.

————, ————, and ————, 1937, *J. Inf. Dis.*, **60**:335.

————, Dragstedt, L. R., Johnson, R., and McCullough, N. B., 1938, *ibid.*, **62**:169.

————, Kirsner, J. B., Dragstedt, L. R., and Johnson, R., 1939, *ibid.*, **65**:200.

Dicker, H., 1938, *Zentr. Bakteriol. Parasitenk., I Orig.*, **141**:37.

Disraely, M. N., and Rogosa, M., 1957, *Prepr. Abstr. Internat. Assoc. Dental Research*, No. 122.

Dobell, C., 1932, *Antony van Leeuwenhoek and His "Little Animals,"* Harcourt, Brace and Company, New York, reprinted 1960, Dover Publications, New York.

Doetsch, R. N., Howard, B. H., Mann, S. O., and Oxford, A. E., 1957, *J. Gen. Microbiol.*, **16**:156.

Dragstedt, L. R., Dack, G. M., and Kirsner, J. B., 1941, *Ann. Surg.*, **114**: 653.

Dubos, R. J., and Middlebrook, G., 1947, *Am. Rev. Tuberc.*, **56**:334.

Eggerth, A. H., and Gagnon, B. H., 1933, *J. Bacteriol.*, **25**:389.

Feldman, W. H., Hester, H. R., and Wherry, F. P., 1936, *J. Inf. Dis.*, **59**: 159.

Finegold, S. M., Siewert, L. A., and Hewitt, W. L., 1957, *Bacteriol. Proc.*, p. 59.

Fisher, A. M., and McKusick, V. A., 1952, *Trans. Am. Clin. Climatol. Assoc.*, **4**:1.

Foley, G. E., 1947, *Science*, **106**:423.

Frühwald, F., 1889, *Jahrb. Kinderheilk.*, **29**:200.

Garrod, L. P., 1928, *Brit. J. Exptl. Pathol.*, **9**:155.

————, 1955, *Brit. Med. J.*, **2**:1529.

Gesner, B. M., and Jenkin, C. R., 1961, *J. Bacteriol.*, **81**:595.

Gibbons, R. J., and Macdonald, J. B., 1960, *ibid.*, **80**:164.

————, and ————, 1961, *ibid.*, **81**:614.

Gilbert, A., and Lippmann, A., 1902, *Compt. Rend. Soc. Biol.*, **54**:718, 989, 1189.

————, and ————, 1904, *ibid.*, **56**:139, 374.

Gins, H., 1942, *Z. Hyg. Infektionskrankh.*, **124**:460

Grumbach, A., and Verdan, C., 1935, *Arch. Hyg. u. Bakteriol.*, **115**:115.

Guillaume, J., Beerens, H., and Osteux, R., 1956, *Ann. Inst. Pasteur*, **90**:229.

Guillemot, L. J. B., 1898, *Récherches sur la gangrene pulmonaire*, Thèse de Paris.

————, Hallé, J., and Rist, E., 1904, *Arch. Méd. Expér. et Anat. Pathol.*, **16**: 571, 677.

Hall, M. W., 1926, *J. Exptl. Med.*, **44**:539.

Hallé, J., 1898, *Récherches de la bacteriologie du canal génital de la femme*, Thèse de Paris.

Hamlin, L. J., and Hungate, R. E., 1956, *J. Bacteriol.*, **72**:548.

Hampp, E. G., Scott, D. B., and Wyckoff, R. W. G., 1960, *ibid.*, **79**:716.

Harris, J. W., and Brown, J. H., 1927, *Bull. Johns Hopkins Hosp.*, **40**:203.

Harris, N. McL., 1901, *J. Exptl. Med.*, **6**:519.
Heck, W. E., and McNaught, R. C., 1952, *J. Am. Med. Assoc.*, **149**:662.
Hehre, E. J., and Sery, T. W., 1952, *J. Bacteriol.*, **63**:424.
Heidelberger, M., and Kendall, F. E., 1931, *J. Exptl. Med.*, **54**:515.
Henriksen, S. D., 1948, *Acta Pathol. Microbiol. Scand.*, **25**:368.
Henthorne, J. C., Thompson, L., and Beaver, D. C., 1936, *J. Bacteriol.*, **31**: 255.
Hine, M. K., and Berry, G. P., 1937, *ibid.*, **34**:517.
Hirschfeld, I., Beube, F., and Siegel, E. H., 1940, *J. Periodontol.*, **11**:89.
Hobson, P. N., and Mann, S. O., 1961, *J. Gen. Microbiol.*, **25**:227.
Hoffman, H., 1955, *Ohio J. Sci.*, **55**:441.
Huhtanen, C. N., and Gall, L. S., 1953, *J. Bacterial.*, **65**:548.
——— Rogers, M. R., and Gall, L. S., 1952, *ibid.*, **64**:17.
Hülphers, G., and Henricson, T., 1942, *Svensk Veterinär. Tidskr.*, **47**:566. (*Biol. Abstr.*).
Hungate, R. E., 1950, *Bacteriol. Revs.*, **14**:1.
Illenyi, A., 1939, *Zentr. Bakteriol. Parasitenk.*, *I Orig.*, **144**:502.
Jackins, H. C., and Barker, H. A., 1951, *J. Bacteriol.*, **61**:101.
Jensen, R., Flint, J. C., and Griner, L. A., 1954, *Am. J. Vet. Research*, **15**:5.
Joliff, C. R., Engelhard, W. E., Ohlsen, J. R., Heidrick, P. J., and Cain, J. A., 1960, *Antibiotics & Chemotherapy*, **10**:694.
Jonsen, J. and Thjötta, T., 1948, *Acta Pathol. Microbiol. Scand.*, **25**:688.
———, and ———, 1950, *ibid.*, **27**:152.
Judicial Commission, 1958, *Internat. Bull. Bact. Nomen. Taxon.*, **8**:163 (*Biol. Abstr.*).
Katz, Y. J., and Hanke, M. E., 1941, *Proc. Soc. Exptl. Biol. Med.*, **47**:263.
King, A. B., Conklin, S. D., and Collette, T. S., 1952, *Ann. Internal Med.*, **37**:761.
Kirchheiner, E., 1939, *Compt. Rend. Soc. Biol.*, **132**:385.
Knorr, M., 1923, *Zentr. Bakteriol. Parasitenk.*, *I Orig.*, **89**:4.
Lahelle, O., 1945, *Acta Pathol. Microbiol. Scand.*, **22**:34.
———, 1947a, *ibid.*, Suppl. 67.
———, 1947b, *ibid.*, **25**:567.
———, and Thjötta, T., 1945, *Acta Pathol. Microbiol. Scand.*, **22**:310.
Landsteiner, K., and Mucha, V., 1906, *Wien. klin. Wochschr.*, **19**:1349.
Laporte, A., and Brocard, H., 1939, *Compt. Rend. Soc. Biol.*, **131**:4.
Larson, W. P., and Barron, M., 1913, *J. Inf. Dis.*, **13**:429.
Lee, H. C., and Moore, W. E. C., 1959, *J. Bacteriol.*, **77**:741.
Lessel, E. F., Jr., and Breed, R. S., 1954, *Bacteriol. Revs.*, **18**:165.
Lev, M., 1958, *Nature*, **181**:203.
———, 1959, *J. Gen. Microbiol.*, **20**:697.
Lewis, C. J., 1911, *J. Pathol. Bacteriol.*, **16**:29.
Lewis, K. H., and Rettger, L. F., 1940, *J. Bacteriol.*, **40**:287.
Lewkowicz, X., 1901, *Arch. Méd. Expér. et Anat. Pathol.*, **13**:633.
Lingard, A., 1888, *Lancet*, **2**:159.
Lodenkämper, H., and Stienen, G., 1955, *Antibiotic Med.*, **1**:653.
Loeffler, F., 1884, *Mitt. kaiserl. Gesundheitsamte*, **2**:421.
Macdonald, J. B., 1953, *The Motile Non-sporulating Anaerobic Rods of the Oral Cavity*, Dissertation, Columbia University, New York.
———, 1959, personal communication.
———, and Gibbons, R. J., 1960, *J. Dental Research*, **39**:655.
———, Knoll, M. L., and Sutton, R. M., 1953, *Proc. Soc. Exptl. Biol. Med.*, **84**:459.

————, and Madlener, E. M., 1957, *Can. J. Microbiol.*, **3**:679.

————, ————, and Socransky, S. S., 1959, *J. Bacteriol.*, **77**:559.

————, and Sutton, R. M., 1957, *Prepr. Abstr. Internat. Assoc. Dental Research*, no. 121.

————, ————, and Knoll, M. L., 1954, *J. Inf. Dis.*, **95**:275.

————, ————, ————, Madlener, E. M., and Grainger, R. M., 1956, *ibid.*, **98**:15.

Madlener, E. M., 1958, *J. Dental Research*, **37**:12.

Malek, J., and Malkova, J., 1938, *Zentr. Bakteriol. Parasitenk.*, *I Orig.*, **143**:126.

Mashimo, P. A., and Ellison, S. A., 1959, *J. Bacteriol.*, **78**:636.

Mayer, E., 1902, *Am. J. Med. Sci.*, **123**:187.

McCullough, N. B., 1938, *J. Inf. Dis.*, **63**:34.

McHenry, M. C., Wellman, W. E., and Martin, W. J., 1961, *A.M.A. Arch. Internal Med.*, **107**:572.

McVay, L. V., Jr., and Sprunt, D. H., 1952, *Ann. Internal Med.*, **36**:56.

Mendel, J., 1918, *Compt. Rend. Soc. Biol.*, **81**:471.

Mergenhagen, S. E., 1960, *J. Dental Research*, **39**:267.

————, Hampp, E. G., and Scherp, H. W., 1961, *J. Inf. Dis.*, **108**:304.

Miller, W. D., 1884, *Deutsche med. Wochschr.*, **10**:781.

————, 1890, *The Microorganisms of the Human Mouth*, S. S. White Company, Philadelphia, pp. 76–79.

Mills, K. C., Shibley, G. S., and Dochez, A. R., 1928, *J. Exptl. Med.*, **47**: 193.

Misra, S. S., 1938, *J. Pathol. Bacteriol.*, **46**:204.

Moore, B., 1954, *ibid.*, **67**:461.

Moureau, M., 1952, *Ann. Inst. Pasteur*, **83**:367.

Mühlens, P., 1909, *Zentr. Bakteriol. Parasitenk.*, *I Orig.*, **48**:523.

Olitsky, P. K., and Gates, F. L., 1921, *J. Exptl. Med.*, **33**:713.

————, and ————, 1922a, *ibid.*, **35**:813.

————, and ————, 1922b, **36**:501.

————, and ————, 1923, *Science*, **57**:159.

————, and McCartney, J. E., 1923, *J. Exptl. Med.*, **38**:427.

Oliver, W. W., and Wherry, W. B., 1921, *J. Inf. Dis.*, **28**:341.

Omata, R. R., 1953, *J. Bacteriol.*, **65**:326.

————, 1959, *ibid.*, **77**:35.

————, and Braunberg, B. C., 1960, *ibid.*, **80**:737.

————, and Disraely, M. N., 1956, *ibid.*, **72**:677.

Orcutt, M. L., 1930, *ibid.*, **20**:343.

Park, R. W. A., and Jeynes, M. H., 1959, *ibid.*, **77**:667.

Patocka, F., and Sebek, V., 1947, *Československ. Gynaekol.*, **12**:24 (*Biol. Abstr.*).

Perez, J. E., Padilla, E. A., Anaya, J. D. R., and Torrech, A., 1956, *J. Agr. Univ. Puerto Rico*, **40**:118 (*Biol. Abstr.*).

Pilot, I., and Brams, J., 1923, *J. Inf. Dis.*, **32**:134.

————, and Kanter, A. E., 1923, *ibid.*, **32**:204.

Plaut, H., 1894, *Deutsche med. Wochschr.*, **20**:920.

Pratt, J. S., 1927, *J. Inf. Dis.*, **41**:461.

Prévot, A.-R., 1938, *Ann. Inst. Pasteur*, **60**:285.

————, 1940a, *Compt. Rend. Soc. Biol.*, **133**:246.

————, 1940b, *Ann. Inst. Pasteur*, **64**:117.

————, 1945, *ibid.*, **71**:317.

————, 1948, *Manuel de classification et de détermination des bactéries anaérobies*, 2d ed., Masson et Cie, Paris.

————, 1957, *ibid.*, 3d ed.

————, and Kirchheiner, E., 1938, *Compt. Rend. Soc. Biol.*, **128**:963.

————, and ————, 1939, *Compt. Rend. Acad. Sci.*, **209**:182.

————, Pouliquen, E., and Tardieux, P., 1954, *Bull. Acad. Nat. de Méd.*, Nos. 19–20, p. 308.

————, and Taffanel, J., 1942, *Ann. Inst. Pasteur*, **68**:420.

————, and Veillon, R., 1940, *Compt. Rend. Soc. Biol.*, **133**:249.

Proske, H. O., and Sayers, R. R., 1934, *Public Health Repts. (U.S.)*, **49**:839.

Rauchfus, 1893, cited by Mayer, 1902.

Repaci, G., 1909, *Compt. Rend. Soc. Biol.*, **66**:630.

————, 1911, *ibid.*, **71**:784.

————, 1912, *Ann. Inst. Pasteur*, **26**:536.

Riddell, M. I., Morton, H. S., and Murray, E. G. D., 1953, *Am. J. Med. Sci.*, **225**:535.

Rist, E., and Ribadeau-Dumas, L., 1907, *Compt. Rend. Soc. Biol.*, **63**:538.

Rosebury, T., 1942, *J. Lab. Clin. Med.*, **27**:1470.

————, Clark, A. R. Engel, G. G., and Tergis, F., 1950*a*, *J. Inf. Dis.*, **87**:217.

————, ————, Tergis, F., and Engel, S. G., 1950*b*, *ibid.* **87**:226.

————, ————, Macdonald, J. B., and O'Connell, D. C., 1950*c*, *ibid.*, **87**:234.

————, and Francis, S., 1950, *Oral Surg., Oral Med., Oral Pathol.*, **3**:1557.

————, Macdonald, J. B., Ellison, S. A., and Engel, S. G., 1951, *ibid.*, **4**:68.

————, and Sonnenwirth, A. C., 1958, in Dubos, R. J. (ed.) *Bacterial and Mycotic Infections of Man*, 3d ed., J. P. Lippincott Company, Philadelphia, p. 626.

————, and ————, 1960, *Bacteriol Proc.*, p. 80.

Ruebner, B., 1957, *J. Pathol. Bacteriol.*, **73**:429.

Ruys, A. C., 1947, *ibid.*, **59**:313.

Ryff, J. F., and Lee, A. M., 1946, *Am. J. Vet. Research*, **7**:41.

Sawyer, S. J., Gibbons, R. J., and Macdonald, J. B., 1961, *J. Dental Research*, **40**:716.

Schierbeek, A., 1959, *Measuring the Invisible World: The Life and Works of Antoni van Leeuwenhoek FRS*, Abelard-Schuman Inc., New York.

Schmorl, G., 1891, *Deut. Z. Thiermed.*, **17**:375, cited by Lahelle (1947).

Schwabacher, H., Lucas, D. R., and Rimington, C., 1947, *J. Gen. Microbiol.*, **1**:109.

Seguin, P., 1928, *Compt. Rend. Soc. Biol.*, **99**:439.

————, and Boisvert, H., 1942, *ibid.*, **136**:317.

Senos, G., and Mattman, L. H., 1955, *J. Bacteriol.*, **70**:483.

Sevin, A., and Beerens, H., 1949, *Ann. Inst. Pasteur Lille*, **2**:108.

————, and ————, 1950, *ibid.*, **3**:65.

————, ————, and Spy, C., 1947, *Ann. Inst. Pasteur*, **73**:926.

————, ————, and ————, 1948, *Ann. Inst. Pasteur Lille*, **1**:223.

Shaw, F. W., and Bigger, I. A., 1934, *J. Am. Med. Assoc.*, **102**:688.

Shevky, M., Kohl, C., and Marshall, M. S., 1933, *J. Lab. Clin. Med.*, **19**:689.

Shmamine, T., 1912, *Zentr. Bakteriol. Parasitenk.*, *I Orig.*, **65**:311.

Slanetz, L. W., and Rettger, L. F., 1933, *J. Bacteriol.*, **26**:599.

Smith, W. E., 1943, *ibid.*, **45**:54.

————, 1948, *ibid.*, **56**:603.

————, and Ropes, M. W., 1945, *New Engl. J. Med.*, **232**:31.

Sonnenwirth, A. C., 1960, *A Study of Certain Gram-negative, Non-sporulating Anaerobic Bacteria Indigenous to Man, with Special Reference to their Classification by Serological Means,* Dissertation, Washington University, St. Louis.

Spaulding, E. H., and Rettger, L. F., 1937, *J. Bacteriol.,* **34**:535, 549.

Steen, E., and Thjötta, T., 1950, *Acta Pathol. Microbiol. Scand.,* **27**:851.

Stevens, W. C., and Harrison, A. P., 1958, *Antibiotics & Chemotherapy,* **8**:192.

Suter, L. S., Ulrich, E. W., and Vaughan, B. F., 1955, *J. Bacteriol.,* **69**:604.

Thomson, D., and Thomson, R., 1924–25, *Ann. Pickett-Thomson Research Labs.,* **1**:229.

Tunnicliff, R., 1906, *J. Inf. Dis.,* **3**:148.

——, 1914, *ibid.,* **15**:350.

——, 1923, *ibid.,* **33**:146.

——, 1926, *ibid.,* **38**:366.

——, 1933, *ibid.,* **53**:280.

——, 1938, *J. Dental Research,* **17**:53.

——, and Jackson, L., 1930, *J. Inf. Dis.,* **46**:12.

Tynes, B. S., and Utz, J. P., 1960, *Am. J. Med.,* **29**:879.

Varney, P., 1927, *J. Bacteriol.,* **13**:275.

——, 1929, *Arch. Surg.,* **19**:1609.

Vedel, R., 1929, *Contribution à l'étude du bacille de la nécrose,* Thèse Vét., Paris, cited by Lahelle (1947).

Veillon, A., and Zuber, A., 1897, *Compt. Rend. Soc. Biol.,* **49**:253.

——, and ——, 1898, *Arch. Méd. Exper. et Anat. Pathol.,* **10**:517.

Velu, H., and Bouffanais, A., 1948, *Ann. Inst. Pasteur,* **74**:253.

Verneuil, A., and Clado, 1889, *Compt. Rend. Acad. Sci.,* **108**:272, cited by Weinberg et al., 1937.

Vincent, H., 1896, *Ann. Inst. Pasteur,* **10**:488.

——, 1899, *ibid.,* **13**:609.

——, 1904, *Compt. Rend. Soc. Biol.,* **56**:311.

——, 1905, *ibid.,* **58**:722, 774.

Walker, P. H., and Dack, G. M., 1939, *J. Inf. Dis.,* **65**:285.

Wallach, R., and Pomeranz, N., 1949, *New Engl. J. Med.,* **241**:690.

Wegner, G. H., and Foster, E. M., 1960, *J. Dairy Sci.,* **43**:566.

Weinberg, M., Nativelle, R., and Prévot, A.-R., 1937, *Les microbes anaérobies,* Masson et Cie, Paris.

——, and Prévot, A.-R., 1926, *Compt. Rend. Soc. Biol.,* **95**:519.

Weinstein, L., 1960, *Bull. Tufts–New Engl. Med. Center,* **6**:31.

Weiss, C., 1937, *Proc. Soc. Exptl. Biol. Med.,* **37**:463.

——, and Mercado, D. G., 1939, *J. Exptl. Med.,* **67**:49.

Weiss, J. E., and Rettger, L. F., 1937, *J. Bacteriol.,* **33**:423.

——, and ——, 1938, *J. Inf. Dis.,* **62**:115.

Wills, M. R., and Reece, M. W., 1960, *Brit. Med. J.,* **2**:566.

CHAPTER 6

THE INDIGENOUS SPIROCHETES

No microorganisms are more characteristically indigenous to the mucous membranes of man than spirochetes, and none have been more neglected. Medical bacteriologists rarely see them. In material examined by the usual cultural procedures they may be entirely overlooked, since they grow only under special and seldom-used conditions complicated by the need for anaerobiosis. Even microscopy is likely to pass them by unless the more readily stained spirochetes happen to be present in abundance, or unless these organisms are specifically looked for by the darkfield or phase contrast methods. To these difficulties, which are matters of custom rather than intrinsic, must be added a real problem of isolation—beyond the lesser obstacles of cultivation itself. Finally, suggestions of elusive pathogenicity or the lack of it have not encouraged the exploration of indigenous spirochetes. In the light of much recent discussion of pure science it nevertheless seems curious that such distinctive and accessible objects should have been so little studied.

We do know enough about these spirochetes to label them with confidence as true amphibionts indigenous to the dentulous mouth, the crypts of the tonsils, and the external genitalia, and probably also to the lower intestine. If we except a description by Veldkamp (1960) of a treponeme (*T. zuelzerae*) said to be free-living, anaerobic, and serologically[1] related to *Treponema pallidum*, there is no suggestion among forms within this group of true saprophytism. Healthy mucous membranes harbor spirochetes only in scant numbers, but in the presence of inflammatory processes that seem entirely nonspecific in the usual sense of that term, enormous overgrowths of these microorganisms may be present. In a healthy mouth, for example—one in which a critical trained eye can find no evidence of gingival disease—spirochetes may be demonstrable only upon careful search. But in a range of pathologic processes from mild, trivial, and almost universal,

---

[1] DeBruijn (1961) has reported that *T. zuelzerae* shares a group-specific protein antigen with the Reiter spirochete (see page 203) but has a distinct polysaccharide fraction.

such as gingivitis associated with a single imperfect dental restoration, to the rare fulminating noma, spirochetes are present in great profusion. Fresh exudate from such a process, examined by competent darkfield microscopy—or less strikingly under the phase contrast microscope—presents a picture of these corkscrew-like forms in furious turmoil that is highly characteristic and likely to be unforgettable. Spirochetes may seem to dominate the picture because of their distinctive morphology and active motility; but many other bacteria are invariably present, including smaller numbers of actively motile vibrios and spirilla, aerobic and anaerobic streptococci, Gram-positive anaerobic rods, bacteroides, and fusiform bacilli—a mixed population loosely termed the fusospirochetal flora.

This flora, with variations, occurs in disease of the areas mentioned, and also pathologically in the lungs, on the skin, and in other locations; and the mixed exudate from such sites is regularly and typically pathogenic when injected in large doses into laboratory animals. The spirochetes persist as characteristic members of the transmissible experimental infection, and may appear in the tissues, in advance of other members of the flora, in such a way as to suggest distinctive pathogenicity. On the other hand it has been possible to reproduce similar if not identical pathologic processes experimentally with deliberate mixtures of pure cultures *not* including spirochetes; and up to the present it has not been shown unequivocally that spirochetes contribute to such pathogenicity.

Dobell (1932) thought that Leeuwenhoek may have seen true spirochetes and that his simple microscopes made use of a darkfield method; but it seems doubtful that the Dutch microscopist could have distinguished clearly between spirochetes and spirilla; the two were certainly confused two centuries later in the early bacteriologic era. The free-living spirochetes, which differ markedly from those considered here (with the possible exception noted above), were known to Ehrenberg, who applied the name to them in 1833. The first pathogenic spirochete, that of relapsing fever, was discovered as early as 1868 by Obermeier, marking one of the first milestones in the development of the germ theory. Parasitic spirochetes were seen in fusospirochetal processes by many early workers [see Smith (1932)]; but the impetus to their systematic study came, albeit haltingly, only with the discovery in 1905 by Schaudinn and Hoffmann of both *Treponema pallidum* and the spirochete now called *Borrelia refringens*. In the following year Landsteiner and Mucha (1906) introduced the darkfield microscope for the study of the syphilis spirochete, adapting the principle of the ultramicroscope of von Siedentopf and Zsigmondy as applied, earlier in 1906, in the darkfield condenser of von Reichert

Fɪɢ. 6-1. *Borrelia* sp. from a case of gingivitis, after 20 minutes' tryptic digestion of cell wall, showing some 12 filaments. Electron micrograph, ×17,000. [*From Swain* (1955), *courtesy of Dr. Swain and J. Pathol. Bacteriol.*]

[Landsteiner and Mucha (1906)]. It may be noted that the water leptospiras were not described until 1914, and the pathogenic leptospiras a year later.

The Problem of Classification

Because of the special difficulties with these organisms it seems particularly wise to confront the inadequacy of our knowledge of them and to put forward only the most tentative classification. It must be recognized, indeed, that the literature contains no assurance that a satisfactory compromise can be made between recognition of such multiplicities of "species" of indigenous spirochetes as have been listed, for example, by Hindle (1931) and by Robinson and Wichelhausen (1946) on the one hand, and the hypothesis that all these forms might be looked upon as variations of a single species, variations induced by differences of environment.[2]

Distinctive Structure. It seems worth noting at the outset that the spirochetes as a group can be defined unequivocally as a result of electron micrographic studies made during the 1950s [Bradfield and Cater (1952); Swain (1955, 1957); Czekalowski and Eaves (1955); Kawata et al. (1956)]. Confirming and extending early optical observations, these studies have established for the parasitic spirochetes as a class a

---

[2] As examples that seem to lend credence to this idea, Noguchi (1912a) noted that "the forms which are commonly observed in a smear from tooth deposit consist of . . . irregular individuals" which he observed in cultures of so-called *T. microdentium* and *T. macrodentium* exposed to imperfect anaerobiosis. The writer has also seen loosely wound and double-contoured spirochetes appear in cultures of the small tightly wound single-contoured oral spirochetes; and he has frequently noted that the loose forms, characteristically absent through repeated passage of mixed fusospirochetal infection in guinea pigs, have reappeared in the exudate from a draining lesion [Rosebury et al. (1951)]. Obviously, however, all these observations might also depend on the presence initially of more than 1 species of spirochete.

distinctive cellular structure. One longitudinal fibril may serve as an uncoiled "axistyle" around which the protoplast is wound helically (in leptospiras), or a bundle of 3 or more fibrils may be closely applied to the protoplast in phase with the helical course of the spirochete. The number of fibrils seems to vary characteristically. *Treponema pallidum* has 3; relapsing fever borrelias have 8 to 12 or more; and the larger, loosely wound spirochetes of the mouth [Swain (1955)] have an approximately equal number (Fig. 6-1). The fibrils of all these spirochetes appear to be approximately 0.02 μ in diameter. They may be broken transversely and detached from the cell by the use of sodium desoxycholate (in leptospiras) or by tryptic or peptic digestion or with distilled water (in *Treponema* and *Borrelia*), when they may appear as flagella-like artefacts. Otherwise no flagella are seen; spirochetal motility is attributed to the intact fibrils. Berger (1958) has provided an electron micrograph of an oral treponeme indicating a comparable fibrillar structure (Fig. 6-2). Additional observations of this kind may provide a more adequate basis for classification of these spirochetes than is now available.

Genera of Parasitic Spirochetes. The parasitic spirochetes, including pathogenic forms, are conventionally classified into 3 genera: (1) *Borrelia*, staining easily with ordinary aniline dyes; (2) *Treponema*, staining with difficulty; and (3) the aerobic, very tightly wound *Leptospira*. The leptospiras can be cultivated with comparative ease, and have recently been grown successfully by several workers as surface colonies [Cox and Larson (1957); Larson et al. (1959); Kirschner and Graham (1959)]; whereas both borrelias and treponemes are cultivable only with difficulty, sometimes not at all. All members of the latter groups that have been cultivated are anaerobes; and, indeed, unusually strict anaerobiosis, or unusual sensitivity to oxidizing conditions, may be a signal difficulty impeding their cultivation [see Soc-

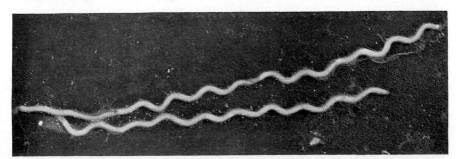

FIG. 6-2. Electron micrograph of an oral treponeme without enzymatic treatment, showing helical fibrils but no flagella. ×10,000. [*From Berger* (1958), *courtesy of Dr. Berger.*]

ransky, Macdonald, and Sawyer (1959)]. Leptospira-like forms have been reported in the human mouth, where the writer has occasionally seen them [see Seguin and Vinzent (1936); Vinzent and Seguin (1939)]. Vinzent and Seguin were of the opinion that a spirochete morphologically identical with true leptospiras is present in the mouth and in respiratory disease; but spirochetes corresponding in other respects with this distinctive genus have not been cultivated from indigenous sites. Both borrelia- and treponeme-like spirochetes, however, are characteristically found in such locations. Among them are forms that resemble the spirochete of syphilis on the one hand and those of relapsing fever on the other. The former can be distinguished from *Treponema pallidum* by critical observation of morphology and especially of motility [Rosebury (1942)]. The need to distinguish the borrelias does not arise in practice, since the relapsing fever spirochetes do not appear on mucous surfaces.

How Many Indigenous Species? The finer classification of the indigenous spirochetes is beset with formidable obstacles that cannot at present be surmounted; indeed, the need to clear these obstacles from the path is seldom recognized. The obstacles may be worth enumerating:

1. The evidence is seldom if ever given or apparent that specific descriptions of spirochetes in the literature were based on true isolations, rather than on mere separation of spirochetes from contaminating bacteria by a variant of the Noguchi procedure. While one hardly expects single-cell isolations in this difficult field, isolation from distinct colonies, as with other microorganisms, is indispensable. Such a procedure is only now becoming technically feasible in this group, and an adequate specific classification must await its more widespread application.

2. Comparative studies of spirochetes have not made use of a sufficient number of cultures to provide convincing evidence that reported differences are not simply strain variations. Before Noguchi such differences were entirely morphologic. Noguchi, in a series of papers (1911–1918), attempted to use both biochemical and serologic as well as morphologic criteria; but his specific designations were nearly all based on a single culture for each (the point is not always explicit); and even so the reported differences do not withstand close scrutiny. For example, the alleged production of "mucin" by *T. mucosum*— coupled with dubious pathogenicity to distinguish it from *T. microdentium*—seems a poor basis for the widespread acceptance the former name achieved; and neither the fermentation data of Akatsu (1917) nor the serologic findings of Noguchi and Akatsu (1917) provide more than suggestions to be explored in adequate future studies. The work

of the French school [e.g., Kritchewski and Seguin (1920, 1924); Seguin (1930); Seguin and Vinzent (1936); Vinzent et al. (1934, 1936, 1939)], supplemented by the more recent studies of Moureau (1955) has been incorporated in the classification presented by Prévot (1957) in which some 13 "species" are listed as commensal or doubtfully pathogenic spirochetes of the human mouth, lung, intestine, and genitalia. This classification is subject to the same deficiencies as the others. It may be noted that Prévot continued to follow Noguchi (1928) in listing all indigenous spirochetes in the genus *Treponema*, reserving the name *Borrelia* for the distinctly pathogenic blood spirochetes of fowl, man, and swine.

3. The criterion of classification that seems to have been most widely accepted in this group, aside from morphology, is *habitat*—varying indigenous locus in man—but no acceptable justification for this practice has been offered. Several workers have in fact challenged it. Noguchi (1912*b*) was uncertain that the mouth and genital spirochetes were clearly distinct, but he applied distinctive names to them. Seguin and Vinzent (1936) observed that spirochetes recovered from respiratory lesions were identical with those of mouth and throat. Vinzent and Seguin (1939*b*) commented on a presumed similar relationship between intestinal and oral forms, although they argued that mouth spirochetes occur in the intestine only pathologically, and described a spirochete which they thought to be peculiar to the bowel. More recent workers (Hampp, Berger), in confining their attention to oral spirochetes, have in effect evaded this question. Here as with other indigenous microorganisms we are guided by the economic hypothesis that the same species is likely to appear in several loci, but it is not denied that only an adequate comparative study can settle the question.

A Tentative Classification

The Minimal Species. It is plain, then, that if any attempt is to be made to resolve the near chaos that now characterizes the classification of indigenous spirochetes—if only for convenience in speaking of these organisms in other contexts—we ought to be willing to err on the side of simplicity rather than of complexity. It can be argued that the minimal probable number of indigenous species is two: (1) that form which is typically tightly wound, pallidum-like, comparatively easy to cultivate, corresponding with the *Spirochaeta dentium* of Mühlens and Hartmann (1906)—not with the *Spirochaeta dentium* of Miller (1890), which seems to have been his name for all the oral spirochetes, and with the *Treponema microdentium* of Noguchi (1912*a*); and (2) a form which, in view of the evidently impenetrable confusion of earlier reports, may be given the specific name *refringens* after Schaudinn and Hoffmann (1905). This organism, as it was cultivated and described by Noguchi (1912*b*), would now be assigned to the genus *Borrelia* as a loosely wound, easily stained spirochete; and this name, pending further elucidation, would include and supplant the names *B. vincenti* and *B. buccale*, oral spirochetes which differ principally or only in *thickness;* the latter being double-contoured, the former single-contoured, as seen by darkfield illumination. Noguchi's description of his 2 strains of *B. refringens* is compatible with descriptions of *B. buccale* in all respects but one; the former seemed to be cultivable with comparative ease, while the oral form, in Noguchi's hands as in those of most other workers, did not appear at all in "pure" culture. Noguchi (1912*b*) stated that he had been unable to cultivate the buccalis spirochete pure, but commented: "In an impure culture of the buccalis, I was much impressed with the morphological similarity that it bears to the refringens. . . . "

The thin spirochete called *B. vincenti* has also seemed to resist cultivation. Vinzent and Seguin (1939*b*) disputed its existence, arguing that spirochetes described by earlier workers under this or analogous names (e.g., *Spirochaeta bronchialis*) together comprise the several other species they suggested. Prévot (1957) also listed *Treponema vincenti* as doubtful, and discarded the specific epithet *buccale* altogether. Hampp has recognized both *B. vincenti* (1950) and *B. buccale* (1954) and has reported their separate cultivation, but in neither instance with convincing details. He has suggested that the latter is more difficult to grow, and has reported that it failed to grow in a simplified medium in which both his *B. vincenti* and the "smaller oral treponemes" were cultivated [Hampp and Nevin (1959)]. Hampp and Fitzgerald have also reported (1959) in a study based on 3 strains of each, that the 3 groups show similar sensitivities to 10 antibiotics with differences mainly in relation to novobiocin, toward which sensitivity increased in the order smaller treponemes, vincenti, buccale. Berger (1958) considered Hampp's classification satisfactory; but his extensive studies were based only on the smaller forms, the others having resisted his attempts at cultivation. In a later study, however, Berger (1959) reported without detail that a single strain of *B. vincenti* was sensitive to 0.5 μg per ml of vancomycin, whereas 6 strains of *T. microdentium* showed sensitivities to the same antibiotic of 10 to 12 μg per ml. Hampp and Fitzgerald (1959) reported the inhibitory concentration of vancomycin in μg per ml to be, for the small treponemes 2.5, and for *B. vincenti* and *B. buccale* 1.2 to 2.5.

Such disagreement, which all careful students of this subject have noted, seems to be intrinsic and cannot be resolved arbitrarily or without further study of demonstrably pure cultures. This is still difficult as compared with analogous studies of other bacteria, but it is no longer prohibitively difficult. In any event, the writer suggests that studies in this field based on species names without adequate characterization ought not to be condoned.

Synonymy. The two "species" of indigenous spirochetes are as follows:

1. *Treponema dentium* [*Spirochaeta dentium*, Mühlens and Hartmann (1906)] is the smaller indigenous form, typically pallidum-like but with wide variation; probably always single-contoured, relatively easily cultivated; it stains poorly with aniline dyes and is Gram-negative. The following alternative specific names, suggested as synonyms pending further elucidation, have been compiled from the data given by Noguchi (1928), Hindle (1931), Robinson and Wichelhausen (1946), and Prévot (1957):

a. microdentium and *mucosum*, Noguchi (1912*a,c*); *calligyrum*, Noguchi (1913); *stenostrepta*, Werner (1909); *dentium*, *orthodontum*, and *skoliodontum*, Hoffmann (1920); (*Leptospira*) *trimerodonta*, Hoffmann (1920); *genitalis*, Noguchi (1923).

b. dentium, Dobell (1912); *urethrale*, Castellani (1915).

c. gracilis, Veszpremi (1907).

d. ambigua and *comandoni*, Seguin and Vinzent (1936).

2. *Borrelia refringens* [*Spirochaeta refringens*, Schaudinn and Hoffmann (1905)] is the larger spirochete, recurrentis-like or still more loosely wound, single- or double-contoured under darkfield, generally more difficult to cultivate; stains relatively easily with aniline dyes; Gram-negative. The following alternative specific names are from the four sources in order as above:

a. vincenti, Blanchard (1906); *bronchiale*, Castellani (1906); *schaudinni*, Prowazek (1907); *aboriginalis*, Cleland (1909); *eurygyrata*, Werner (1909); *macrodentium* and *phagedenis*, Noguchi (1912*d*); *noguchii*, Strong (1923).

b. balanitidis, Hoffmann and Prowazek (1906); *intermedia*, Dobell (1912); *minima*, Aragao and Vianna (1913); *vaginalis* and *urethrae*, Macfie (1916, 1917); *intestinalis*, Macfie and Carter (1917).

c. inequalis, *undulata*, *tenuis*, and *recta*, Gerber (1910); *buccale*, Dobell (1912).

d. vincenti, Brumpt (1922); *enterogyrata*, Vinzent and Seguin (1939).

Occurrence

Man. In the *mouth*, spirochetes are characteristic of the gingival crevice. Braïlovsky-Lounkevitch (1915) found them with other anaerobes only in that site and considered them part of the fundamental flora of the adult. Although they are widely held to be absent from both the predentulous and the edentulous mouth, Rosenthal and Gootzeit (1942) found spirochetes in 7 of 212 (3.3 per cent) of completely edentulous mouths with no visible areas of inflammation. Rosebury, Macdonald, and Clark (1950) found the various morphologic types of spirochetes (other than leptospiras) in darkfield studies in suspensions of gingival scrapings from 5 of 10 adults with healthy gingival tissues. In such persons they were both less common and, when found, much less numerous than in the presence of gingivitis or periodontal disease, as is true of the fusospirochetal flora in general.

Their occurrence in other sites in the clinical absence of local inflammation is less clear. Pilot and Brams (1923) found spirochetes, together with fusiform organisms, α- and β-streptococci, and other bacteria, in 25 of 100 excised *tonsils* but in only 2 of 46 adenoids. Okabe (1936) found spirochetes in the nose, the tonsils, and elsewhere in the pharynx in 27 healthy persons, less regularly than in the mouth and more often in the presence of nasal or pharyngeal infection. Wolbach (1914–15) recorded the almost constant presence of spirochetes in human *feces*. Parr (1923) found them in smears of feces in 27.7 per cent of all subjects, comprising 38.9 per cent of 95 men, 28.5 per cent of 28 women, 17.6 per cent of children 14 days to 14 years old; but in none of 33 babies less than 14 days old. Spirochetes cultured from the *gastrointestinal tract* seem to have come only from pathologic processes —e.g., Noguchi (1912c: *B. refringens*); Hogue (1922: *Sp. eurygyrata*); and Vinzent and Seguin (1939b: *T. microdentium, T. calligyra,* and *Sp. enterogyrata*). The last workers considered *T. microdentium,* found in appendicitis, as foreign to the intestine, perhaps transported there from the mouth via blood or lymph.

Parr (1923) suggested that the site in the intestinal tract in which spirochetes are found in man is the *cecum.* Palmer (1954) has examined the claims of earlier workers that spirochetes may be found in sections of the *stomach* at autopsy; he failed to find spirochetes in gastric mucosal biopsies from 1,000 adults taken by a vacuum technique.

As for the *genitourinary tract,* Stoddard (1917) found spirochetes of several kinds, including refringens-like forms, treponemes, and leptospira-like organisms, in the urine and the urethra of men, in health and more often in the presence of various illnesses. Noguchi (1918) and Noguchi and Kaliski (1918) reported that various spirochetes were present in smegma, similar in men and women. Pilot and Kanter (1923) observed spirochetes in stained smears of smegma from the clitoris of 36 normal pregnant primiparas, and also noted that the forms found were similar in men and women. More recently, Coutts et al. (1952) have remarked on the occurrence of *T. macrodentium* and *T. microdentium* on the human genitalia in terms of their differentiation from *T. pallidum*.

Indigenous spirochetes have been seen in the foregoing sites and many others under pathologic conditions, including the *lower respiratory tract* [Castellani (1906)], the *skin* [Vincent (1896); Strong et al. (1926)] and elsewhere in fusospirochetal disease [see Smith (1932)].

Animals. Scattered references seen by the writer suggest that indigenous spirochetes are widely distributed in animals under natural conditions and that some of them may resemble the spirochetes of man. Parr (1923) found spirochetes in the intestinal tract, chiefly the cecum, of all of 62 white rats and of nearly all of a group of guinea pigs and white mice. On the other hand, only 21 per cent of wild rats and 22 per cent of wild mice showed them; no spirochetes appeared in any of 37 rabbits. Bryant (1952, 1959) has reviewed the literature on the spirochetes of the rumen of cattle and sheep. Kasai and Kobayashi (1919) observed treponeme-like spirochetes in the stomachs of 43 out of 49 dogs, 1 of 13 cats, 1 of 38 wild rats, all of 13 monkeys, but not in rabbits, guinea pigs, white rats, mice, or field voles. These workers were unable to find similar organisms in the mouth or cecum of any of 26 animals of various species, all of which had spirochetes in the stomach. Spirochetes have been reported in animals in necrotic disease, presumably or clearly fusospirochetal, in sheep [Ludovic and Blaizot (1928)]; pigs [Chick et al. (1938); Hofferd (1950)]; dogs [Phillips and Berry (1930); Michel (1930)]; horses [Yakimoff and Rastjapin (1930)] and an orangutan [Pilot (1938)].

Morphology and Motility

Treponema dentium. *T. dentium* is relatively tightly wound, with a mean pitch [distance between two coils from crest to crest on one side; see Rosebury (1942)] of approximately 1.2 μ. The coils are typically regular and uniform but they may be complex ["spiral on spiral"— e.g., the *Spirochaeta comandoni* of Seguin and Vinzent (1936); see also Rosebury and Foley (1939)]. Length varies over wide limits (Fig. 6-3). The number of coils is typically 6 to 12, the over-all width approximately 1 μ. Thickness seems to vary within the approximate limits 0.2 to 0.3 μ, as indicated especially from the writer's estimates of the electron micrographs of Hampp, Scott, and Wycoff (1948). These figures may be too high, since a thickness of 0.3 μ would be expected to show double contouring under critically set darkfield optics; double contours, however, do not appear on these spirochetes. Swain's measurements (1955) for thickness of *T. pallidum*, based on his electron micrographs, are 0.09 to 0.18 μ, average 0.13 μ; this organism is probably slightly thinner than *T. dentium*. The electron micrographs of Hampp and his coworkers (1948) [see also Berger (1958) and Fig. 6-2] suggest the presence of a bundle of 3 or more fibrils wound as a helix around the helical protoplast—a picture that would correspond with Swain's finding for *T. pallidum*.

Motility. Under conditions that seem optimal—in fresh material from natural sources or in vigorously growing cultures—these spirochetes show active motility, with rapid rotation variably accompanied by darting progression which may include frequently repeated alternation of direction. Flexion is associated with less active movement and is characteristically slow and jerky, giving an impression of stiffness. (In *T. pallidum*, which appears soft, graceful movements of flexion are characteristic and progressive movement is usually absent, or if present is more deliberate.) In *T. dentium* as in other treponemes, pitch and amplitude do not change during movement, in contrast to *B. refringens*.

Borrelia refringens. *B. refringens* is distinctly more loosely wound than the preceding, with a pitch of 2.5 to 4 μ or even more [see Noguchi (1928), plates X and XI; Rosebury (1942), table 1]. Careful students of these organisms are generally agreed that the coils are always regular when the spirochetes are viable and active; irregularity

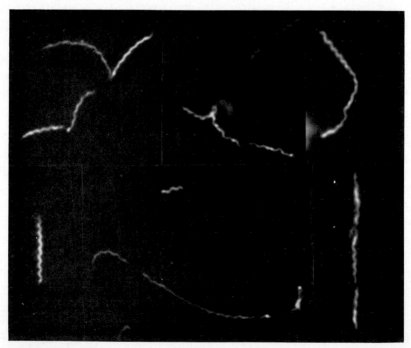

Fɪɢ. 6-3. Oral spirochetes from separated cultures showing long and dividing forms. Darkfield illumination, ×1,400.

is due to artefact or abnormality. The number of coils varies from 2 to 10 or more, with the length correspondingly varied. Over-all width ranges approximately from 1 to 3 μ and is a function in part of active motility as noted below. In an electron micrograph of an intact *"Borrelia* sp. from a case of gingivitis" presented by Swain (1955), the thickness is approximately 0.3 μ or slightly more, including a well-defined cell membrane. Swain gave the figures for thickness of *B. vincenti* as 0.23 to 0.64 μ (average 0.42 μ) which would include both single- and double-contoured forms under darkfield optics. Electron micrographs of these organisms after tryptic digestion revealed 8 to 11 fibrils approximately 0.02 μ in diameter, which as in treponemes appear to be wound helically as a bundle around the helical protoplast (see Fig. 6-1).

Motility. The motility of these organisms under optimum circumstances is highly characteristic. They spin rapidly and, stretching their coils almost taut, move progressively in the line of the long axis, which appears to be a straight line as they do so. Intermittently they stop for a moment and then move again in either the same or the reverse direction; during the immotile instant the coils relax and their amplitude increases [see Rosebury (1942)]. Slower-moving forms may show "serpentine" progression—winding forward along the path of the helix —but movements of flexion are not characteristic.

Methods of Cultivation

Mühlens [Mühlens and Hartmann (1906)] seems to have been the first to obtain a bacteriafree culture of an indigenous spirochete (*T. dentium*). He used horse-serum agar in shake cultures in deep tubes by the method of Veillon and Zuber (1898). His paper includes excellent photomicrographs of typical treponemes in apparently pure culture. Similar methods were used successfully in the next few years by Paul (1908) and by Shmamine (1910).

The Isolation Problem. Subsequent isolation techniques for *T. dentium* derive from Noguchi (1911, 1912, 1913) and have been reviewed by Rosebury et al. (1941, 1951) and by Berger (1958). Noguchi's basic isolation method made use of stab cultures in deep columns of infusion agar containing ascitic fluid and a piece of fresh sterile tissue, usually rabbit kidney. In successful cultures, which had not been disrupted by gas-forming bacteria, spirochetes appeared as a haze growing in the agar away from the mixed bacterial growth in the stab; and bacteria-free growth could be obtained by breaking the tube aseptically and transferring a portion of agar containing spirochetes to fresh medium. This method with variations of medium has been used by many workers including the writer. It suffers from two serious defects: (1) it is at long range too laborious to permit the study of adequate numbers of

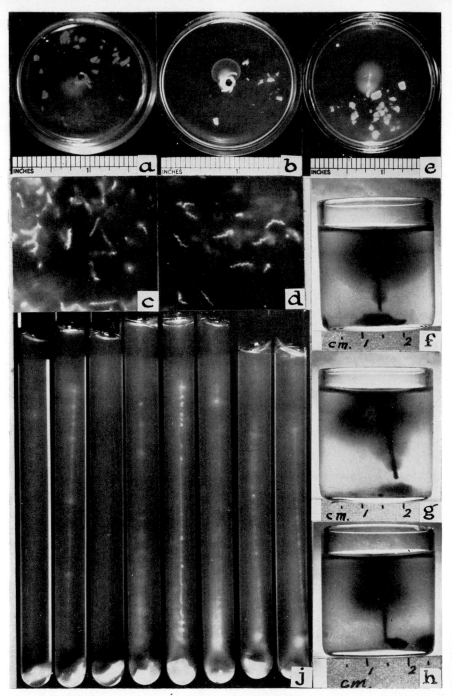

Fig. 6-4. Indigenous (oral) spirochetes, showing the author's modification of Noguchi's method of cultivation. *a*, *b*, shallow-dish cultures seen from

cultures; and, (2), as noted earlier, it provides no assurance that the cultures, although they can be obtained free from bacteria other than spirochetes, are pure in the sense of being the progeny of a single spirochete.

The first of these difficulties but not the second was largely overcome in the writer's laboratory [Rosebury and Foley (1941, 1942); Rosebury et al. (1951)] by using deep-dish cultures rather than tubes. In the initial studies, small petri dishes were used containing a layer 7 mm or more thick of serum-, ascitic fluid-, or serum ultrafiltrate-infusion agar with minced sterile guinea-pig kidney. Mixed material was inoculated by stab into a well cut with 2 mm glass tubing into the center of the agar. The plates were incubated inverted for 4 to 7 days at 37° in sealed jars made anaerobic with platinum-catalyzed hydrogen and containing 5 per cent CO_2. Spirochetal growth was visible from the surface of the plate as a haze growing into the agar beyond the central zone of mixed bacterial growth (Fig. 6-4a,b). A piece of agar containing spirochetes free from other bacteria could easily be removed with a sterile knife or capillary and transferred to a tube of the same medium.

The proportion of successful bacteriafree cultures was later [Rosebury and Foley (1942)] made gratifyingly higher by using for primary isolation specially made small deep petri dishes. The inner or containing member had an inside diameter of 25 mm and was 28 mm deep; it was filled to an agar depth of approximately 25 mm. By inoculating as before with a stab through the bottom of a shallow central well with care to avoid contaminating the agar surface and incubating anaerobically in a hydrogen-CO_2 jar, abundant and easily recognizable spirochete growth could be removed by aspirating with a capillary pipet and transferred to deep tubes of Noguchi medium (see Fig. 6-4).

---

above, showing central well surrounded by mixed bacterial growth and, beyond this, in a, extending to the left and below, diffuse haze of spirochete growth, and in b, extending above, demarked haze. Peripheral particles are guinea-pig kidney fragments. c, d, tightly and more closely wound spirochetes derived respectively from diffuse and demarked hazes; darkfield illumination, ×800. e, a cuture of spirochetes separated from other bacteria, growing in a similar shallow dish culture. f,g,h, deep-dish stab cultures with covers removed, all inoculated with eighth passage guinea-pig fusospirochetal exudate, showing growth of spirochetes extending into the agar from the mixed growth in the central stab; the fragment below the stab is guinea-pig kidney. j, separated spirochete cultures in Noguchi tubes. [a,b,e, from Rosebury and Foley (1941), courtesy of Proc. Soc. Exptl. Med.; c,d,f,g,j, from Rosebury et al. (1951), courtesy of Oral Surg. Oral Med. Oral Pathol.; h, previously unpublished.]

Two morphologically different spirochetes were seen frequently in both shallow and deep plate cultures [Rosebury and Foley (1941); Rosebury et al. (1951)]: one growing as a "diffuse haze"—with an indefinite outer boundary—and appearing as typical small tightly wound spirochetes; the other growing as a "demarked haze"—with a sharply defined margin like a bubble—and containing small loosely wound spirochetes, having 4 or 5 turns rather than 6 or 8 as in the first form, in a length of 8 to 10 μ. The loosely wound form was found alone in the outermost zone when the two appeared together, suggesting more rapid or more persistent motility. Spirochete growth intermediate between the diffuse and demarked types also appeared, and in 3 of 25 instances spirochetes were recovered in the absence of visible haze. The occurrence of loosely wound double-contoured spirochetes in primary culture in one instance, but not in subculture (which showed only single-contoured forms), and the appearance of loosely wound forms in subcultures of another strain that had originally been tightly wound, emphasized the uncertain purity of the cultures and the difficulties of morphologic classification.

This deep-dish or cup-plate procedure for isolation of small spirochetes has been used successfully by Macdonald and his coworkers (1954, 1956) and by Berger (1958; Fig. 6-5). Hampp (1943) used essentially the same procedure with small beakers substituted for the deep petri dishes. All these workers have made modifications of the culture medium; these details have been reviewed by Berger.

Growth as Colonies. Wichelhausen and Wichelhausen (1942) were able to grow small spirochetes from the mouth in standard poured rabbit blood agar plates, in which the organisms appeared as hazy nonhemolytic colonies; but the procedure was less regularly effective in their hands than shake-tube (Veillon) cultures, and was used for only part of their "isolations." These workers noted that Gates (1923), Fortner (1928, 1929), and Aksjansew-Malkin (1933) had reported cultivating mouth spirochetes, as well as less fastidious "culture pallidum" (see page 202) on the surface of blood agar plates. Wichelhausen and Wichelhausen were able to grow the mouth organisms in this way only twice in many attempts. Berger (1958) obtained both deep and surface colonies of oral treponemes in plate cultures using 5 to 10 per cent rabbit blood agar. Such growth

Fig. 6-5. Separated culture of an oral treponeme in guinea-pig kidney medium. [*From Berger* (1958), *courtesy of Dr. Berger.*]

seemed to require adaptation, since it was more effective with older laboratory strains. Hemolysis was seen around deep but not surface colonies, and it was noted that greening appeared in the presence of small amounts of oxygen, suggesting formation of hydrogen peroxide, which would be in line with the finding of Gordon, Holman, and McLeod (1952) for other anaerobes. The studies of Socransky, Macdonald, and Sawyer (1959) in which these spirochetes were cultivated with almost uniform success on streaked blood agar plates maintained continuously under anaerobic conditions suggest that an unusually fastidious requirement for anaerobiosis may be an important key to this problem.

Subcultures. Subculture of these spirochetes, if successful in the first instance (seemingly dependent mainly upon viability in the original culture at the time of transfer, as a function in part of maintained anaerobiosis) can usually be continued without difficulty by inoculation of visible portions of haze into the depths of a long column (10 to 12 cm in 12×200 mm tubes) of one of the variants of the Noguchi medium, using a capillary pipet attached to a 5-ml dry Luer syringe. Rosebury et al. (1951) obtained best results with an unfiltered veal-heart infusion base [Proske and Sayers (1934)] containing 1.8 per cent agar, 30 per cent ascitic fluid, 0.1 per cent neutralized cysteine hydrochloride, and pieces of minced fresh sterile guinea-pig kidney—the standard AFK isolation medium. Many attempted substitutions were unsuccessful or less successful, but nearly all strains grew well when the agar concentration was reduced to 0.2 per cent (yielding a fluid medium), although not when it was lowered further to 0.1 per cent or to zero. Moderately good growth was obtained in a few trials when Bacto heart infusion broth was substituted for the Proske-Sayers base and when 0.5 per cent of a 10 per cent (weight per volume) sterile guinea pig kidney extract was substituted for whole tissue.

Since even low concentrations of agar are objectionable for certain purposes—e.g., they interfere with centrifugation—other workers have also tried to grow these spirochetes in agarfree broth. Robinson and Wichelhausen (1946) used a pancreatic digest of beef heart containing 0.1 per cent 2-mercaptoethanol as a reducing agent, in florence flasks filled to the neck, and containing 10 per cent ascitic fluid or 1 per cent defibrinated rabbit blood. They were unable to substitute hemoglobin solution for whole blood. Hampp (1947) used a medium containing 0.1 per cent agar and approximately 2 per cent gastric mucin in an unfiltered veal-heart base enriched with 10 per cent ascitic fluid and 0.1 per cent glutathione. As antigen for microscopic agglutination tests this worker used the water of condensation of slant cultures made in the same base medium containing 1.4 per cent agar but without mucin.

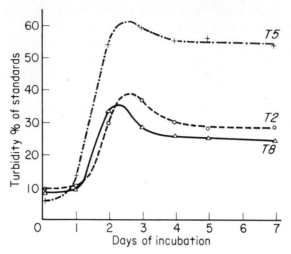

Fig. 6-6. Growth curves of oral spirochetes in pancreatin–ascitic fluid–thioglycolate fluid medium ("PAT"). [*From Berger* (1958a), *courtesy of Dr. Berger.*]

Neither the Robinson-Wichelhausen nor the Hampp fluid media were effective in the writer's laboratory [Rosebury et al. (1951)].

Berger (1958), on the other hand, after a meticulous but unrewarding trial of leads in the earlier literature, was able to devise an effective fluid medium by modification of the procedure of Robinson and Wichelhausen (1947). His best results were obtained with a pancreatic digest [Brown (1948)] of fresh lean veal hearts, titrated to pH 7.4, filtered only through glass wool, sterilized fractionally, decanted to clarify, containing 0.1 per cent autoclaved sodium thioglycollate (in preference to either cysteine-HCl or glutathione) and 10 per cent ascitic fluid, filled into 25-ml volumetric flasks [as suggested by Fitzgerald and Hampp (1952)], closed with rubber stoppers, and incubated aerobically. Good growth was also obtained in rubber-stoppered test tubes. Berger was able to use this procedure for biochemical as well as for serologic tests. He presented growth curves of 3 strains of oral treponemes based on turbidity measurements in the fluid medium, showing a lag phase of 1 to 1.5 days, a peak of growth between the second and third days, and in all 3 instances a subsequent atypical fall in turbidity (lysis?) to a nearly stationary level that continued through the 7-day study period (Fig. 6-6).

Biochemical Studies

The So-called Culture-Pallidum (Cul-Pal) Strains. Relation to *Treponema pallidum.* An attempt to piece together in some semblance of order the fragmentary data bearing on the nutritional and metabolic activity of the spirochetes under study can be made only after a detour (if indeed it is such) into the taxonomic terra incognita of the so-called culture-pallidum organisms, especially the widely studied Reiter strain. The question of the origin of these organisms has never been resolved; whether they, or some of them, were in fact originally virulent syphilis spirochetes that rapidly lost virulence and changed in other respects, or whether from the start they were what is popularly called "sapro-phytes"—a word which in the present context is probably equivalent to "indigenous spirochetes." As the various strains have been main-tained and transferred in laboratories through the years they have lost any compelling stigmata of kinship they may once have had with either group. More sophisticated workers avoid calling them *Treponema pallidum* and refer to them principally by the strain names of the workers who first isolated them: Reiter, Nichols-Hough (not to be confused with the rabbit-virulent Nichols strain of true *T. pallidum*), Noguchi, Króo, Kasan, and others. For lack of a better short general name for these organisms we here abbreviate "culture-pallidum" and speak of these forms as the "cul-pal" spirochetes. In general, these spirochetes can be cultivated easily under anaerobic conditions in such media as standard thioglycollate broth containing 10 per cent serum. In morphology they vary from pallidum-like to loosely wound and even double-contoured. The ease with which they can be handled in the laboratory has encouraged their relatively intensive study in the hope that it might illuminate problems of cultivation and antigenicity of true *T. pallidum*. These studies have, indeed, led through the work of Nelson and Mayer (1949) on the specific immobilization of rabbit-virulent *T. pallidum* to the development of media in which the spirochete of syphilis can be kept alive for limited periods, and via the early work of Gaehtgens (1929), the more recent studies of D'Ales-sandro and his coworkers (1949, 1950, 1953), Dardanoni and Censuales (1957), and Cannefax and Garson (1959), to the widespread use of the Reiter spirochete as antigen in a serum test for syphilis. Antigenic re-lationships of the cul-pal spirochetes to the indigenous forms proper will be considered later. Our present concern is with biochemical studies.

It should be noted parenthetically that Moureau (1955*b*) suggested that the Reiter treponeme may be identical with *B. refringens* on the basis of active deamination [see Barban (1954)]—a suggestion adopted by Prévot (1957) but objected to by Berger (1958) because of alleged differences in indole production and morphology.

Growth Requirements. Biochemical studies of the cul-pal spiro-chetes were initiated by Little and SubbaRow in 1945. These workers noted that all cul-pal strains require animal fluid for growth, some after laboratory cultivation for more than 20 years; but that whereas as much as 33 per cent of ascitic fluid or hydrocele fluid had been needed at first, they could now usually be grown with 10 per cent rabbit serum. Little and SubbaRow were able to replace such fluid with refined serum albumin at concentrations of 0.1 to 0.5 per cent in a medium containing casamino acids, 0.1 per cent glucose, sodium thioglycollate, cystine, asparagine, tryptophane, and an unheated alcohol-soluble liver extract, with or without agar. A limited number of transfers was possible when liver extract was replaced by choline chloride, niacin, pantothenate, pyridoxine, riboflavin, thiamin, and ascorbic acid.

In 1948 Whitely and Frazier obtained 9 subcultures of the Reiter strain in a mixture of amino acids with sodium thioglycollate, glucose, vitamins, dibasic potassium phosphate, and serum albumin. In the same year Eagle and Steinman (1948) introduced a fruitful series of studies by reporting growth of the Reiter spirochete in a mixture of acetic acid, arginine and any one of several SH- compounds, crystalline serum albumin, and minute amounts of yeast extract, in an enzymatic casein digest–glucose medium. Subsequently, Steinman and Eagle (1950) were able to use a medium containing arginine, cysteine and phenylalanine, pantothenic acid, glutamine, sodium acetate, and crystalline serum albumin with only 0.01 per cent enzymatic casein hydrolysate; and in 1952 they (Steinman, Eagle, and Oyama) replaced the casein hydrolysate to obtain a medium defined except for crystalline albumin, by using additional amino acids, vitamins, purines, and pyrimidines, with 1 per cent glucose, inorganic ions, and albumin [see also Steinman, Oyama, and Eagle, (1952)]. In 1953 Steinman, Eagle, and Oyama found that 13 amino acids were essential for growth of the parent Reiter organism; but variant strains, showing unusual variation "toward autotrophy" could dispense with aspartic acid and either glutamic acid or proline (which were mutually replaceable for the parent strain). Either uracil or cytosine was also essential, but purines were not, although adenine increased growth. This ability to dispense with purines, as well as a requirement for large amounts of ammonium ion in addition to amino acids (the NH_4^+ replaceable by glutamine) were noted as particularly unusual microbic characteristics.

In a further study by this group [Oyama, Steinman, and Eagle (1953)], the need of the Reiter strain for crystalline egg albumin was found to depend on a mechanism similar to that shown to operate for the tubercle bacillus by Dubos and Davis (1946); i.e., to supply an essential lipid, which the protein binds and detoxifies. The lipid could be replaced by certain unsaturated fatty acids, especially by oleic acid. More recently, Power and Pelczar (1959) found that increased yields of the Reiter treponeme could be obtained in commercial (BBL) "spiro-late" broth (a trypticase–yeast extract–glucose-L-cysteine–sodium thioglycollate medium), with 10 per cent inactivated sheep serum, when the medium was enriched with monoglyceride tartaric acid esters, especially diacetyl tartaric acid ester of tallow monoglycerides ("TEM 4t"). This enrichment could be replaced with a mixture of equal parts of palmitic, stearic, and oleic acids at a total concentration in the medium of 0.2 to 0.23 mg per ml. It may be noted that albumin has been substituted effectively for serum for growth of *Leptospira canicola* and *Plasmodium knowlesii* [Schneiderman et al. (1951)] and for *Trichomonas vaginalis* [Sprince and Kupferberg (1947)]; for the latter protozoan growth-promoting activity was also shown by linoleic acid (see Chap. 8).

Metabolic Activity. In view of the orientation of studies with these cul-pal spirochetes it is not surprising that little has been done to explore their catabolic behavior. Supniewski and Hano (1933) reported them relatively inactive metabolically. Scheff (1935) regarded them as true anaerobes, capable of producing lactic acid and CO_2 from glucose without significant oxygen uptake. Bucca et al. (1951) presented evidence of the presence in the Reiter strain of dehydrogenase activity for many amino acids, carbohydrates, monohydric and polyhydric alcohols, dicarboxylic acids, and fatty acids. The Reiter strain was reported by Barban (1954) to deaminate the L forms of glutamate, histidine, cysteine, arginine, and threonine. Glutamate and histidine, but not the other amino acids, could also be decarboxylated; and histidine could be further dissimilated by rupture of the imidazole ring. The chief end products of glutamate metabolism were found to be NH_3, CO_2 and succinic acid; glutamic dehydrogenase was demonstrated spectrophotometrically in sonic extracts and found to be specifically dependent on DPN. Formation of NH_3 from glutamate presumably explains the ability of glutamine to replace the requirement of the Reiter organism for extra ammonium ion as noted above [Steinman, Eagle, and Oyama (1953)]. In a later paper, Barban (1956) reported that the Reiter spirochete catalyzes transaminations of several amino acids and their keto analogues. Glutamic acid, aspartic acid, and alanine were formed from their respective keto compounds in this way, and glycine from glyoxylic acid; transamination was also noted between glutamine and α-keto acids; the coenzyme for these reactions seemed to be pyridoxal phosphate.

While it appears from the foregoing that glucose and probably other carbohydrates may be fermented by the cul-pal spirochetes, no study of their carbohydrate metabolism is known to have been made. Wichelhausen and Wichelhausen (1942) cited unpublished data obtained by

Eagle indicating a serologic relationship between the Reiter and Kasan strains and two other "large, regularly coiled spirochetes [isolated from the mouth] which do not require blood for the maintenance of pure subcultures." These oral spirochetes were found to ferment glucose with acid production, whereas, as will be noted, more typical *Treponema dentium*, which is evidently more exacting nutritionally, has usually been found inactive or only weakly active in glucose fermentation. This observation points to a possible prototype of the cul-pal spirochetes —or of some of them—among the more easily cultivated indigenous forms.

The Indigenous Spirochetes Proper. Biochemical studies of indigenous spirochetes up to about 1950 were in general superficial and, being usually based on a few strains of uncertain identity, tend to appear conflicting whether because of strain or species variation or differences in method or both. Thus, Akatsu (1917), working with Noguchi's spirochete collection, examined 1 strain each labeled *T. microdentium*, *T. mucosum*, and *T. calligyrum* (which we lump together as *T. dentium*) and 1 of *T. refringens*. Only *T. mucosum* showed improved growth in the presence of carbohydrate, while *T. microdentium* produced the most acid from glucose or glycogen, titrated as 2.8 ml of 0.1N acid in 10 ml of medium. Okabe (1936) reported that oral spirochetes have little effect on sugars, but form indole and H_2S. The loosely wound intestinal spirochete called *Spirochaeta enterogyrata* by Vinzent and Seguin (1939)—here *B. refringens*—failed in their hands to form H_2S or to liquefy gelatin or coagulated serum. Wichelhausen and Wichelhausen (1942) noted that of 15 strains of oral spirochetes identifiable as *T. dentium*, 8 that were studied failed to ferment glucose; the comparatively fastidious growth requirements of these organisms were suggested by their need for blood in the stock medium used. Of the 4 other strains of oral spirochetes studied by these workers, 3 grew without blood and formed acid from glucose; 2 of these, as noted above, were reported by Eagle as serologically related to the Reiter and Kasan cul-pal spirochetes. Carbohydrate fermentation was not determined for a single additional strain which, having failed to grow in blood agar poured plates (unlike all the others) may hence have been more fastidious than any of them.

The principal biochemical reactions of indigenous spirochetes as given by Prévot (1957), with additions from Moureau (1955), are summarized in Table 6-1, with "species" names as given by the French workers assembled in the 2 categories adopted here. Gaps in the table indicate absence of information in the originals; where the indicated information is not given for a named "species" (e.g., *T. macrodentium*) it has not been listed. Prévot noted specifically for *T. microdentium* and

TABLE 6-1

BIOCHEMICAL REACTIONS OF INDIGENOUS SPIROCHETES
(AFTER MOUREAU, 1955, AND PRÉVOT, 1957)

	Gelatin liquefied	Coagulated serum or egg-white* digested	H_2S	Indole	NH_3	Products of "fermentation"			
						Acetic acid	Propionic acid	Lactic acid	Other products
Treponema dentium type									
T. microdentium	+	+	+	+	+	+			
T. ambigua	0	0	+	+	+	+			
T. comandoni	0	0	±	±	+	+	+	+	Traces of amines
T. skoliodonta	0	0							
T. trimerodonta	0	0							
T. minutum	0	0		+	+	+	+		Ketones, traces of amines
Borrelia refringens type									
T. refringens			±	+	+	+			Amines, traces of butyric acid
T. phagedenis			±	±	+	±			Butyric acid

* Or other coagulated protein.

T. minutum that carbohydrates are not fermented. The term "fermentation" as he (and presumably Moureau as well) used it evidently signifies the anaerobic dissimilation of amino acid complexes. Berger (1958), working with oral treponemes, presumably *T. dentium*, recorded strong proteolytic activity including indole and H_2S production, but also found that glucose and possibly glycogen (alone among carbohydrates tested) were weakly fermented. Omata and Hampp (1961) have reported that spirochetes of both *T. dentium* and *Borrelia refringens* types are proteolytic, the former more actively so.

In 1952 Bryant isolated 3 strains of small loosely wound spirochetes (considered as *Borrelia sp.*) from the cattle rumen, of which they appeared to be a normal inhabitant; a similar spirochete had been seen by others in the rumen of both cattle and sheep. This organism as depicted resembles the form seen by the writer from the demarked haze of AFK plates (see page 200); it was found by Byrant to grow anaerobically at 39° on media containing rumen fluid and sugar. Its growth was stimulated by many monosaccharides and some disaccharides. It formed CO_2, ethyl alcohol, formic, acetic, lactic, and succinic acids from glucose. More recently, Wegner and Foster (1960) isolated what may have been the same organism in roller tubes of a trypticase–phytone–glucose–

rumen fluid medium. The requirement of these spirochetes for rumen fluid could be replaced by a mixture of fatty acids found in the rumen. Five strains grew well with a mixture of n-valerate and isovalerate and appreciably with isovalerate alone.

Fragmentary nutritional studies of spirochetes indigenous to man have appeared in the literature of the 1950s. Steinman, Oyama, and Schulze (1954)[3] found a strain of *T. dentium* that failed to grow in their chemically defined Reiter cul-pal medium unless it was supplemented with small amounts of Brewer's thioglycollate medium and whole blood. As with the Reiter treponeme, serum albumin, functioning as a nontoxic carrier of lipid, could replace the nondialyzable fraction of serum. The dialyzable fraction could be replaced with 5 per cent CO_2 added to the growth atmosphere (95 per cent H_2). A dialysate of laked red blood cells could be replaced with cocarboxylase; thiamin or thiamine monophosphate were many times less active. Growth factors supplied by the thioglycollate medium, contained in its yeast extract component, were identified as citrovorum factor (L-leucovorin), coenzyme A, and sodium pyruvate. Carbohydrate was included in the medium, but whether it was essential was apparently not determined. It was noted that these nutritive requirements indicate an unusually fastidious microorganism, implying "a high degree of dependency on the environment," and that virulent *T. pallidum* failed to grow in the complete medium.

In 1959 Hampp and Nevin reported a study of the so-called *Borrelia vincenti*, in which they found that ascitic fluid, usually required for growth, could be replaced by a mixture of 5 coenzymes (cocarboxylase, codecarboxylase, coenzyme A, ATP, and DPN) with glucose-1-phosphate. With this medium, maximal growth was obtained through 12 transfers of 1 strain. It was also satisfactory for 4 strains of *T. dentium* ("oral treponemes") and 3 additional strains of *B. vincenti*, but failed to support growth of 3 strains of *B. buccale*. These workers [Nevin and Hampp (1959)] have described a partially defined medium for *B. vincenti* consisting of vitamin-free casamino acids, tryptophane, purines, pyrimidines, glucose (0.25 per cent), vitamins, glutathione, and salts, supplemented by a minimum of 1.33 per cent ascitic fluid and by 1 μg per ml of cocarboxylase and 0.5 μg per ml of oleic acid—the best

---

[3] This paper finds its place here unexpectedly but unequivocally. In its text, Steinman and his coworkers characterize the spirochete studied as "one of [the] . . . saprophytic strains of *Treponema pallidum*" other than the Reiter treponeme, the latter having been studied extensively by this group, as noted above; but the "saprophyte" was identified in a footnote as one of the strains described by Wichelhausen and Wichelhausen (1942) and Robinson and Wichelhausen (1946). It can be clearly identified from the data given by the latter authors as a strain of *T. dentium* (*T. microdentium*) from the human mouth.

of a series of fatty acids—which reduced the formation of granules. Riboflavin, biotin, and folic acid were found to be essential, and ATP was required with 1.33 per cent ascitic fluid but not with 3.33 per cent. At the lower ascitic fluid concentration the further addition of coenzyme A brought the yield to the level attained with 10 per cent ascitic fluid [see also Nevin and Jordan (1961)].

Antigen-Antibody Reactions

Immunologic studies with these spirochetes have dealt with two questions, neither of which has been definitively answered: their relationship to the cul-pal organisms and to *Treponema pallidum* as part of the problem of the specificity of serum tests for syphilis; and the matter of taxonomy of the indigenous forms themselves.

Relationship to Cul-pal Forms and to *T. pallidum.* The earliest study of this question appears to be that of Craig and Nichols (1912) who, using alcohol extracts of Noguchi's cultures of *T. pallidum, T. pertenue,* and *T. microdentium,* found that they all reacted with syphilitic serums to fix complement as did the Wassermann tissue lipid. Noguchi and Akatsu (1917) extended these studies to include the *calligyra-refringens* and *microdentium-mucosum* strains as well as 4 of Noguchi's culture strains of *T. pallidum.* The cultures were grown with rabbit serum in place of ascitic fluid, as well as rabbit kidney, and were used apparently in viable form to immunize rabbits by the intravenous route. Homologous and cross titrations by several methods indicated some quantitative heterogeneity within the "pallidum" group and cross reactions between the groups at low titers; between *pallidum* and *calligyra,* slightly between *pallidum* and *refringens,* more markedly between *calligyra* and *refringens,* slightly between *microdentium* and *mucosum,* and between *mucosum* and many of the others. *T. microdentium* seemed to be the least related to the other strains. It was noted that a virulent *T. pallidum* from rabbit testicle reacted only slightly with culture pallidum antiserums.

Several papers published in Germany during the latter half of the 1920s proposed the use of avirulent cul-pal spirochetes, either as alcohol extracts or as phenolized suspensions, to replace tissue lipid in the complement-fixation test for syphilis [reviewed by Gaehtgens (1937–38)]. A careful study of this question reported by Beck in 1939 included a mouth spirochete labeled Jahnel,[4] not otherwise identified, as well as the cul-pal strains Reiter 36, Króo, Kasan II, and Noguchi. When culture spirochetes suspended in "0.3 per cent carbol saline solu-

---

[4] Koch (1940) reported that a "saprophytic" genital spirochete isolated by Jahnel was antigenically distinct from culture pallidum.

tion" were used as antigens in complement-fixation tests with 1,100 serums—542 from known syphilis, 62 from doubtful cases, and 496 from controls—the percentage values for sensitivity/specificity were: Reiter, 89/0.6; Kasan, 96.3/1.8; Króo, 79.1/1.7; and the mouth spirochete, 59.2/4.4. The mouth spirochete antigen thus cross-reacted with syphilitic serums, but less often than those of the cul-pal spirochetes, and gave reactions with nonsyphilitic serums more often. Beck noted that the reactions of the mouth spirochete recorded as positive were weak ($\pm$) in about half the cases. He cited Gaehtgens (1929) as having obtained positive reactions with syphilitic serums in only a few instances with a strain of *Spirochaeta dentium*. Beck further observed, in tests with absorbed antispirochete serums from immunized rabbits, by both agglutination and complement fixation, that the Kasan and Reiter strains were identical; whereas the Noguchi, Króo, and mouth spirochetes differed from the first two and from one another. These findings are not in full agreement with those of Noguchi and Akatsu given previously.

In 1941 Kolmer, Kast, and Lynch (1941*a*) undertook similar studies with cul-pal spirochetes and included cultures of mouth spirochetes called by them *Sp. microdentium* and *Sp. macrodentium*. They compared Kolmer, Kahn, and Kline test findings with those of complement-fixation tests using culture spirochete antigens prepared in both phenolized and formalinized saline and as alcohol extracts. They tested 139 syphilitic serums and 260 nonsyphilitic serums, as well as syphilitic and nonsyphilitic cerebrospinal fluid, and serums from cases of leprosy and malaria. Their results differed from those of earlier workers in demonstrating naturally occurring spirochetal complement-fixing antibody, especially for the *microdentium* strain. Thus in 114 serums all of which were negative in standard serum tests for syphilis, the following percentages were positive for the organisms noted: Nichols-Hough, 22.9; Noguchi, 38.7; Króo, 61.4; *macrodentium*, 61.4; *microdentium*, 79.4; and for *C. diphtheriae* antigens, 2.2. One spinal fluid out of fifteen from nonsyphilitic subjects reacted positively with the Króo and Reiter antigens and with both mouth spirochetes; none was positive with Nichols-Hough or Noguchi culture antigens or in standard STS. All but 1 of 25 serums from leprosy reacted with *microdentium*, as did all of 6 from malaria, suggesting an increase in antibody to this spirochete in these diseases. In a subsequent study by the same workers (Kolmer, Kast, and Lynch, 1941*b*), the complement-fixation titers were found distinctly higher in syphilitic than in nonsyphilitic serums for Reiter and *microdentium* antigens, whereas agglutination titers were much the same in STS-positive and STS-negative serums for the Nichols-Hough (range 0 to 1:50), Noguchi (0 to 1:50), Króo (0 to 1:100), and Reiter (1:500

to 1:1000) strains and for both *macrodentium* (1:200 to 1:1000) and *microdentium* (1:200 to 1:10,000). Titers of *microdentium* antigens were conspicuously higher than those of the other spirochetes. Rabbit serums prepared by immunization with both living and heat-killed Nichols-Hough antigens reacted significantly in agglutination only with homologous and Noguchi antigens. Complement-fixation tests with a wider range of rabbit antiserums yielded apparently nonspecific results; the 2 mouth spirochete antigens reacted not only with their homologous and other spirochetal serums but also with antidiphtheria serum.

The data of Robinson and Wichelhausen (1946) with precipitin reactions that separated a group of oral spirochetes into distinct serotypes contain interesting support of the findings of both Beck and the Kolmer group. Beck's observation that the Kasan and Reiter strains were serologically identical was confirmed, as was that of the latter workers of a close relationship between the Nichols and Noguchi strains. The first 2 cul-pal organisms, moreover, crossed with 2 strains of mouth spirochetes called *Treponema macrodentium*; while the latter 2 formed a group by themselves. Robinson and Wichelhausen observed no reactions by their precipitin technique with normal (human?) serum; but they noted in passing that positive results in normal serum appeared in agglutination tests, which also showed cross-reactions between morphologically different spirochetes.

In more recent studies that have led to development of the Reiter complement-fixation test for syphilis [Oddo and Dardanoni (1947); D'Alessandro et al. (1949, 1950, 1953); Dardanoni and Censuales (1957); DeBruijn (1958, 1959); Pillot and Faure (1959); Cannefax and Garson (1959); Christiansen (1960)], the indigenous spirochetes do not appear to have been studied.

Serology of the Indigenous Spirochetes Proper. The findings given above of Noguchi and Akatsu (1917) and of Kolmer, Kast, and Lynch (1941*a*) both suggested serologic heterogeneity among indigenous spirochetes. Those of Robinson and Wichelhausen (1946) indicated that at least 7 serotypes are distinguishable among the mouth spirochetes by the precipitin method of those workers. The small spirochetes we call *T. dentium* fell into 5 such groups, and the larger form, *B. refringens*, formed 2 serotypes, of which the first (1 strain) was characterized as irregular and loosely coiled but not named, while the second (2 strains), called by Robinson and Wichelhausen *T. macrodentium* ("large, regularly coiled") cross-reacted with Reiter and Kasan cul-pal spirochetes as noted above. Hampp (1947) has described a method for microscopic agglutination tests with oral spirochetes but seems to have reported only homologous titers. The need for additional serologic studies of these organisms is apparent.

Pathogenicity

The particular contribution to disease made by indigenous spirochetes—if there is one—remains unclear. Such evidence as we have for pathogenicity points to *T. dentium* rather than to *B. refringens:* the connection of the so-called *B. vincenti* (syn., *B. refringens*) with Vincent's or other fusospirochetal disease is entirely one of guilt by association. Attempts to induce transmissible lesions with cultures containing only indigenous spirochetes have been overwhelmingly negative [reviewed by Berger (1958)]. Fitzgerald, Hampp, and Newton (1958) have reported negative results with cultures of both *T. dentium* and *B. refringens* in guinea pigs pretreated with cortisone as well as in untreated animals, and also in germfree guinea pigs. Small transient abscesses have been produced in rabbits and guinea pigs by Hampp and Mergen-

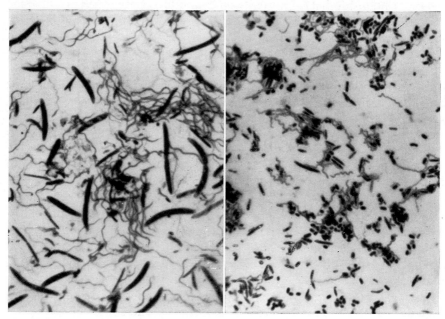

Fig. 6-7. Fusospirochetal exudates. Left, gingival scrapings from periodontal disease in man, showing profusion of spirochetes, principally loosely wound, and large curved granular organisms, presumably *Spirillum sputigenum*. Typical fusobacteria, much smaller than the preceding, are also present, as well as vibrio-like forms and scattered cocci and rods. Right, exudate from guinea-pig fusospirochetal exudate in the fourteenth passage, originally produced with material from gingival disease in man, showing typical alteration in the flora: spirochetes are all small and predominantly tightly wound; spirilla are absent; cocci and short rods are more abundant. Goldsworthy-Ward stain, ×1,000.

hagen (1961) by intracutaneous inoculation of 6×10^7 cells. The evidence for pathogenicity of *T. dentium* rests rather upon 3 points: (1) prominence and persistence of spirochetes as a component of experimental fusospirochetal infections; (2) their occasional presence apart from other microorganisms in viable tissue beyond the necrotic zone of mixed infection in sections of fusospirochetal lesions; and (3) their reported participation in experimentally recombined mixtures of pure cultures having fusospirochetal infectivity. The last point, which ought to be crucial, is in fact ambiguous. Details of the 3 points follow.

Spirochetes in Lesions. It has been found consistently (see Fig. 6-7) that even though the larger spirochetes may occur in profusion in the original fusospirochetal inoculum from a lesion in man, the experimental exudate from guinea pigs or other animals after several passages contains spirochetes of the *T. dentium* type only [see Rosebury and Foley (1939, 1942); Hemmens and Harrison (1942); Shpuntoff and Rosebury (1949)]. An exception has been noted in the instance of draining abscesses, in which small numbers of loosely wound spirochetes, both single- and double-contoured, have reappeared [Rosebury et al. (1951)]. The suggestion has been offered [e.g., by Noguchi (1912a)] that the larger forms appear in response to imperfect anaerobiosis (see footnote, page 188). Rosebury and collaborators (1950b) estimated that the LD_{50} for guinea pigs in a volume of 0.1 ml of exudate contained 1.7×10^9 spirochetes in a total flora of 8×10^9 mixed bacteria, the ratio of spirochetes to total flora being roughly 1:5. The corresponding values for ID_{50} were approximately 6.8×10^7 and 3.2×10^8. These values indicate, at most, an extremely low order of virulence. In the experiment of Rosebury and his group (1950c) in which a mixed cup-plate culture of guinea pig fusospirochetal exudate was transferred culture-to-culture for 10 passages without loss of typical infectivity, spirochetes persisted without observed change in both cultures and guinea pigs inoculated at each passage.

Spirochetes in Tissue Sections. The occurrence of spirochetes in silver-impregnated tissue sections, extending into viable tissue in advance of the mixed flora of severe spreading fusospirochetal disease, has been described for lesions in man by Stewart (1911), Tunnicliff (1919), Zinserling (1928), and Tunnicliff, Fink, and Hammond (1936); the last-named workers gave additional references. The writer has seen such sections from the mouth of a chimpanzee naturally infected with a noma-like illness, in which a profusion of spirochetes appeared without other bacteria, giving a picture indistinguishable from that of congenital syphilitic tissue. In the writer's laboratory, Ehrenhaus (1940) was able to reproduce this picture with material from fatal experimental fusospirochetal disease in guinea pigs. Ehrenhaus, and

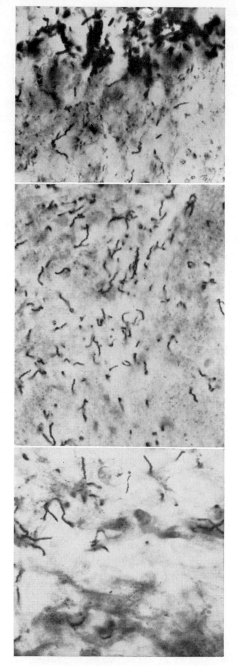

Fig. 6-8. Fatal fusospirochetal cellulitis. Guinea-pig tissue stained by Levaditi's method, showing, above, invasion principally of spirochetes beyond (beneath) the mixed bacterial flora, which is limited to necrotic tissue; center, spirochetes infiltrating viable tissue; and below, vanguard spirochetal invasion. × 800.

also Kunert (1955) have presented photomicrographs of such sections (see Fig. 6-8).

Spirochetes in Experimental Culture Mixtures. Early attempts to reproduce experimental fusospirochetal disease with culture combinations were reviewed by Rosebury et al. (1950a). These studies culminated in the work of D. T. Smith (1927, 1930, 1932) which was soon duplicated by Proske and Sayers (1934). Both groups found a spirochete of the *T. dentium* type to be a member of their only effective combination, which also included a fusiform bacillus, a vibrio, and a streptococcus, all anaerobic. Extended attempts to confirm these findings in the writer's laboratory [Rosebury et al. (1950a,b,c)] were unsuccessful, as were efforts to find any combination of up to 17 different microorganisms, including spirochetes, that would yield more than transient or atypical lesions in guinea pigs. These workers (1950c) found that mixed cultures prepared from whole guinea pig exudate either in spirochete cup-plates or as "spot" cultures on blood agar were capable of reproducing typical transmissible lesions in guinea pigs after repeated culture passage. Continuing these studies, Macdonald, Sutton, and Knoll (1954) recombined cultures prepared from 16 separate isolations, not identical with those of the previous group, by streaking them on blood agar plates as separate "spoke" lines toward a common center, at which spirochetes were added. With mixed growth from the center of some of these "wheel" plates they succeeded in initiating typical transmissible fusospirochetal disease in guinea pigs. In subsequent studies, these workers [Macdonald et al. (1956)] recombined these cultures in smaller groups and reported producing typical lesions with mixtures of organisms containing bacteroides, but in which spirochetes were no longer present. Whether this finding indicates that spirochetes actually play no part in the natural and experimental diseases in which they occur, or whether these workers confused fusospirochetal disease with the similar but probably not identical mixed anaerobic infections of Meleney (1931), Hite, Locke, and Hesseltine (1949) and others [see Rosebury and Sonnenwirth (1958); Berger (1958)] remains to be determined.

Other Data on Pathogenicity. Wichelhausen and Wichelhausen (1942) found partial hemolysis in pour plate cultures of both large and small mouth spirochetes that grew in blood agar; 3 cul-pal strains also showed hemolysis. Berger (1958) also found hemolysis around deep colonies of *T. dentium*. This worker's attempts to demonstrate a soluble hemotoxin or leukocidin in these spirochetes were negative, but he reported evidence for weak hyaluronidase activity. Hampp, Mergenhagen, and Omata (1959), on the other hand, were unable to demonstrate hyaluronidase or other mucopolysaccharidase activity in either small or large oral spirochetes. Endotoxic activity was found in both tightly and loosely wound oral spirochetes by Mergenhagen, Hampp, and Scherp (1961).

Antibiotic and Drug Sensitivity

A series of studies of the in vitro drug sensitivity of indigenous (oral) spirochetes has been reported by Fitzgerald and Hampp (1952), Hampp and Fitzgerald (1958, 1959), and Berger (1956, 1958b,c, 1959, 1960); see also Berger and Marggraf (1960). The following have been found actively antispirochetal by either or both groups of workers: penicillin, tetracyclines, chloramphenicol, bacitracin, neomycin, spiramycin, and carbomycin. The following showed considerable strain variation or were only moderately active: erythromycin, streptomycin, oleandomycin, novobiocin, celesticetin, and streptolidigin. Generally inactive were tyrothrycin, polymyxin B, cycloserine, anisomycin, Furacin, and Furadantin. It may be noted that the pattern of sensitivity is generally that of Gram-positive bacteria.

Fitzgerald and Hampp (1952) reported that both tightly and loosely wound oral spirochetes were sensitive to 50 to 100 μg per ml of sulpharsphenamine. Arsphenamines were used effectively in treatment of experimental fusospirochetal disease by Rosebury, Foley, and Rights (1939), and penicillin has been found active under similar conditions in the writer's laboratory. Penicillin has been widely used with well-marked effect in treatment of fusospirochetal disease in man [briefly reviewed by Rosebury (1946)]. Such sensitivity, which suggests an effect dependent upon elimination of the spirochetes, contrasts with the findings in anaerobic mixed (bacteroides) infections (see Chap. 5) and adds an additional suggestion of a contribution made by spirochetes to pathogenicity.

References

Akatsu, S., 1917, *J. Exptl. Med.*, **25**:375.
Aksjanzew-Malkin, S., 1933, *Zentr. Bakteriol. Parasitenk.*, *I Orig.*, **129**:405.
Aragão, H. de B., and Vianna, G., 1913, *Mem. Inst. Oswaldo Cruz*, **5**:211, cited by Hindle (1931).
Barban, S., 1954, *J. Bacteriol.*, **68**:493.
————, 1956, *ibid.*, **71**:274.
Beck, A., 1939, *J. Hyg.*, **39**:298.
Berger, U., 1956, *Arch. Hyg. u. Bakteriol.*, **140**:605.
————, 1958a, *Die Treponemen der Mundhöhle und ihre Bedeutung für die Pathogenese der oralen Fusospirochätosen, Beitr. Hyg. u. Epid.*, vol. 12, J. A. Barth, Leipzig.
————, 1958b, *Z. Hyg. Infektionskrankh.*, **144**:480.
————, 1958c, *ibid.*, **145**:1, 160.

————, 1959, *Arch. Hyg. u. Bakteriol.*, **143**:316.
————, 1960, *Arch. klin. u. exptl. Dermatol.*, **210**:537.
————, and Marggraf, H., 1960, *ibid.*, **210**:400.
Blanchard, R., 1906, *Arch. Parasitol.*, **10**:129.
Bradfield, J. R. G., and Cater, D. B., 1952, *Nature*, **169**:944.
Braïlovsky-Lounkevitch, Z. A., 1915, *Ann. Inst. Pasteur*, **29**:379.
Brown, J. H., 1948, *J. Bacteriol.*, **55**:871.
Brumpt, 1922, cited by Prévot (1957), p. 333.
Bryant, M. P., 1953, *J. Bacteriol.*, **64**:325.
————, 1959, *Bacteriol. Revs.*, **23**:125.
Bucca, M. A., Thayer, J. D., Roberts, H. B., and Tager, B., 1951, *J. Venereal Disease Inform.*, **32**:6.
Cannefax, G. R., and Garson, W., 1959, *J. Immunol.*, **82**:198.
Castellani, A., 1906, *Lancet*, **1**:1384.
Chick, H., MacRae, T. F., Martin, A. J. P., and Martin, C. J., 1938, *Biochem. J.*, **32**:10, 844, 2207.
Christiansen, A. H., 1960, *Acta Pathol. Microbiol. Scand.*, **50**:106.
Cleland, J. B., 1909, *J. Trop. Med. Hyg.*, **12**:143.
Coutts, W. E., Silva-Inzunza, E., and Valadares-Prieto, J., 1952, *Dermatologia* (Basel), **1–5**:79 (*Biol. Abstr.*).
Cox, C. D., and Larson, A. D., 1957, *J. Bacteriol.*, **73**:587.
Craig, C. F., and Nichols, H. J., 1912, *J. Exptl. Med.*, **16**:336.
Czekalowski, J. W., and Eaves, G., 1955, *J. Pathol. Bacteriol.*, **49**:129.
D'Alessandro, G., and Dardanoni, L., 1953, *Am. J. Syphilis, Gonorrhea, Venereal Diseases*, **37**:137.
————, Oddo, F., Comes, R., and Dardanoni, L., 1949, *Riv. Ist. Sieroterap. Ital.*, *Sez. II*, **24**:134 (*Biol. Abstr.*).
————, ————, and Dardanoni, L., 1950, *J. Venereal Disease Inform.*, **31**: 314.
Dardanoni, L., and Censuales, S., 1957, *Riv. Ist. Sieroterap. Ital.*, **32**:489, cited by Christiansen (1960).
DeBruijn, J. H., 1958, *Antonie van Leeuwenhoek J. Microbiol. Serol.*, **24**: 253 (*Biol. Abstr.*).
————, 1959, *ibid.*, **25**:41 (*Biol. Abstr.*).
————, 1961, *ibid.*, **27**:98.
Dobell, C. C., 1912, *Arch. Protistenk.*, **26**:117, cited by Hindle (1931).
————, 1932, *Antony van Leeuwenhoek and His "Little Animals,"* Harcourt, Brace and Company, New York, reprinted 1960, Dover Publications, New York.
Dubos, R. J., and Davis, B. D., 1946, *J. Exptl. Med.*, **83**:409.
Eagle, H., and Steinman, H. G., 1948, *J. Bacteriol.* **56**:163.
Ehrenberg, C. B., 1833, cited by Noguchi (1928).
Ehrenhaus, J., 1940, *Columbia Dental Rev.*, **11**:11.
Fitzgerald, R. J., and Hampp, E. G., 1952, *J. Dental Research*, **31**:20.
————, ————, and Newton, W. L., 1958, *ibid.*, **37**:11.
Fortner, J., 1928, *Zentr. Bakteriol. Parasitenk.*, *I Orig.*, **108**:155.
————, 1929, *ibid.*, **110**:233.
Gaehtgens, W., 1929, *Z. Immunitätsforsch.*, **63**:398.
————, 1937–38, *Arch. Dermatol. Syphilol.*, **176**:42.
Gates, F. L., 1923, *J. Exptl. Med.*, **37**:311.
Gerber, P., 1910, *Zentr. Bakteriol. Parasitenk.*, *I Orig.*, **56**:508.

Gordon, J., Holman, R. A., and McLeod, J. W., 1952, *J. Pathol. Bacteriol.*, **46**:527.

Hampp, E. G., 1943, *J. Am. Dental Assoc.*, **30**:1066.

——, 1947, *ibid.*, **34**:606.

——, 1950, *ibid.*, **40**:1.

——, 1954, *J. Dental Research*, **33**:660.

——, and Fitzgerald, R. J., 1958, *ibid.*, **37**:11.

——, and ——, 1959, *ibid.*, **38**:947.

——, and Mergenhagen, S. E., 1961, *J. Inf. Dis.*, **109**:43.

——, ——, and Omata, R. R., 1959, *J. Dental Research*, **38**:979.

——, and Nevin, T. A., 1959, *J. Bacteriol.*, **77**:800.

——, Scott, D. B., and Wycoff, R. W. G., 1948, *ibid.*, **56**:755.

Hemmens, E. S., and Harrison, R. W., 1942, *J. Inf. Dis.*, **70**:131.

Hindle, E., 1931, *A System of Bacteriology in Relation to Medicine* (London), **8**:141.

Hite, K. E., Locke, M., and Hesseltine, H. C., 1949, *J. Inf. Dis.*, **84**:1.

Hofferd, R. M., 1950, *Vet. Med.*, **45**:227.

Hoffmann, E., 1920, *Deutsche med. Wochschr.*, **46**:625.

——, and Von Prowazek, S., 1906, *Zentr. Bakteriol. Parasitenk., I Orig.*, **41**:741, 817.

Hogue, M. J., 1922, *J. Exptl. Med.*, **36**:617.

Kasai, K., and Kobayashi, R., 1919, *J. Parasitol.*, **6**:1.

Kawata, T., and Aoi, H., 1956, *Japan. J. Bacteriol.*, **11**:471.

——, Matsuo, J., and Aoi, H., 1956, *ibid.*, **11**:911.

Kirschner, L., and Graham, L., 1959, *Brit. J. Exptl. Pathol.*, **40**:507.

Koch, F., 1940, *Zentr. Bakteriol. Parasitenk., I Orig.*, **145**:338.

Kolmer, J. A., Kast, C. C., and Lynch, E. R., 1941*a*, *Am. J. Syphilis, Gonorrhea, Venereal Diseases*, **25**:300.

——, ——, and ——, 1941*b*, *ibid.*, **25**:412.

Kritchewski, B., and Seguin, P., 1920, *Rev. Stom.*, **22**:613.

——, and ——, 1924, *Dental Cosmos*, **66**:511.

Kunert, H., 1955, *Z. Hyg. Infektionskrankh.*, **141**:384.

Landsteiner, K., and Mucha, V., 1906, *Wien. klin. Wochschr.*, **19**:1349.

Larson, A. D., Treick, R. W., Edwards, C. L., and Cox, C. D., 1959, *J. Bacteriol.*, **77**:361.

Little, P. A., and SubbaRow, Y., 1945, *J. Immunol.*, **50**:213.

Ludovic, M. M., and Blaizot, P., 1928, *Compt. Rend. Acad. Sci.*, **187**:911.

Macdonald, J. B., Sutton, R. M., and Knoll, M. L., 1954, *J. Inf. Dis.*, **95**:275.

——, ——, ——, Madlener, E. M., and Grainger, R. M., 1956, *ibid.*, **98**:15.

Macfie, J. W. S., 1916, *Ann. Trop. Med. Parasitol.*, **10**:305.

——, 1916–17, *Parasitology*, **9**:274.

——, and Carter, H. F., 1917, *Ann. Trop. Med. Parasitol.*, **11**:75.

Meleney, F. L., 1931, *Ann. Surg.*, **94**:961.

Mergenhagen, S. E., Hampp, E. G., and Scherp, H. W., 1961, *J. Inf. Dis.*, **108**:304.

Michel, 1930, *Rev. Gén. Méd. Vét.*, **34**:330.

Miller, W. D., 1890, *The Micro-Organisms of the Human Mouth*, S. S. White Company, Philadelphia.

Moureau, M., 1955*a*, *Ann. Inst. Pasteur*, **88**:231.

——, 1955*b*, *ibid.*, **89**:127.

Mühlens, P., and Hartmann, M., 1906, Z. Hyg. Infektionskrankh., 55:81, 82.

Nelson, R. A., Jr., and Mayer, M. M., 1949, J. Exptl. Med., 89:369.

Nevin, T. A., and Hampp, E. G., 1959, J. Bacteriol., 78:263.

———, and Jordan, H. V., 1961, J. Dental Research, 40:622.

Noguchi, H., 1911, J. Am. Med. Assoc., 57:102.

———, 1911, J. Exptl. Med., 14:99.

———, 1912a, ibid., 15:81.

———, 1912b, ibid., 15:466.

———, 1912c, ibid., 16:194.

———, 1912d, ibid., 16:261.

———, 1913, ibid., 17:89.

———, 1918, ibid., 27:575, 667.

———, 1923, Laboratory Diagnosis of Syphilis, New York, cited by Noguchi (1928), p. 483.

———, 1928, in Jordan, E. O., and Falk, I. S., The Newer Knowledge of Bacteriology and Immunology, University of Chicago Press, Chicago, p. 452.

———, and Akatsu, S., 1917, J. Exptl. Med., 25:765.

———, and Kaliski, D. J., 1918, ibid., 28:559.

Obermeier, O. (1868), 1873, Berl. klin. Wochschr., 10:152, 378, 391, 445.

Oddo, F., and Dardanoni, L., 1947, Boll. Soc. Ital. Biol. Sper., 23:1090 (Biol. Abstr.).

Okabe, S., 1936, Zentr. Bakteriol. Parasitenk., I Orig., 136:485.

Omata, R. R., and Hampp, E. G., 1961, J. Dental Research, 40:171.

Oyama, V. I., Steinman, H. G., and Eagle, H., 1953, J. Bacteriol., 65:609.

Palmer, E. D., 1954, Gastroenterology, 27:218.

Parr, L. W., 1923, J. Inf. Dis., 33:369.

Paul, E., 1908, Ber. 80 Vers. deutsch. Naturforsch. Artze, Köln; in 1909, Deut. Monatsschr. Zahnh., 27:24, cited by Berger (1958).

Phillips, J. McI., and Berry, F., 1930, J. Inf. Dis., 27:136.

Pillot, J., and Faure, M., 1959, Ann. Inst. Pasteur, 96:196.

Pilot, I., 1938, Arch. Pathol., 25:601.

———, and Brams, J., 1923, J. Inf. Dis., 32:134.

———, and Kanter, A. E., 1923, ibid., 32:204.

Power, D. A., and Pelczar, M. J., Jr., 1959, J. Bacteriol., 77:789.

Prévot, A.-R., 1957, Manuel de classification et de détermination des bactéries anaérobies, 3d ed., Masson et Cie, Paris.

Proske, H. O., and Sayers, R. R., 1934, Public Health Repts. (U.S.), 49:839, 1212.

Prowazek, S. von, 1907, Arch. Protistenk., 10:129, cited by Noguchi (1928), p. 483.

Robinson, L. B., and Wichelhausen, R. H., 1946, Bull. Johns Hopkins Hosp., 79:436.

Rosebury, T., 1942, J. Lab. Clin. Med., 27:1470.

———, 1946, J. Periodontol., 17:122.

———, Clark, A. R., Engel, S. G., and Tergis, F., 1950a, J. Inf. Dis., 87:217.

———, ———, Tergis, F., and Engel, S. G., 1950b, ibid., 87:226.

———, ———, Macdonald, J. B., and O'Connell, D. C., 1950c, ibid., 87:234.

———, and Foley, G., 1939, J. Am. Dental Assoc., 26:1798.

————, and ————, 1941, *Proc. Soc. Exptl. Biol. Med.*, **47**:368.

————, and ————, 1942, *J. Dental Research*, **21**:308.

————, ————, and Rights, F. L., 1939, *J. Inf. Dis.*, **65**:291.

————, Macdonald, J. B., and Clark, A. R., 1950, *J. Dental Research*, **29**: 718.

————, ————, Ellison, S. A., and Engel, S. G., 1951, *Oral Surg., Oral Med., Oral Pathol.*, **4**:68.

————, and Sonnenwirth, A. C., 1958, in Dubos, R. J. (ed.) *Bacterial and Mycotic Infections of Man*, 3d ed., J. B. Lippincott Company, Philadelphia, ch. 31, p. 626.

Rosenthal, S. L., and Gootzeit, E. H., 1942, *J. Dental Research*, **21**:373.

Schaudinn, F., and Hoffman, E., 1905, *Arb. kaiserl. Gesundh.*, **22**:527.

Scheff, G., von, 1935, *Zentr. Bakteriol. Parasitenk., I Orig.*, **134**:35.

Schneiderman, A., Greene, M. R., Schieler, L., McClure, L. E., and Dunn, M. S., 1951, *Proc. Soc. Exptl. Biol. Med.*, **78**:777.

Seguin, P., 1930, *Compt. Rend. Soc. Biol.*, **104**:247.

————, and Vinzent, R., 1936, *ibid.*, **121**:408.

————, 1938, *Ann. Inst. Pasteur*, **61**:255.

Shmamine, T., 1910, *Zentr. Bakteriol. Parasitenk., I Orig.*, **65**:311.

Shpuntoff, H., and Rosebury, T., 1949, *J. Dental Research*, **28**:7.

Smith, D. T., 1927, *Am. Rev. Tuberc.*, **16**:584.

————, 1927, *Arch. Surg.*, **14**:(II):231.

————, 1930, *J. Inf. Dis.*, **46**:303.

————, 1932, *Oral Spirochetes and Related Organisms in Fuso-Spirochetal Disease*, The Williams & Wilkins Company, Baltimore.

Socransky, S., Macdonald, J. B., and Sawyer, S., 1959, *Arch. Oral Biol.*, **1**: 171.

Sprince, H., and Kupferberg, A. B., 1947, *J. Bacteriol.*, **53**:441.

Steinman, H. G., and Eagle, H., 1950, *ibid.*, **60**:57.

————, ————, and Oyama, V. I., 1952, *ibid.*, **64**:265.

————, ————, and ————, 1953, *J. Biol. Chem.*, **200**:775.

————, Oyama, V. I., and Eagle, H., 1952, *Bacteriol. Proc.*, 135.

————, ————, and Schulze, H. O., 1954, *J. Biol. Chem.*, **211**:327.

Stewart, M. J., 1911, *J. Pathol. Bacteriol.*, **16**:221.

Stoddard, J. L., 1917, *Brit. Med. J.*, **2**:416.

Strong, R. P., 1923, *Science*, **57**:514.

————, Shattuck, G. C., Bequaert, J. C., and Wheeler, R. E., 1926, *Medical Report of the Hamilton Rice 7th Expedition to the Amazon, 1924–25*, Harvard University Press, Cambridge.

Supniewski, J. W., and Hano, J., 1933, *Bull. Intern. Acad. Polon. Sci., Classe Méd.* 181, cited by Bucca et al. (1951).

Swain, R. H. A., 1955, *J. Pathol. Bacteriol.*, **69**:117.

————, 1957, *ibid.*, **73**:155.

Tunnicliff, R., 1919, *J. Inf. Dis.*, **25**:132.

————, Fink, E. B., and Hammond, C., 1936, *J. Am. Dental Assoc.*, **23**:1959.

Veillon, A., and Zuber, A., 1898, *Arch. Méd. Expér. et Anat. Pathol.*, **10**:517.

Veldkamp, H., 1960, *Antonie van Leeuwenhoek J. Microbiol. Serol.*, **26**: 103 (*Biol. Abstr.*).

Veszpremi, D., 1907, *Zentr. Bakteriol. Parasitenk., I Orig.*, **44**:332, 408, 515.

————, 1908, *ibid.*, **45**:15.

Vincent, H., 1896, *Ann. Inst. Pasteur*, **10**:488.

Vinzent, R., and Daufresne, M., 1934, *Compt. Rend. Soc. Biol.*, **116**:490.

———, and Seguin, P., 1939*a*, *ibid.*, **130**:12.

———, and ———, 1939*b*, *Bull. Acad. Méd.*, **121**:407.

———, ———, and Daufresne, M., 1936, *Compt. Rend. Soc. Biol.*, **121**:406.

Wegner, G. H., and Foster, E. M., 1960, *J. Dairy Sci.*, **43**:566.

Werner, H., 1909, *Zentr. Bakteriol. Parasitenk.*, *I Orig.*, **52**:241.

Whitely, H. R., and Frazier, C. N., 1948, *Am. J. Syphilis, Gonorrhea, Venereal Diseases*, **32**:43.

Wichelhausen, O. W., and Wichelhausen, R. H., 1942, *J. Dental Research*, **21**:543.

Wolbach, S. B., 1914–15, *Am. J. Trop. Dis. Prev. Med.*, **2**:494.

Yakimoff, W. L., and Rastjapin, T., 1930, *Arch. Protistenk.*, **71**:543.

Zinserling, W., 1928, *Ueber die Fusospirochetose (Gangran und einige Prozesse vorsugsweise bei Kindern)*, Gustav Fischer, Jena, in 1929, *Veröffentl. aus der Kriegs- und Konstitutionspathologie 5*, **19**:1.

CHAPTER 7

INDIGENOUS FUNGI

Fungi in General

The eumycetes or true fungi—as distinguished from the actinomycetes, which as we have seen in Chap. 3 are now placed unequivocally among the bacteria—are less well understood than bacteria in their ecologic relations with man. Only the yeastlike form *Candida albicans* has been studied extensively as an undoubtedly indigenous fungus. Additional species are included, some more tentatively; and there is reason to believe that still others will emerge into this category as they are more directly looked for.

Saprophytism and Pathogenicity. A conspicuous difficulty in this field is the ubiquity of fungi in the environment. The distinctions between saprophyte, amphibiont, and pathogen among these microorganisms are even more clouded than elsewhere, lacking, for instance, the positive clarity found among the streptococci or the distinctive negativity of the clostridia. In other words, nearly all fungi, including those that induce disease, seem to behave like environmental contaminants. In recent years the suggestion advanced early by Sabouraud (1893) has been put forward strongly [Emmons (1950, 1954); Ajello (1956)] that fungi pathogenic for man are, like the clostridia, properly saprophytes of soil. Saprophytism in soil has been demonstrated for several important disease-producing fungi, including *Coccidioides immitis, Aspergillus fumigatus, Cryptococcus* spp., *Allescheria boydii*, the dermatophyte *Microsporum gypseum*, and most conspicuous in more recent studies, *Histoplasma capsulatum. Sporotrichum schenkii* is perhaps exceptional in its capacity to proliferate in living plant tissue as well as in animals and saprophytically. Ajello (1956) compiled from the literature a list of species of pathogenic or potentially pathogenic fungi isolated from nonliving sources. Emmons (1954) has suggested that "the epidemiology of most of the deep mycoses is that of a group of diseases caused by fungi which are primarily saprophytes capable of living and reproducing indefinitely in soil, without any necessary relationship to a living animal host." There appear to be exceptions, however. Among patho-

222

genic or parasitic fungi that do not seem to have been found multiplying saprophytically are *Blastomyces dermatitidis* [Emmons (1950)], dermatophytes other than *Microsporum gypseum* [Baer et al (1955)], and *Pityrosporum* spp. (see below). *Candida albicans* has been recovered in a few instances from decaying vegetation [Negroni and Fisher (1941)] and from soil [DiMenna (1955)]; Ajello (1956) reported its recovery from 2 of 1,141 soil samples [see also McDonough et al. (1961)]. Van Uden and his coworkers (1956) also recovered this fungus in 5 instances from vegetable sources, and more recently DiMenna (1958) isolated it from grasses in an area lightly stocked with sheep.[1] These findings, as Van Uden et al. pointed out, do not establish saprophytism, but probably reflect survival in the environment of yeasts derived from human or animal sources. Skinner and Fletcher (1960) agreed that *C. albicans* is probably adventitious in nonanimal habitats.

Autochthony. The problem is equally complex when approached from the other side, in the effort to determine whether fungi found on human or animal body surfaces can be considered indigenous to those areas, or only transient environmental contaminants. The ubiquity of fungi in soil and in the immediate environment of man is the principal difficulty. *Candida albicans*, whose preference for a parasitic habitat seems definite although unexplained, may be considered essentially amphibiotic. Fungi with nutritional requirements that suggest dependence on parasitism— such as *Pityrosporum* spp.—are also clearly eligible for indigenous status. The problem of environmental ubiquity may be met by modifying the first rule developed in Chap. 1 in the instance of fungi to read: *encountered in one or more typical (indigenous) locations frequently, and distinctly more frequently than in the adjacent environment.* The other criteria seem applicable to fungi as well as to bacteria.

The necessary conditions are abundantly met by *Candida albicans*, which is considered in detail below. Certain other *Candida* species also require treatment as saprophytic amphibionts. Other fungi are either less well studied or more doubtfully indigenous and may be treated briefly.

Connell and Skinner (1953) among more recent students of this subject set out to determine how the distribution of species of yeasts and yeastlike fungi on skin compared with that in the air and on environmental surfaces that might have served as sources of skin contamination. Their attempts to recover such forms from floors, walls, window panes, furniture, table tops, and rugs were virtually all negative; and the distribution of species found in air was distinctly diffrent from that found on skin surfaces. The skin disclosed a predominance of ferment-

[1] Van Uden, DoCarmo Sousa, and Farinha (1958) reported finding *C. albicans* in the cecum of 4.2 per cent of 503 sheep.

TABLE 7-1

DISTRIBUTION OF YEASTLIKE FUNGI ON HEALTHY HUMAN BODY
SURFACES AND IN THE ENVIRONMENT (COMPILED AND
CONDENSED FROM DiMENNA, 1954)

	Children*					Adults†					
	Mouth	Throat	Feces	Nails	Arm skin	Mouth	Throat	Nails	Arm skin	Contaminated surfaces	Air
Number of samples	448‡	278	188	278	190	255§	103	103	103	220	220
Saccharomyces sp.	0	1	4			2	0				
Debaromyces spp.	2	2	2	34	1	2	0	3	0	19	32
Cryptococcus spp.	2	0		15	5	0	0	0	0	40	56
Torulopsis spp.	9	2	7	6	0	4	0	0	0	3	9
Candida albicans	113	14	58			90	9				
Candida spp. (other)	1	1	12	4	0	3	1	0	0	8	7
Trichosporon sp.	0	0		2	1	1	0	0	0	1	5
Rhodotorula sp.	7	2	4	22	4	0	0	1	0	34	29
Cladosporium sp.	1			13	8			1	0	16	19
Sporobolomyces sp.										0	10

* 278 school children aged 2 to 13.
† 152 young adults, mainly fourth-year medical students and a few trainee nurses.
‡ 278 gum swabs + 170 mouth washings.
§ 103 gum swabs + 152 mouth washings.

ing nonpigmented species of the genera *Saccharomyces, Torulopsis,* and *Candida,* of which 507 strains were found, or 64.7 per cent of the total from skin, as compared with 26 from air, or 11.1 per cent of the air cultures. Nonfermenting, nonpigmented forms, chiefly *Cryptococcus* and *Candida,* accounted for another 180 skin cultures (23 per cent) and 27 air cultures (11.5 per cent); while other forms, comprising only 97 (12.4 per cent) of the skin cultures, were represented by 182, or 77.5 per cent of the yeastlike forms from air. Fermenting and nonfermenting yeasts appeared in similar ratio in the different skin areas sampled, their concentrations being highest between the toes and fingers, lowest in the axilla, and intermediate in inframammary, umbilical, and lumbar skin. The predominant group of fermenting yeasts was not identified as to species. The authors concluded that the skin surface may be a true habitat for yeasts.

Somewhat different results were reported by DiMenna (1954) and are summarized in Table 7-1. With important exceptions to be noted, this author found the yeasts on skin and those in the air similar both in the proportions of the various genera and in the species recovered. That the environmental fungi are particularly well represented in the nail swabbings of children is hardly surprising, otherwise it would appear that DiMenna chose a poor source area in arm skin, especially in her group of adults. It may be noted that the genera *Rhodotorula* and *Sporobolomyces* were among those found principally in air by Connell and Skinner, with a group of *Dematiaceae*—"black yeasts"—which were either not recovered by DiMenna or were excluded by her as not yeast-like. The results of the 2 studies are thus not incompatible; it is of interest that DiMenna had seen only a brief preliminary abstract of the Connell-Skinner study. More recently, Rieth (1958*b*) reported the results of an extensive search for yeasts in clinical material, in which a total of 15,592 specimens were cultured. Skin, nails, and hair were included among other body sites and materials; but cultures from air or environment were not made. Of 3,128 yeastlike cultures recovered, 2,114 were candidas, or 67.2 per cent, including 1,111 *C. albicans;* 686 were identified as *Torulopsis* (21.9 per cent); other groups were found less frequently. The predominance in cultures from skin and nails of yeast groups other than candidas and torulopses, of species of candida other than *C. albicans*, and less strikingly of *Torulopsis* spp. other than *T. glabrata*, suggests a general accord with the findings of the previous workers.

Pityrosporum (Fig. 7-1)

While it is difficult to judge from these findings that any fungus other than *Candida albicans* is indigenous, other data given by Di-Menna (1954) and by other workers have more positive implications. A yeast, *Pityrosporum ovale* [Castellani and Chalmers (1913)] has been cultivated from skin, especially from dandruff, on media containing fat, fatty acid, or glycerol, one of these substances having been found necessary for continued growth [Benham (1939); Emmons (1940)]. This yeast produces small oval to spherical cells with elongated buds having a broad base—"bottle-bacillus" forms (Fig. 7-1*a*). Gordon (1951) recovered 15 strains of a related yeast which he called *Pityrosporum orbiculare*, 13 from the lesions of tinea versicolor and 2 from healthy glabrous skin. Similar fungi were seen in 7 of 8 samples of normal skin. *P. orbiculare* forms spherical cells, usually with single buds slightly elongated and attached by a narrow isthmus; the mature cells are 2.1 to 4.8 μ in diameter, mainly 2.8 to 3.8 μ (Fig. 7-1*b*). This fungus grew well on Sabouraud's glucose agar slants overlaid with 2 ml of sterile olive oil, best at 37°, more slowly at 30°, poorly at 25°.

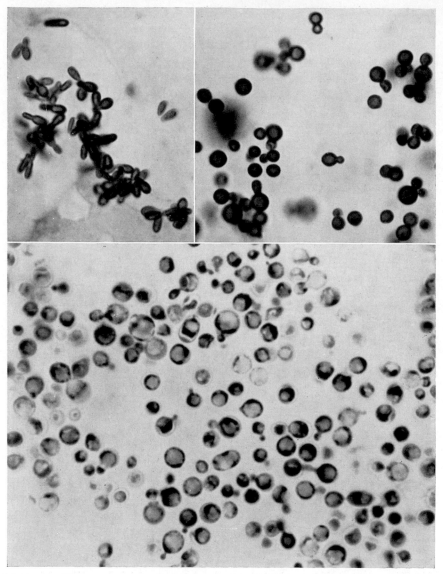

Fig. 7-1. *Pityrosporum ovale* (upper left, ×645) and *P. orbiculare* (upper right, ×1,470), Hotchkiss-McManus stain, ×645. Below *P. orbiculare*, mounted in lactophenol cotton blue, ×1,470. [*From Gordon* (1951), *courtesy of Dr. Gordon and Mycologia.*]

Incorporation of penicillin and streptomycin in the agar favored isolation by inhibiting bacterial growth.

For cultivation of this yeast, olive oil could be replaced by other fatty oils or by the saturated fatty acids lauric, myristic, palmitic, and stearic, but not by oleic or linoleic acids nor, with 1 exception, by glycerol; and growth occurred only when the adjuvant was layered on the agar, not when it was emulsified. *P. ovale* grew in the emulsified media; Benham (1939) had reported excellent growth of this species with oleic acid but much less with saturated fatty acids. All her strains showed some growth in the presence of glycerol. Gordon (1951*b*) also recovered other lipophilic yeasts from skin, some of which resembled *P. ovale;* he found these strains as well as *P. orbiculare* incapable of inducing skin lesions in rabbits or guinea pigs or in human volunteers. DiMenna (1954) also found yeasts typical of the genus *Pityrosporum* in 82 of 87 samples of dandruff; most of these seemed to be *P. ovale.* She considered *P. ovale* to be the dominant species and to constitute with *P. orbiculare* members of the truly indigenous fungal flora of the human skin. Martin-Scott (1952) found *P. ovale* on the skin of animals other than man, and Gustafson (1959, 1960) found the same yeast in the external ear of swine, cattle, and horses. DiMenna suggested that "search may profitably be made for further human or mammalian yeasts with exacting nutritional requirements, not detectable by the use of the conventional Sabouraud or malt extract agars."

Torulopsis

Torulopsis glabrata is another yeast that appears to be indigenous, perhaps obligately so. Benham and Hopkins (1933) included it among their "Cryptococcus group I" as occurring on human skin and mucous membranes. Van Uden et al. (1958) reported that it shows cells 2.5 × 4.5 μ, fails to form a pseudomycelium, grows well at 20°, and when grown at 37° requires biotin, niacin, pyridoxine, and thiamin. These workers noted the similarities between this species and 4 other yeasts (*Torulopsis p:ntolopesii, Saccharomyces tellustris, Candida bovina,* and *C. sloofii*) which they constituted as the "glabrata group": the 5 species differ in average cell size, in having or lacking a pseudomycelium, and in their minimum growth temperature. Among them only *T. glabrata* ferments trehalose, but the 5 forms are otherwise identical in their fermentation and assimilation patterns, and similar in their vitamin requirements. Other evidence of a close relationship between the genera *Torulopsis* and *Candida,* including pseudomycelium formation by the former after cultivation for several years and also mating between members of the 2 groups, has been remarked by Skinner and Fletcher (1960). Hasenclever and Mitchell (1960), moreover, found that *T. glabrata* was antigenically related to the indigenous species of *Candida* although it also contained species-specific antigens. Kemp and Solotorovsky (1961) have demonstrated an antigenically identical glucomannan protein in the cell walls of *T. glabrata* and *C. albicans*, and have shown that the 1, 2, 3, 5, 6, and 7 thermostable antigens of Tsuchiya (1956) are present in both species—*C. albicans* differs only in containing antigen 4 in addition (see page 235 and Table 7-2).

DiMenna (1954) stated that *T. glabrata* had been found only on human body surfaces, including the mucous membranes of mouth, intestine, and genitourinary tract. She recovered it in 10 instances, all from children—mouth, 4; throat, 2; feces, 3; nail swabs, 1. [See also Batista, Oliveira, and Silveira (1957)]. Rieth (1958) recovered 686 strains identified as 17 species of *Torulopsis* from clinical material. Of the total, 84 were *T. glabrata*, and this species was generally more commonly recovered from sputum, the mouth, feces, and especially from the vulva and vagina than were the other species, which appeared principally in material from skin and nails. The latter may presumably be considered nonindigenous.

Lopez Fernandez (1952) found *T. glabrata* pathogenic for rabbits, guinea pigs, rats, and mice by intravenous or intraperitoneal inoculation, which produced nodules in which the yeasts appeared within a heavy concentration of macrophages—a picture resembling histoplasmosis. Wickerham (1957) reported finding 9 strains of *T. glabrata* in pathologic material from man and suggested that its prevalence may be increasing as an effect of antibiotic therapy. He noted that it produces gas from trehalose and is distinctive among yeasts in fermenting that sugar; it does not assimilate maltose, sucrose, or cellobiose [see also Wickerham (1951)]. Vörös-Felkai and Novák (1961) have also recovered *Torulopsis* species from pathologic human material. Van Uden et al. (1958) [see also Van Uden and Do Carmo Sousa (1956)] recovered *T. glabrata* from the cecum of swine, cattle, horses, and goats.

Dermatophytes

That the dermatophytes *Trichophyton rubrum*, *T. mentagrophytes* (*T. gypseum*, *T. interdigitale*), and *Epidermophyton floccosum* may be indigenous to the skin of the feet is suggested especially by the studies of Baer and his associates (1955, 1956) on tinea pedis, or "athlete's foot." In earlier literature these fungi were demonstrated on the feet of persons with no clinical symptoms of tinea pedis [e.g., Strickler and Friedman (1931)]. The distribution of fungous species during an outbreak at a military post was such as not to suggest a communicable disease [Hopkins et al. (1947)]. Dermatophytes have been recovered inconsistently from the usually implicated floor surfaces [Ajello and Getz (1954); English and Gibson (1959*b*)]. Moreover, experimental reproduction of the disease in man has required "severe, highly artificial measures" such as maceration of the skin for several days before and after inoculation [e.g., Von Graffenreid (1918)]. Baer and his coworkers were able to demonstrate dermatophytes on 14 per cent of clinically normal feet, compared with 40.8 per cent as observed by Strickler and Friedman (1931) and only 1.7 per cent as reported by Ajello et al. (1945). Rosenthal et al. (1956), using media containing the antibiotic, cyclohexamide [see Georg, Ajello, and Papageorge (1954)] as well as penicillin and streptomycin, were able to recover dermatophytes from 12.5 per cent of 40 subjects with healthy feet. They failed to find the fungi in public shower stalls, locker-room floors, or areas around swimming pools. Baer and his coworkers (1955) exposed 45 volunteers to contaminated footbath water; none developed disease, 23 showed fungi on the exposed foot and 15 on the unexposed (control) foot, and 2 of the subjects yielded *T. rubrum* although they had been exposed to *T. mentagrophytes*. Details of studies of a larger series of subjects, with similar findings, were given in a later paper [Baer et al. (1956)]. These authors concluded that "acute attacks of fungous infections of the feet are usually due to a flare-up of a preexisting latent, clinically or mycologically often not detectable infection." They compared this pattern with that of tuberculosis, but a more apt comparison might be with the archetype of endogenous infective disease associated with the normal flora.

The opinions of Baer and his coworkers are, however, objected to in several quarters, although principally, it seems to the writer, as a matter of emphasis. Georg (1960), for instance, in a review of the epidemiology of these infections, suggested that the difficulties of the preceding workers in producing experimental disease depended on their failure to "create the proper conditions" for doing so; and emphasized that some workers have been able to isolate dermatophytes from floors, foot baths, and footwear. (This would of course be expected; it has not been shown that the also-to-be-expected transmission of fungi from floors to feet leads in any predictable way to disease.) Desai and Bhat (1960) argued that experimental disease is producible in man by inoculation of mycelia rather than of spores, and by introducing the inoculum on abraded skin. It is of interest that Huppert and Keeney (1959), whose primary interest was immunization rather than epidemiology, were able to infect only half of a group of 16 control volunteers, by placing a cylindrical 1-in. disk cut from a 2 weeks' agar culture of *T. mentagrophytes* with a cork borer, on the fourth web of the foot after roughening the skin with gauze, covering the inoculum with cotton, strapping the fourth and fifth toes together with adhesive tape, and leaving the bandage in place for 2 days. The irregular success of such heroic measures hardly argues against the principle of endogenous infection. Similarly, the extensive studies of English and Gibson (1959, 1960) and English, Gibson, and Duncan (1960) on the epidemiology of tinea pedis in British school children, did not establish clearly that this disease, or the more common minor lesions with which its fungi (principally *T. mentagrophytes*) were found associated, can be regarded as communicable. These workers, it is true, were hardly ever able to find fungi in interdigital scrapings from the feet of "symptomless carriers"; and, on the other hand, they recovered them repeatedly from swimming-pool floors. Yet they could find no clear relationship between incidence of disease and attendance at school swimming classes or the use of school showers. They concluded that "whatever the reasons, tinea pedis is not a highly infectious disease," and suggested that a higher incidence among boys than among girls may depend partly on more frequent bathing out of school, and on the circumstance that girls' shoes and socks were found to be much lighter and cooler than boys', especially in summer—indications, consistent with the endogenous hypothesis, of host determinants in pathogenesis. In a study of *T. rubrum* infection in household groups in New Orleans, Many, Derbes, and Friedman (1960) also uncovered little evidence of communicability. For example, in only 2 of 15 conjugal couples were both spouses involved. On the other hand, a further report by the workers at Bristol [English, Gibson, and Warin (1961)] adduced evidence for a small group of boarding-school boys that the lesionfree carrier state is nearly always transient. In a paper that seemed to sum up this important investigation, English (1961) has argued strongly in favor of exogenous infection as a determinant of tinea pedis. She continued nevertheless to emphasize the factors of susceptibility of the inoculated foot and of associated circumstances such as footwear. Whether infection with these dermatophytes is endogenous or exogenous is of practical importance in relation to control measures and deserves further exploration.

The Genus *Candida*

Taxonomy and Synonymy

The genus *Candida* consists of dimorphic yeastlike imperfect fungi. They are imperfect in that sexual elements are not produced,[2] yeastlike in that they form unicellular elements, and dimorphic in that the

[2] Wickerham and Burton (1952) have presented evidence that members of this group, including *C. guilliermondi*, may be capable of producing ascospores when mated with other candidas; hence becoming "perfect" forms.

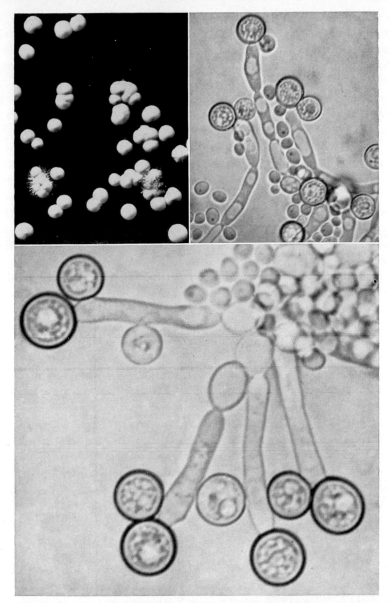

Fig. 7-2. *Candida albicans.* Upper left, smooth and rough colonies on agar, ×½. Upper right, pseudomycelium developing from elongated and vacuolated blastospores; the large round cells are chlamydospores. Below, typical chlamydospores and pseudomycelium with a clump of blastospores above, ×2,200. [*From Rieth* (1958a,b), *courtesy of Dr. Rieth and Springer-Verlag* (*Arch. klin. exp. Dermatol.*).]

yeast phase alternates under suitable conditions with a branching filamentous or mycelial type of growth. Intermediate between the 2
phases is a characteristic pseudomycelium of elongated budding cells
clinging together in chains. The budding cells or blastospores are especially characteristic; no arthrospores or mycelial fragments are
formed (see Fig. 7-2). Some species, particularly *C. albicans*, produce
chlamydospores, heavy-walled resistant asexual elements [see Skinner
(1947); Wickerham (1952); Scherr and Weaver (1953)]. The classification of species within the genus has been subject to much disagreement which seems to be moving toward resolution, at least in terms of
species commonly isolated from man. A former multiplicity of species
is being pared down to manageable numbers. The species now generally
agreed upon as significant to the present context are listed in Table 7-2
with their principal metabolic and antigenic distinguishing features,
as explained below. Further details, especially of colonial and cellular
morphology, may be found in Lodder and Kreger-van Rij (1952) and
Benham (1957). The following synonyms have been selected from the
long lists given in the former work as the most frequent in the more
recent medical literature. Genus *Candida* = *Oidium, Monilia, Syringospora;* species *albicans* = *pinoyi, psilosis; tropicalis* = *candida; parapsilosis* = *parakrusei;* and *pseudotropicalis* = *mortifera.*

Assimilation Tests. The data given in Table 7-2 under "assimilation"
depend upon the use of substrates as sole sources of carbon or nitrogen
tested by the auxanographic method originally developed by Beijerink
in 1899 [see Wickerham (1946); Wickerham and Burton (1948);
Lodder and Kreger-van Rij (1952); Benham (1955)]. The organisms
are usually seeded into a pour plate of defined agar medium lacking
the class of substrates under test, and crystals or small amounts of the
test substances are placed at various points on the surface. Assimilation
is determined by growth in the area of diffusion of the test substance.
Wickerham and Burton (1948) performed carbon assimilation tests
in a liquid medium, and such media are now commercially available.
Drouhet and Couteau (1954) used impregnated paper disks. The
replica plating method has been applied for this purpose by Shifrine,
Phaff, and Demain (1954) to facilitate multiple testing. A rapid testing method involving agitation during growth has been described by
Ahearn et al. (1960). Possibilities of further developments of biochem-
ical identification tests for candidas have been discussed by Skinner and
Fletcher (1960).

The Status of *C. stellatoidea* **(see Fig. 7-3).** Among the forms separated as species in Table 7-2, the status of *C. stellatoidea* is particularly
disputed. This name was proposed as a separate species by Jones and
Martin (1938), who found the organism more often than *C. albicans*

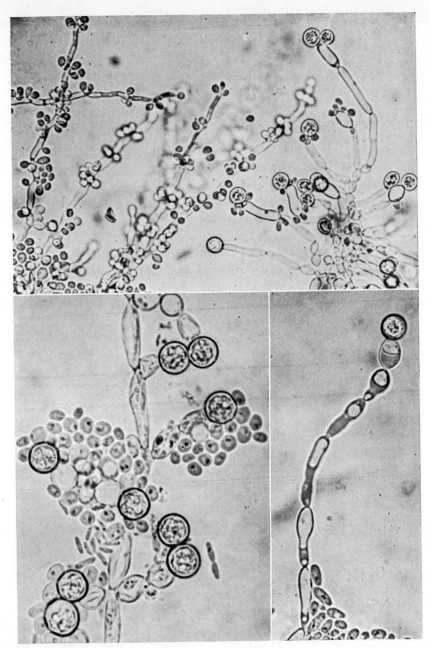

F<small>IG</small>. 7-3. Mixed culture of *Candida tropicalis* (left) and *C. albicans* (right, with chlamydospores). Below left, *C. stellatoidea*, showing mature and immature chlamydospores, long pseudomycelial cells, round and elongated blastospores. Below right, *C. stellatoidea*, vacuolated pseudomycelial cells with a terminal chlamydospore. [*From Rieth and Schönfeld* (1959), *courtesy of Dr. Rieth and Springer-Verlag* (*Arch. klin. exp. Dermatol.*).]

TABLE 7-2

DIFFERENTIAL CHARACTERISTICS OF *Candida* SPECIES MOST
FREQUENTLY ISOLATED FROM MAN (COMPILED FROM DATA GIVEN
BY LODDER AND KREGER-VAN RIJ, 1952; TSUCHIYA ET AL.,
1956; AND BENHAM, 1957)

	C. albicans	*C. stellatoidea*	*C. tropicalis*	*C. parapsilosis*	*C. krusei*	*C. guilliermondi*	*C. pseudotropicalis*
Chlamydospores formed	+	rare	rare	0	0	0	0
Fermentation:							
Glucose	AG	AG	AG	AG	AG	AG	AG
Maltose	AG	AG	AG	0*	0	0	0
Sucrose	A	0	AG	0	0	AG	AG
Lactose	0	0	0	0	0	0	AG
Assimilation:							
Glucose	+	+	+	+	+	+	+
Lactose	0	0	0	0	0	0	+
Sucrose	+	0	+	+	0	+	+
Galactose	+	+	+	+	0	+	+
Maltose	+	+	+	+	0	+	0
Raffinose	0		0	0	0	+	+
Thermostable antigens:							
3	+	+	+	+	0	+	0
4	+	+	+	0	0	+	0
5	+	+	+	+	+	0	0
6	+	0	+	0	0	0	0
7	+	0	0	0	0	0	0
8	0	0	0	0	0	0	+
9	0	0	0	0	0	+	0
Thermolabile antigens:							
a	0	0	0	0	0	0	+
b	0	0	0	0	+	0	0
c	0	0	0	+	0	0	0

* One of 12 strains studied by Lodder and Kreger-van Rij fermented maltose weakly; the other workers reported this fermentation as negative.

in the healthy vagina and distinguished it as producing mycelium readily but chlamydospores rarely—2 of 29 strains each showed only a single chlamydospore. It differed from *C. albicans* especially in failing to acidify sucrose and in being entirely nonpathogenic for rabbits. Winter and Foley (1955) reported that 41 strains of candidas among 162 isolated from the mouth or from internal viscera were "very weak" acid producers from sucrose. Comparative studies of these strains and others identified as *C. stellatoidea* showed a range of variation in morphology, biochemical characters, and rabbit pathogenicity such as not to justify separating *C. stellatoidea* as a species. Widra (1956) and Benham (1957) continued to give the organism separate status, the former author considering it a variant of *C. albicans*. In a more recent paper, Pollack and Benham (1957) also decided that *C. stellatoidea* is probably an avirulent variant of *C. albicans*. In a study of 164 strains of candidas found in man, Newton et al. (1960) observed that 103 of 104 strains of *C. albicans* and all of 15 strains of *C. stellatoidea* produced filamentous colonies when grown on 5 per cent sheep blood agar plates for 2 days in candle jars. Other species failed to form such colonies under these conditions; 10 per cent human blood gave less specific results. Serologic findings reviewed below emphasize the relationship between *C. albicans* and *C. stellatoidea* and do not completely resolve the question of identity.

Serologic Classification. Data permitting a satisfactory serologic classification of both indigenous and other species of *Candida* have emerged especially from the work of Tsuchiya and his colleagues (1954, 1955, 1956). These workers, employing monospecific absorbed rabbit antiserums in slide agglutination tests, have defined a series of heat-stable and heat-labile antigens, of which 7 of the former, numbered 3 through 9, and 3 of the latter (*a, b, c*) have differential value for the indigenous candidas and correlate well with biochemical distinctions, as shown in Table 7-2. According to their procedures both *C. stellatoidea* and *C. tropicalis* are antigenically closely related to *C. albicans*, but the 3 are distinguishable by the absence of antigens 6 and 7 in the first and of 7 in the second [for a review of these and other serologic studies of candidas, see Tsuchiya, Fukuzawa, and Kawakita (1961)]. The findings of the Japanese group have been confirmed by Kemp and Solotorovsky (1961). Gordon (1958) has reported independently that *C. albicans* and *C. stellatoidea* can be distiguished by the use of specific fluorescein isocyanate–conjugated rabbit globulin. On the other hand, Biguet et al. (1961) have found *C. albicans* and *C. stellatoidea* antigenically related by gel immunoelectrophoresis; and Hasenclever and Mitchell (1961), in a brief note, have reported that *C. stellatoidea* was indistinguishable by tube agglutination and absorption from one group of *C. albicans*, designated B. These workers also reported that *C. tropicalis* is antigenically similar to another group of *C. albicans*, called by them group A.

Occurrence

Man, in Health. In Table 7-3 the percentages of instances are set out in which the principal species of *Candida* have been recovered from different human body surfaces in the absence of disease. The data are taken only from reports in which the number of samples tested was given, and in which the organisms recovered were identified, in most instances in terms of the separate *Candida* species in addition to *C. albicans*. In the report of Marwin (1949) "other species" were listed only as such without further identification. Much additional material is available in reports in which one or more of these conditions were not met; the findings in such reports are not inconsistent with those in the table. Table 7-3 indicates that (1) members of the genus have

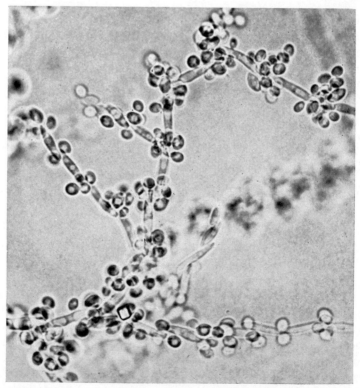

Fig. 7-4. *Candida parapsilosis*, showing pseudomycelium and blastospores, ×980. (*Courtesy of Dr. Morris Moore, St. Louis.*)

TABLE 7-3

DISTRIBUTION OF *Candida* SPECIES ON HEALTHY HUMAN BODY SURFACES

Source	Number of samples	C. albicans	C. tropicalis	C. krusei	C. para-psilosis	Other Candida spp.
		Per cent of samples				
Mouth[a]	100	6.0		1.0		
Mouth[b]	146	23.9	3.4	3.4	3.4	1.4
Mouth[c]	703	38.8			4.2	1.4
Throat[d]	125	28.0	9.8	7.2	3.2	4.6
Throat[c]	381	6.0			2.6	
Feces[a]	100	18.0		13.0	2.0	3.0
Feces[e]	314	16.5	4.1	5.8	5.8	
Feces[f]	50	14.0	6.0	30.0	6.0	12.0
Feces[g]	102	15	5	10	4	5
Feces[c]	188	30.9		2.6	0.5	3.2
Vagina[h]	68	27.9	5.9	5.9	4.4	42.6*
Skin[a]	300	0		0.3	0.7	1.0
Skin[i]	100	0	0	0	12.0	6.0
Skin[j]	200	1.5				14.5
Skin[c]	674	0				5.6
Bile, duodenal fluid[k]	220	11.4	3.6	1.0	0.5	3.6

* Representing 29 isolations of *C. stellatoidea;* see text.
[a] Benham and Hopkins (1933)   [g] Lawler et al (1942); cited by Skinner (1947)
[b] Knighton (1939)   [h] Jones and Martin (1938)
[c] DiMenna (1954)   [i] Croft and Black (1938)
[d] Brygoo (1952a)   [j] Marwin (1949)
[e] Schnoor (1939)   [k] Brygoo (1952b)
[f] Negroni and Fisher (1941)

been recovered from all the areas sampled; (2) *C. albicans* is found on all the mucous membrane areas listed, and is generally the commonest species found there, being roughly as frequent in its occurrence as all other species combined; (3) *C. albicans* is not strikingly more or less common in any one of these areas, although the results of individual studies [Benham and Hopkins (1933); DiMenna (1954)] may suggest otherwise, presumably by chance; and (4) *C. albicans* is rare on healthy skin, but other species of *Candida* may not be.

Skinner and Fletcher (1960) listed several habitats other than higher animals for *C. krusei*, *C. guilliermondii*, and *C. parapsilosis*, principally plants and their products and insects. DiMenna (1954) recovered *C. parapsilosis* in two instances from air; and the common occurrence of this species in samples from skin and nails as recorded by Rieth (1958), as well as the presence of *C. krusei* in such locations more often than in mucous membrane sites, suggest that they are not true amphibionts. *C. albicans*, on the other hand, as noted earlier, seems to be essentially parasitic on man and animals. From the indications of relationships given previously, as well as the absence of data to the contrary, the same may be suggested for *C. tropicalis* and *C. stellatoidea*.

In the mouth, candidas are commonly found with lactobacilli on the pH 5 plates used for counts of the latter group as an index of activity of dental caries (Fig. 7-5). Counts of the yeastlike organisms per ml of saliva are usually 10^3 or lower and seldom exceed 10^4 [see Rosebury and Waugh (1939); Lilienthal (1950); Young, Rusca, and Sullivan (1951); Krasse (1954)]. In the vagina, *Candida* species seem also to form part of the so-called aciduric flora, accompanying acid-forming bacilli and showing a tendency to occur more commonly in pregnant than in nonpregnant women [see Plass, Hesseltine, and Borts (1931); Carter and Jones (1937); Woodruff and Hesseltine (1938); Hite, Hesseltine, and Goldstein (1947); Petru (1956); Krupp and St. Romain (1960)]. An association of vaginal candidas with *Trichomonas vaginalis* has also been reported [e.g., Pereira-Barreto et al. (1958); see also Chap. 8].

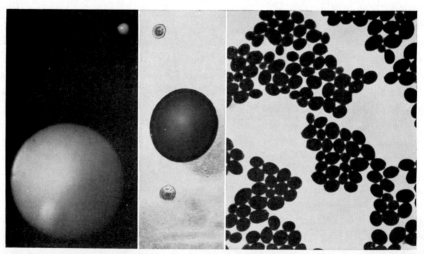

Fɪɢ. 7-5. Candida and lactobacillus colonies from the mouth on a pH 5.0 tomato agar plate at 4 days: left, photographed by reflected light; center, by transmitted light, ×6.5; right, budding yeast cells in Gram-stained smear, ×1,200.

Man, in Disease. *C. albicans,* with or without other candidas, or undifferentiated yeastlike fungi, has been recovered frequently from sputum [Brygoo (1951); Sharp (1954); Armstrong and Hall (1956); Baum (1960)]; from gastric washings [Drouhet and Couteau (1954)]; from urine [Drouhet and Couteau (1954); Carpenter (1955); Higaki (1955)] and in cultures of nose and throat and of skin [Carpenter (1955)], all under pathologic conditions which, however, do not necessarily implicate these organisms as pathogens. Lea, Schuster, and Harrell (1958) found *C. albicans* in the healthy external ear; and Batista, Silveira, and Oliveira (1959), as well as Brygoo (Table 7-3), have reported their presence in bile. Batista, Silveira, and Oliveira (1957) also found them in the appendix [see also Vörös-Felkai and Novák (1961)]. The occurrence of candidas pathologically in more incriminating locations is mentioned under Pathogenicity, page 241.

Animals. *Candida albicans* appears to be indigenous to the crop of chickens [Jordan (1953)] and turkeys [Manfre et al. (1958); see also Blaxland and Fincham (1950); Blaxland and Markson (1954)]. In the healthy bovine cecum, van Uden and Do Carmo-Sousa (1957) found *C. tropicalis, C. parapsilosis, C. krusei,* and other *Candida* species; but *C. albicans* was not isolated [see also Loken et al. (1959)]. The distribution of *C. albicans* and other members of the genus in the cecums of horses, sheep, goats, and swine, however, was found by van Uden et al. (1958) to be comparable with that in man except that an additional species, *C. sloofii,* was the predominant member of the genus in the cecum of swine and also appeared, although much less prominently, in the horse. Van Uden (1960) has also reported the presence of *C. albicans* in the digestive tracts of wild animals and crows in Africa [see also van Uden and Do Carmo-Sousa (1956); Saez (1959); and the reference to candidas under *Torulopsis glabrata,* above]. Clarke and DiMenna (1961) have found *C. albicans* and others candidas in the bovine rumen.

Pathogenic *Candida,* Especially *C. albicans*

Identification

The principal points of distinction between *C. albicans* and other species of this genus, and the distribution of this species, have been dealt with in the preceding section. There remain for consideration certain aspects of *C. albicans* itself as the most common member and the principal pathogen of the genus. For general methods of cultivation and staining of this organism see, in addition to the references given below, Muskatblit, Taschdjian, and Franks (1953); Bakerspigel,

(1954); Johnson, Guzman, and Aguilera (1954); Negroni and de Negroni (1958); and Taubert and Smith (1960).

C. albicans is one of the indigenous microorganisms that have acquired increased importance since the advent of antibiotic therapy. Its precise identification has accordingly become increasingly necessary. The data in Table 7-2 indicate that such identification properly requires a battery of biochemical tests and a determination of pathogenicity as well as morphologic study; but the desirability of a simplified diagnostic procedure is obvious. Since other varieties of *Candida* that produce chlamydospores (1) show them rarely, and (2) are so closely related to *C. albicans* that their separate status is questionable, demonstration of these spores is the primary step in identification and is often regarded as sufficient. They are spherical, 7 μ or more in diameter, thick-walled, and appear mainly at the ends of hyphae either singly or in clusters.

Chlamydospores are usually easily demonstrated on "starvation" media at 18 to 25°. The medium most commonly used to induce their formation is yellow corn meal agar, of which many variants have been proposed [see Benham (1931, 1957)]. Gordon, Bradley, and Gant (1952) and Benham herself have noted a preference for "homemade" corn meal agar over commercially available products. Reid, Jones, and Carter (1953) devised a medium containing zein, the protein of maize, in place of corn meal. Nickerson and Mankowski (1953) proposed a defined medium for this purpose that contained ammonium sulfate and, as the carbon source, either glycogen or soluble starch freed from reducing sugar; added trypan blue was selectively accumulated by the chlamydospores. Addition of glucose or cysteine prevented mycelium or chlamydospore formation. Other media have been suggested by Liu and Newton (1955), Sina and Reiss (1957), and Taschdjian (1957). Distinctive pigmentation of *C. albicans* in an agar medium containing 1.9 mg per ml of phosphomolybdic acid has been described by MacLaren and Armen (1958). Pollack and Benham (1957) compared commercial Nickerson-Mankowski medium with another soluble starch agar and with Benham's original (1931) corn meal agar, and found the last superior in terms both of frequency and of rapidity of chlamydospore production. Skinner and Fletcher (1960), on the other hand, recommended the commercial Nickerson-Mankowski medium.

Pagano, Levin, and Trejo (1957–58) presented data suggesting that the relative inability of *C. albicans*, as compared with other *Candida* species and other yeasts or yeastlike fungi, to reduce tetrazolium salts to colored formazan compounds could be used in a differential medium. The so-called Pagano-Levin medium, commercially available, has been used by several workers [Kutscher et al. (1959); Rosenthal and Furnari

(1960); Sinski (1960); Kelly, Kutscher, and Tuoti (1961)]. A rapid identification procedure for *C. albicans* entailing the use of eosin-methylene blue and corn meal–Tween albumin media combined with commercial paper disk fermentation tests has been devised jointly by Walker and Huppert (1959, 1960) and Kelly and Funigiello (1959); but objections to these methods have been reported by Dean and Haley (1959). According to Taschdjian, Burchall and Kozinn (1960) the production of initial mycelial growth—germ tubes—within 4 hours at 37 to 42° after inoculation into human or animal serum permits identification of *C. albicans*. A fluorescent staining method for pathogenic fungi, including *C. albicans*, in tissue sections has been reported by Pickett et al. (1960).

Chemically defined media for *C. albicans* have been described by Wickerham (1946); Wickerham and Burton (1948); McClary (1952); Kapicka and Blank (1957); and Firestone and Koser (1960). Biotin is required by many strains and thiamin by some. References to metabolic studies with this organism, which seem to have been few, have been given by Skinner and Fletcher (1960) and Rao, Ramakrishnan, and Sirsi (1960). The latter workers reported that the glucose dissimilation of *C. albicans* proceeds by both Embden-Meyerhof and hexose-monophosphate shunt pathways.

Serologic Identification. Gordon (1958), in the paper mentioned previously, applied the fluorescent antibody procedure in what appears to be a promising means for the rapid identification of *C. albicans*. The procedure also distinguished the other species listed in Table 7-2, including *C. stellatoidea*, most clearly after absorption of the rabbit antiserum with *C. parapsilosis* cells; but *C. tropicalis* could not be separated from *C. albicans* by this means. Tsuchiya, Fukazawa, and Kawakita (1959) have applied their techniques with absorbed rabbit antiserums in slide agglutination tests to the identification of clinical cultures. Their findings were well correlated with morphologic and biochemical data, and the authors suggested that the serologic method is useful and reliable for rapid identification of species.

Pathogenicity

The following discussion is limited to experimental studies with *C. albicans* and other candidas. *C. albicans* has a degree of pathogenic capacity, readily demonstrable experimentally, that seems at first glance to distinguish this microorganism from most other members of the indigenous biota; but the distinction loses sharpness on close inspection. Very large infecting doses, usually combined with selected routes of inoculation and with adjuvant factors, are nearly always required for establishment of progressive disease under experimental conditions. This microorganism thus belongs in the amphibiotic band of the ecologic spectrum, albeit near the pathogenic region. Before considering the principal part of this subject—the pathogenicity of *C. albicans* for experimental animals—we may note two peripheral but very significant points: (1) that pathogenicity among *Candida* species is not strictly limited to the one species; and (2) that experimental *C. albicans* disease has been produced in man.

Species other than *C. albicans.* Several workers have reported that *C. tropicalis*, which is closely related to *C. albicans* (see page 235) may be capable of pathogenic activity. Urso (1951) was able to produce generalized fatal bronchial moniliasis in a guinea pig, 3 mice, and a rabbit by repeated insufflation of large doses of *C. tropicalis.* Stovall and Pessin (1933) reported that doses of this species five to fifteen times as large as were required with *C. albicans* were capable of killing rabbits by the more customary intravenous route. Drouhet and Couteau (1954) also found that 3 of 6 strains of *C. tropicalis*, when freshly isolated, were lethal for rabbits. That the other species found on human mucous membranes are potentially capable of inducing disease is indicated by the findings of Salvin (1952) that *C. krusei, C. pseudotropicalis*, and *C. stellatoidea*, as well as *C. tropicalis*, all killed mice when given intraperitoneally with 5 per cent mucin in dosages of 1.8 to 6.6×10^6 cells—not greatly in excess of those required with *C. albicans* under similar circumstances, as will be seen; and that similar results could be obtained with *C. parapsilosis* and *C. guilliermondii* in the dosage range 5.3 to 14.7×10^6. All these forms, moreover, were found to be toxic, as was *C. albicans*, when killed cells mixed with dried tubercle bacilli were inoculated. Hasenclever (1959), on the other hand, found that by intravenous inoculation of either mice or rabbits, *C. guilliermondii, C. krusei, C. parapsilosis, C. pseudotropicalis*, and *C. stellatoidea* were innocuous at dosage levels a hundredfold or more higher than the average LD_{50} of *C. albicans* by this route. *C. tropicalis*, in this worker's hands, had an intravenous LD_{50} for mice of 2.3×10^6 organisms but failed to kill rabbits in a dosage of more than 5×10^8.

The implication of candidas other than *C. albicans* in disease in man, especially *C. tropicalis*, but also *C. parapsilosis* and other species, has been reported by Drouhet (1957), Manchester and Georg (1959), Conn et al. (1959), and Richart and Dammin (1960).

Experimental Disease in Man. The role of *C. albicans* as the immediate determinant of certain diseases of skin and mucous membranes of man was made clear by a series of early experiments with human subjects. Frank (1932) reproduced a perlèche-like syndrome in himself by rubbing a culture of *C. albicans* isolated from perlèche into the scarified skin at the angle of the mouth. The fungus, mixed with bacteria, was recovered from the lesions repeatedly for 32 days. Frank also produced pruritic pustular lesions with associated tender lymphadenitis by inoculation of his scarified skin. The other studies are of questionable propriety [see Beecher (1959)]. Finnerud (1929) reproduced perlèche in 9 of 10 orphanage children by inoculation of scarified commissure skin. Hesseltine et al. (1934) described the appearance of thrushlike vaginitis in 15 of 22 pregnant and 6 of 9 nonpregnant women, after implantation of *Candida* on their previously fungusfree mucous membranes; similar manipulation led to the development of oral thrush in 9 of 29 newborn infants. Bland et al. (1937) also reported the production of thrush by inoculation of the vagina of both pregnant and nonpregnant women; some of the latter showed cutaneous involvement, with pruritis or marked inflammation mainly on the perivulvar skin, sometimes spreading to the inner surface of the thighs. Hesseltine and Campbell (1938) reported that when *Candida* organisms (or cryptococci) were present in the vagina, application of glucose as powder or in aqueous solution induced a vulvovaginal mycosis or an exacerbation of an existing mycosis, and concluded that fungal vulvitis in diabetes depends on the presence of glucose in the urine.

Rabbits. Experimental pathogenicity of *C. albicans* has traditionally been demonstrated by intravenous inoculation of rabbits. For confirmation of identification of the species, Benham (1957) suggested a dosage of 0.1 ml of a 1 per cent suspension by volume of packed cells obtained by washing 24- to 48-hour cultures on Sabouraud's glucose agar with 0.85 per cent NaCl and centrifuging at 1500 rpm for 15 minutes. Death occurs usually in 4 or 5 days with abscesses especially in the kidneys, from which the organisms can be recovered. Evans and Winner (1954) have described the pathology of the experimental process produced in the rabbit by intravenous injection of 1 to 2×10^7 organisms. Abscesses appeared in various organs, particularly in the kidneys, where hyaline thickening was found in the glomerular basement membrane. These workers remarked the absence of reactive hyperplasia in spleen, bone marrow, or liver, and the lack of lymph-node enlargement. Ishida (1959) has been able to produce lung abscesses in rabbits by sensitizing them with lung tissue and adjuvants intramuscularly and later introducing *C. albicans* intratracheally together with either homologous or heterologous lung antigen. The candidas seemed to multiply actively in the allergic lesions.

Mice. The mouse began to be used widely as an experimental animal for studies with *C. albicans* in 1951, when Strauss and Kligman reported that 5 per cent gastric mucin, inoculated intraperitoneally with this or several other fungi, greatly increased mortality. Salvin, Cory, and Berg (1952) confirmed this result with the finding that 1.25 to

22×10^6 *Candida albicans* cells, innocuous alone, killed 24 to 100 per cent of white Swiss mice when mixed with 2.5 per cent mucin; 21-day-old mice were more susceptible than older animals, the intracerebral route of injection most effective, the subcutaneous route least, the intraperitoneal and intracardial routes intermediate. In a separate report mentioned previously, Salvin (1952) pointed out that the pathogenicity of species of *Candida* other than *C. albicans* was demonstrable in mice when the organisms were given with mucin, and that all species showed evidence of toxicity when the killed yeasts were injected together with dried tubercle bacilli. Ansel and Gauthier (1955) have also found that 5 per cent mucin enhances the infectivity of *C. albicans* given intraperitoneally to mice. These workers reported male mice to be more susceptible than females [see also Scherr (1955)]. Solotorovsky and his coworkers (1954) were able to infect mice intravenously with *C. albicans*. Adriano and Schwartz (1955) reported that intravenous inoculation of mice is evidently capable of killing at lower dosage levels than the intraperitoneal route more customary with this animal: intravenously, 10^5 organisms killed within 13 days, average about 3.5 days; 10^6 organisms were more rapidly fatal. Autopsy showed disseminated disease, with interstitial inflammation, abscesses and granulomas; the lesions were found in heart, kidneys, brain, and spleen, and sometimes in the liver. Hasenclever (1959) found that the LD_{50} of *C. albicans* by the intravenous route is less for the mouse than for the rabbit, ranging for 10 strains of *C. albicans* from 2.7×10^3 to 2.6×10^5 for mice and from 8×10^5 to 2.3×10^8 for rabbits; or per gram of animal from 1.5×10^2 to 1.4×10^4 for mouse and from 4.8×10^2 to 1.2×10^5 for rabbit. In these experiments, as mentioned above, the LD_{50} for *C. tropicalis* for mice was 2.3×10^6; this species did not infect rabbits intravenously, and other candidas were nonpathogenic by this route for both animal species.

Salvin's (1952) suggestion of an endotoxin in *C. albicans* is supported by the finding of Vogel (1957) that the organism may contain a lipopolysaccharide antigen similar to those of Gram-negative bacteria. Substances lethal for mice when inoculated intravenously in large doses (equivalent to 10^8 organisms or more) were found by Mourad and Friedman (1961a) in sonically disrupted *C. albicans* and also in 2 saprophytic candidas. Aksoycan and LeMinor (1960) reported that *C. albicans*, *C. tropicalis*, and *C. guilliermondii* cross-reacted in agglutination tests with what appeared to be minor O antigens of *Salmonella* and members of the Arizona group; the latter also reacted with *C. stellatoidea*; but *C. krusei* and *C. parapsilosis* failed to show such relationships.

Other Animals. The guinea pig has been found less suitable as an experimental animal for *C. albicans* than either rabbits or mice [see Winner (1960)]. Visco (1959) reported that chick embryos less than 12 days old are highly susceptible to yolk sac inoculation with either *C. albicans* or *C. tropicalis;* inoculation via the allantoic cavity was much less effective.

Virulence; Enhancement

Cortisone or x radiation, or both agencies together, have been used to enhance the pathogenicity of *C. albicans* for mice; a synergistic effect of the combination has been described [see Syverton et al. (1952); Friedman et al. (1952); Mankowski and Littleton (1953); Seligmann (1953); Roth, Friedman, and Syverton (1957)]. Louria, Fallon, and Browne (1960) reported that the enhancing effect of cortisone on renal localization of infection in mice following intravenous inoculation of *C. albicans* was much more marked than corresponding effects with *Histoplasma capsulatum* or *Cryptococcus neoformans*. Henry and Fahlberg (1960) have studied the combined enhancing effect of hydrocortisone acetate and tetracycline on infection of mice with *C. albicans*.

Several observations indicate that strains of *C. albicans* recovered from healthy mucous membranes are capable of inducing disease in experimental animals. Knighton (1939) found that his oral strains could induce generalized candidiasis in rabbits; Lilienthal (1955) reported that strains from the mouth were as pathogenic for mice and rats as those from thrush, as tested by the development of local inflammatory lesions; and Young (1958) used cultures of *C. albicans* from healthy mouths in her studies of pathology in mice described below. Eisman, Geftic, and Mayer (1953) reported that smooth variants of *C. albicans* were more virulent for mice than rough ones. Winsten and Murray (1956) found that addition of cysteine to a normal growth medium enhanced mouse virulence of this fungus.

Pathogenesis

The foregoing studies with rabbits and mice, although they establish the potential pathogenicity of *C. albicans*, throw little light on the question of pathogenesis of the more common varieties of candidiasis in man. Since such disease in recent years has been closely associated with antibiotic therapy, especially with the broad-spectrum drugs, several workers have attempted to demonstrate enhancement of growth or of pathogenicity of *C. albicans* by antibiotics.

Seligmann (1952) first reported that chlortetracycline augmented pathogenicity for mice. Injected intraperitoneally, 3.2×10^8 cells were innocuous alone, but fatal in nearly all instances when mixed with 2 mg of the antibiotic, which was also nontoxic by itself. The drug was found to have some effect in increasing pathogenicity when given 24 hours before or as much as 4 hours after the organisms, but not later. The enhancement disappeared with the antibiotic activity of the drug upon aging or boiling; no enhancing effect of chlortetracycline on *C. albicans* could be demonstrated in vitro. In a later paper, this worker [Seligmann (1953)] reported that oxytetracycline had a similar enhancing effect, but that penicillin, streptomycin, bacitracin, and chloramphenicol did not. Roth et al. (1957) found that a substance released from viable *C. albicans* cells by vibration was lethal to mice pretreated with chlortetracycline; oxytetracycline was less active and chloramphenicol and streptomycin were inactive. These workers also found that guinea pigs, rabbits, and monkeys could be killed by intraperitoneal injection of 5 to 15×10^6 viable *C. albicans*, but only when the animals were pretreated with chlortetracycline. By intratracheal instillation in rabbits of 5×10^7 *C. albicans* spores together with 10^4 μg of any of the tetracyclines, Felisati, Bastianini, and de Mitri (1959) produced much more severe granulomatous and hemorrhagic lesions than were elicited without antibiotic or with penicillin, streptomycin, or chloramphenicol. Jackson and Axelrod (1954) and Forney and Hedrick (1961) have reported that chlortetracycline enhances infection of the chick embryo; the former group worked with *C. albicans*, the latter with *C. krusei*.

A growth-stimulating effect of certain antibiotics, measured in terms of total cell nitrogen by the micro-Kjeldahl procedure, has been reported by Huppert, MacPherson, and Cazin (1953) and Huppert and Cazin (1955); see also Johnson, Guzman, and Aguilera (1954); Carpenter (1955); Privitera (1957); and Mandel et al. (1958). This effect could be demonstrated with chlortetracycline, neomycin, and bacitracin, but not with penicillin, chloramphenicol, oxytetracycline, streptomycin, Magnamycin, or erythromycin; nor did the effect appear when chlortetracycline containing the fungicides methyl or propyl *p*-hydroxybenzoate were used.

Since the occurrence of clinical candidiasis is associated with a wider range of drugs than have been found active in the foregoing experiments either in vivo or in vitro, it is apparent that additional mechanisms must operate under clinical conditions. Huppert, Cazin, and Smith (1955) have been able to show that all antibiotics tried—chlortetracycline, oxytetracycline, tetracycline, chloramphenicol, dihydrostreptomycin, Magnamycin, neomycin, erythromycin, and penicillin—when given orally to mice, predisposed toward the establishment of *C. albicans* in the intestinal biota; one breed of mice was found to be more susceptible to such implantation than another [see also Winter and Foley (1956)]. These findings are in agreement with those of McGovern et al. (1953) and Sharp (1954) with human subjects—they point to the mouse as a useful subject for further study of the mechanism of candidiasis in man.

Rather thin lines of evidence, to be detailed in later pages (Chap. 11) suggest that this mechanism, as has been widely suspected, is to be found in the influence of antibiotic drugs on ecologic phenomena, including indirect effects involving disturbances of vitamin synthesis by antibiotic-sensitive bacteria. The complexity of the problem is suggested by a finding that seems to point in the opposite direction from that implied in the foregoing discussion, as reported for chicks and turkey poults by Sieburth and Roth (1954). *C. albicans* could easily be established in the intestinal tracts of these fowl regardless of their diet; addition of therapeutic levels of chlortetracycline or oxytetracycline seemed to prevent fatal moniliasis, perhaps by stimulating growth of *Proteus mirabilis*, a *Candida* antagonist. While chicks and turkey poults may well differ from man in respects significant in this connection, these findings emphasize how much remains to be learned on this subject.

Mixed cultures in serum broth prepared by inoculation either with mouse feces or with human throat swabbings, treated with tetracycline for 24 hours, were reported by Campbell and Heseltine (1960) to contain a "growth factor" for *C. albicans*.

The report by Kapicka and Blank that both *C. albicans* (1957) and *C. parapsilosis* (1958) were able to utilize keratin as the sole nitrogen source and to hydrolyze it to amino acids, in a medium containing glucose, salts, and vitamins, was offered as bearing on the problem of pathogenicity for skin. The possible relation of these findings as well to the pathogenesis of dental caries, in which candidas are frequently found, in connection with enamel keratin breakdown as well as decalcification, seems worth suggesting.

In contrast to most pathogenic dimorphic yeastlike fungi [see Scherr and Weaver (1953)], *C. albicans* has been found to appear in host tissues more often in the mycelial than in the yeast phase. Both Stovall and Pessin (1933) and Hill and Gebhardt (1956) have related the rapid formation of filamentous forms in the tissues to the greater pathogenicity of *C. albicans* as compared with other species of *Candida*. Young (1958), using 18-hour cultures of *C. albicans* in a dosage of 4 $\times 10^7$ cells inoculated intraperitoneally into male mice without adjuvants, found that 60 per cent of the cells showed some pseudomycelium formation after 1 hour and 80 per cent after 2 hours. Since yeast-phase cells but not filaments were found to be ingested, and sometimes apparently digested, by larger monocytes, there seemed to be a connection between mycelium formation and pathogenicity [see also Whittle and Gresham (1960)].

Bichel and Stenderup (1955) studied the effect in mice of repeated intraperitoneal inoculation of sublethal doses (2×10^5 or 1×10^6 cells per injection) at daily intervals. Gross signs of illness appeared only at the higher dosage level after 8 injections, but many of the animals at both levels showed a lymphopenia, and all manifested slight to moderate leukocytosis. Of 15 mice given 1.5×10^6 cells per day, all but one appeared ill after the second injection, some were moribund after the fifth, and all showed similar changes in their white blood cells. Aspects of the pathology of *C. albicans* infection have been studied in mice by Blyth (1959) and in guinea pigs by Sacenti (1957, 1959).

Immunity

The question of immunity to *C. albicans* is curiously interwoven with others, among them the matter of the source, in infancy, of the indigenous *Candida* organisms. Opinion is at present divided as to whether these organisms are derived directly from the birth canal [e.g., Bret et al. (1958)] or indirectly via the hands of mother or nurse [e.g., Holzel (1953); Csillag, Vince, and Simon (1958)]. The findings of Kozinn et al. (1959)—notably that the incidence of oral thrush in infants in a hospital nursery was not reduced by isolation of clinical cases during the first 2 weeks of life—suggest that *C. albicans* is not transmitted from infant to infant. There is general recognition, however, that the occurrence of *C. albicans* in mouth, throat, or feces is much more likely to have pathologic implications in newborn infants than in older children or adults [Ludlam and Henderson (1942); Taschdjian and Kozinn (1957); Csillag et al. (1958)]. Ludlam and Henderson reported that babies that recovered from thrush did not suffer a second attack even though they still harbored the fungus. It would be of interest to determine whether passive maternal antibodies to *C. albicans* can be demonstrated in the newborn (see page 368).

Antibodies to the organism are found in adults. Todd (1937) reported that the serums of 259 out of 1,150 healthy persons, or 22.5 per cent, agglutinated *C. albicans*, and that a striking relationship existed between the presence of the organism in mouth or throat and the agglutinin titer, as shown in Table 7-4. Duncan (1937), in reviewing Todd's paper, noted that he had observed antibodies to these fungi correlated with their presence in feces. Drake (1943) found antibodies to this organism in from 45 to 88 per cent of human serums, as well as in 70 per cent of normal rabbit serums. Low titers of antibody to *C. albicans* have also been reported in man by Norris and Rawson (1947).

TABLE 7-4
RELATIONSHIP OF SPECIFIC AGGLUTININ TITER IN SERUM TO PRESENCE
OF *Candida albicans* IN THE MOUTH OR THROAT OF HEALTHY
PERSONS (AFTER TODD, 1937)

Agglutinin titer	C. albicans				
	Mouth and throat	Mouth only	Throat only	Total	Absent
	Number of persons				
0	6	1	2	9	520
±	3	0	0	3	10
+1:10	1	1	2	4	12
+1:20	6	6	3	15	22
+1:40	12	3	4	19	23
+1:80	14	6	5	25	5
+1:160	18	3	4	25	1
+1:320	8	0	0	8	0
+1:640	1	0	0	1	0

Beemer, Pryce, and Riddell (1954) suggested that high titers may
have diagnostic significance, and that the absence of agglutinins may be
indicative of susceptibility to moniliasis. A positive "monilial complement-fixation" (MCF) has been reported by Peck et al. (1955) in 13.5
and 17.5 per cent of patients with diseases other than candidiasis, and in
75 per cent of 48 subjects with clinical evidence of this disease. These
workers were unable to correlate long-term tetracycline therapy, or the
more common gastrointestinal symptoms that may follow such therapy,
with the MCF test; but 21 of 27 patients who reacted positively in the
test prior to therapy developed anogenital pruritis after treatment with
tetracyclines. Winner (1955) reported that 31.6 per cent of 1,017 persons showed positive slide agglutination tests with *C. albicans;* but they
could not always associate infection with a high titer. Attempts to use
serologic means for diagnosis of candidiasis have also been made by
Akiba, Iwata, and Inouye (1957) using skin tests and precipitin reactions with *C. albicans* polysaccharide; by Vogel and Padula (1958) by
means of a fluorescein-coupled Coombs serum; and by Tomsikova and
Wagner (1958) with an agglutination test for incomplete as well as
complete antibodies in human serum to *C. albicans* and the other common candidas [see also Gargani, Carloni, and Pin (1959); Gracheva
(1959)]. Hypersensitivity to candidas in man has also been noted by
Pepys (1959) and briefly reviewed by Salvin (1959).

Winner (1956) was unable to protect rabbits by immunization

against intravenous challenge with *C. albicans*. Marcus and Rambo (1955) reported that immunization of mice with formalin-killed yeast-phase organisms did not affect mortality on challenge with *C. albicans*, but kidney cultures of sacrificed survivors were usually sterile in immunized animals and positive in unimmunized controls. Kemp and Solotorovsky (1961) were able to protect about 45 per cent of mice against intravenous inoculation of *C. albicans* by intravenous passive immunization with rabbit antiserum prepared against either the homologous organism or against *C. stellatoidea*. Prior absorption of the immunizing *C. albicans* antiserum with either *C. stellatoidea* or *C. krusei* had little effect. Relative protection of mice by active immunization has also been reported by Mourad and Friedman (1961*b*).

Sensitivity to Antibiotics

C. albicans, like other fungi, is not inhibited by any of the usual antibiotic drugs. As noted above this organism may be stimulated by several of them either in vitro or in vivo or both. Distinctive antibiotics have, however, been developed as fungicides. Among these, nystatin [Hazen and Brown (1951); Brown, Hazen, and Mason (1953)] has been most extensively studied and used for treatment of undisseminated candidiasis as well as prophylactically [for literature, see Wright, Graham, and Sternberg (1957); Hazen and Brown (1960); Dobias and Hazen (1961)]. Other antibiotic drugs reported as useful in vivo against *C. albicans* include candicidin [Kligman and Lewis (1953); Franks, Taschdjian, and Thorpe (1954)]; trichomycin [Magara et al. (1954)]; amphotericin B [Huang, Sarria, and High (1957–58); Montana and Sery (1958); Stough, Groel, and Kroeger (1959); Louria and Dineen (1960); Louria (1961)]; candidin [Solotorovsky, Quabeck, and Winsten (1958)]; malucidin [Parfentjev (1958)]; and Pimaricin [Manten and Hoogerheide (1958); Cazemier et al. (1959)].

References

Adriano, S. M., and Schwarz, J., 1955, *Am. J. Pathol.*, **31**:857.
Ahearn, D. G., Roth, F. J., Jr., Fell, J. W., and Meyers, S. P., 1960, *J. Bacteriol.*, **79**:369.
Ajello, L., 1956, *Science*, **123**:876.
————, and Getz, M. E., 1954, *J. Invest. Dermatol.*, **22**:17.
————, Keeney, E. L., and Broyles, E. N., 1945, *Bull. Johns Hopkins Hosp.*, **77**:440.
Akiba, T., Iwata, K., and Inouye, S., 1957. *Japan J. Microbiol.*, **1**:11.
Aksoycan, N., and LeMinor, L. and S., 1960, *Ann. Inst. Pasteur*, **99**:723.
Ansel, M., and Gauthier, C., 1955, *Ann. Parasitol. Humaine et Comparée*, **30**:312.

Armstrong, E. C., and Hall, J. A., 1956, *Month. Bull. Med. Res. Council* (U.K.), **15**:220 (*Biol. Abstr.*).

Baer, R. L., Rosenthal, S. A., Litt, J. Z., and Rogachefsky, H., 1956, *J. Am. Med. Assoc.*, **160**:184.

————, ————, Rogachefsky, H., and Litt, J. Z., 1955, *Am. J. Public Health*, **45**:784.

Bakerspigel, A., 1954, *J. Inf. Dis.*, **94**:141.

Batista, A. C., de Oliveira, D., and Silveira, G., 1957, *Univ. Recife, Inst. Micol., Comun. Cient.*, **3**:1 (*Biol. Abstr.*).

————, Silveira, G., and de Oliveira, D., 1957, *ibid.*, **1**:1 (*Biol. Abstr.*).

————, ————, and ————, 1959, *Rev. Assoc. Med. Brasil*, **4**:360 (*Biol. Abstr.*).

Baum, G. L., 1960, *New Engl. J. Med.*, **263**:70.

Beecher, H. K., 1959, *Experimentation in Man*, Charles C Thomas, Publisher, Springfield, Ill.; reprinted from 1959, *J. Am. Med. Assoc.*, **169**:461.

Beemer, A. M., Pryce, D. M., and Riddell, R. W., 1954, *J. Pathol. Bacteriol.*, **68**:359.

Beijerinck, M. W., 1889, *Arch. Neerl. Sci.*, **23**:367, cited by Wickerham and Burton (1948).

Benham, R. W., 1931, *J. Inf. Dis.*, **49**:183.

————, 1939, *J. Invest. Dermatol.*, **2**:187.

————, 1955, *Trans. N.Y. Acad. Sci. II*, **17**:418.

————, 1957, *J. Chronic Diseases*, **5**:46.

————, and Hopkins, A. M., 1933, *Arch. Dermatol. Syphilol.*, **28**:532.

Bichel, J., and Stenderup, A., 1955, *Acta Pathol. Microbiol. Scand.*, **37**:157.

Biguet, J., Havez, R., Tran Van Ky, and Degaey, R., 1961, *Ann. Inst. Pasteur*, **100**:13.

Bland, P. B., Rakoff, A. E., and Pincus, I. J., 1937, *Arch. Dermatol. Syphilol.*, **36**:760.

Blaxland, J. D., and Fincham, I. H., 1950, *Brit. Vet. J.*, **106**:221.

————, and Markson, L. M., 1954, *ibid.*, **110**:139.

Blyth, W., 1959, *Mycopathol. et Mycol. Appl.*, **10**:269.

Bret, J., Coupe, C., Solle, R., and Marchand, H., 1958, *Presse Méd.*, **66**:937.

Brown, R., Hazen, E. L., and Mason, A., 1953, *Science*, **117**:609.

Brygoo, E. R., 1951, *Ann. Inst. Pasteur*, **81**:676.

————, 1952a, *ibid.*, **83**:818.

————, 1952b, *ibid.*, **83**:816.

Campbell, P. J., and Heseltine, W. W., 1960, *J. Hyg.*, **58**:95.

Carpenter, A. M., 1955, *Am. J. Clin. Pathol.*, **25**:98.

Carter, B., and Jones, C. P., 1937, *Southern Med. J.*, **30**:298.

Castellani, A., and Chamers, A. J., 1913, *Manual of Tropical Medicine*, Balliére, Tindall & Cox, London.

Cazemier, C., Goslings, W. R. O., Houwert, K. A. F., van Leeuwen, D. P., Lubbers, G. J., and Kok, P. C., 1959, *Antibiotic Med. & Clin. Ther.*, **6**:601.

Clarke, R. T. J., and DiMenna, M. E., 1961, *J. Gen. Microbiol.*, **25**:113.

Conn, N. K., Crean, G. P., Maccabe, A. F., and Maclean, N., 1959, *Brit. Med. J.*, **1**:944.

Connell, G. H., and Skinner, C. E., 1953, *J. Bacteriol.*, **66**:627.

Croft, C. C., and Black, L. A., 1938, *J. Lab. Clin. Med.*, **23**:1259.

Csillag, A., Vince, I., and Simon, G., 1958, *Ann. Pediat. Basel*, **190**:352.
Dean, K. F., and Haley, L. D., 1959, *Am. J. Med. Technol.*, **25**:395.
Desai, S. C., and Bhat, M. L. A., 1960, *J. Invest. Dermatol.*, **35**:297.
DiMenna, M. E., 1954, *J. Pathol. Bacteriol.*, **68**:89.
———, 1955, *J. Gen. Microbiol.*, **12**:54.
———, 1958, *Nature*, **181**:1287.
Dobias, B., and Hazen, E. L., 1961, *Chemotherapia*, **3**:108.
Drake, C. H., 1943, *J. Bacteriol.*, **46**:486.
Drouhet, E., 1957, *Semaine Hôp.*, **33**:897 (abstr., 1957, *J. Am. Med. Assoc.*, **164**:1013).
———, and Couteau, M., 1954, *Ann. Inst. Pasteur*, **86**:602.
Duncan, J. T., 1937, *Bull. Hyg.*, **11**:604.
Eisman, P. C., Geftic, S. G., and Mayer, R. L., 1953, *Proc. Soc. Exptl. Biol. Med.*, **82**:263.
Emmons, C. W., 1940, *Public Health Repts. (U.S.)*, **55**:1306.
———, 1950, *Proc. 7th Intern. Botan. Congr. Stockholm.*
———, 1954, *Trans. N.Y. Acad. Sci.*, Series II, **17**:157.
English, M. P., 1961, *Brit. Med. J.*, **1**:1068.
———, and Gibson, M.D., 1959a, *ibid.*, **1**:1442.
———, and ———, 1959b, *ibid.*, **1**:1446.
———, and ———, 1960, *ibid.*, **1**:1860, **2**:577.
———, ———, and Duncan, E. H. L., 1960, *ibid.*, **2**:573.
———, ———, and Warin, R. P., 1961, *ibid.*, **1**:1083.
Evans, W. E. D., and Winner, H. I., 1954, *J. Pathol. Bacteriol.*, **67**:531.
Felisati, D., Bastianini, L., and deMitri, T., 1959, *Antibiotics & Chemotherapy*, **9**:744.
Finnerud, C. W., 1929, *Arch. Dermatol. Syphilol.*, **20**:454.
Firestone, B. Y., and Koser, S. A., 1960, *J. Bacteriol.*, **79**:674.
Forney, C. E., and Hedrick, L. R., 1961, *Appl. Microbiol.*, **9**:52.
Frank, L. J., 1932, *Arch. Dermatol. Syphilol.*, **26**:451.
Franks, A. G., Taschdjian, C. L., and Thorpe, G. A., 1954, *J. Invest. Dermatol.*, **23**:75.
Friedman, J., Werder, A. A., Roth, F. J., Graham, A. B., Mira, O. J., and Syverton, J. T., 1954, *Am. J. Roentgenol. Radium Therapy Nuclear Med.*, **71**:709.
Gargani, G., Cardoni, M., and Pin, R., 1959, *Ann. Sclavo*, **1**:263 (*Biol. Abstr.*).
Georg, L. K., 1960, *Ann. N.Y. Acad. Sci.*, **89**:69.
———, Ajello, L., and Papageorge, C., 1954, *J. Lab. Clin. Med.*, **44**:422.
Gordon, M. A., 1951a, *Mycologia*, **43**:524.
———, 1951b, *J. Invest. Dermatol.*, **17**:267.
———, 1958, *ibid.*, **31**:123.
———, Bradley, E. G., and Grant, V. Q., 1952, *J. Lab. Clin. Med.*, **40**:316.
Gracheva, N. M., 1959, *J. Microbiol. Epidemiol. Immunobiol. (U.S.S.R.)*, (transl.) **30**:96.
Graffenried, C. von, 1918, *Dermatol. Wochschr.*, **66**:361.
Gustafson, B. A., 1959, *Acta Pathol. Microbiol. Scand.*, **45**:275.
———, 1960, *ibid.*, **48**:51.
Hasenclever, H. F., 1959, *J. Bacteriol.*, **78**:105.
———, and Mitchell, W. O., 1960, *ibid.*, **79**:677.
———, and ———, 1961, *Bacteriol. Proc.*, p. 121.

Hazen, E. L., and Brown, R., 1951, *Proc. Soc. Exptl. Biol. Med.*, **76**:93.
————, and ————, 1960, *Ann. N.Y. Acad. Sci.*, **89**:258.
Henry, B., and Fahlberg, W. J., 1960, *Antibiotics & Chemotherapy*, **10**:114.
Hesseltine, H. C., and Campbell, L. K., 1938, *Am. J. Obstet. Gynecol.*, **35**:272.
————, Gorts, I. C., and Plass, E. D., 1934, *ibid.*, **27**:112.
Higaki, M-A., 1955, *Japan. J. Bacteriol.*, **10**:925.
Hill, D. W., and Gebhardt, L. P., 1956, *Proc. Soc. Exptl. Biol. Med.*, **92**:640.
Hite, K. E., Hesseltine, H. C., and Goldstein, L., 1947, *Am. J. Obstet. Gynecol.*, **53**:233.
Hopkins, J. G., Hillegas, A. B., Ledin, R. B., Rebell, G. C., and Camp, E., 1947, *J. Invest. Dermatol.*, **8**:291.
Holzel, A., 1953, *Arch. Disease Childhood*, **28**:412.
Huang, N. N., Sarria, A., and High, R. H., 1957–58, *Antibiotics Ann.*, p. 59.
Huppert, M., and Cazin, J., Jr., 1955, *J. Bacteriol.*, **70**:435.
————, ————, and Smith, H., Jr., 1955, *ibid.*, **70**:440.
————, and Keeney, E. L., 1959, *J. Invest. Dermatol.*, **32**:15.
————, MacPherson, D. A., and Cazin, J., 1953, *J. Bacteriol.*, **65**:171.
Ishida, M., 1959, *J. Osaka City Med. Center*, **8**:273 (*Biol. Abstr.*).
Jackson, G. G., and Axelrod, S. C., 1954, *Antibiotics & Chemotherapy*, **4**:277.
Johnson, S. A. M., Guzman, M. G., and Aguilera, C. T., 1954, *A.M.A. Arch. Dermatol. Syphilol.*, **70**:49.
Jones, C. P., and Martin, D. S., 1938, *Am. J. Obstet. Gynecol.*, **35**:98.
Jordan, F. T. W., 1953, *Brit. Vet. J.*, **109**:527.
Kapicka, L., and Blank, F., 1957, *Dermatologica*, **115**:81.
————, and ————, 1958, *ibid.*, **117**:433.
Kelly, J., Kutscher, A. H., and Tuoti, F., 1961, *J. Invest. Dermatol.*, **86**:403.
Kelly, J. P., and Funigiello, F., 1959, *J. Lab. Clin. Med.*, **53**:807.
Kemp, G., and Solotorovsky, M., 1961, *Bacteriol. Proc.*, p. 120.
————, and ————, 1961, personal communication from Dr. Solotorovsky.
Kligman, A. M., and Lewis, F. S., 1953, *Proc. Soc. Exptl. Biol. Med.*, **82**:399.
Knighton, H. T., 1939, *J. Dental Research*, **18**:103.
Kozinn, P. J., Wiener, H., Taschdjian, C. L., and Burchall, J. J., 1959, *J. Am. Med. Assoc.*, **170**:1172.
Krasse, B., 1954, *Odontologisk Revy*, **5**:241.
Krupp, P. J., and St. Romain, M. J., 1960, *J. Louisiana State Med. Soc.*, **112**:176 (*Biol. Abstr.*).
Kutscher, A. H., Seguin, L., Zegarelli, E. V., Rankow, R. M., Mercadante, J., and Piro, J. D., 1959, *J. Invest. Dermatol.*, **33**:41.
Lea, W. A., Jr., Schuster, D. S., and Harrell, E. R., 1958, *ibid.*, **31**:137.
Lilienthal, B., 1950, *Australian J. Exptl. Biol. Med. Sci.*, **28**:279.
————, 1955, *Oral Surg., Oral Med, Oral Pathol.*, **8**:1214.
Liu, P., and Newton, A., 1955, *Am. J. Clin. Pathol.*, **25**:93.
Lodder, J., and Kreger-van Rij, N. J. W., 1952, *The Yeasts. A Taxonomic Study*, North Holland Publishing Co., Amsterdam.
Loken, K. I., Thompson, E. S., Hoyt, H. H., and Ball, R. A., 1959, *J. Am. Vet. Med. Assoc.*, **134**:401 (*Biol. Abstr.*).
Lopez Fernandez, J. R., 1952, *Anales. Fac. Med. Montevideo*, **37**:470.
Louria, D. B., 1961, *Chemotherapia*, **3**:95.
————, and Dineen, P., 1960, *J. Am. Med. Assoc.*, **174**:273.

————, Fallon, N., and Browne, H. G., 1960, *J. Clin. Invest.*, **39**:1435.

Ludlam, G. B., and Henderson, J. L., 1942, *Lancet*, **1**:64.

MacLaren, J. A., and Armen, D., 1958, *Am. J. Clin. Pathol.*, **30**:411.

Magara, M., Yokouti, E., Senda, T., and Amino, E., 1954, *Antibiotics & Chemotherapy*, **4**:433.

Manchester, P. T., and Georg, L. K., 1959, *J. Am. Med. Assoc.*, **171**:1339.

Mandel, M., Hood, F., and Cohen, J. R., 1958, *Antibiotics & Chemotherapy*, **8**:187.

Manfre, A. S., Wheeler, H. O., Feldman, G. L., Rigdon, R. H., Ferguson, T. M., and Couch, J. R., 1958, *Am. J. Vet. Research*, **19**:689.

Mankowski, Z. T., and Littleton, B. J., 1954, *Antibiotics & Chemotherapy*, **4**:253.

Manten, A., and Hoogerheide, J. C., 1958, *ibid.*, **8**:381.

Many, H., Derbes, V. J., and Friedman, L., 1960, *A.M.A. Arch. Dermatol.*, **82**:226.

Marcus, S., and Rambo, F. R., 1955, *Bacteriol. Proc.*, p. 92.

Martin, D. S., and Jones, C. P., 1940, *J. Bacteriol.*, **39**:609.

Martin-Scott, I., 1952, *Brit. J. Dermatol.*, **64**:257.

Marwin, R. M., 1949, *J. Invest. Dermatol.*, **12**:229.

McClary, D. O., 1952, *Ann. Missouri Botan. Garden*, **39**:137.

McDonough, E. S., Ajello, L., Ausherman, R. J., Balows, A., McClellan, J. T., and Brinkman, S., 1961, *Am. J. Hyg.*, **73**:75.

McGovern, J. J., Parrott, R. H., Emmons, C. W., Ross, S., Burke, F. G., and Rice, E. C, 1953, *New Engl. J. Med.*, **248**:397.

Montana, J. A., and Sery, T. W., 1958, *A.M.A. Arch. Ophth.*, **60**:1.

Mourad, S., and Friedman, L., 1961*a*, *J. Bacteriol.*, **81**:550.

————, and ————, 1961*b*, *Proc. Soc. Exptl. Biol. Med.*, **106**:570.

Muskatblit, E., Taschdjian, C. L., and Franks, A. G., 1953, *A.M.A. Arch. Dermatol. Syphilol.*, **67**:507.

Negroni, P., and Fisher, I., 1941, *Rev. Inst. Bacteriol. Malbràn*, **10**:334.

————, and de Negroni, C. B., 1958, *Anales Soc. Cient. Arg.*, **166**:93.

Newton, A., Shaw, E. D., Goode, C. S., and Riggall, F. O., 1960, *J. Invest. Dermatol.*, **35**:123.

Nickerson, W. J., and Mankowski, Z., 1953, *J. Inf. Dis.*, **92**:20.

Norris, R. F., and Rawson, A. J., 1947, *Am. J. Clin. Pathol.*, **17**:813.

Pagano, J., Levin, J. D., and Trejo, W., 1957–58, *Antibiotics Ann.*, p. 137.

Parfentjev, I. A., 1958, *J. Inf. Dis.*, **103**:1.

Peck, S. M., Bergamini, R., Kelcec, L. C., and Rein, C. R., 1955, *J. Invest. Dermatol.*, **25**:310.

Pepys, J., 1959, *Postgrad. Med. J.*, **35**:436.

Pereira-Barreto, M., Zago, H., Oliveira, P. V., Marques, W., Mendonca, J., Saquis, J., Guimaraes, J., and Villa, E., 1958, *Rev. Assoc. Med. Brasil*, **4**:126 (*abstr. Rev. Mycol. Vet. Med.*, 1959, no. 1030).

Petru, V., 1956, *Ceskoslov. Epidemiol. Mikrobiol. Immunol.*, **5**:199, *Referat. Zhur. Biol.*, 1957, No. 68690 (*Biol. Abstr.*).

Pickett, J. P., Bishop, C. M., Chick, E. W., and Baker, R. D., 1960, *Am. J. Clin. Pathol.*, **34**:197.

Plass, E. P., Hesseltine, H. C., and Borts, I. H., 1931, *Am. J. Obstet. Gynecol.*, **21**:320.

Pollack, J. D., and Benham, R. W., 1957, *J. Lab. Clin. Med.*, **50**:313.

Privitera, F., 1957, *Giorn. Mal. Infettive e Parassit.*, **9**:492, 494, 496 (*Biol. Abstr.*).

Rao, G. R., Ramakrishnan, T., and Sirsi, M., 1960, *J. Bacteriol.*, **80**:654.

Reid, J. D., Jones, M. M., and Carter, E. B., 1953, *Am. J. Clin. Pathol.*, **23**: 938.

Richart, R., and Dammin, G. J., 1960, *New Engl. J. Med.*, **263**:474.

Rieth, H., 1958*a*, *Arch. klin. u. exptl. Dermatol.*, **205**:541.

———, 1958*b*, *ibid.*, **207**:413.

———, and Schönfeld, J., 1959, *ibid.*, **208**:343.

Rosebury, T., and Waugh, L. M., 1939, *Am. J. Diseases Children*, **57**:871.

Rosenthal, S. A., Baer, R. L., Litt, J. Z., Rogachefsky, H., and Furnari, D., 1956, *J. Invest. Dermatol.*, **26**:41.

———, and Furnari, D., 1960, *ibid.*, **34**:229.

Roth, F. J., Jr., Friedman, J., and Syverton, J. T., 1957, *J. Immunol.*, **78**: 122.

———, and Murphy, W. H., Jr., 1957, *Proc. Soc. Exptl. Biol. Med.*, **94**:530.

Sabouraud, R., 1893, *Ann. Dermatol. Syphilis*, **3**:561.

———, 1893, *Ann. Inst. Pasteur*, **7**:497, cited by Ajello (1956).

Sacenti, M., 1959, *Sperimentale*, **109**:434 (*Biol. Abstr.*).

———, and Marraccini, G. F., 1957, *Giorn. Mal. Infettive e Parassit.*, **9**:322 (*Biol. Abstr.*).

Saez, H., 1959, *Rec. Méd. Vét. École d'Alfort*, **135**:629 (*Biol. Abstr.*).

Salvin, S. B., 1952, *J. Immunol.*, **69**:89.

———, 1959, *Am. J. Med.*, **27**:97.

———, Cory, J. C., and Berg, M. K., 1952, *J. Inf. Dis.*, **90**:177.

Scherr, G. H., 1955, *Mycologia*, **47**:305.

———, and Weaver, R. H., 1953, *Bacteriol. Revs.*, **17**:51.

Schnoor, T. F., 1939, *Am. J. Trop. Med.*, **19**:163.

Seligmann, E., 1952, *Proc. Soc. Exptl. Biol. Med.*, **79**:481.

———, 1953, *ibid.*, **83**:778.

Sharp, J. L., 1954, *Lancet*, **1**:390.

Shifrine, M., Phaff, H. J., and Demain, A. L., 1954, *J. Bacteriol.*, **68**:28.

Sieburth, J. McN., and Roth, F. J., Jr., 1954, *ibid.*, **67**:460.

Sina, B., and Reiss, F., 1957, *J. Invest. Dermatol.*, **29**:263.

Sinski, J. T., 1960, *ibid.*, **35**:131.

Skinner, C. E., 1947, *Bacteriol. Revs.*, **11**:227.

———, and Fletcher, D. W., 1960, *ibid.*, **24**:397.

Solotorovsky, M., Ironson, E. J., Gregory, F. J., and Winsten, S., 1954, *Antibiotics & Chemotherapy*, **4**:165.

———, Quabeck, G., and Winsten, S., 1958, *ibid.*, **8**:364.

Stough, A. R., Groel, J. T., and Kroeger, W. H., 1959, *Antibiotic Med. & Clin. Therapy*, **6**:653.

Stovall, W. D., and Pessin, S. B., 1933, *Am. J. Clin. Pathol.*, **3**:347.

Strauss, R. E., and Kligman, A. M., 1951, *J. Inf. Dis.*, **88**:151.

Strickler, A., and Friedman, R., 1931, *Arch. Dermatol. u. Syphilis*, **24**:430.

Syverton, J. T., Werder, A. A., Friedman, J., Roth, F. J., Jr., Graham, A. B., and Mira, O. J., 1952, *Proc. Soc. Exptl. Biol. Med.*, **80**:123.

Taschdjian, C. L., 1957, *Mycologia*, **49**:332.

———, Burchall, J. J., and Kozinn, P. J., 1960, *A.M.A. J. Diseases Children*, **99**:212.

————, and Kozinn, P. J., 1957, *J. Pediat.*, **50**:426.

Taubert, H. D., and Smith, A. G., 1960, *J. Lab. Clin. Med.*, **55**:820.

Todd, R. L., 1937, *Am. J. Hyg.*, **25**:212.

Tomšiková, A., and Wagner, V., 1958, Z. *Immunitätsforsch.*, **116**:239 (*Rev. Mycol. Vet. Med.*, **8**:1166).

Tsuchiya, T., Fukazawa, Y., and Kawakita, S., 1959, *Mycopathol. et Mycol. Appl.*, **10**:191.

————, ————, and ————, 1961, *Studies on Candidiasis in Japan*, p. 34.

————, ————, Miyasaki, F., and Kawakita, S., 1955, *Japan. J. Exptl. Med.*, **25**:75.

————, ————, Iwahara, I., Miyasaki, F., and Fukuzawa, Y., 1954, *ibid.*, **24**:95.

————, ————, and ————, 1954, *Japan. J. Bacteriol.*, **9**:449.

————, Kamijo, K., Fukazawa, Y., Kawakita, S., and Nishikawa, Y., 1956, *Japan. J. Med. Sci. Biol.*, **9**:103.

Uden, N. van, 1960, *Ann. N.Y. Acad. Sci.*, **89**:59.

————, and do Carmo-Sousa, L., 1956, *Portugaliae Acta Biol.*, Sér. A, **4**:7.

————, and ————, 1957, *J. Gen. Microbiol.*, **16**:385.

————, ————, and Farinha, M., 1958, *ibid.*, **19**:435.

————, Faia, M. de M., and Assis-Lopes, L., 1956, *ibid.*, **15**:151.

Urso, B., 1951, *J. Trop. Med. Hyg.*, **54**:94.

Visco, G., 1959, *Riv. 1st. Sieroterop. Ital.*, **34**:29 (*abstr. Rev. Mycol. Vet. Med.*, 1959, No. 1045).

Vogel, R. A., 1957, *Proc. Soc. Exptl. Biol. Med.*, **94**:279.

————, and Padula, J. F., 1958, *ibid.*, **98**:135.

Vörös-Felkai, G., and Novák, E. K., 1961, *Acta Microbiol. Acad. Sci. Hungar.*, **8**:89.

Walker, L., and Huppert, M., 1959, *Am. J. Clin. Pathol.*, **31**:551.

————, and ————, 1960, *ibid.*, **32**:190.

Whittle, C. H., and Gresham, G. A., 1960, *Mycopathol. et Mycol. Appl.*, **12**:207.

Wickerham, L. J., 1946, *J. Bacteriol.*, **52**:293.

————, 1951, *Tech. Bull.*, *U.S. Dept. Agr.*, p. 1029.

————, 1952, *Ann. Rev. Microbiol.*, **6**:317.

————, 1957, *J. Am. Med. Assoc.*, **165**:47.

————, and Burton, K. A., 1948, *J. Bacteriol.*, **56**:363.

————, and ————, 1952, *ibid.*, **63**:449.

————, and ————, 1954, *ibid.*, **69**:594.

Widra, A., 1957, *J. Inf. Dis.*, **100**:79.

Winner, H. I., 1955, *J. Hyg.*, **53**:509.

————, 1956, *J. Pathol. Bacteriol.*, **71**:234.

————, 1960, *ibid.*, **79**:420.

Winsten, S., and Murray, T. J., 1956, *J. Bacteriol.*, **71**:738.

Winter, W. F., and Foley, G. E., 1955, *J. Inf. Dis.*, **97**:227.

————, and ————, 1956, *ibid.*, **98**:150.

Woodruff, P. W., and Hesseltine, H. C., 1938, *Am. J. Obstet. Gynecol.*, **36**:467.

Wright, E. T., Graham, J. H., and Sternberg, T. H., 1957, *J. Am. Med. Assoc.*, **163**:92.

Young, G., 1958, *J. Inf. Dis.*, **102**:114.

————, Rusca, H. G., and Sullivan, M. T., 1951, *J. Dental Research*, **30**:426.

CHAPTER 8

THE INDIGENOUS PROTOZOA

The data to be reviewed in this chapter make plain the need to treat protozoa in this book in accordance with the criteria set forth in Chap. 1. Certain protozoa appear in the human mouth and intestinal and genitourinary tracts often enough in the absence of disease, overt or latent, to justify regarding them as indigenous. The label, here as elsewhere, does not imply that they have necessarily met the requirements for admission to a select organization; no moral judgment, whether of approval or aversion, is intended. This point is emphasized here because qualified opinion, in what seems to be an extraordinarily distinctive way, runs heavily against considering protozoa as "normal" to man in any sense of that broad word. The common term "normal flora" attests negatively to this point: protozoa are, of course, "fauna," although the distinction at this level between animals and plants is perhaps no sharper than other biological boundaries [e.g., see Lwoff (1951)].

Medical opinions in the writer's experience seem to make little distinction in terms of the relevant judgment between the less and the more overtly pathogenic protozoa, or between protozoa and metazoan parasites; with rare exceptions medical parasitologists associate them all with primitive conditions of environmental sanitation or with poor personal or group hygiene—in short, with filth. The common preoccupation of these parasitologists with feces—the basis of more than one ribald joke—may be partly responsible for this attitude. It might be augmented by the association of the one species among these protozoa most widely considered pathogenic—*Trichomonas vaginalis*—with venereal disease, with all the odious implications of that category. It is of interest that this very protozoan has been cited as an exception. McEwen (1960) has suggested that the trichomonad "is often a normal inhabitant in the vagina, just as it is of the rectum and mouth," and that the participation of the vaginal form in disease depends on predisposing conditions in the host, as is true of other typical endogenous infections. This is not a unique opinion, but it is distinctly a minority one. Whether or not the foregoing helps to explain the contrary view that prevails, the view itself is foreign to the writer's approach and is rejected out of hand. But its existence demands that the question of the autochthony of protozoa—or, conversely, their acutal relationship to the conditions so widely considered responsible for their presence in man—be examined carefully on its merits.

Indigenous Species

Detailed descriptions of the morphology and distinguishing features of protozoa are available in specialized texts of protozoology and need only be briefly summarized here. The protozoa that may qualify for indigenous status all fall into the 2 classes of *Mastigophora* or flagellates and *Rhizopoda* or amebas. Except where indicated otherwise, the morphologic data that follow have been compiled from Belding (1952), Kudo (1954), and Faust and Russell (1957).

Flagellates

Trichomonads (Fig. 8-1). *Trichomonas tenax* (syn., *T. buccalis, T. elongata), T. hominis,* and *T. vaginalis* are found in the human mouth, intestine, and genitourinary tract, respectively. They are ovoid, squat, fusiform or pear-shaped organisms with 4 free flagella originating in 1 or more granules (blepharoplasts) at the anterior pole, the flagella being approximately as long as the body of the organism. An undulating membrane carries a fifth flagellum on its outer margin and a costa or

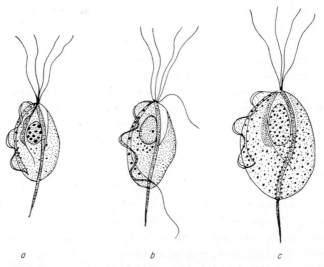

a   b   c

Fig. 8-1. Indigenous trichomonads. *a, T. tenax. b, T. hominis. c, T. vaginalis.* Diagrammatic, ×2,000. [*Redrawn by the writer after Wenrich* (1944), *courtesy of Dr. Wenrich and Am. J. Trop. Med.*]

basal rod at its base. A thick axostyle or solid central body extends from the anterior axial pole (from which the undulating membrane also originates) and projects through the opposite pole, tapering to a point. An ovoid nucleus is near the anterior pole. A parabasal apparatus (especially in *T. tenax* and *T. vaginalis*) comprising a slender fibril extends from the anterior pole between the nucleus and the base of the undulating membrane, carrying a shorter thicker parabasal body at its anterior end; and a cytostome, usually most conspicuous in *T. hominis*, appears as a cleft or mouth adjoining the anterior end of the axostyle [see Wenrich (1944); Kirby (1945)]. Nearly all workers agree that these trichomonads do not form cysts, but Wantland and Wantland (1960) have stated that *T. tenax* forms cysts with 2 to 8 nuclei. Electron micrographs of *T. vaginalis* have been presented by Inoki, Nakanishi, and Nakabayashi (1959) and of *T. tenax* by Ohno (1960).

Most competent observers are agreed that the 3 trichomonads of man are distinct species [e.g., Dobell (1939); Wenrich (1944, 1947); Honigberg and Lee (1959)]; but the 3 forms overlap in size and morphology, and perhaps in other respects; and the differences are hardly striking enough to permit microscopic identification of single organisms without knowledge of their sources. *T. vaginalis* is usually larger than the others. It is 7 to 23 μ long, average 13 μ, exclusive of flagella or the posterior extension of the axostyle; comparable averages for *T. tenax* and *T. hominis* are 6.5 and 7 to 8 μ *T. vaginalis* is also usually widest, *T. tenax* most slender. *T. hominis* is said to show 5 anterior flagella at times [Wenrich (1944, 1947); Kirby (1945)]. Other morphologic and minor cultural differences have also been suggested [Wenrich (1947)].

MacDonald and Tatum (1948a) found *T. vaginalis* and *T. hominis* alike in their sensitivity to antiseptics, and the same authors (1948b) found these 2 forms antigenically identical, but distinct from the animal trichomonad, *T. foetus*. In a brief note, Inoki and Hamada (1953) reported that in mice pretreated by intravenous injection of young chicken erythrocytes, *T. vaginalis*, nonlethal in untreated mice, produced transmissible fatal infection and became altered in growth characteristics and morphology so as to resemble *T. foetus*. More recently, Honigberg and Read (1960) have presented evidence of a DNA-dependent transformation to virulence in the bird trichomonad *T. gallinae*, which closely resembles *T. tenax* [Honigberg and Lee (1959)].

Trichomonas hominis has been mentioned among the protozoan population of the cecum of rats [Peterson (1960)].

Giardia (Fig. 8-2). *G. lamblia* (syn. *G. intestinalis*), a common intestinal flagellate, exists as both trophozoite and cyst. The trophozoite is bilaterally symmetrical with paired nuclei, axostyles, and flagella. It

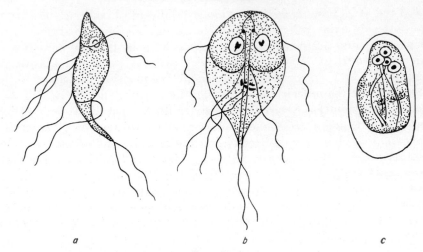

FIG. 8-2. *Giardia lamblia. a,* side view of living organism. *b,* stained trophozoite. *c,* stained mature cyst, ×2,000. [*Redrawn by the writer after Kudo* (1954), *with Dr. Kudo's permission and by courtesy of Charles C Thomas, Publisher.*]

is shaped roughly like half a pear, flattened dorsally and convex ventrally, rounded anteriorly and tapering to a fine point posteriorly, usually 12 to 20 μ long, 6 to 8 μ wide and 3 to 4 μ thick. Occupying most of the anterior part of the flat dorsal surface is a concave sucking disk. The 2 needlelike axostyles lie close together in the midline near the dorsal surface; from different points along their length arise 4 or perhaps 5 pairs of flagella. The 2 oval nuclei, each with a single karyosome, lying one on each side of the axostyles anteriorly, and the bifurcated parabasal body, combine to give the trophozoite its odd facelike appearance. The cysts are ovoid, slightly smaller than the trophozoites, with 2 or 4 nuclei nearer one pole; paired structures representing axostyles, flagella, and fibrils are seen in stained specimens. The cell contents appear shrunken within the cell wall.

Chilomastix mesnili (Fig. 8-3*a,b*). This enteric flagellate has an asymmetrical pear-shaped trophozoite 10 to 15 μ or more long and an ovoid cyst averaging 8 μ long with a lemonlike projection at one pole. The trophozoite appears helically twisted, with a groove spiraling around the body toward the tapered posterior pole. The spherical nucleus, lying close to the blunt anterior pole, has a small karyosome joined by radial linin fibrils to peripheral chromatin masses. A cytostome with irregular borders extends from the anterior pole backward about half the length of the organism. Two short and three long flagella project from the anterior pole; a short fourth flagellum lies along

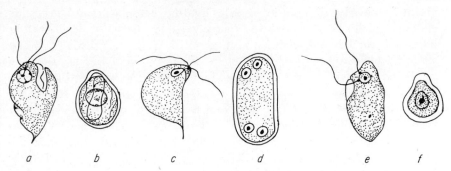

a   b   c   d   e   f

FIG. 8-3. Small indigenous flagellates. *a,b, Chilomastix mesnili, a,* stained trophozoite. *b,* stained cyst. *c,d, Enteromonas hominis, c,* stained trophozoite, *d,* stained cyst. *e,f, Retortomonas intestinalis, e,* stained trophozoite, *f,* stained cyst. ×2,000 [*Redrawn by the writer after Kudo* (1954), *with Dr. Kudo's permission and by courtesy of Charles C Thomas, Publisher.*]

the floor of the cytostome. In the cyst can be seen a single nucleus similar to that of the trophozoite, the cytostome with its contained flagellum, and 3 blepharoplast granules close to the bulging anterior pole.

Enteromonas hominis (Fig. 8-3*c,d*). *E. hominis* (syn., *Tricercomonas intestinalis*) is a small intestinal flagellate, the trophozoite 4 to 10 × 3 to 6 μ, varying from spherical to piriform, with 4 flagella, 3 attached anteriorly and a fourth projecting from the posterior pole. The nucleus is round or irregularly ovoid, has a large karyosome, and lies close to the anterior pole. The cysts are ovoid and contain 1, 2, or 4 nuclei.

Retortomonas intestinalis (Fig. 8-3*e,f*). Another flagellate of the intestine, *R. intestinalis* (syn., *Embadomonas intestinalis*), appears in its trophozoite form as a small, variable pyriform or ovoid organism 4 to 9 μ × 3 to 4 μ, with a nucleus and karyosome near the anterior end, a large cystostome and 2 unequal flagella. The cyst is pearshaped and shows only 1 nucleus.

Amebas (Fig. 8-4)

All the amebas are enteric forms except the first.

Entamoeba gingivalis. The ameba of the human mouth (syn., *Endamoeba buccalis*) is said nearly universally to occur only as a trophozoite. Wantland and Wantland (1960), however, have stated that this form as well as *Trichomonas tenax* may produce cysts, and that in both species the cysts may contain from 2 to 8 nuclei. The trophozoite is usually 10 to 20 μ in diameter and in the living state generally appears irregularly round or ovoid or with one or more pseudopodia; the cytoplasm is clearly differentiated into hyaline ectoplasm and granular endoplasm, the latter containing many vacuoles, bacteria, degenerating host cell nuclei, cell debris, and greenish refractile bodies. When stained, the nearly spherical nucleus, 2 to 4 μ in diameter, shows a small central karyosome and irregular chromatin masses lining the nuclear membrane. This ameba is usually smaller than *Ent. coli* or the larger variety of *Ent. histolytica*, and is distinguished from the latter especially by the abundance of its cell contents and the generally accepted absence of cysts. Tumka (1960) has reported that both the trophozoite of *Ent. gingivalis* and its contained nucleus are significantly larger in the presence of gingival inflammation than when found in healthy mouths.

Entamoeba coli. This intestinal ameba (syn., *Endamoeba hominis*) occurs in trophozoite and cyst stages and in several intermediate forms. The trophozoite is usually 20 to 35 μ in diameter, the cytoplasm is not clearly differentiated, movement is more sluggish than in either *Ent. gingivalis* or *Ent. histolytica*, and the pseudopods are endoplasmic and usually granular rather than (as in the others) ectoplasmic and hyaline. The nucleus is more apparent in the living state than in either of the

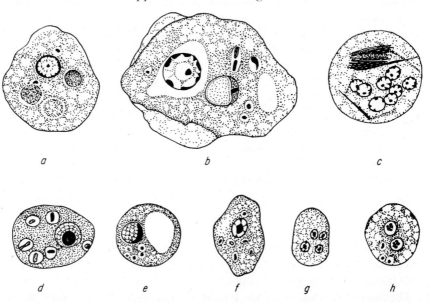

Fig. 8-4. Indigenous amebas, stained. *a, Entamoeba gingivalis. b,c, E. coli, b,* trophozoite, *c,* mature cyst. *d,e, Iodamoeba bütschlii, d,* trophozoite, *e,* cyst, *f,g, Endolimax nana, f,* trophozoite, *g,* cyst. *h, Dientamoeba fragilis,* binucleate trophozoite, 2,000. [*Redrawn by the writer after Kudo* (1954), *with Dr. Kudo's permission and by courtesy of Charles C Thomas, Publisher.*]

other *Entamoeba* species. In stained specimens, the karyosome is eccentric, the peripheral chromatin ring irregular and coarse. The cytoplasm contains vacuoles and less cellular debris but more bacteria and fungi than *Ent. gingivalis;* erythrocytes, characteristic of *Ent. histolytica,* are rarely or never seen in *Ent. coli.* Cyst formation, as observed in cultures, entails rounding and the elimination of cytoplasmic inclusions (the precyst), followed by nuclear division leading typically in the mature cyst to 8 (occasionally to 16 or 32) nuclei all with eccentric karyosomes. Immature cysts, containing 1, 2, or 4 nuclei, show one or more distinctly outlined large glycogen vacuoles and several acicular, filamentous or splinter-like so-called chromatoid bodies which tend to disappear in the mature cyst. Immature cysts are not distinguishable from those of *Ent. histolytica,* but the mature cyst of *Ent. coli* is usually larger (up to 30 μ in diameter) and is distinguished especially by the morphology and number of its nuclei (*Ent. histolytica* has 4) and by its chromatoid bodies, which are less numerous and more irregular in form. Cysts are likely to be found alone in formed stools, trophozoites or both in diarrhea.

Iodamoeba bütschlii. I. bütschlii (syn., *Entamoeba williamsi, Endolimax williamsi*) is characterized by its nucleus, which contains a large karyosome rich in chromatin, usually centrally located in the trophozoite, markedly eccentric or in contact with the nuclear membrane in the cyst. The karyosome is surrounded by a layer of lightly staining granules, with achromatic strands extending from the karyosome to the membrane. The trophozoite is usually 8 to 15 μ in diameter and shows fairly active progressive movement. Its cytoplasm is not well differentiated. Bacteria and yeasts appear in its food vacuoles. The cysts are slightly smaller than the vegetative cells, vary widely in shape, and typically contain a large glycogen vacuole (staining with Lugol's solution, whence the generic name).

Endolimax nana. The small trophozoite of *E. nana* (syn., *E. intestinalis, Entamoeba nana*) is usually less than 10 μ in diameter, with a vesicular nucleus containing a relatively large irregular karyosome with achromatic roughly radial threads. Motility is fairly active, usually with a single broad pseudopodium. Food vacuoles contain bacteria. Precystic stages occur. The cyst is usually oval; it is thin-walled and contains 1 to 4 nuclei.

Dientamoeba fragilis. This intestinal ameba is known only as the trophozoite which may contain 1 but more often has 2 nuclei, each with a large karyosome made up of separate chromatin granules connected to the nuclear membrane by radial strands. The organism is small (average 5 to 12 μ), shows clear cytoplasmic differentiation, and active ameboid movement. Bacteria occur in its food vacuoles.

Incidence of the Protozoa in Man

The Intestine

The question whether protozoa may properly be considered indigenous to man should be answerable in terms of incidence; but with these microorganisms, because of the suggestion noted at the head of this chapter that incidence may be modified or determined by environmental circumstances, such circumstances must be taken into account. It is appropriate to begin the inquiry with the intestinal protozoa, not only because this category encompasses most of the forms in question, but because one may expect that the influence of environmental conditions would be most apparent in this body area.

Table 8-1 presents a compilation of data, in terms of percentage incidence and number of subjects, on the intestinal fauna of man, excluding *Entamoeba histolytica* and *Balantidium coli* as overt pathogens, *Isospora belli* for reasons of rarity as well as pathogenicity, and the so-called coprozoic amebas, which are evidently transients. The data have been assembled from older compilations, with overlapping avoided in so far as this could be done, and from the original reports chiefly of more recent investigations. Aside from the separation of "mental hospital inmates" given in the bottom rows, an attempt has been made to divide the data into groups for adults and children, on the one hand, and for each of these into populations of North America–Western Europe, for Alaskan Eskimos and Greenlanders, and for all other areas. Since age data are frequently not given, and since no correlation of a possibly contributing influence (such as environmental sanitation) can be made confidently with the geographic distinction employed—and for other obvious reasons—the data must be treated with caution. They represent, however, much of the basis for the prevalent view that protozoa are not indigenous to man, and it is this view that we purpose to examine.

Adults. The data in Table 8-1 for groups I and II (principally adults, with the geographic separation noted above) are given in 2 sets for each representing minimum and maximum values for individual surveys. For group I, 7 different compilations or surveys are represented, and it seems of interest that the two that recur as minima, representing U.S. students and military personnel and their dependents, might be thought of as subject to "cleaner" environmental conditions than the 5 more miscellaneous groups that recur as maxima. In group II are found just 2 surveys in which, when both are represented, the Marshallese present lower values than the Egyptian–Turkish group except for *Trichomonas hominis*, where the reverse relation appears. The inclusion of children in the latter geographic group does not seem sufficient, in light of the data for children given below, to explain this difference;

TABLE 8-1
PER CENT INCIDENCE OF LESS PATHOGENIC INTESTINAL PROTOZOA IN DIFFERENT POPULATION GROUPS*

	Enta-moeba coli	Endo-limax nana	Ioda-moeba bütschlii	Dienta-moeba fragilis	Giardia lamblia	Chilo-mastix mesnili	Tricho-monas hominis	Entero-monas hominis	Retorto-monas intesti-nalis
I. Western min.	3.2^a	9.3^c	1.4^c	0.2^a	2.9^c	0.4^c	0.3^c	0.1^a	0.1^a
adults† max.	32.1^b	16.0^d	5.0^e	5.9^f	14.7^b	6.1^g	4.1^g	3.2^g	1.3^g
II. Non-Western min.	40.0^h	31.8^h	1.6^h §	4.8^i	2.4^h	4.4^h §	3.5^i	11.3^i	
adults max.	52.6^i	36.4^i	15.3^i		13.5^i	7.6^i	29.4^h		
III. Alaskan Eskimos^k	51	8	4		1	0	0		
IV. Greenlanders, 15 or over^l	46.1	24.3	3.7		2.1	2.7			
V. Greenlanders, under 15^l	70.9	32.0	5.9		13.5	4.5			
VI. Western children‡	11.2^m	14.8^m	1.8^m	5.3^m	7.7^m 17.6^g	1.2^m	3.0^m 0.4^n		
VII. Non-Western	26.3^m	22.8^m	4.2^m	20.4^m	3.0^m	1.8^m		2^p	4.6^p
children	47.6^p	36.8^p	23.0^p	4.8^p	19.9^p	6.4^p	7.3^p		1.5^t
VIII. Mental hospital	76–81^r	19–63^r	6–11^r	36–51.4^s	5–11^r	10–26^r	11–17^r		
patients	41.6^u	24.5^u	9.4^u		4.4^u	21.6^u	6.9^u		

* Numbers of subjects are given in parentheses in the references below.
† Adults or general populations, North America or western Europe.
‡ Children, North America or western Europe.
a Brown and Garber (1960) military personnel, California (18,064).
b Meleney et al. (1932) Tennessee (20,237).
c Kean and Smillie (1954) U.S. students going abroad and returning; Kuntz et al. (1959) U.S. military personnel and dependents in Formosa (1,104).
d Craig and Faust (1951) compilations (10,279 to 18,322).
e Belding (1952) compilations, U.S. (8,029 to 38,577).
f Knoll and Howell (1945) hospital patients and others, Chicago (2,937).
g Belding (1952) compilations of world-wide surveys (7,120 to 65,295).
h Goldman and Carver (1959) natives of Rongelap (Marshall Islands) aged 21 or over (85) or (§) all ages (181).
i Kuntz et al. (1958) children and young adults, Egypt, Turkey (1,757).
k Hitchcock (1950) Bethel area (S.W. Alaska) Eskimos (100).
l Babbott et al. (1961) Greenlanders, aged 14 or under (288) or 15 or over (375).
m Weiner et al. (1959) native white (169) or Puerto Rican (167) children in Philadelphia.
n Summerlin, cited by Wenrich (1947) San Diego children (513).
p Goldman and Carver (1959) Rongelap natives under 21; Kuntz (1960) East Pakistan children aged 6–18; Kuntz and Lawless (1958) lower Egypt, infants aged 26–51 months; Wells and Blagg (1956) northern Egypt, children aged 8–12 years (323–778).
q Wenrich (1947) compilation (797).
r Jeffery (1960) South Carolina state hospital, aged 18–76 (110).
s Craig and Faust (1951) compilations, Holland, Sweden, Panama (numbers not given).
t Young and Felsenfeld (1944) Chicago area state hospital (1,029).
u Svensson (1935) Swedish mental hospitals (1,323).
w Wenrich (1945) compilation, adults (1,418).

nor can it explain the Rongelap value for *T. hominis*, the maximum for that protozoan in the table. It may be noted that the Rongelap group was small.

Comparing groups I and II as such, it is evident that the values for *Entamoeba coli* and *Endolimax nana* are distinctly higher in the non-Western group II, and that a tendency in the same direction is also to be found for *Iodamoeba bütschlii*, *Chilomastix mesnili*, and *Enteromonas hominis,* with, indeed, only *Dientamoeba fragilis* and *Giardia lamblia* clearly failing to conform to the trend. On the other hand, considering especially the maximum values for group I, all representing large samples, it is apparent that all forms listed occur in man often enough to be considered indigenous.

Primitives. The data for groups III, IV, and V (Alaskan Eskimos and arctic Greenlanders) are given separately because they probably represent environmental conditions as primitive as any to be found on earth. The samples were small, especially in group III. Babbot, Frye, and Gordon (1961) in the Greenland study referred to, noted that "environmental and living conditions of the indigenous population [to which the study was limited] resemble those of the Alaskan Eskimos"; and the details supplied amply substantiate the designation, "primitive." Yet, except for *Ent. coli* in both groups and *End. nana* among the Greenlanders, the findings are distinctly closer to those of group I than of group II. To the degree that these findings can be considered valid, it must be concluded that something other than or in addition to primitive living conditions—presumably climate?—influences the prevalence of intestinal protozoa generally.

Children. The values for children in Table 8-1 are generally consistent with those for adults in terms of comparison of the Western (group VI) and non-Western (group VII) categories, but they also convey the odd suggestion that Western but not non-Western children tend to be more heavily parasitized than their adult counterparts—a suggestion hardly to be taken seriously. The common view that *Giardia lamblia* is more prevalent in children than in adults is given limited but hardly striking support from the data in the table. The view can be traced back to a study by Maxcy (1921) of 98 children without gastrointestinal disease, of whom 18, or 20 per cent, had *G. lamblia* in their stools. Chandler (1954) has also reported that among these protozoa studied in Egyptian villages, only *Giardia* was more common in children than in adults. Isolated high values in Table 8-1 for *I. bütschlii* and *D. fragilis* in children may also be noted. The textbook statement that *Trichomonas hominis* is more common in children [e.g., Belding (1952)] finds little support in these data.

Included within the second row under Group VII in Table 8-1 are 28 children in a typical lower Egyptian village studied by Kuntz and Lawless (1958), the findings for which seem worth separate scrutiny. The children were 26 to 47 months old at the beginning of a 4-month survey, and were compared with 2 younger groups of 23 children 1 to 6 months old and of 30 children 13 to 24 months old. The pertinent findings are set out in Table 8-2. For all protozoan species the incidence increased with age and except for *Dientamoeba fragilis* reached values

TABLE 8-2

PER CENT INCIDENCE OF CERTAIN INTESTINAL PROTOZOA IN GROUPS
OF EGYPTIAN CHILDREN EXAMINED WEEKLY FOR 4 MONTHS
(EXTRACTED FROM KUNTZ AND LAWLESS, 1958)

	Age at beginning of survey, months		
	1–6	13–24	26–47
Number of children	23	30	28
Entamoeba coli	0	10	71
Endolimax nana	0	13	43
Iodamoeba bütschlii	0	10	21
Dientamoeba fragilis	0	0	10
Giardia lamblia	30	70	82
Chilomastix mesnili	0	10	32
Trichomonas hominis	9	30	50
Enteromonas hominis	0	7	32

well above those given for children in Table 8-1. Only *Giardia* and
T. hominis were found in the youngest group. The authors noted that
these two species did not coexist in the children studied. They remarked
that living conditions in the village were such that the children were
exposed to infection almost constantly beginning a few days after
birth, and considered that "host parasite relationships among [such]
peoples . . . leave an investigator baffled." Clearly, here as with indigenous bacteria and fungi, much remains to be learned.

Mental Patients. Table 8-1 includes data on the incidence of these
protozoa among the inmates of mental hospitals, who are notoriously
subject to intestinal parasitism and disease—with poor hygiene the
accepted reason. It is apparent that the values for intestinal protozoa
are for the most part high indeed in this group, especially for *Entamoeba coli*, *Endolimax nana*, *Dientamoeba fragilis*, and *Chilomastix
mesnili*, for all of which the maximum values are well above those
given elsewhere in the table. The maxima for *Trichomonas hominis*
and *Iodamoeba bütschlii* are also high but within the range reached by
the group II populations, while those for *Giardia lamblia* and *Retortomonas intestinalis* are within or near normal limits. If the high levels
in this group are dependent upon poor hygiene, it seems again that not
all intestinal protozoa are affected by this circumstance.

Some of the data for mental hospital patients given in Table 8-1
were taken from a 3-year study by Jeffery (1960) of 110 female inmates, aged 18 to 76, at South Carolina State Hospital. Between the
first and eight subsequent surveys for parasites, this whole group was

moved from "an extremely old building, poorly designed . . . [which] made any but a very low level of sanitation most difficult" to "a new building of modern design . . . [in which] a high level of sanitation was possible."

The cumulative incidence of 6 protozoan species as given by Jeffery is shown graphically in Fig. 8-5 together with plots, calculated from Jeffery's data, for the total number of new infections with the 6 species at each survey, and the total of such infections minus *Ent. coli* and *End. nana*, which tended toward saturation. The data are difficult to interpret. It would have been useful to have determined infection rates in the old building by several surveys before the population was moved. The report noted that, in addition to the data of immediate interest here, transmission of hookworm ceased and that of two other worms, *Trichuris trichuria* and *Strongyloides stercoralis*, was greatly reduced coincident with the changed environment. It was also noted, although the data were not given, that *Chilomastix mesnili* and *Trichomonas hominis* showed a net decrease between the initial and final examinations.

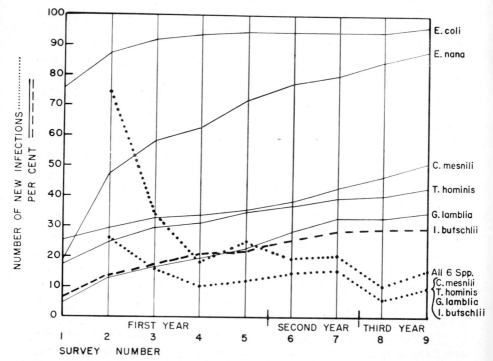

FIG. 8-5. Cumulative incidence of certain intestinal protozoa in 110 inmates of a mental hospital. [*From the data of Jeffery* (1960).]

TABLE 8-3

PER CENT INCIDENCE OF INDIGENOUS INTESTINAL PROTOZOA
IN SWEDEN AND FINLAND (DATA OF SVENSSON, 1935)

	Rural			Mental hospital inmates
	Stockholm	Sweden	Helsingfors	
Number studied	300	300	157	1,323
Entamoeba coli	7.3	16.0	29.3	41.6
Endolimax nana	6.0	12.3	14.0	24.5
Iodamoeba bütschlii	1.3	1.7	5.7	9.4
Giardia lamblia	4.7	7.0	6.4	4.4
Chilomastix mesnili	0.7	1.0	3.2	21.6

The new infection rate diminished sharply, for all 6 species combined and for the 4 of lower incidence, after the third survey. As Jeffery put it, "transmission of intestinal protozoa continued, although probably at a somewhat reduced rate" after the change of environment. It is obvious that environment alone might have failed to complete the hygienic transformation of a group of this sort, or that even if in effect it did so, infection starting at so high a rate might not have been controlled. The difficulties of the problem are manifest.

Influence of Sanitation. An intensive study by Svensson (1935) on the intestinal protozoa attempted to come to grips with "the connexion between their distribution and hygienic conditions," and it is of interest that this worker omitted any reference to hygiene in her summary. Her principal findings are given in Table 8-3. It will be seen that except for *Giardia lamblia* these species all increased in incidence from left to right in the order given. From a compilation of the literature, Svensson discerned a definite relationship between "good social standing" or "poor" or "primitive" living conditions, the latter together with a warm climate, and, respectively, low or high incidence rates of intestinal protozoa. As representatives of both primitive living conditions and a warm climate she mentioned "natives in a Southern state of U.S.A. . . . subtropical America" as well as Chinese in Peking, referring for the former group to a paper by Faust (1930) dealing with the mountainous and by no means subtropical Wise County in southwestern Virginia. With regard specifically to the groups listed in Table 8-3, Svensson observed that outpatients in Helsingfors showed almost as high incidence values as the Chinese despite living conditions corresponding with Western hygienic standards; and she did not present any but the vaguest suggestion of parallelism between the

TABLE 8-4

PER CENT INCIDENCE OF INDIGENOUS INTESTINAL PROTOZOA IN
1,323 MENTAL HOSPITAL INMATES IN SWEDEN CLASSIFIED
BY TYPE OF WARD (DATA OF SVENSSON, 1935)

	"Quiet and cleanly"	"Restless and uncleanly chronic"		"Excitable and violent"	"Indolent, decrepit, uncleanly, chronic"
		1	2		
Number studied	164	122	221	92	143
Entamoeba coli	51.2	44.3	49.3	56.5	42.7
Endolimax nana	19.5	35.2	21.7	28.3	27.3
Iodamoeba bütschlii	9.1	19.7	9.5	12.0	8.4
Giardia lamblia	2.4	5.7	4.5	2.2	3.5
Chilomastix mesnili	18.9	36.9	26.2	21.7	24.5

trend of the values in the table and a sequence of decreasing "social standing" or living conditions.

The subjects studied by Faust (1930) consisted of rural, urban, and semiurban groups including those of mining camps, who were examined for intestinal protozoa because of a high *Ascaris* infection rate, especially among the children, as demonstrated by Cort, Otto, and Spindler (1930). Faust found the incidence of protozoa

. . . higher than has thus far been discovered in any population save in the tropics or in the Orient or in asylum cases . . . comparable to those found in an environment where local factors favor propagation of the parasite and where personal hygiene is almost entirely lacking . . . [but] the *Ascaris* and protozoan data do not coincide, so that the underlying factors must be essentially different . . . .

Svensson (1935), to return to her report of mental hospital patients, studied the incidence of intestinal protozoa in different wards in which the inmates were classified in the groups given in Table 8-4. It is obvious from these findings that although the values are high throughout except for *Giardia*, there is no simple relationship between cleanliness as defined by this worker and the incidence of any of the protozoan species listed. The findings for the sexes have been combined in the table: Svensson found consistently higher values among men.

An attempt to approach directly the question of the effect of improved sanitation on intestinal parasites has been made by Chandler (1954), who studied two villages near Cairo, Egypt, one of which had been provided about 2 years earlier with greatly improved sanitary facilities, an uncontaminated water supply, and a health center [see

TABLE 8-5

PER CENT INCIDENCE OF INDIGENOUS INTESTINAL PROTOZOA IN TWO
EGYPTIAN VILLAGES WITH DIFFERING SANITARY FACILITIES
(SUMMARIZED FROM CHANDLER, 1954)

Village	Number examined	Ent. coli	End. nana	Iodamoeba	Dientamoeba	Giardia	Chilomastix	Trichomonas hominis
Sindbis: sanitation improved	229	58	49	35	12	11	10	1.8
Aghour El Kubra: unaltered	169	56	50	40	11	7.5	10	1.2

also Weir (1952)]. The data revealed a distinct reduction in the incidence of most *helminth* infections in the cleaner village, but no difference in the general incidence of protozoan infection. The results are summarized in Table 8-5. Chandler suggested that the absence of a reduction in incidence of protozoa at Sindbis, despite sanitary improvements, may have depended on persistence of the infections that had existed 2 years before. He also noted that "the installation of latrines and availability of pump wells does not necessarily mean that they are used." In general, the provision of good sanitary facilities does not of itself bring the level of community hygiene up to the standard the facilities make possible. It cannot therefore be suggested that any of the information presented above negates the idea that sanitation and the incidence of intestinal protozoa are related, but the relationship is evidently not established. The evidence does, on the other hand, suggest that some factor or factors associated with the conditions of life in certain geographic localities or in certain institutions tends to increase the incidence of intestinal protozoa, but the nature of the factor or factors is not made clear by these data.

The Mouth

The 2 protozoan species, *Entamoeba gingivalis* and *Trichomonas tenax*, have been found in the mouth, most frequently in the gingival area, of a variable, often high, proportion of persons in many parts of the world. A connection between the occurrence of both species and hygiene has generally been assumed, with "hygiene" having here a somewhat more restricted meaning than is usually given to it in studies of intestinal protozoa. The incidence of *Ent. gingivalis* in the mouth, in the findings of different workers with subjects variously described, has ranged from 0 to 100 per cent; the corresponding range for *T. tenax* in the literature reviewed is 4.0 to 33.8 per cent. In mouths considered normal or healthy, the range for *Ent. gingivalis* is 0 [Drew and Griffin (1917); Fisher (1927)] to 72.6 per cent [Westphal (1941)]; in the presence of gingivitis or periodontal disease it is 83.3 [Goodey and Wellings (1917)] to 100 per cent [Barrett (1914); Drew and Griffin (1917); Hinshaw and Simonton (1928)]. Beatman (1933) found *T. tenax* in 11.4 per cent of 105 healthy mouths. The lower values for this species in gingival disease, as compared with the ameba [10.0 to 26.5 per cent, Drew and Griffin (1917); Beatman (1933); Wenrich (1947)] may reflect only its greater fragility. Jepps (1923) found the trichomonad in the mouths of 16, or 32 per cent, of 50 hospitalized Indian and Chinese coolies at Kuala Lumpur, none of whom complained of mouth disease, and some of whom were said to have kept their mouths very clean. The incidence of *Ent. gingivalis* reported by Jepps for the same group was 56 per cent. Burch, Rees, and Reardon (1959) reported the presence of *T. tenax* in the mouth as associated significantly ($P = {<}0.001$) with the occurrence of *T. vaginalis* in the vagina. Of 213 women who harbored the latter protozoan, 33.8 per cent had *T. tenax* in their mouths; while among 369 women with negative vaginal cultures, only 19.2 per cent harbored the oral trichomonad. The sample comprised 176 white and 406 Negro women, but the data were not given separately for the 2 groups. The same authors [Burch et al. (1959)], as noted below, reported, in agreement with others, a markedly greater incidence of *T. vaginalis* in Negro than in white women. It is thus curious that Beatman (1933), in the only study of this kind known to the writer, found no significant difference in the incidence of *T. tenax* in the mouths of Negro and white subjects under either normal or pathologic conditions, although the difference between normal and pathologic was well marked in this instance. Beatman's findings are summarized in Table 8-6.

Relationship to Disease. The findings for both oral protozoa, more strikingly for *Entamoeba gingivalis*, suggest a relationship between their occurrence in the mouth and the presence of gingival and periodontal disease, a relationship reminiscent of the fusospirochetal group of bacteria, which, indeed, the protozoa often accompany. This relationship led Barrett (1914) and Bass and Johns (1915) to suggest *Ent. gingivalis* as "the cause" of pyorrhea, a suggestion long since discredited [see Kofoid, Hinshaw, and Johnstone (1929)]. In the literature on the protozoa of the mouth a curious thread of evident prejudice is sometimes apparent—the designation of a mouth as "normal," "clean," "healthy," or "well cared for" has been made as if to suggest that these terms are interchangeable. Conversely, their opposites— a "dirty" or "neglected" mouth, or, in actual effect, a mouth with severe gingivitis or suppurative periodontal disease, is regarded as if it

TABLE 8-6

INCIDENCE OF *Trichomonas tenax* IN THE MOUTHS OF PREGNANT
WOMEN AT ANTENATAL CLINICS AND IN DENTAL CLINIC
PATIENTS, PHILADELPHIA (DATA OF BEATMAN, 1933)*

	Pathologic mouths	Normal mouths	Total
White patients	29.7/155	9.3/54	24.4/209
Negro patients	21.1/90	13.7/51	18.4/141
Totals	26.5/245	11.4/105	22.7/350

* Per cent per number of patients.

By the χ^2 method, P for white versus Negro, pathologic mouths, = >0.1; white versus Negro, normal mouths, P = >0.3; both groups combined, pathologic versus normal, P = <0.01.

were sinful and as though it might be cured with a scrubbing brush. Shades of the lazar house, the Victorian view of syphilis, and the still current revulsion against mental illness! The protozoa of the mouth, apparently in contrast to other and doubtless more significant microorganisms, seem to symbolize the modern variant of Shakespeare's "creeping venomed thing." Their significance in relation to health and disease remains, however, obscure. No relationship between their presence in the mouth and habits of cleanliness or other desirable attributes of civilized man can be called established.

The Genitourinary Tract

The single protozoan species of the human genitourinary mucous membranes, *Trichomonas vaginalis*, is the subject of a larger literature than any of the other protozoa treated in this chapter. Two monographs deal with this microorganism [Trussell (1947); Keutel (1957)] and it has been a subject of three international symposia [see Catterall and Nicol (1960); Gallai and Sylvestre (1960); Sylvestre and Gallai (1960)]. While the reason for this popularity is not obvious, it is evidently associated with the nearly unanimous imputation of pathogenicity mentioned in the opening paragraph of this chapter. *T. vaginalis* is widely distributed in the general population, and might accordingly be considered indigenous. Evidence suggestive of an inverse relationship between its incidence and the economic level of the population is less equivocal for this species than for the intestinal and oral protozoa.

Data on the incidence of *T. vaginalis*, summarized from the compilations of Trussell (1947) and Wenrich (1947) and supplemented principally from more recent reports, are given in Table 8-7. Diverse sources and conditions impose the usual cautions. Most of the values are based on more than one study. The wide variation especially in the "Pathologic" column for men warns against comparisons between rows, but comparisons within each row and of the data for the two sexes are of interest.

Women. From the upper row of values for women it appears, first, that the incidence of *T. vaginalis* is approximately the same in pregnant and nonpregnant women. In several studies cited by Trussell (1947)—those of Hoehne; Fukushima; and Jirovec et al.—higher incidence values were obtained for pregnant than for nonpregnant groups. A difference of this kind is conspicuous in the data of Lang et al. (1956)—not included in the table—in which pregnant and nonpregnant women *with vaginitis* were compared. Of 275 in the former group, 54.2 per cent, and of 324 in the nonpregnant group, 24.8 per cent, harbored vaginal trichomonads. From the data as a whole it is difficult to be certain whether pregnancy of itself encourages the growth of these protozoa in the vagina, or whether vaginitis—a clearly related factor—is of particular importance in pregnancy. The data in Table 8-7 for the pathologic as compared with the normal or unspecified groups for both sets of women show that *T. vaginalis* is distinctly more common under pathologic conditions. Of particular interest are the findings for this microorganism in white as compared with Negro subjects of both sexes, and in female private patients as compared with clinic patients. Consistently and distinctly higher incidence values have been found for the latter groups in all instances. Of the two private- versus clinic-patient comparisons, the value for the clinic group is based in one [Burch et al. (1959)] on a preponderance of Negroes, and the same may be true of the other [Davis (1955)], although the author did not say so. According to Davis, "It is generally recognized that *T. vaginalis* infections are commoner among the segment of the population that depends on public clinics for medical care."

An economic factor affecting the incidence of this trichomonad is suggested—and, indeed, such a factor might well be the basis for the greater incidence among Negroes than among whites; but the manner in which such a factor may operate, and whether it is connected in any way with "hygiene," is not clear.

Additional light on the question of prevalence of trichomonads in Negro and white women has been furnished in a careful study of 405 women prisoners in the Detroit area by Herbst, Olszewski, and Thompson (1960). The subjects comprised 159 white and 246 Negro women aged 17 to 79, studied by single cultures in 5-year age groups between 21 and 50 and in 4 groups by length of confinement (less than 1 year, 1 to 2 years, 2 to 5 years, and more than 5 years). It was noted

TABLE 8-7

INCIDENCE OF *Trichomonas vaginalis* IN THE VAGINA AND
IN THE MALE GENITOURINARY TRACT

	Normal or un-specified	Preg-nant	Patho-logic	White	Negro	Patients	
						Private	Clinic
Women:							
Number[a]	4,685	2,219	993	4,298	2,412		
Per cent	24.9	25.6	36.4	23.5	44.7		
Number[b-i]	10,403		3,061	1,833	1,382	6,965	3,053
Per cent	9.9		19.5	9.8	48.1	9.9	28.3
Men:							
Number[b,i,k]			1,905	482	1,532		
Per cent			5.7	10.4	17.0		
Number[e-n]			271				
Per cent			28.0				
Number[o]			2,482				
Per cent			68				

[a] Compiled from Trussell (1947)
[b] Compiled from Wenrich (1947)
[c] Bland and Rakoff (1937)
[d] Feo (1953)
[e] Davis (1955)
[f] Brizio (1957)
[g] Burch et al. (1959)
[h] Koss and Wolinska (1959)

[i] Bauer et al. (1959)
[j] Feo (1944)
[k] Lanceley (1953)
[l] Valina (1950)
[m] Feo et al. (1956)
[n] Lomuto and Ciaula (1955)
[o] Coutts et al. (1955)

that during this period the 2 ethnic groups were integrated in housing and shared the same general environment, nutrition, and sexual limitations, constituting in the opinion of these authors probably the most closely controlled study of the race factor ever reported. The results showed the over-all prevalence of *T. vaginalis* to be higher among the Negro women by a small but significant margin ($P = 0.01$), being 67 per cent among the former and 53 per cent among the white prisoners. Differences attributable either to age or to length of prison stay were generally insignificant, but the prevalence of trichomonads tended to be lowest among the oldest inmates (none were found in 11 women over 60) and among the group of 31 who had been in prison for more than 5 years (10, or 32 per cent, infected). Except for these groups (or up to age 60 and 5 years' imprisonment) prevalence before imprisonment and persistence of infection seemed to determine the rates. It was noted that many of the prisoners had vaginitis, but no attempt was made to relate symptoms to infection.

Men. The incidence of *T. vaginalis* in men has been a matter of considerable recent interest, and has been closely associated with the question of possible venereal transmission of this trichomonad, a matter considered on page 286. The wide variation of the values for men in Table 8-7 reflects varying opinion. Here as elsewhere in the study of parasitic protozoa the principal errors are probably false negatives, so that true incidence values are always thought to be higher than those reported. Among the reasons given for missing this protozoan in men are (1) that it needs to be sought for in several sites, e.g., in the preputial sac as well as in urethral exudates or scrapings, urinary sediment, or prostatic fluid [see Trussell (1947); Lanceley (1953)]; (2) that different methods of disclosing it—stained smears, fresh preparations examined under darkfield or phase-contrast conditions, or cultures—are of differing sensitivity [see, for example, Frühwald (1957); Jira (1958); Catterall and Nicol (1960)]; and (3) that the forms occurring in the male differ from the more typical ones seen in the vagina and may therefore be missed. On this last point, Frühwald (1957) stated that round forms of *T. vaginalis* are more characteristic in men than the typical pear-shaped vaginal forms, and Keutel (1958) noted that aflagellate forms occurring in dense groups in men may make their identification difficult. Lanceley (1953), on the other hand, limited identification to "the unequivocal presence of a motile or flagellated organism morphologically indistinguishable from *T. vaginalis*," and suggested that "a belief in the existence of an encysted or resting stage would tend to produce higher figures" for its incidence.

In nearly all instances *T. vaginalis* has been looked for in men only in the presence of genitourinary symptoms, and the question of the occurrence of the organism on healthy tissues of the male is unresolved. Lanceley (1953) studied 40 married men he described as "normal" and found one symptomless "vector" who showed the organism in urethral scrapings "for as long as 24 hours after each marital coitus." He also examined preputial washings from 60 "promiscuous males" and failed to find trichomonads in any. Verheye and Kanda (1958) reported the presence of trichomonads in the urethra of 15 per cent of 912 men presumed to be normal, but three-quarters of these were found to have a urethral discharge. Burch et al. (1959) cultured *T. vaginalis* from urethral swabs or prostatic secretions of 13 (41.9 per cent) of 31 spouses of infected women; they noted, without further details, that the finding "is probably biased since men with symptoms would probably be most apt to volunteer for examination." In much of the literature the finding of *T. vaginalis* is itself accepted as evidence of disease, although in women without doubt and in men with very little doubt the presence of the organism is compatible with complete freedom from symptoms of any kind [see, e.g., Feo (1944); Draper (1955); Catterall and Nicol (1960)].

Summary: Protozoa as Indigenous to Man

The data reviewed in the foregoing section leave little room for doubt that certain protozoa are as much a part of the indigenous biota of man as are bacteria and fungi. Protozoa have been found in the mouth, and in the intestinal and genitourinary tracts of people everywhere in the world, some species commonly although presumably never universally, others much less so. The view that a high infection rate with any of these protozoa depends on poor hygiene, uncleanliness, primitive living conditions, or inadequate environmental sanitation is not supported by the data. Different groups, however, certainly show widely different rates of parasitism with many of these protozoa. Among the intestinal forms, *Giardia lamblia* tends to be more common among children than among adults, but does not otherwise show the variation characteristic of most of the other indigenous protozoa of the intestinal tract. These others are in general more common, in climates other than arctic or subarctic, among many non-Western peoples than among groups in North America and western Europe (except for *Dientamoeba fragilis*), and among patients in mental hospitals than elsewhere. In the mouth there is a clear association of prevalence of both *Ent. gingivalis* and *T. tenax* with disease of the local soft tissues, of which protozoan infection is evidently a consequence rather than a determinant. In the genitourinary tract there is a distinctly higher prevalence of *T. vaginalis* among Negroes than among whites, but again there is no objectively measured evidence of a corresponding difference in hygiene or correlated factors. An associated economic factor is inferred and directly suggested by a higher prevalence of trichomonads among clinic patients than among private patients. As will be seen on page 285, *T. vaginalis* is widely regarded as an inciting agent of genitourinary disease, and it is certainly found more frequently under pathologic conditions than on healthy tissues.

The probability of the occurrence of a given member of this group of protozoa in a slide or culture made from an indigenous locus is doubtless influenced by its concentration at the source, and a high prevalence rate would therefore imply active proliferation of the parasite in many of the subjects. Such active proliferation could result from tissue damage induced by conditions other than infection with the given protozoan. It seems possible, in other words, that the key factor in the prevalence of protozoa, in the intestine and vagina as well as in the mouth, is disease of the local tissues. Such a circumstance would not, of course, negate the possibility that any of these protozoa may themselves manifest pathogenic activities; on the contrary, it is characteristic of many amphibionts that they flourish in the presence of local tissue damage and in doing so themselves contribute to the damage.

Growth of Indigenous Protozoa

Physiologic and biochemical studies of this group of protozoa are scarce except for a small literature on *Trichomonas vaginalis*. For reviews and references on this organism, see Trussell (1947); and on other protozoa see Lwoff (1951), Nakamura (1953), Porter (1953), Hutner and Lwoff (1955), and Provasoli (1958). The following discussion is limited to selected aspects of the questions of cultivation and metabolism of the indigenous species.

Cultivation

Media and methods for cultivation of both amebas and trichomonads have been described by Dobell and Laidlaw (1926), Boeck and Drbohlav (1925), and Balamuth (1946). Using modifications of the earlier methods, the intestinal protozoa (*Entamoeba histolytica, Ent. coli, Endolimax nana, Dientamoeba fragilis, Chilomastix mesnili, Trichomonas hominis,* and *Enteromonas hominis*—but not *Giardia lamblia*) were cultivated by Svensson (1935); *Iodamoeba bütschlii* did not survive more than 4 culture generations. Mandoul, Dargelos, and Bour (1959, 1960), more recently, have reported studies of *Chilomastix mesnili* grown in Dobell's medium. *Entamoeba gingivalis* has been cultivated by similar methods [see Kofoid and Johnstone (1929); Westphal (1941)]. Balamuth (1946) cultivated *Dientamoeba, Endolimax, Iodamoeba, Trichomonas,* and *Chilomastix,* as well as *Ent. histolytica,* but not *Ent. coli,* in an egg-yolk medium. Cultivation of *Ent. coli* was noted by this worker without details in a later paper [Balamuth (1953)]. *Trichomonas vaginalis* and trichomonads found in hosts other than man have been grown in unequivocally pure cultures—that is, apart from other microbic species ("axenic"); whereas the other protozoa have been grown in mixtures with other microbes, sometimes with a single accompanying species ("monoxenic"), either bacterial or other [e.g., *Trypanosoma cruzei* or other blood flagellates; see Balamuth and Thompson (1955); Chia-Tung Pan (1960)]. It is of interest that among bacteria grown in association with *Ent. histolytica* has been a species of *Bacteroides* [see Shaffer, Schuler, and Key (1958); Reeves and Frye (1960); Reeves, Schweinfurth, and Frye (1960)].

Ent. gingivalis has been grown mixed with bacteria in the Locke solution–egg albumin medium developed for *Enteromonas hominis* by Boeck (1924); see Drbohlav (1925); Howitt (1925); Kofoid and Johnstone (1929). Westphal (1941) grew *Ent. gingivalis* in a medium developed by him for *Trichomonas vaginalis*, consisting of a fluid filtrate of coagulated serum in diluted Ringer's solution, layered over peptone-serum agar; rice starch was "occasionally" added. Balamuth and Thompson (1955) stated that the general pattern of media for cultivation of amebas includes the use of highly complex animal products (hen's egg, serum, or organ extracts) combined with plant products, usually rice powder or rice starch.

Media for trichomonads, including *T. hominis*, have been reviewed by Trussell (1947). He noted that all successful media had contained serum or whole blood. The original bacteriafree culture of *T. vaginalis* was obtained by accident [Trussell (1940)]; but his subsequent studies and those of other workers successfully utilized penicillin or streptomycin for separation of trichomonads from bacteria. See also Kott and Adler (1961).

Aided by these pure culture methods, Sprince and Kupferberg (1947*a,b*) and Sprince (1948) have been able to initiate studies of the nutrition of *T. vaginalis*. They showed that the organism grew axenically in a medium containing trypticase, B vitamins, purines, pyrimidines, acetate, asparagine, bicarbonate, ascorbic acid, and ribose enriched with 10 per cent serum [Sprince and Kupferberg (1947*a*)]; that among the active components of serum were linoleic acid and serum albumin (1947*b*), and that serum could be separated into two essential fractions, a proteinfree lipid and the proteins precipitable by 50 per cent alcohol.

A medium devised by Diamond (1957) has been adapted by Ivey (1961) to the growth of isolated colonies of *T. vaginalis* in pour plates incubated in anaerobic jars. Ryigas (1960–61) has suggested a means for separation of *T. vaginalis* from accompanying yeasts by inoculating antibiotic-treated material into sterile burettes containing the medium of Laan (1960–61) made semisolid by addition of 0.1 per cent agar. The protozoan, growing in the lower portion of the burette, could be recovered via the stopcock.

Early studies of the cultivation of *Trichomonas tenax* were referred to by Kofoid, Hinshaw, and Johnstone (1929). More recently, this organism has been grown with bacteria in a yolk infusion–serum medium [see Honigberg and Lee (1959)]. Wantland and Wantland (1960) found cultures more sensitive than direct examination for disclosure of both *T. tenax* and *Ent. gingivalis* in the mouth; they used the egg-yolk fluid medium of Balamuth (1946) layered on the solid egg slants of Dobell and Laidlaw (1926), and also the fluid medium of St. John (1932).

Cultivation of *Giardia lamblia* together with candidate has been reported by Karapetyan (1960), who used chick fibroblast tissue culture for initial growth and later a human serum–chick embryo extract medium.

Carbohydrate Metabolism. Anaerobiosis. Magara, Amino, and Yakouti (1953) were able to obtain separated colonies of *T. vaginalis* in deep agar tubes after isolating bacteriafree cultures in a beef–beef liver–glucose–serum–penicillin medium. Asami, Nodake, and Uento (1955) grew this protozoan on the surface of Fortner plates, using *Escherichia coli* to absorb oxygen. The isolation medium used by these workers contained meat extract, peptone, cysteine HCl, glucose, methylene blue, human serum, penicillin, streptomycin, and 0.05 per cent agar. The plating medium was similar but contained 2 per cent agar without cysteine or methylene blue. It is now recognized that trichomonads and parasitic amebas, in so far as the latter have been studied, have a growth requirement for reducing conditions approaching or actually equivalent to strict anaerobiosis. It is of interest that rumen protozoa, which fall into genera distinct from those of man, are all obligate anaerobes [see Hungate (1955)].

Nakamura (1953) reviewed the evidence which led him to conclude that anaerobic conditions are necessary for optimum growth and metabolism of *Entamoeba histolytica*, while Johnson (1942) found complete anaerobiosis optimal for *Trichomonas vaginalis*. Read and Rothman (1955) showed that acid, including lactic, as well as CO_2 and H_2 are produced anaerobically by *T. vaginalis* in the presence of glucose. Hutner and Provasoli (1955) noted that the essentially anaerobic metabolism of trichomonads is manifested by their preference for reducing conditions in the growth medium, their dependence on sugars as energy sources, and their inability to oxidize lower fatty acids, amino acids, or tricarboxylic acid cycle intermediates, as well as their production of hydrogen and of acids including lactic [see also Baernstein (1959, 1961)]. Ninomiya and Suzuoki-Ziro (1952) found that catalase, present as a trace in *Trichomonas foetus* of cattle, is absent in *T. vaginalis*. Kupferberg (1960) noted that cytochromes had not been reported in *T. vaginalis*, and was himself unable to find cytochrome C in it, but obtained evidence of flavin mononucleotide and of a DPN coenzyme system. According to this worker, who mentioned other substantiating literature, *T. vaginalis* seems to follow the classic Embden-Meyerhof pathway of glucolysis forming principally lactic acid and, in addition, malic and a third unidentified acid. Fixation of radioactive CO_2 was also reported by Kupferberg (1960), with all the radioactivity found to be localized in the carboxyl carbon of lactic acid.

Trussell and Johnson (1941) reported that *T. vaginalis* utilized only glucose and its polymers maltose, soluble starch, glycogen, and dextrin. Fructose and galactose increased growth slightly but no depression of pH appeared in their presence. Read (1957) reported utilization of galactose and also of melibiose.

Infectivity and Pathogenicity

Protozoa and Disease of the Mouth

Trichomonas tenax. Inoculation experiments with *Trichomonas tenax* in animals [briefly reviewed by Wenrich (1947)] seem to have resulted in no more than persistence of the parasite—that is, in infection without obvious disease. Hinshaw (1927) was unable to infect normal dogs, cats, rabbits, guinea pigs, mice, or scorbutic guinea pigs, by inoculating this organism mixed with *Ent. gingivalis* into the gingival sulcus, but he observed persistence of both protozoa for more than 14 months after such inoculation into a dog with a preexisting gingivitis. Trussell (1947) stated that Westphal "successfully inoculated his mouth with *T. elongata (buccalis* or *tenax)* and the infection persisted ten months to the time of his report. Swallowing cultures of *T. elongata* on four different occasions failed to cause an intestinal infection." Despite the frequent presence of this trichomonad in periodontal exudates it does not seem to have been thought of seriously as a pathogen, nor is there any evidence known to the writer to suggest such a connection.

Entamoeba gingivalis. The buccal ameba, on the contrary, has been indicted as a periodontal pathogen [Barrett (1914); Bass and Johns (1915)], but only by association; and subsequent workers have come to general agreement that this ameba is nonpathogenic. Hinshaw (1927), in experiments reported with those mentioned in the preceding paragraph, found that *Ent. gingivalis* could be implanted gingivally in dogs, but only in those with "more or less inflammation and gingival pocket formation" preceding implantation; the infection did not persist more than 4 months, and no symptoms were attributed to it. Kofoid, Hinshaw, and Johnstone (1929) reported similar results, with successful implantation in 5 of 11 dogs. These protozoa seem to have attracted little attention as possible pathogens in recent years. Their increase in size in gingival disease as reported by Tumka (1960) was noted above (page 262).

Enteric Protozoa

As a group, the protozoa of the intestine selected for treatment in this chapter are not commonly considered pathogenic, but disease has occasionally been attributed to some of them. It is of interest that even

Ent. histolytica has been found incapable of producing ulcerative enteric lesions when given by mouth to germfree guinea pigs in monoxenic cultures with trypanosomes, unless at least 1 bacterial species
was also inoculated[1] [see Phillips and Wolfe (1958)].

Implantation in Man. That *Ent. coli* is nonpathogenic has been generally accepted since the early studies of Walker and Sellards (1913)
on human volunteers. More recently, Rendtorff has explored possible
means by which infections with *Ent. coli* and other enteric protozoa
may be transmitted to man, and the duration of such infection, in a
series of papers that may be recommended as models of experiments
in this important area of indigenous microbiology. In most of these
studies, cysts for inoculation were obtained fresh, from donor feces,
by a procedure involving selective centrifugation, washing in saline,
and separation and enumeration with a micromanipulator [see Rendtorff 1954b)].

Working with male prisoner volunteers previously found free from
the parasites in question, Rendtorff (1954a) was able to implant *Ent.
coli* cysts, given in gelatin capsules by mouth, in 8 of 26 subjects, including 1 of 8 given only a single cyst and 3 of 10 given 10 cysts.
Prepatent periods ranged from 6 to 22 days, averaging 10 days. The
parasites continued to appear in stool specimens intermittently throughout the subsequent period of examination, from 56 to 162 days. "No
case was observed which was considered to show a spontaneous disappearance of the infection." No clinical signs or symptoms could be
clearly attributed to the infections, although mild transient changes in
stool pattern, of no clinical importance, occasionally accompanied the
first appearance of parasites in the stools.

In another study [Rendtorff and Holt (1954a)], attempts to transmit
infection with cysts of either *Ent. coli* or *Giardia lamblia* with food
contaminated via house flies (*Musca domestica*) succeeded only once
(with *Ent. coli*) in 32 volunteers. On the other hand, both *Ent. coli*
and *G. lamblia*, in further experiments [Rendtorff and Holt (1954b)],
were transmitted readily in drinking water. Tap water containing 100
cysts each of the 2 species, stored at 8° for 0, 1, 2, 4, 8, and 16 days,
yielded infections at all the storage intervals, with *Ent. coli* in a total
of 12 of 17 and with *G. lamblia* in 11 of 17 volunteers. With *Ent. coli*
the prepatent periods were 4 to 14 days, average 8.3; with *G. lamblia*
they were 9 to 22 days, average 13.1. *Ent. coli* infections were persistent as before, whereas the flagellate disappeared spontaneously
within 60 days. A tendency toward looser and more frequent stools

---

[1] In curious contrast is the finding of Newton, Reardon, and DeLeva (1960) that
germfree but not conventional guinea pigs were susceptible to *subcutaneous* infection with *Trichomonas vaginalis* (see page 288 and Chap. 11).

appeared in 2 of the subjects who harbored both protozoa, while a single instance of "a very mild and innocuous gastrointestinal disorder" occurred in another subject in whose stools both species appeared early.

In a further study by Rendtorff and Holt (1955), 12 volunteers were each given a mixture containing 100 cysts each of 3 species of amebas —*E. coli, Iodamoeba bütschlii,* and *Endolimax nana.* Infection resulted with the species in the order named in 5, 5, and 6 instances, including 1 with *I. bütschlii* and *E. nana* together, and 3 with all 3 species; 9 of the 12 subjects were infected with 1 or more species. Five control subjects given sterile saline remained free from infection. Prepatent periods showed the following ranges and averages: for *I. bütschlii,* 4 to 13 (days), 7.3; for *E. coli,* 5 to 16, 10.2; and for *E. nana,* 7 to 21, 12.0. No significant symptoms were noted. Infections with all 3 species were heavy, and all persisted throughout the study period, 65 to 157 days.

Rendtorff (1954b) has also studied infection with *Giardia lamblia* alone by administering graded doses of cysts in gelatin capsules by mouth. None of 5 subjects who ingested a single cyst became infected, but implantation appeared after ingestion of as few as 10 cysts, and all of 13 subjects who received 100 cysts or more were infected. In all, 21 of 40 subjects (52.5 per cent) responded positively, while 21 controls remained uninfected. The prepatent period ranged from 6 to 15 days with an average of 9.1 days. Of 14 subjects examined adequately for persistence of parasites, spontaneous disappearance occurred in 12 after 5 to 41 days; in the other 2 subjects, infection persisted through the observation periods, 129 and 132 days. Transient tendencies toward looser and more frequent stools were associated in some instances with first appearance of the organisms. No significant clinical symptoms appeared.

Clinical Observations, *Giardia lamblia.* The foregoing data make it appear doubtful that the severe symptoms—including diarrhea, epigastric pain, and migraine headache—recorded by Tsuchiya and Andrews (1930) as associated with a laboratory infection with *G. lamblia* were actually due to the flagellate. There is, however, a common opinion among clinicians that this protozoan may be responsible for disease. McMurray and Cayer (1951) are among the more conservative, suggesting that it can be no more than a secondary determinant of disease, and noting that it has not been shown to invade tissue; but they recommended treatment if it coexists with gastrointestinal symptoms. The clinical literature has been reviewed more recently by Cortner (1959) who presented 4 cases in children of so-called giardiasis accompanied by celiac-like malabsorption of fat. Several reports have associated the presence of *Giardia* with gastrointestinal symptoms, and in some of these treatment leading to disappearance of the parasites from the stool also brought about symptomatic relief [Rai Chaudhuri (1959); Grott, Borko, and Pedrycz (1959); see also Payne et al. (1960)]. Although such associations may seem clinically convincing they do not, of course, exclude the possibilities (1) that the parasitism may coexist with or result from the symptomatic illness, and (2) that the treatment may eliminate disease and parasite coincidentally. This reasoning is at least as old as Koch's postulates. It should be recognized, on the other hand, that Rendtorff's negative findings dealt with adults; *G. lamblia* is associated particularly with children, and the question of its possible pathogenicity is not resolved by these observations. Dekhkan-Khodzhaeva (1960) has reported suggestive evidence of pathologic effects in both spontaneous and experimental *G. lamblia* infections of mice.

Other Enteric Protozoa. Pathogenicity has also been suggested for other intestinal protozoa, but on slender evidence. Knoll and Howell (1945) observed that *Dientamoeba fragilis* could be found in the presence of every gradation of symptomatology from nil to acute gastroenteritis; they were unable to infect kittens by feeding or rectal injection. Burrows and Swerdlow (1954) thought this ameba might be responsible for fibrosis of the appendix, especially in children [see also Swerdlow and Burrows (1955)]. In another paper, these workers [Burrows and Swerdlow (1956)] reported evidence that *D. fragilis* may be transmitted in the egg of the pinworm, *Enterobius vermicularis*. They found that appendices harboring the ameba also contained the nematode—either or both adults and eggs—with an association 20 times as frequent as would be expected by chance; and that sections of pinworms from subjects known to harbor *D. fragilis* showed bodies in the eggs resembling this protozoan.

Amebas identified as probably *Iodamoeba bütschlii* were found in large numbers in a fatal chronic granuloma of the brain in a 6-year-old child [Kernohan, Magath, and Schloss (1960)]. Mueller (1959) has suggested a relationship between *Chilomastix mesnili* and diarrheal disease. Young and Felsenfeld (1944) found *Retortomonas intestinalis* in stools under both normal and pathologic conditions and did not consider it pathogenic.

Trichomonas hominis, according to Trussell (1947) has been successfully implanted orally in rats and both orally and rectally in cats. He mentioned that Westphal, following his unsuccessful attempt to implant *T. tenax* in the intestine, succeeded in such implantation with *T. hominis* by drinking cultures of the protozoan. Several workers, on the other hand, have failed in attempts to implant *T. hominis* in the vagina. These findings were presented by Trussell as evidence that the 3 species of trichomonads are distinct. The literature on implantation experiments with *T. hominis* has also been reviewed by Wenrich (1947), again principally for its taxonomic implications. Despite occasional textbook statements to the contrary [e.g., Pelczar and Reid (1958)], this protozoan, which is found relatively uncommonly in the intestine, calls for no serious consideration as a pathogen.

Trichomonas vaginalis

In apparently sharp contrast to all the protozoa discussed above, the trichomonad of the genitourinary tract is widely thought of as a frank pathogen. The common opinion is based on the insecure grounds of clinical association and less-than-crucial experiments with human subjects, but in recent years evidence has been accumulating of an elusive but perhaps quite significant experimental pathogenicity that may provide a sound basis for the common view. In its general outline if not in detail this phenomenon is hardly distinctive among indigenous microorganisms. On the contrary, it provides another example, useful in the context of this book, of peculiar or qualified pathogenicity.

The evidence of pathogenicity may be considered under the following heads: (1) the clinical conditions in which *T. vaginalis* is found; (2) the question of its venereal transmission; (3) the crucial matter of experimental pathogenicity; and (4) the effects of therapy as they bear on pathogenicity.

Trichomoniasis. We have seen (Table 8-7) that *T. vaginalis* is more common in the vagina under pathologic conditions than otherwise, that no unequivocal data on this point are available for men, and that certainly in women and probably in men the trichomonad may be found in the absence of symptoms. When disease is present, its manifestations do not appear to be distinctive. In women the clinical findings are most commonly leukorrhea and vaginitis, and a discharge may be present that is said to be characteristically frothy or bubbly. According to Trussell (1947) this feature is not constant. It was noted above that *T. vaginalis* produces gas in fermentation, so that in vivo gas formation might be due to it directly; but accompanying bacteria, notably *Veillonella alcalescens* [Trussell (1947); see also Chap. 2] have also been incriminated. In men, *T. vaginalis* has been associated particularly with urethritis, prostatitis, and balanitis. Lanceley (1953) considered that a hazy urine specimen containing "many fine light threads" was "highly suggestive of trichomonad infection"; but this worker and others [e.g., Trussell (1947); Feo (1944)] have not suggested that trichomoniasis in men is clinically distinctive. In both sexes these microorganisms share honors especially with *Candida albicans* (Chap. 7) and the so-called pleuropneumonia organisms (Chap. 9) as presumed agents of nonspecific urethritis or vaginitis. Catterall (1960) found 126 men in a British clinic positive for *T. vaginalis* among 2,300 infections described as nongonococcal urethritis: i.e., 5.5 per cent of the total were "trichomoniasis," but 18 of the 126 were described as having no symptoms referable to the genitourinary tract. Sylvestre, Belanger, and Gallai (1960) in a brief but well-documented review of trichomoniasis in the male, tabulated data from the literature from 1940 to 1959 showing a wide range of values for incidence of *T. vaginalis* urethritis as percentage of nongonococcal urethritis—from 5.5 to 68.0; but of 17 values all but 3 were under 20 per cent and the median was less than 15 per cent.

Venereal Transmission. That *Trichomonas vaginalis* is likely to be transmitted between sexual partners must follow from its characteristic habitat. Whether such transmission justifies calling trichomonas infection "venereal disease" is a question perhaps too lightly answered in the affirmative in the clinical literature; its resolution depends on the relationship for this parasite of infection and disease, which is evidently unclear. The literature frequently assumes that the two are the same. The higher incidence of these trichomonads among Negroes in the United States (Table 8-7) and the associated but unexplained relationship between their presence and true venereal disease, notably gonorrhea, are not proper evidence that trichomoniasis is a venereal disease. Trussell (1947) may be technically correct when he says: "Parasitism of the male urinary tract may be regarded as almost solely a result of the sex act"; but the statement has less meaning than appears on the surface. The important question is suggested by a statement of Catterall and Nicol (1960): "Sexual intercourse should be forbidden until *T. vaginalis* is eradicated from the genital tracts of both partners."[2]

Lanceley (1953), who apparently considered trichomoniasis in the male a venereal disease, has noted that such infection is usually short-lived and followed by spontaneous cure; he suggested that "apparently chronic infections are in reality recurrent re-infections." The suggestion that such infection is more elusive in men than in women may be

---

[2] *Escalus.* . . . . What do you think of the trade, Pompey? Is it a lawful trade?
Pompey. If the law would allow it, sir.
   Escalus. But the law will not allow it, Pompey; nor it shall not be allowed in Vienna.
   Pompey. Does your worship mean to geld and splay all the youth of the city?
   Escalus. No, Pompey.
   Pompey. Truly, sir, in my poor opinion, they will to't then. If your worship will take order for the drabs and the knaves, you need not to fear the bawds.
   Escalus. There is pretty orders beginning, I can tell you; it is but heading and hanging.
   Pompey. If you head and hang all that offend that way but for ten year together, you'll be glad to give out a commission for more heads. If this law hold in Vienna ten year, I'll rent the fairest house in it after threepence a bay; if you live to see this come to pass, say Pompey told you so.
                                              Measure for Measure, Act II, Scene i.

considered in relation to experimental studies with sex hormones mentioned below.

If trichomoniasis is to be accepted as a venereal disease, it must be demonstrated that sexual contact with a person of either sex leads predictably or in a significant proportion of instances, and within a definable incubation period, to symptomatic disease in the other partner. Such information is not available. The literature indicates rather that sexual intercourse with *women* who harbor *T. vaginalis* in the genital tract is sometimes followed by the appearance of the protozoan in the urinary tract of the man. Symptoms may or may not be present in either partner. As will be seen, such symptoms may disappear under therapy together with the trichomonads, and may disappear only when both partners are treated, but whether the symptoms precede or follow or have any true connection with the trichomonads is not established by such data [see Sylvestre, Gallai, and Ethier (1958); Chappaz (1960); Kean (1960); Bertrand and Leulier (1960); and Watt and Jennison (1960)].

Moore and Simpson (1954) and McEwen (1960), on the other hand, have suggested that trichomonads are normal inhabitants of the vagina which may produce disease as a result of predisposing conditions, especially associated with emotional stress. If trichomoniasis is to be considered as an endogenous infective disease it cannot also be thought of as venereal; it would belong rather in the same class as genitourinary fusospirochetosis, which was also once thought to be venereal but is no longer [see Rosebury (1942)]. Nicol (1961) in an otherwise extensive listing of venereal diseases, does not mention fusospirochetal disease.

Experimental Pathogenicity. Since 1950 evidence has been accumulating that *T. vaginalis*, inoculated in pure culture, is capable of proliferating in the tissues of experimental animals under certain circumstances, and that in certain instances fatal disease may result. The subject has a curious history, since repeated attempts to demonstrate such pathogenicity were consistently negative in the earlier trials. Trussell (1947) has reviewed these negative experiments in tabular form. Rabbits, guinea pigs, dogs, rats, mice, cats, monkeys, fowl, and farm animals were used, with *T. vaginalis* from various sources including axenic cultures, either seeded on the vaginal or other mucous membranes or inoculated by various routes. The result was an essentially uniform lack of pathologic effect; even survival seldom resulted except in abscesses attributed to accompanying bacteria. Trussell and McNutt (1941) [see also Trussell and Plass (1940)] alone reported a positive finding: implantation in the vagina of *Macacus rhesus* monkeys with persistence for a few weeks without symptoms. In 1950 Schnitzer, Kelly, and Leiwant reported the production of nonfatal abscesses in mice with bacteriafree cultures of *T. vaginalis*. Using inocula of 0.5

ml, the minimum infective concentration per milliliter was, intra-peritoneally, 4 to 7×10^6; intramuscularly, 2.5×10^5; and subcutane-ously, 3×10^3. Higher doses yielded more persistent lesions. The ani-mal-pathogenic species *Trichomonas gallinae* and *T. foetus* were more infective for mice; the last alone yielded fatal disease. These findings have been confirmed by Honigberg and Braunthal (1957), who found little difference in a statistical comparison of lesions produced in mice with *T. gallinae* and *T. vaginalis*, and considered the latter "a truly pathogenic species." They have also been confirmed by Iwai (1957) and Orita (1960). Reardon and Jacobs (1958) reported further that of 2 culture strains of *T. vaginalis* tested intraperitoneally in mice, one that had been isolated from a severe case of vaginitis was regularly fatal for 6 strains of mice in doses of 10^6 parasites or more, whereas another culture, recovered from a relatively mild case, was nonlethal. Using the same 2 cultures, Newton, Reardon, and DeLeva (1960), in a paper referred to earlier, reported the production of abscesses in *germ-free* guinea pigs following subcutaneous inoculation of the more "viru-lent" one. Smaller lesions or none were produced with the same strain in conventional guinea pigs. The other culture was active at lower levels of virulence, with a similar difference between germfree and conventional guinea pigs.

Interesting results, as yet unconfirmed, have been reported by Inoki and Hamada (1953) following inoculation into suitably treated mice. These workers had previously found that the lethality of *Trichomonas foetus* for mice could be increased by prior treatment of the animals with peanut oil or nitrogen mustard (mechlorethamine hydrochloride) and, subsequently, that this species could be enhanced in virulence by successive transfers under these conditions. They were then able to pro-duce fatal infections with *T. vaginalis* in young (10-Gm) mice which received prior intravenous injections of washed erythrocytes of young chickens. Two culture strains of *T. vaginalis*, neither lethal for un-treated mice, were successfully used. In such treated mice, 70 per cent of which died, large numbers of trichomonads were found in the peri-toneal cavity 14 to 40 days after intraperitoneal inoculation; and 0.05 ml of such peritoneal fluid, containing approximately 5×10^5 parasites, was found lethal for 100 per cent of *untreated* mice within 5 days. As noted earlier in this chapter, moreover, the organisms after such pas-sage were said to have changed in growth characteristics and morphol-ogy so as to resemble *Trichomonas foetus*.

McNutt and Trussell (1941) reported cultivation of *T. vaginalis* in the allantoic sac of chick embryos without pathogenic effect. Kean and Weld (1955) were able to grow this protozoan through 14 serial pas-sages in the anterior chamber of the rabbit eye. Such methods, augment-ing pure in vitro cultures and now feasible animal experiments, may be expected to lead to further elucidation of the pathogenicity of *T. vaginalis*.

Implantation of this trichomonad on the mucous membrane of the vagina or the male urethra has been successful, although irregularly, in human subjects and more recently in experimental animals. The successful experiments of Trussell and McNutt (1941) in monkeys were noted previously. Omitting earlier experiments in which variable results followed seeding into the human vagina of *T. vaginalis* mixed with bacteria [reviewed by Trussell (1947)], we may note that varying results have also been obtained with pure cultures of this trichomonad. Trussell and Plass (1940) succeeded in implanting the organism into the vagina of 1 nonpregnant and 8 of 28 pregnant women. One of the pregnant subjects showed no symptoms and another showed only a slight discharge. In the remaining 7 the symptoms ranged from slight hyperemia and moderate purulent discharge without subjective complaints to distinct and painful vaginitis. These workers found no relation between susceptibility to trichomonal disease and the presence of the so-called Döderlein bacillus (Chap. 3) or the pH of the vaginal secretion.

Hesseltine, Walters, and Campbell (1942), working with the same culture strain of *T. vaginalis*, reported the production of vaginal trichomoniasis in 7 of 53 pregnant women. Only 3 of the 7 had subjective symptoms, and, in general, the trichomonads disappeared after several days. In this latter study 6 of the 7 subjects that were successfully infected had presented with an abnormal vaginal flora, in which Gram-positive acidogenic bacilli were scant or lacking. Such an abnormal vaginal flora, or the relatively high vaginal pH associated with it, is commonly regarded as predisposing to vaginal trichomoniasis [see Lang, Rakoff, and Menduke (1956); Hesseltine (1959)].

Lanceley and McEntegart (1953) have reported on the experimental intraurethral inoculation of volunteer males. Ten hospital inpatients without genitourinary disease were studied. Five controls given sterile culture medium remained negative. The others, who received a pure culture of *T. vaginalis*, responded in varying degrees: 2 with a transient urethritis unaccompanied by demonstrable protozoa, 1 with a moderately severe urethritis with the organism demonstrable for 4 days, and 2 with more severe and more persistent urethritis and prostatitis; only one of these complained of subjective symptoms.

The suggestion of a possible mechanism of susceptibility to *T. vaginalis* infection is given in 2 French studies, both of which utilized rats as experimental subjects. Cavier and Mossion (1956) administered estradiol benzoate subcutaneously in oily solution to castrated rats, and found that they were then susceptible to vaginal implantation of *T. vaginalis*. Combescot, Pestre, and Domenech (1956) found that implantation was successful not only in such rats but also in uncastrated rats given large doses of estrogen; and that in both groups administration of progesterone led to rapid disappearance of the trichomonads.

Therapy. Treatment of trichomoniasis is relevant here only as the subject bears on that of pathogenicity. At present, no single drug or therapeutic regimen seems to have found general acceptance, and none of the remedies considered effective is sufficiently specific for trichomonads to exclude the probability that other antimicrobial effects may have contributed to a clinical result. It is of interest that antibiotics and other new drugs—e.g., "flagyl" or metronidazole [1-β-hydroxyethyl-2-methyl-5-nitroimidazol, Cosar and Julou (1959)] seem to be employed by some workers, whereas others prefer such remedies as potassium permanganate or mercuric oxycyanide [Catterall (1960); see also Jírovec et al. (1959)].

It cannot be stated categorically that good results reported from any given mode of treatment throw any significant light on the question at issue. It seems of interest that one recommended remedy, Carbasone (Editorial, 1954) was among the agents reported by Read (1957) as not inhibiting gaseous fermentation of *Trichomonas vaginalis*. Tramontano (1957) found that nystatin gave good results in treatment of vaginal discharge whether it was associated with *Candida albicans* or with *T. vaginalis* [which frequently appear in vaginitis together, see, e.g., Lang, Fritz, and Menduke (1960), and Chap. 7]. Cazemier et al. (1959) found pimaricin effective in both trichomonal and fungal vaginitis, although more so in the latter. Metronidazole ("flagyl") has been reported as effective against trichomoniasis but not against candida infections [Moffett and McGill (1960); Rodin et al. (1960)]; but Sylvestre et al. (1959, 1960) have reported the same drug active against other forms of nongonococcal urethritis as well as trichomoniasis; and Scott-Gray and Murrell (1961) reported a case in which the clinical response to flagyl was immediate but trichomonads did not completely disappear for 4 weeks. For other aspects of the therapy of trichomoniasis see Trussell (1947), MacDonald and Tatum (1948a), Seneca and Ides (1949), Feo (1952, 1960), Frank and Reiner (1954), Durel et al. (1960), and Durel (1960).

Serology

The meager serologic data available on indigenous protozoa are all concerned with trichomonads.[3] Trussell et al. (1942) were able to

---

[3] Zaman (1960) reported that specific immobilization could be used in taxonomic studies of the genus *Entamoeba*; but *Ent. coli*, the only indigenous species studied, was found unsuitable because of its restricted activity.

demonstrate complement-fixing antibodies against *T. vaginalis* in 47.3 per cent of 110 women infected with the organism, and in only 16.6 per cent of 290 women without *T. vaginalis*. They did not consider the test useful for diagnostic purposes. MacDonald and Tatum (1948*b*), using agglutination and the technique of agglomeration as developed for trypanosomes and applied by other workers to veterinary trichomonads, were able to show that *T. vaginalis* and *T. hominis* are antigenically identical, and that both are related to but distinct from *T. foetus*. More recently, Kott and Adler (1961), using axenic cultures of *T. vaginalis* and *T. hominis* and cultures of *T. tenax* containing bacteria, were able to distinguish all 3 by agglutination, hemagglutination, and cross-absorption tests, and to define serotypes among the first 2. Mc-Entegart (1952) developed a hemagglutination test for *T. vaginalis* using sheep erythrocytes treated with a formamide extract of the organism. The serum of a rabbit immunized with culture trichomonads showed a titer of 1:100. Positive hemagglutination reactions with human serums were obtained with titers not exceeding 1:20 in 19 of 50 normal men, in 11 of 50 normal women, and in 7 of 13 normal children. The maximum titer in the children was 1:10. On the other hand, all but 1 of 50 women with *T. vaginalis* infection gave hemagglutination ranging in titer from 1:5 to 1:250 with a median of 1:20 to 1:40. The low titers in normal subjects were thought to suggest non-specific effects. More recently, Robertson (1960) has successfully applied the Ouchterlony gel-diffusion technique to separated protein and polysaccharide antigens of *Trichomonas foetus*.

References

Asami, K., Nodake, Y., and Uento, T., 1955, *Exptl. Parasitol.*, **4**:34.

Babbott, F. J., Jr., Frye, W. W., and Gordon, J. E., 1961, *Am. J. Trop. Med. Hyg.*, **10**:185.

Baernstein, H. D., 1959, *J. Parasitol.*, **45**:491.

———, 1961, *ibid.*, **47**:279.

Balamuth, W., 1946, *Am. J. Clin. Pathol.*, **16**:380.

———, 1953, *Am. J. Trop. Med.*, **2**:191.

———, and Thompson, P. E., 1955, in Hutner and Lwoff, 1955, p. 277.

Barrett, M. T., 1914, *Dental Cosmos*, **56**:948.

Bass, C. C., and Johns, F. M., 1915, *J. Am. Med. Assoc.*, **64**:553.

Bauer, A. C., Epifanio, A., and Redner, W. J., 1959, *Obstet., Gynaecol.*, **14**:391.

Beatman, L. H., 1933, *J. Dental Research*, **13**:339.

Belding, D. L., 1952, *Textbook of Clinical Parasitology*, 2d ed., Appleton-Century-Crofts, Inc., New York.

Bertrand, P., and Leulier, J., 1960, *Gynaecologia* 149 (Suppl.):93.

Bland, P. B., and Rakoff, A. E., 1937, *J. Am. Med. Assoc.*, **108**:2013.

Boeck, W. C., 1924, *Am. J. Trop. Med.*, **4**:519.

———, and Drbohlav, J., 1925, *Am. J. Hyg.*, **5**:371.

Brizio, P. D., 1957, *Giorn. Mal. Infettive. e Parassit.*, **9**:411 (*Biol. Abstr.*).

Brown, R. L., and Garber, M. J., 1960, *Am. J. Trop. Med. Hyg.*, **9**:262.

Burch, T. A., Rees, C. W., and Reardon, L. V., 1959, *ibid.* **8**:312.

Burrows, R. B., and Swerdlow, M. A., 1954, *ibid.*, **3**:1033.

———, and ———, 1956, *ibid.*, **5**:253.

Catterall, R. D., 1960, *Brit. Med. J.*, **2**:113.

———, and Nicol, C. S., 1960, *ibid.*, **1**:1177.

Cavier, R., and Mossion, X., 1956, *Compt. Rend. Acad. Sci.*, **242**:2412.

Cazemier, C., Goslings, W. R. O., Houwert, K. A. F., van Leeuwen, D. P., Lubbers, G. J., and Kok, P. C., 1959, *Antibiotic Med. & Clin. Therapy* **6**:601.

Chandler, A. C., 1954, *Am. J. Trop. Med. Hyg.*, **3**:59.

Chappaz, G., 1960, *Gynaecologia*, **149** (Suppl.):1.

Chia-Tung, Pan, 1960, *J. Inf. Dis.*, **106**:284.

Combescot, C., Pestre, M., and Domenech, A., 1956, *Compt. Rend. Soc. Biol.*, **151**:332.

Cort, Otto, and Spindler, 1961, cited by Faust, E. C., 1961 (personal communication).

Cortner, J. A., 1959, *Am. J. Diseases Children*, **98**:311.

Cosar, C., and Julou, L., 1959, *Ann. Inst. Pasteur*, **96**:238.

Coutts, W. E., Vargas-Salazar, R., Silva-Inunza, E., Olmedo, R., Turtetaub, R., and Saavedra, J., 1955, *Brit. Med. J.*, **2**:885.

Craig, C. F., and Faust, E. C., 1951, *Clinical Parasitology*, 5th ed., Lea & Febiger, Philadelphia.

Davis, C. H., 1955, *J. Am. Med. Assoc.*, **157**:126.

Dekhkan-Khodzhaeva, N. A., 1960, *Med. Parazitol. Parazitar. Bolezni*, **29**:226 [1961, *Referat. Zhur., Biol.*, No. 4E45 (transl.)] (*Biol. Abstr.*).

Diamond, L. S., 1957, *J. Parasitol.*, **43**:488.

Dobell, C., 1939, *Parasitology*, **31**:138.

———, and Laidlaw, P. P., 1926, *ibid.*, **18**:283.

Draper, J. W., 1955, *Intern. Rec. Med. Gen. Prac. Clin.*, *N.Y.*, **168–9**:563 (abstr., 1957, *Exerpta Med. Sect. 13*, **11**:97).

Drew, A. H., and Griffin, U. D., 1917, *J. Royal Microscopic Soc.*, p. 185 (Apr.).

Drbohlav, J., 1925, *Ann. Parasitol.*, **3**:361.

Durel, P., 1959, *Urol. Intern.*, **9**:306.

———, Couture, J., Collart, P., and Girot, C., 1960, *Brit. J. Venereal Diseases*, **36**:154.

Editorial, 1954, *J. Am. Med. Assoc.*, **156**:991.

Faust, E. C., 1930, *Am. J. Hyg.*, **11**:371.

———, and Russell, P. F., 1957, *Craig and Faust's Clinical Parasitology*, 6th ed., Lea & Febiger, Philadelphia.

Feo, L. G., 1944, *Am. J. Trop. Med.*, **24**:195.

———, 1952, *Am. J. Trop. Med. Hyg.*, **1**:623.

———, 1953, *Am. J. Obstet.*, **65**:1330.

———, 1960, *Gynaecologia*, **149** (Suppl.):101.

———, Fetter, T. R., Peoples, D. M., and Morton, H. E., 1956, *J. Urol.*, **75**:711.

Fisher, J. H., 1927, *Am. J. Pathol.*, **3**:169.

Frank, H. G., and Reiner, L., 1954, *J. Immunol.*, **72**:191.

Frühwald, R., 1957, *XIth Intern. Conf. Dermatol.* [*Excerpta Med. Sect. 13*, 11 (Suppl.):124, C224].

Gallai, Z., and Sylvestre, L., eds., 1960, *Gynaecologia*, 149 Suppl. parts 3–4.

Goldman, M., and Carver, R. K., 1959, *Am. J. Trop. Med. Hyg.*, **8**:417.

Goodey, T., and Wellings, A. W., 1917, *Parasitology*, **9**:537.

Grott, J. W., Borko, W., and Pedrycz, W., 1959, *Wiadomošci Parazytol.*, **5**:509 (*Biol. Abstr.*).

Herbst, S., Olszewski, B., and Thompson, P. E., 1960, *J. Parasitol.*, **46**:743.

Hesseltine, H., 1959, *Ann. N.Y. Acad. Med.*, **83**:245.

————, Walters, S. L., and Campbell, A., 1942, *J. Inf. Dis.*, **71**:127.

Hinshaw, H. C., 1927, *Proc. Soc. Exptl. Biol. Med.*, **25**:430.

————, and Simonton, F. V., 1928, *J. Dental Research*, **8**:507.

Hitchcock, D. J., 1950, *J. Parasitol.*, **36**:232.

Honigberg, B. M., and Braunthal, S. D., 1957, *ibid.*, **43**, Sec. 2 (Suppl.): 40.

————, and Lee, J. J., 1959, *Am. J. Hyg.*, **69**:177.

————, and Read, C. P., 1960, *Science*, **131**:352.

Howitt, B. F., 1925, *Univ. Calif. Publ. Zoöl.*, **28**:65.

Hungate, R. E., 1955, in Hutner and Lwoff, 1955, p. 159.

Hutner, S. H., and Lwoff, A., 1955, *Biochemistry and Physiology of Protozoa*, vol. 2, Academic Press, Inc., New York.

————, and Provasoli, L., 1955, in Hutner and Lwoff, 1955, p. 17.

Inoki, S., and Hamada, Y., 1953, *J. Inf. Dis.*, **92**:1.

————, Nakanishi, K., and Nakabayashi, T., 1959, *Biken's J.*, **2**:21.

Ivey, M. H., 1961, *J. Parasitol.*, **47**:539.

Iwai, 1957, *Japan. J. Parasitol.*, **6**:136, cited by Reardon and Jacobs (1958).

Jeffery, G. M., 1960, *Am. J. Hyg.*, **71**:1.

Jepps, M. W., 1923, *Parasitology*, **15**:343.

Jira, J., 1958, *Zentr. Bakteriol Parasitenk.*, *I Orig.*, **172**:310.

Jírovec, O., Rudolf, P., Jindrich, J., and Miroslav, P., 1959, *J. Hyg. Epidemiol. Microbiol. Immunob.*, **3**:195 (*Biol. Abstr.*).

Johnson, G., 1942, *J. Parasitol.*, **28**:369.

Karapetyan, A. E., 1960, *Med. Parazitol. Parazitar. Bolezni*, **29**:84 [1961, *Referat. Zhur.*, *Biol.*, No. 4E46 (transl.)] (*Biol. Abstr.*).

Kean, B. H., 1960, *Gynaecologia*, **149** (Suppl.):97

————, and Smillie, W. G., 1954, *New Engl. J. Med.*, **251**:471.

————, and Weld, J. T., 1955, *Proc. Soc. Exptl. Biol. Med.*, **89**:218.

Kernohan, J. W., Magath, T. B., and Schloss, G. T., 1960, *Arch. Pathol.*, **70**:576.

Keutel, H. J., ed., 1957, *Les infestations à Trichomonas*, Masson et Cie, Paris.

————, 1958, *Z. Urol.*, **51**:25 (abstr., 1959, *Exerpta Med. Sect. 13*, **13**:265).

Kirby, H., 1945, *J. Parasitol.*, **31**:163.

Knoll, E. W., and Howell, K. M., 1945, *Am. J. Clin. Pathol.*, **15**:178.

Kofoid, C. A., Hinshaw, H. C., and Johnstone, H. G., 1929, *J. Am. Dental Assoc.*, **16**:1436.

————, and Johnstone, H. G., 1929, *Am. J. Public Health*, **19**:549.

Koss, L. G. and Wolinska, W. H., 1959. *Cancer*, **12**:1171.

Kott, H. and Adler, S., 1961, *Trans. Roy. Soc. Trop. Med. Hyg.*, **55**:333.

Kudo, R., 1954, *Protozoology*, 4th ed., Charles C Thomas, Publisher, Springfield, Ill.

Kuntz, R. E., 1960, *Am. J. Trop. Med. Hyg.*, **9**: 168.

———, and Lawless, D. K., 1958, *ibid.*, **7**:353.

———, ———, and Langbehn, H. R., 1958, *ibid.*, **7**:298.

———, ———, ———, and Malakatis, G. M., 1958, *ibid.*, **7**:630.

———, ———, and Malakatis, G. M., 1959, *ibid.*, **8**:63.

Kupferberg, A. B., 1960, *Gynaecologia*, **149** (Suppl.):114.

Laan, I. A., 1960, *Lab. Delo*, **4**:41; *Referat Zhur.*, Biol. No. 7E17 (*Biol. Abstr.*).

Lanceley, F., 1953, *Brit. J. Venereal Diseases*, **29**:213.

———, and McEntegart, M. G., 1953, *Lancet*, **1**:668.

Lang, W. R., Fritz, M. A., and Menduke, H., 1960, *Gynaecologia*, **149** (Suppl.):55.

———, Rakoff, A. E., and Menduke, H., 1956, *Obstet. Gynecol.*, **7**:378.

Lomuto, G., and Ciaula, V., 1955, *Dermatologia (Naples)*, **6**:271 (1957, *Exerpta Med. Sect. 13*, **11**:46).

Lwoff, A., 1951, *Biochemistry and Physiology of Protozoa*, Academic Press, Inc., New York.

MacDonald, E. M., and Tatum, A. L., 1948a, *J. Immunol.*, **59**:301.

———, and ———, 1948b, *ibid.*, **59**:309.

Magara, M., Amino, E., and Yakouti, E., 1953, *Am. J. Trop. Med. Hyg.*, **2**:267.

Mandoul, R., Dargelos, R., and Bour, Y., 1959 (1960) *Bull. Soc. Pathol. Éxotique*, **52**:607, 613 (*Biol. Abstr.*).

Maxcy, K. F., 1921, *Bull. Johns Hopkins Hosp.*, **32**:166.

McEntegart, M. G., 1952, *J. Clin. Pathol.*, **5**:275.

McEwen, D. C., 1960., *Gynaecologia* **149** (Suppl.):63.

McMurray, C. M., and Cayer, D., 1951, *Am. J. Digest. Diseases*, 18:90.

McNutt, S. H., and Trussell, R. E., 1941, *Proc. Soc. Exptl. Biol Med.*, **46**:489.

Meleney, H. E., Bishop, E. L., and Leathers, W. S., 1932, *Am. J. Hyg.*, **16**:523.

Moffett, M., and McGill, M. I., 1960, *Brit. Med. J.*, **2**:910.

Moore, S. F., Jr., and Simpson, J. W., 1954, *Am. J. Obstet. Gynecol.*, **68**:974.

Mueller, J. F., 1959, *J. Parasitol.*, **45**:170.

Nakamura, M., 1953, *Bacteriol. Revs.*, **17**:189.

Newton, W. L., Reardon, L. V., and DeLeva, A. M., 1960, *Am. J. Trop. Med. Hyg.*, **9**:56.

Nicol, C. S., 1961, *Brit. Med. J.*, **1**:445.

Ninomiya, J., and Suzuoki-Ziro, 1952, *Biochem. J.*, **39**:321.

Ohno, M., 1960, *Osaka Univ. Med. J.*, **12**:563 (in Japanese).

Orita, Y., 1960, *J. Osaka City Med. Center*, **9**:1873 (*Biol. Abstr.*).

Payne, F. J., Atchley, F. O., Wasley, M. A., and Wenning, M. E., 1960, *J. Parasitol.*, **46**:742.

Pelczar, M. J., Jr., and Reid, R. D., 1958, *Microbiology*, McGraw-Hill Book Company, Inc., New York, p. 186.

Peterson, W. J., 1960, *Exptl. Parasitol.*, **10**:293.

Phillips, B. P., and Wolfe, P. A., 1959, *Ann. N.Y. Acad. Sci.*, **78**:308.

Porter, R. J., 1953, *Ann. Rev. Microbiol.*, **7**:273.

Provasoli, L., 1958, *ibid.*, **12**:279.

Rai Chaudhuri, M. N., 1959, *Bull. Calcutta School Trop. Med.*, **7**:112 (*Biol. Abstr.*).

Read, C. P., 1957, *J. Parasitol.*, **43**:385.

————, and Rothman, A. H., 1955, *Am. J. Hyg.*, **61**:249.

Reardon, L. V., and Jacobs, L., 1958, *J. Parasitol.*, **44**(Sect. 2):21.

Reeves, R. E., and Frye, W. W., 1960, *ibid.*, **46**:187.

————, Schweinfurth, D. I., and Frye, W. W., 1960, *Am. J. Hyg.*, **72**:211.

Rendtorff, R. C., 1954a, *ibid.*, **59**:196.

————, 1954b, *ibid.*, **59**:209.

————, and Holt, C. J., 1954a, *ibid.*, **60**:320.

————, and ————, 1954b, *ibid.*, **60**:327.

————, and ————, 1955, *ibid.*, **61**:321.

Robertson, M., 1960, *J. Hyg.*, **58**:207.

Rodin, P., King, A. J., Nicol, C. S., and Barrow, J., 1960, *Brit. J. Venereal Diseases*, **36**:147.

Rosebury, T., 1942, *J. Am. Dental Assoc.*, **29**:823.

Ryigas, E. M., 1960, *Lab. Delo*, **4**:43; 1961, *Referat. Zhur., Biol.* No. 7E16 (*Biol. Abstr.*).

Schnitzer, R. J., Kelly, D. R., and Leiwant, B., 1950, *J. Parasitol.*, **36**:343.

Scott-Gray, M., and Murrell, M., 1961, *Practitioner*, **186**:218.

Seneca, H., and Ides, D., 1953, *Am. J. Trop. Med. Hyg.*, **2**:1045.

Shaffer, J. G., Schuler, R. W., and Key, I. D., 1958, *ibid.*, **7**:302.

Sprince, H., 1948, *J. Bacteriol.*, **55**:169.

————, and Kupferberg, A. B., 1947a, *ibid.*, **53**:435.

————, 1947b, *ibid.*, **53**:441.

St. John, J. H., 1932, *Am. J. Trop. Med.*, **12**:301.

Svensson, R., 1935, *Acta Med. Scand., Suppl.* 70.

Swerdlow, M. A., and Burrows, R. B., 1955, *J. Am. Med. Assoc.*, **158**:176.

Sylvestre, L., Belanger, M., and Gallai, Z., 1960, *Can. Med. Assoc. J.*, **83**:1195.

————, and Gallai, Z., 1960, *Union Méd. Canada*, **89**:735 (transl. Poulenc, Ltd., Doc. 8A, Aug. 1, 1960).

————, ————, and Ethier, J., 1958, *ibid.*, **87**:710.

————, ————, and ————, 1959, *Urol. Intern.*, **9**:356.

Tramontano, A., 1957, *Giorn. Mal. Infettive e Parassit.*, **9**:443 (*Biol. Abstr.*).

Trussell, R. E., 1940, *J. Iowa Med. Soc.*, **30**:66.

————, 1947, *Trichomonas Vaginalis and Trichomoniasis*, Charles C Thomas, Publishers, Springfield, Ill.

————, and Johnson, G., 1941, *Proc. Soc. Exptl. Biol. Med.*, **47**:176.

————, and McNutt, S. H., 1941, *J. Inf. Dis.*, **69**:18.

————, and Plass, E. D., 1940, *Am. J. Obstet. Gynecol.*, **40**:883.

————, Wilson, M. E., Longwell, F. H., and Laughlin, K. A., 1942, *ibid.*, **44**:292.

Tsuchiya, H., and Andrews, J., 1930, *Am. J. Hyg.*, **12**:297.

Tumka, A. F., 1960, *Zool. Zhur.*, **39**:509 [1961, *Referat. Zhur., Biol.*, No. 9E54 (transl.)] (*Biol. Abstr.*).

Valina, F., 1950, *Ceskoslov. Dermatol.*, **25**:51 (1951, *Excerpta Med. Sect. 13*, **5**:167).

Verheye, H., and Kanda, D., 1958, *Ann. Soc. Belge. Méd. Trop.*, **38**:231. (abstr; 1959, *Excerpta Med. Sect. 13*, **13**:450).

Walker, E. L., and Sellards, A. W., 1913, *Philippine J. Sci., Sect. B.*, **8**:253.
Wantland, W. W., and Wantland, E. M., 1960, *J. Dental Research*, **39**:863.
Watt, L., and Jennison, R. F., 1960, *Brit. J. Venereal Diseases*, **36**:163.
Weiner, D., Brooke, M. M., and Witkow, A., 1959, *Am. J. Trop. Med. Hyg.*, **8**:625.
Weir, J., 1952, *J. Egypt. Public Health Assoc.*, **27**:56.
Wells, W. H., and Blagg, W., 1956, *Am. J. Trop. Med. Hyg.*, **5**:266.
Wenrich, D. H., 1944, *Am. J. Trop. Med.*, **24**:39.
————, 1947, *J. Parasitol.*, **33**:177.
Westphal, A., 1941, *Deut. tropenmed. Z.*, **45**:685.
Young, V. M., and Felsenfeld, O., 1944, *J. Parasitol.*, **30**:34.
Zaman, V., 1960, *Ann. Trop. Med. Parasitol.*, **54**:381.

CHAPTER 9

PLEUROPNEUMONIA-LIKE ORGANISMS, SPHEROPLASTS, AND PROTOPLASTS

A diverse and ambiguous category of biologic formations, ranging from what have been widely accepted as distinctive microorganisms intermediate between bacteria and viruses on the one hand to damaged or altered derivatives of a wide range of familiar microorganisms on the other, has been clarified in recent years by fundamental research on the anatomy and chemistry of the microbial cell wall. Much evidence now suggests that all such formations depend upon injury to, or loss of, the cell wall, leaving crippled vestiges of bacteria [or of fungi: see Bachman and Bonner (1959) and McQuillen (1960)]. Yet in important instances no such typical microbic source has been identified. Since the formations in question occur naturally among the normal flora, they require treatment in this book; but the assumption is made that they are not taxonomically separable from organisms described in others chapters. Only the more relevant aspects of this fast-growing subject can be dealt with here. For recent reviews see McQuillen (1956, 1960); Weibull (1958); Brenner et al. (1958); Lederberg and St. Clair (1958); Kalina (1958); and Klieneberger-Nobel (1960). The biology of the pleuropneumonia-like organisms was the topic of an extensive symposium held in New York in 1959 [Nelson (1960)].

The unifying features of the forms to be considered are the occurrence among them of spherical cells lacking, altogether or in part, the rigid cell walls of typical microorganisms, having some degree of osmotic fragility, and having either an incapacity or a limited capacity for multiplication under normal growth conditions, with multiplication, when it occurs, leading to distinctive colony characteristics. Penicillin resistance is a constant feature. Cell formations or reproductive bodies other than spheres occur in certain "species."

Pleuropneumonia-like Organisms: PPLO

Among the forms to be considered, the so-called *pleuropneumonia-like* organisms—abbreviated PPLO—head the list in decreasing order both of complexity and of uncertainty. In common with the type "species" in this group, the agent of pleuropneumonia of cattle [Nocard and Roux (1898)], are forms recovered from other animals (sheep, goats, dogs, swine, rats, mice, fowl) and from man, as well as from sewage and other saprophytic sites. These forms have been classified with the bacteria as a separate order, Mycoplasmatales (alternative, Mollicutales) and in the genus *Mycoplasma* [Edward and Freundt (1956)]. The PPLO are particularly distinctive in that no alternative microbic species of origin is known to exist. They are said to differ as well from the groups described below in that PPLO (1) require cholesterol for growth [Edward and Fitzgerald (1951); Edward (1953); Smith and Lynn (1958); see also Butler and Knight (1960)]; (2) contain "minimal reproductive units" [Cuckow and Klieneberger-Nobel (1955)] that are smaller (100 mμ) than those of L forms and therefore more easily filtered [Klieneberger-Nobel (1956, 1960)]; and (3) form a distinctive branching mycelium in addition to spherical cells, granules, and other structures [Freundt (1952, 1960); see also Liebermeister (1960)]. Smith and Rothblat (1960), Smith and Boughton (1960), and Rodwell and Abbot (1961) have studied the role of cholesterol and other nutrients in the growth and nutrition of PPLO.

In common with the L forms considered below, PPLO have been cultivated principally on solid or semisolid agar media containing high concentrations (usually 30 per cent) of ascitic fluid or serum. The characteristic colonies are minute, with a dense granular central area penetrating into the agar and a translucent flat periphery [Freundt (1954)]. Opinion continues to be sharply divided as to whether these forms, in particular the PPLO of human origin, are distinctive microorganisms [e.g., Freundt (1960)] or L forms of as yet undefined bacteria [e.g., Ruys (1960); van Iterson and Ruys (1960)].

L Forms

The so-called L forms or L phase organisms or variants ["L" from Lister Institute, Klieneberger (1935)] have for some years been regarded by certain workers [e.g., Dienes and Weinberger (1951); Kellenberger, Liebermeister, and Bonifas (1956)] as identical with PPLO, except that by definition PPLO are not, and L forms are, known to have been derived from typical bacteria. More recently, Dienes (1960) has suggested that the question remains unsettled. A group of students of these structures [Basserman et al. (1957)] have pointed out that the word "form" as used in "L form" is not equivalent to the French "forme" but should be translated by the French "formation" or the German "phase". These workers would distinguish between "L forms" on the one hand and "pleomorphic bacteria, globular forms, filterable forms, etc." on the other; but the distinction is by no means clear. More recently, Klieneberger-Nobel (1960), a member of the group referred to, has attempted to distinguish between L forms as *stable* derivatives of bacteria, showing no tendency to revert to typical bacterial morphology, aiid "L phase" or transition forms, from which the source organisms are regenerated. Stability, however, is unlikely to be absolute, and its determinants are for the present unknown. A similar suggestion has been put forward by Tulasne et al. (1960), who would distinguish *reversible* forms as "type B" L forms—having "temporarily incomplete cell-walls," and those "having lost the factors necessary to reconstitute the original bacteria" together with complete loss of cell wall, as L forms of "type A." These 2 groups correspond with *spheroplasts* and *proto-plasts*, respectively, as will be seen. The fluidity even of arbitrary boundaries in this territory is symbolized by the studies of Smith, Peoples, and Morton (1957), which indicated that a well-established PPLO would have to be reclassified as an L formation if it could be induced to revert to a typical bacterium. These workers reported success in accomplishing such a change with established PPLO strains, which were converted irreversibly to diphtheroids; and they suggested that "eventual establishment of a relationship between PPLO strains and some microbial species is not improbable." Similar studies of a probable relationship between avian PPLO and *Haemophilus gallinarum* have been described by McKay and Truscott (1960) who emphasized that "binding proof" of the relation of PPLO to bacteria will require not only reversion of a classic strain of PPLO to a bacterium, but the reverse transformation as well.

Spheroplasts

The uncertainity of a distinction between PPLO and L formations is repeated at the next presumed boundary, between the latter and what are coming to be called spheroplasts [Hurwitz, Reiner, and Landau (1958); Michael and Braun (1959)]. Whereas the L forms can either occur in nature or be recovered from cultures, spheroplasts are by definition induced artificially by injury to the cell wall such that remnants of wall are retained, actually or presumably. The term "spheroplast" refers only to the globular or spherical osmotically fragile body; the relationship to such bodies of granular and other structures found in both L forms [Klieneberger-Nobel (1951); Pulvertaft (1953)] and PPLO [Freundt (1954); Klieneberger-Nobel (1960)] has not been clarified [see also Thorsson and Weibull (1958); Welsch and Oster-rieth (1958)]. Spheroplasts and spherical L formations are evidently indistinguishable except in terms of pedigree, or perhaps in characters that reflect differences between species of origin. It is therefore appropriate to consider the properties of the whole group together; and, except where granular or other formations are specifically intended, the terms "spheroplast" and "L formation" (or equivalent) are used interchangeably in the following discussion.

Species of Origin. The list of bacterial species from which spheroplasts have been derived is a long one, and need not be recounted here in full. It is significant that many of its members are Gram-negative, as contrasted with protoplasts (see page 302). Among the species of particular interest to the present context are *Escherichia coli* and other enterobacteria, *Proteus vulgaris* and *P. morganii, Pseudomonas aeruginosa, Alcaligenes faecalis, Haemophilus influenzae,* and *Bacteroides funduliformis* [see Dienes and Weinberger (1951)]; *Moraxella lacunata* [Klieneberger-Nobel (1951*b*)]; diphtheroids and staphylococci [Dienes and Sharp (1956); Schonfeld (1959)]; nonhemolytic streptococci [Dienes (1953); Hijams and Dienes (1955); A. Abrams (1959)]; group A hemolytic streptococci [Sharp (1954); Sharp, Hijams, and Dienes (1957); Crawford, Frank, and Sullivan (1958)]; pneumococci [Madoff and Dienes (1958)]; *Actinomyces bifidus* [Sundman and Björksten (1958)]; and mycobacteria including tubercle bacilli and *M. smegmatis* [Mattman et al. (1960)]. Recent studies have dealt with *Klebsiella aerogenes* [Gebicki and James (1960)] and *Aerobacter cloacae* [B. S. W. Smith, Payne, and Watson (1960)].

Induction. Procedures used to induce spheroplast formation include treatment with *penicillin* [Dienes (1949); Tulasne (1949); Medill and Hutchinson (1954); Stempen (1955); Lederberg (1957); Marston (1961)]; or—for Gram-negative species—with *lysozyme* under appropriate conditions, namely, at pH 9 [Zinder and Arndt (1956)], in conjunction with chelating agents [see Brenner et al. (1958); Schweighofer and Starlinger (1958)] or with freezing and thawing [Kohn and Szybalski (1959); Kohn (1960)]. Other means of inducing cell-wall damage or impairment of cell-wall synthesis [see Weibull (1958); McQuillen (1960); Pitzurra and Szybalski (1959)], include lysis in the presence of specific antibody and complement [Michael and Braun (1959); Muschel, Carey, and Baron (1959); Carey, Muschel, and Baron (1960)]. The use of *glycine* and other amino acids for inducing L formations has been reviewed by Michel and Hijmans (1960), who reported that glycine actively promotes spheroplast formation of group A streptococci in the presence of penicillin, that a combination of D-cycloserine and glycine or DL-serine was as effective with this organism as the same amino acids with penicillin. These procedures are all known to entail damage to the cell wall or inhibition of its synthesis. Kawata, Asaki, and Takagi (1961) have reported the production of flagellated spheroplasts of *Bacillus megaterium* by autolysis occurring at 37°, in a medium containing 15 per cent sucrose, after interruption of aeration early in the exponential growth phase.

Growth. Among the properties of spheroplasts in addition to those they share with PPLO and which have already been noted, the following are of interest, and in general distinguish spheroplasts from protoplasts, discussed on page 302. Spheroplasts are capable both of cell growth and of cell division in liquid as well as on solid media [see R. Y. Abrams (1955); Weibull and Beckman (1960); Altenbern and Landman (1960)]. Dienes (1949) [see also Dienes and Weinberger (1951)] described 2 types of colonies for L forms of proteus as 3A and 3B, designations which have frequently been followed by other writers. The 3A colony is the typical small one like those of PPLO, appearing only in soft agar and only in the presence of ascitic fluid or serum. The 3B colony is larger (1 to 2 mm) and seems to be a stage in reversion to the bacillary form in transitional or L-phase organisms. Prozorovskii (1959) has described transitional pleomorphic stages of coagulase-positive staphylococci between normal cells and stable L forms, induced by passage through a semisolid medium with various amounts of penicillin. Altenbern (1961a) has reported that the 3A type of *Proteus mirabilis* gave rise to 3B colonies on soft penicillin agar after incubation for 7 days at 37° or 10 days at 30°, with increasing conversion approaching completion during succeeding days. An inhibitor of the change formed in the medium by autoclaving was tentatively identified as formic acid [see also Altenbern (1961b)]. The influence of agar concentration and other factors on the growth of a stable L form of *Proteus mirabilis* has been studied by Weibull and Lundin (1961).

The spheroplasts of motile organisms are usually nonmotile [McQuillen (1960)], but Welsch and Osterrieth (1958) [see also Welsch (1958)], using glycine to induce spheroplast formation, reported that the resulting bodies were less osmotically fragile than those induced with penicillin; those from motile forms retained their motility for some time and, in addition, their H- as well as O- and Vi-antigens. Kawata et al. (1961) (see above) have also produced flagellated spheroplasts. Maccacaro and Turri (1959) described fimbriated spheroplasts of *E. coli* K12 which, unlike nonfimbriated recombinants, retained their hemagglutinating properties. Spheroplasts of *E. coli* can still be infected with specific bacteriophages [Mahler and Fraser (1956)]; and Weidel, Koch, and Lohss (1954) and Weidel and Primosigh (1957) have shown that phage infection depends on retention in the spheroplast of parts of the bacterial cell wall. According to Taubeneck and Böhme (1958) it is the 3B colony (of *Proteus mirabilis*)—which is capable of rapid regeneration into the bacterial form—that contains the phage-sensitive cells. Mahler and Fraser (1959) found that *E. coli* spheroplasts that have ceased to be infected by phage T2 can still be infected by an agent derived from T2, designated π, and thought to be phage DNA with other components including part of the protein envelope of the phage head. Marston (1961) studied L forms induced with penicillin from 8 strains of penicillin-sensitive *Staphylococcus aureus*. Six of these were recovered as cocci; the phage types of those 3 of the 6 that had been typable were identical in parent and recovered strains.

Metabolism. In their metabolic properties, spheroplasts have been found similar to their associated microbic forms with exceptions attributable to cell wall damage—e.g., spheroplasts are resistant to penicillin. The spheroplasts of anaerobes, e.g., clostridia or bacteroides, grow only anaerobically [Dienes and Weinberger (1951)]. It is noteworthy that anaerobic forms regarded as PPLO have also been described [Ruiter and Wentholt (1950–1955)]. Szybalski and Pitzurra (1959) found that the frequencies of spontaneous and induced mutations in *E. coli* and its spheroplasts were nearly identical. Serologic parallelism between spheroplasts and their source cells has also been found, except that cell-wall antigens may have been lost [see Klieneberger-Nobel (1960)]. Sharp, Hijams, and Dienes (1957) reported that the group-specific polysaccharide was lacking in penicillin-induced spheroplasts of group A streptococci, although some M-substance activity was retained. By using the lysin associated with group C streptococcal phage, Freimer, Krause, and McCarty (1959) recovered from group A streptococci what appear to have been true protoplasts, in which both the group A polysaccharide and the M protein were lacking, but which were nevertheless still capable of forming colonies on solid media, so that they seem to constitute a bridge between this group and protoplasts.

Panos, Barkulis, and Hayashi (1960) have described the formation from streptococcal L forms, by sonic treatment, of viable granular elements, the smallest of which were approximately 0.3 μ in size, thought to be comparable with the granular reproductive units described in 1950 by Weinberger, Madoff, and Dienes. Weibull and Beckman (1961) found that the smallest elements in cultures of a stable L form of proteus, which were less than 0.3μ in diameter, respired at about the same rate as whole cultures but showed little or no biosynthetic activity and contained little if any DNA.

Protoplasts

The term used to describe the simplest or most rigorously defined structure in this category is *protoplast*—here as in general botanic usage, that part of the cell that lies within the cell wall, or a structure in which the cell wall is known to be absent [Brenner et al. (1958)].

Studies of bacterial protoplasts, on which a literature has appeared in recent years far too large to be done justice to here, was initiated by Weibull (1953), who found that the spherical cells liberated from *Bacillus megaterium* by lysozyme could be retained without lysis in media osmotically balanced with sucrose or polyethylene glycol. It has long been known that the mucopolysaccharide substrate of lysozyme is an important constituent of the bacterial cell wall, and with the development of methods for separation of cell walls from other bacterial cell components it became possible to determine that lysozyme induces complete dissolution of the cell wall of certain Gram-positive species [see Salton (1957)]. To characterize a bacterial protoplast, absence of cell wall is demonstrated by absence of one or more sets of substances or properties peculiar to that structure—antigens, substances such as DAP, or phage-tail receptor sites. Until recently, all true bacterial protoplasts had been produced with lysozyme acting on lysozyme-sensitive Gram-positive bacterial species; and all such structures had been found incapable of colony formation or of cell division by any means tried, although cell growth without division had been obtained [McQuillen (1955, 1956); Fitz-James (1958); Weibull and Beckman (1960)]. It is clear, however, from the work of Freimer, Krause, and McCarty (1959) cited above, that not all true bacterial protoplasts need behave this way. These workers found that apparently true protoplasts of the lysozyme-insensitive group A streptococcus, induced and maintained by growth in penicillin, contained no cell-wall carbohydrate or protein but were capable of growth and cell division. During growth in the presence of penicillin they synthesized M protein, which was released into the medium. After many transfers the protoplast colonies reverted to the original group A streptococcal type when penicillin was removed from the growth medium.

Interrelationships

Although there is much resistance to an economic and unified hypothesis concerning these forms [see Nelson (1960)], and it is and will doubtless long remain short of rigorous "proof," the evidence surveyed briefly in the foregoing pages would seem clearly to justify the view that all of these forms, from PPLO to protoplasts, are manifestations of microbic cell wall damage or disappearance, with differences depending upon the degree or completeness of such damage and upon peculiarities of the microbe from which the forms were derived. The formations, according to this hypothesis, are microbic manifestations rather than microbes as such; and the application to them of distinctive generic and specific names is inappropriate. The assumed microbic sources of many PPLO await identification.

Occurrence

Since the recovery of PPLO from the human genitourinary tract by Dienes and Edsall in 1937, more interest by far has attached to their presence in that area than in any other. These formations seem nevertheless to have been found in all microbially inhabited areas, including skin [in disease, Ruiter and Wentholt (1955)], both in man and in many animal species [see Ito (1960)]. There is no reason to assume that they are more important in one area than another. Principal interest attaches to attempts to associate them with disease.

In Disease. Much effort has been devoted to the question of a possible relationship between PPLO and *nonspecific urethritis*, among other disease processes, but the matter has not been settled. It has been known since 1946 that L forms of *Neisseria gonorrhoeae* can be produced by growth in vitro in the presence of penicillin [Salaman (1946)]. An attempt has been made more recently to explain increasing clinical resistance of this bacterium to penicillin by assuming a pathogenic L form induced in vivo by therapy [Barile, Van Zee, and Yaguchi (1959)]. It is by no means clear, however, that PPLO or spheroplasts recovered in that state from natural sources in man are ever overtly pathogenic. Since virulence is often associated in bacteria with peripheral cell structures, if PPLO are indeed cells deficient in these structures it would not be surprising to find them less virulent than their parent microbes. Prozorovskii (1959), working with coagulase-positive staphylococci, reported that the stable L form was coagulase-negative, had no necrotizing properties, and was avirulent for white mice.

A general account of the occurrence and possible significance of PPLO and L forms in the genitourinary tract of man was published in 1948 by Dienes and his coworkers. The suggestion that they are associated with disease particularly in men, perhaps transmitted from women in whose genital tracts they may occur normally, was put forward as early as 1943 by Beveridge. Several workers have since found that PPLO occur more often in a variety of disease states in these areas than in the absence of disease. For example, they are found in gonococcal infections and in trichomonal vaginitis [Salaman (1946)] as well as in complications of pregnancy or in the postpartum uterus [Klieneberger-Nobel (1945); Schaub and Guilbeau (1949)]. More recently they have been implicated in Reiter's disease [Oates, Whittington, and Wilkinson (1959); Kuzell and Mankle (1960); Csonka and Furness (1960)]. Klieneberger-Nobel (1959) found PPLO in the genitourinary tract much more often in disease than in health. Dienes et al. (1948) considered the association of PPLO with disease as evidence of pathogenicity, but noted that the forms recovered from man were not pathogenic for animals. They also suggested that the presence of PPLO may be related to penicillin treatment, and noted that L forms of gonococci and other neisseriae, and of *Haemophilus influenzae* and *Escherichia coli* could be produced in vitro by growth in the presence of penicillin. Lack of pathogenicity for animals has also been reported by Wagner and Kuhns (1953) and by Homma and Kusano (1954); while Nicol and Edward (1953), Freundt (1956), and Huijmans-Evers and Ruys (1956b) suggested that absence of association with any particular pathologic condition argued against pathogenicity. Ruiter and Wentholt (1952, 1953a) reported that anaerobic or microaerophilic PPLO recovered from several cases of fusospirochetal disease in the genital area showed "a certain degree" of pathogenicity for young mice, yielding purulent joint swelling after inoculation into the foot pad. Similar tests with aerobic strains of PPLO from genital infections [Ruiter and Wentholt (1953b)] and with an anaerobic PPLO strain from a fusospirochetal skin lesion [Ruiter and Wentholt (1955)] showed no pathogenicity. Barile and Sheingorn (1960) cultivated a PPLO from an inflamed dental pulp.

It may be noted that clear pathogenicity has been found in PPLO isolated from animals, including the classic instances of pleuropneumonia in cattle and agalactia in sheep and goats, and also in PPLO isolated from and generally accepted as parts of the normal flora of rats and mice [see Sabin (1939, 1941); Nelson (1954, 1957); Klieneberger-Nobel and Kwok-Kew Cheng (1955)].

On Healthy Tissues. In man, PPLO or L formations have been found in the absence of disease, in the normal vagina or male urethra [Salaman (1946); Salaman et al. (1946); Nicol and Edward (1953); Freundt (1953, 1956); Somerson et al. (1955)]; in the vagina of children [Olarte (1960)]; in the healthy mouth [Morton et al. (1951, 1952); Dienes and Madoff (1953); Freundt (1954); Huismans-Evers and Ruys (1956a); see also Gilmore and Burnet (1959)]; in the throat [Dienes et al. (1948)]; and in the intestine [Dienes and Madoff (1953)]. Nicol and Edward (1953) recovered PPLO in cultures from the anal canal of men and women with and without proctitis. According to Berg and his coworkers (1960), who gave additional literature on the occurrence of PPLO in man, the incidence of PPLO in the anorectal area is lower than those in the genitourinary tract and mouth and may originate from the genitourinary tract.

In addition to the evidence cited above that PPLO occur in man more commonly in disease than in health, there are several suggestions in the record to the effect that recovery of PPLO from a mucous membrane is more likely in the presence of an abundant rather than a scanty bacterial flora, itself presumably a concomitant or consequence of disease [Freundt (1953, 1956); Shepard (1954); Klieneberger-Nobel (1959)]. Such findings are of course consistent with the hypothesis that PPLO are derived from bacteria or other walled cells.

References

Abrams, A., 1959, *J. Biol. Chem.*, **234**:383.

Abrams, R. Y., 1955, *J. Bacteriol.*, **70**:251.

Altenbern, R. A., 1961*a*, *ibid.*, **81**:586.

———, 1961*b*, *ibid.*, **81**:762.

———, and Landman, O. E., 1960, *ibid.*, **79**:510.

Bachman, B. J., and Bonner, D. M., 1959, *ibid.*, **78**:550.

Barile, M. F., and Sheingorn, A., 1960, *Oral Surg., Oral Med., Oral Pathol.*, **13**:756.

———, Van Zee, G. K., and Yaguchi, R., 1959, *Antibiotic Med. & Clin. Therapy*, **6**:470.

Basserman, J., Carrere, L., Fasquelle, R., Hauduroy, P., Klieneberger-Nobel, E., Penso, G., Roux, J., and Tuncman, Z. M., 1957, *Nature*, **179**:461.

Berg, R. L., Daggett, W., Madden, J., and Dienes, L., 1960, *Ann. N.Y. Acad. Sci.*, **79**:635.

Beveridge, W. I. B., 1943, *Med. J. Australia*, **2**:479.

Brenner, S., Dark, F. A., Gerhardy, P., Jaynes, M. H., Kandler, O., Kellenberger, E., Klieneberger-Nobel, E., McQuillen, K., Rubio-Huertos, M., Salton, M. R. J., Strange, R. E., Tomcsik, J. and Weibull, C., 1958, *Nature*, **181**:1713.

Butler, M., and Knight, B. C. J. G., 1960, *J. Gen. Microbiol.*, **22**:483.

Carey, W. F., Muschel, L. H., and Baron, L. S., 1960, *J. Immunol.*, **84**:183.

Crawford, Y. E., Frank, P. F., and Sullivan, B., 1958, *J. Inf. Dis.*, **102**:44.

Csonka, G. W., and Furness, G., 1960, *Brit. J. Venereal Diseases*, **36**:181.

Cuckow, F. W., and Klieneberger-Nobel, E., 1955, *J. Gen. Microbiol.*, **13**:149.

Dienes, L., 1949, *J. Bacteriol.*, **57**:529.

———, 1953, *Proc. Soc. Exptl. Biol. Med.*, **83**:579.

———, 1960, *Ann. N.Y. Acad. Sci.*, **79**:356.

———, and Edsall, J., 1937, *Proc. Soc. Exptl. Biol. Med.*, **36**:740.

———, and Madoff, S., 1953, *ibid.*, **82**:36.

———, Ropes, M. W., Smith, W. E., Madoff, S., and Bauer, W., 1948, *New Engl. J. Med.*, **238**:509, 563.

———, and Sharp, J. T., 1956, *J. Bacteriol.*, **71**:208.

———, and Weinberger, H. J., 1951, *Bacteriol. Revs.*, **15**:245.

Edward, D. G., 1953, *J. Gen. Microbiol.*, **8**:256.

———, and Fitzgerald, W. A., 1951, *ibid.*, **5**:576.

———, and Freundt, E. A., 1956, *ibid.*, **14**:197.

Fitz-James, P. C., 1958, *J. Biophys. Biochem. Cytol.*, **4**:257.

Freimer, E. H., Krause, R. M., and McCarty, M., 1959, *J. Exptl. Med.*, **110**:853.

Freundt, E. A., 1952, *Acta Pathol. Microbiol. Scand.*, **31**:508.

———, 1953, *ibid.*, **32**:468.

———, 1954, *ibid.*, **34**:127.

————, 1956, *Brit. J. Venereal Diseases*, **32**:188.

————, 1960, *Ann. N.Y. Acad. Sci.*, **79**:312.

Gebicki, J. M., and James, A. M., 1960, *J. Gen. Microbiol.*, **23**:9.

Gilmore, E., and Burnet, G. W., 1959, *J. Bacteriol.*, **77**:147.

Gunsalus, I. C., and Stanier, R. Y., eds., 1960, *The Bacteria: A Treatise on Structure and Function*, vol. 1, Academic Press, Inc., New York.

Hijams, W., and Dienes, L., 1955, *Proc. Soc. Exptl. Biol. Med.*, **90**:672.

Homma, Y., and Kusano, N., 1954, *Japan. J. Bacteriol.*, **9**:1121.

Huijsmans-Evers, A. G. M., and Ruys, A. C., 1956a, *Antonie van Leeuwenhoek J. Microbiol. Serol.*, **22**:371.

————, and ————, 1956b, *ibid.*, **22**:377.

Hurwitz, C., Reiner, J. M., and Landau, J. V., 1958, *J. Bacteriol.*, **76**:612.

Ito, S., 1960, *Japan. J. Bacteriol.*, **15**:1193 (*Biol. Abstr.*).

Kalina, G. P., 1958, *J. Microbiol. Epidemiol. Immunobiol.*, (transl.) **29**:143.

Kawata, T., Asaki, K., and Takagi, A., 1961, *J. Bacteriol.*, **81**:160.

Kellenberger, E., Liebermeister, K., and Bonifas, V., 1956, *Z. Naturforsch.*, **11**:206.

Klieneberger, E., 1935, *J. Pathol. Bacteriol.*, **11**:93.

Klieneberger-Nobel, E., 1945, *Lancet*, **2**:46.

————, 1951a, *Bacteriol. Revs.*, **15**:77.

————, 1951b, *J. Gen. Microbiol.*, **5**:525.

————, 1956, *Zentr. Bakteriol. Parasitenk., I Orig.*, **165**:329.

————, 1959, *Brit. Med. J.*, **1**:19.

————, 1960, in Gunsalus and Stanier (1960), p. 361.

————, and Kwok-Kew Cheng, 1955, *J. Pathol. Bacteriol.*, **70**:245.

Kohn, A., 1960, *J. Bacteriol.*, **79**:697.

————, and Szybalski, W., 1959, *Bacteriol. Proc.*, p. 126.

Kuzell, W. C., and Mankle, E. A., 1960, *Ann. N.Y. Acad. Sci.*, **79**:650.

Lederberg, J., 1957, *J. Bacteriol.*, **73**:144.

————, and St. Clair, J., 1958, *ibid.*, **75**:143.

Liebermeister, K., 1960, *Ann. N.Y. Acad. Sci.*, **79**:326.

Maccacaro, G. A., and Turri, M., 1959, *Giorn. Microbiol.*, **7**:69 (*Biol. Abstr.*).

Madoff, S., and Dienes, L., 1958, *J. Bacteriol.*, **76**:245.

Mahler, H. R., and Fraser, D., 1956, *Biochim. et Biophys. Acta*, **22**:197.

————, and ————, 1959, *Virology*, **8**:401.

Marston, J., 1961, *J. Inf. Dis.*, **108**:75.

Mattman, L. H., Tunstall, L. H., Mathews, W. W., and Gordon, D. L., 1960, *Am. Rev. Resp. Diseases*, **82**:202.

McKay, K. A., and Truscott, R. B., 1960, *Ann. N.Y. Acad. Sci.*, **79**:465.

McQuillen, K., 1955, *Biochim. et Biophys. Acta*, **18**:458.

————, 1956, in *Bacterial Anatomy*, 6th Symposium Soc. Gen. Microbiol., Cambridge University Press, London, p. 127.

————, 1960, in Gunsalus and Stanier (1960) p. 249.

Medill, M. A., and Hutchinson, W. G., 1954, *J. Bacteriol.*, **68**:89.

Michael, J. G., and Braun, W., 1959, *Proc. Soc. Exptl. Biol. Med.*, **100**:422.

Michel, M. F., and Hijams, W., 1960, *J. Gen. Microbiol.*, **23**:35.

Morton, H. E., Smith, P. F., Williams, N. B., and Eickenberg, C. F., 1951, *J. Dental Research*, **30**:415.

————, ————, and Keller, R., 1952, *Am. J. Public Health*, **42**:913.

Muschel, L. H., Carey, W. F., and Baron, L. S., 1959, *J. Immunol.*, **82**:38.

Nelson, J. B., 1954, *J. Exptl. Med.*, **100**:311.

———, 1956, *ibid.*, **106**:179.

———, editor, 1960, *Biology of the Pleuropneumonialike Organisms, Ann. N.Y. Acad. Sci.*, **79**:305.

Nicol, C. S., and Edward, D. G., 1953, *Brit. J. Venereal Diseases*, **29**:141.

Nocard and Roux, 1898, *Ann. Inst. Pasteur*, **12**:240.

Oates, J. K., Whittington, M. J., and Wilkinson, A. E., 1959, *Brit. J. Venereal Diseases*, **35**:184.

Olarte, J., 1960, *Ann. N.Y. Acad. Sci.*, **79**:632.

Panos, C., Barkulis, S. S., and Hayashi, J. A., 1960, *J. Bacteriol.*, **80**:336.

Pitzurra, M., and Szybalski, W., 1959, *ibid.*, **77**:614.

Prozorovskii, S. V., 1959, *J. Microbiol. Epidemiol. Immunobiol.* (transl.) **30**:117.

Pulvertaft, R. J. V., 1953, *J. Pathol. Bacteriol.*, **65**:175.

Rodwell, A. W., and Abbot, A., 1961, *J. Gen. Microbiol.*, **25**:201.

Ruiter, M., and Wentholt, H. M. M., 1950, *J. Invest. Dermatol.*, **15**:301.

———, and ———, 1952, *ibid.*, **18**:313.

———, and ———, 1953a, *Acta Dermato-Venereol.*, **33**:123.

———, and ———, 1953b, *ibid.*, **33**:130.

———, and ———, 1955, *J. Invest. Dermatol.*, **24**:31.

Ruys, A. C., 1960, *Antonie van Leeuwenhoek J. Microbiol. Serol.*, **26**:1 (*Biol. Abstr.*).

Sabin, A. B., 1939, *Science*, **90**:18.

———, 1941, *Bacteriol. Revs.*, **5**:1.

Salaman, M. H., 1946, *Brit. J. Venereal Diseases*, **22**:47.

———, King, A. J., Bell, H. J., Wilkinson, A. E., Gallagher, E., Kirk, C., Howorth, I. E., and Keppich, P. H., 1946, *J. Pathol. Bacteriol.*, **58**:31.

Salton, M. R. J., 1957, *Bacteriol. Revs.*, **21**:82.

Schaub, I. G., and Guilbeau, J. A., 1949, *Bull. Johns Hopkins Hosp.*, **84**:1.

Schonfeld, J. K., 1959, *Antonie van Leeuwenhoek J. Microbiol. Serol.*, **25**:325.

Schweighofer, D., and Starlinger, P., 1959, *Arch. Mikrobiol.*, **32**:219 (*Biol. Abstr.*).

Sharp, J. T., 1954, *Proc. Soc. Exptl. Biol. Med.*, **87**:94.

———, Hijams, W., and Dienes, L., 1957, *J. Exptl. Med.*, **105**:153.

Shepard, M. C., 1954, *Am. J. Syphilis, Gonorrhea, Venereal Diseases*, **38**:113.

Smith, B. S. W., Payne, J. I., and Watson, R. W., 1960, *Can. J. Microbiol.*, **6**:485.

Smith, P. F., and Boughton, J. E., 1960, *J. Bacteriol.*, **80**:851.

———, and Lynn, R. J., 1958, *ibid.*, **76**:264.

———, Peoples, D. M., and Morton, H. E., 1957, *Proc. Soc. Exptl. Biol. Med.*, **96**:550.

———, and Rothblat, G. H., 1960, *J. Bacteriol.*, **80**:842.

Somerson, N. L., Rubin, A., Smith, P. F., and Morton, H. E., 1955, *Am. J. Obstet. Gynecol.*, **69**:848.

Stempen, H., 1955, *J. Bacteriol.*, **70**:170.

Sundman, V., and Björksten, K. af, 1958, *J. Gen. Microbiol.*, **19**:491.

Szybalski, W., and Pitzurra, M., 1959, *J. Bacteriol.*, **77**:621.

Taubeneck, U., and Böhme, H., 1958, *Z. Naturforsch.*, **13b** (7):471 (*Biol. Abstr.*).

Thorsson, K. G., and Weibull, C., 1958, *Nature*, **181**:1348.

Tulasne, R., 1949, *ibid.*, **164**:876.

———, Minck, R., Kirn, A., and Krembel, J., 1960, *Ann. Inst. Pasteur*, **99**:859.

Van Iterson, W., and Ruys, A. C., 1960, *Antonie van Leeuwenhoek J. Microbiol. Serol.*, **26**:9.

Wagner, B. M., and Kuhns, D. M., 1953, *Bacteriol. Proc.*, p. 37.

Weibull, C., 1953, *J. Bacteriol.*, **66**:688.

———, 1958, *Ann. Rev. Microbiol.*, **12**:1.

———, and Beckman, H., 1960a, *Nature*, **188**:428.

———, and ———, 1960b, *J. Bacteriol.*, **79**:638.

———, and ———, 1961, *J. Gen. Microbiol.*, **24**:379.

———, and Lundin, B.-M., 1961, *J. Bacteriol.*, **81**:812.

Weidel, W., Koch, G., and Lohss, F., 1954, *Z. Naturforsch.* **9b**:398, cited by Salton (1957).

———, and Primosigh, J., 1957, *ibid.*, **12b**:427 (*Biol. Abstr.*).

Weinberger, H. J., Madoff, S., and Dienes, L., 1950, *J. Bacteriol.*, **59**:765.

Welsch, M., 1958, *Schweiz. Z. allgem. Pathol. u. Bakteriol.*, **21**:741 (*Biol. Abstr.*).

———, and Osterrieth, P., 1958, *Antonie van Leeuwenhoek J. Microbiol. Serol.*, **24**:257 (*Biol. Abstr.*).

Zinder, N. D., and Arndt, W. F., 1956, *Proc. Nat. Acad. Sci.*, **42**:586.

CHAPTER 10

DISTRIBUTION AND DEVELOPMENT OF THE MICROBIOTA OF MAN

Having dealt separately in the preceding chapters with the individual groups of microorganisms that make up the human microbiota, we must now revert to a more traditional view of the general subject, the distribution of these microorganisms in the various inhabited regions of man. We continue to exclude from our purview certain microbic species which we assume to be transient saprophoyes, e.g., aerobic spore-bearers and certain fungi. On the other hand, we may here include some of the frank pathogens that were not treated in the earlier chapters, notably *Streptococcus pyogenes*. Furthermore, we shall attempt to make direct comparisons of the biota of the various areas in order to bring out their similarities and differences. Since most previous studies have tended directly or by default to emphasize differences, we shall look particularly for similarities. These comparisons are based on tabular material which continues and extends a theme of the writer's chapters in the successive editions of the Dubos text [e.g., Rosebury and Sonnenwirth (1958)].

The Inhabited Areas

In considering the inhabited regions of the human body we are concerned only with those in which a microbiota of bacteria, which may be augmented by fungi and protozoa, is present in appreciable concentration and appears to be proliferating. Such areas include all parts of the skin and the mucous surfaces most contiguous with it; the conjunctiva, the upper respiratory tract down to and including the oropharynx; of the alimentary tract only the mouth and the lower intestinal tract, and the external genitourinary passages including the vagina and the anterior portion of the urethra. In other regions, the rule is either microbiologic sterility or the presence of a sparse biota approaching extinction or in passage. These regions include the larynx, trachea, bronchi, and accessory nasal sinuses; the esophagus, stomach, and the upper portions of the intestinal tract; the upper urinary tract including the posterior urethra and the corresponding posterior genital tract of men or, in women, the passages above the cervix. The presence of a more abundant or persistent biota in these latter areas—or else-where, for example in blood—is accepted as having pathologic import; and, indeed, such a finding may be thought of as providing as re-liable a marker as can be found for the imaginary line that divides health from disease. That such a rule is short of absolute needs no emphasis. It is noteworthy that Schweinburg and Sylvester (1953) found *Clostridium perfringens* widely distributed in the tissues of healthy dogs, and to a lesser degree, of rabbits.

Perekhozheva and Kalshteyn (1956) reported that the maxillary antrum is sterile in many children even in the presence of inflamma-tion, but always contaminated in adults with chronic sinusitis. Bron-chial secretions have been found sterile in most instances in normal adults [Herzog and Schild (1953); Kortekangas (1959); Lees and Mc-Naught (1959)]. By contrast, it is of passing interest that Elmes, Dutton, and Fletcher (1959) found that approximately half of a group of postmen and one quarter of a group of female postal sorters in London, aged 40 to 59, produced morning sputum, often with no ad-mitted symptoms of respiratory disease. The sputum contained appreci-able numbers of *Haemophilus influenzae* in 35 to 48 per cent of in-stances, often accompanied by purulence, and pneumococci in 12 to 26 per cent. Cregan and Hayward (1953) confirmed previous workers in finding the small intestine, sampled by syringe aspiration during gynecologic operations, to contain only a few transient bacteria, most of which seemed to be derived from the mouth. Nadel and Gardner (1956) also found few bacteria in the small intestine by intubation. Anderson and Langford (1958) obtained similar results in children, with sug-gestions of a resident flora in the lower ileum. Cregan, Dunlop, and Hayward (1953) reported that only a few bacteria can be recovered from the small intestine even when free acid is absent from the stomach; and Dixon (1960) confirmed Dack and Petran (1934) in ex-periments with rats suggesting that the mechanism of removal of bac-teria from the small intestine is principally the rapid mechanical action of peristalsis.

Helmholz (1950), using a washing technique, found the urethra sterile increasingly from 21 per cent to 59 per cent of instances in suc-cessive centimeter segments posteriorly. Kass and Finland (1956) found catheterized urine specimens sterile in 46 per cent of asymptomatic women outpatients. Philpot (1956) reported a sterility rate of 18 per cent of clean voided urine samples from 50 men and of 66 per cent of such samples from 50 women. The findings of Monzon et al. (1958)

and Pryles et al. (1959) on urine obtained by suprapubic needle aspiration indicate that the bladder itself is normally sterile.

Development of the Indigenous Biota

It is self-evident that the true amphibionts that make up the most characteristic elements of the indigenous biota, as well as its obligately parasitic members that occupy the more pathogenic band of the spectrum—in short, all those forms that are not found saprophytically in nature—must come to the biota from other human beings or possibly from animals. There is much circumstantial evidence that this is so. It is clear that the fetus is free from microorganisms before birth [see Schweitzer (1919)]—leaving aside the question of viruses[1]—and, indeed, the findings with germfree animals considered in Chap. 11 carry the inescapable implication for man that the biota is derived entirely from the outside world.

The first contribution comes normally from the maternal vagina and perineal area and is demonstrable principally in the infant mouth [Braïlovsky-Lounkevitch (1915); Schweitzer (1919)], nose [Bret et al. (1958)] and oropharynx [Cornelison, Johnson, and Fisher (1946)]. But such contamination may be transient. The characteristic biota of these and other regions does not appear until several hours after birth and in all probability comes largely if not entirely from other sources. In the mouth, bacteria are regularly demonstrable directly or by culture only after the sixth to the tenth hour [Braïlovsky-Lounkevitch (1915)], in the nose and throat after the thirteenth to the eighteenth [Torrey and Reese (1945)] and in the lower intestine after the tenth to the twentieth hour [Tissier (1900, 1905)]. At such times the sources of contamination have become manifold and could be traced only by precise typing or labeling of strains.

The rudimentary data available at present point as sources of infection of infants in hospital nurseries, in the case of antibiotic-resistant coagulase-positive staphylococci, to hospital personnel rather than to the mothers [Sanchez-Torres et al. (1959); Farrer et al. (1959)] or to older infants [Hurst (1960)]. On the other hand both Gareau et al. (1959) and Cooper et al. (1959) have found *E. coli* serotypes in the throats and rectums of infants corresponding in many instances to those of the mother.

---

[1] It is of interest that Moscovici and Maisel (1961), using monkey kidney and human epithelial or cancer cell tissue cultures, were unable to recover viruses from rectal swabs of premature infants in a hospital nursery during the first month of life. The methods used would have been expected to reveal polio, Coxsackie group B, ECHO, and adenoviruses.

It may be assumed that whatever the sources, the process of contamination of man includes microbic species without limit, so that any given microorganism is encountered intermittently but continually. Most of the saprophytes are destroyed soon after contact or excreted. Those microbes that persist do so because they reach an area in sufficient numbers and find growth conditions to their taste and the obstacles not insurmountable. The resultant is a selection of the environmental microbiota which, in part because of its principal source—other human beings—and probably in larger part because the growth conditions and obstacles tend toward uniformity, itself approaches a characteristic pattern despite wide qualitative and quantitative variation.

The development of the biota of each anatomical region depends in part on growth changes in the host—such as eruption of the teeth and maturation of the vagina—and in part on characteristic changes in diet —such as occurs at weaning. There is at present no convincing evidence that geographic differences among human beings, whether they be associated with climate, diet, or cultural or sanitary conditions, play any considerable role in the character of the biota, many statements to the contrary notwithstanding. Nor is any evidence known to the writer of a consistent or definable trend or change in the microbiota (excluding ectoparasites!) with the advance of human history, even including the modern era of antibiotics and the associated decline of serious infective disease. In the individual, and evidently in the mass, the microbiota tends to revert to "normal" when antibiotic therapy is stopped. That the continued use of antibiotics over longer periods, as well as conditions in today's rapidly changing world, may ultimately alter the microbiota is of course not to be excluded; the increasing emergence of antibiotic-resistant staphylococci may be a portent.

Additional details pertaining to the development of the biota of individual areas are given below.

Concentrations of the Total Bacterial Flora in Different Areas

A conspicuous point of difference between the characteristic biotas of different regions of man is quantitative, as may be seen from the data in Table 10-1. The range of variation is suggested by the lowest value given for the nose and the highest value for feces; from hundreds per milliliter to hundred-billions per gram. The actual limits are possibly not so wide. The values for the nose are based on aerobic and anaerobic blood agar counts of a 20-ml wash, and represent a dilution of the actual secretion. On the other hand, the value for feces of 10^{11} [Gyllenberg et al. (1957)] is itself an upper limit for *Actinomyces bifidus* counts in

TABLE 10-1

CONCENTRATIONS OF UNDIFFERENTIATED NORMAL BACTERIAL FLORA IN VARIOUS AREAS*

	Skin			Nose	Mouth			Lower intestine		Urine
	Hands: soap rinse	Scapula-deltoid, per cm²	Nasolabial, per 23-mm circle	Per ml in 20 ml washings	Per ml scrapings tooth surface	Per mg gingival scrapings	Per ml saliva	Upper levels, per ml aspirate	Feces, per Gm wet	Clean midstream, per ml
Microscopic (total)					7^a	8^b				
Aerobic colonies	6^c	2^d	6^e	$1–4^{f,g}$	6^a	7^b	$7^{h,j,k}$ $7–8\dagger^l$	6^m	$7–8\ddagger$	$0–3^{n,o,p}$
Anaerobic colonies		5^d	6^e	$2–5^g$	6^a	7^b	8^j $8–9^k$		$9–11\ddagger$	

* Values are given as $\log_{10}$; e.g., $6 = >5 \times 10^5 < 5 \times 10^6$.
† Edentulous.
‡ Based on differential counts given in Table 10-2.

[a] Kligler (1915).	[i] Richardson and Jones (1958).
[b] Dale et al. (1961).	[k] Rosebury, unpublished.
[c] Price (1938).	[l] Pejrone (1935).
[d] Evans et al. (1950).	[m] Cregan and Hayward (1953).
[e] Pachtman et al. (1954).	[n] Kass and Finland (1956).
[f] Grubb and Puetzer (1947).	[o] Philpot (1956).
[g] Watson et al. (1962).	[p] Clabaugh et al. (1960).
[h] Kraus and Gaston (1956).	

feces of nurselings. Such a count suggests the centrifuged sediment of a pure culture—a wet mass or mud consisting almost entirely of bacteria.

Comparing the two principal rows of Table 10-1 clearly shows that in 4 of 5 areas for which data are available, anaerobic counts have proved higher than the corresponding aerobic count. The exception, scrapings from tooth surfaces [Kligler (1915)], may be entirely valid despite its age, having been obtained in a most careful study. It suggests what seems obvious, although not necessarily so, that so exposed a location as the tooth surface would be unsuitable for the overgrowth of anaerobes. The highly ventilated nasal passages have been found to have a higher anaerobic count [Watson et al. (1961)]. The values for the gingival crevice are those of Dale and her coworkers (1961), in which the average for total viable anaerobes $(3.6 \times 10^{10}$ per Gm) was only slightly higher than that for aerobes $(1.5 \times 10^{10}$ per Gm). The high anaerobic counts do not, of course, point without question to strict anaerobes; facultative forms like viridans streptococci may grow in larger numbers under anaerobic conditions. But in feces the higher anaerobic counts directly reflect bacteroides; on skin they reveal the initially anaerobic or microaerophilic *Corynebacterium acnes*. In the mouth, the difference seems to be smaller and its basis more complex, as the data in Table 10-2 suggest.

The values given in Table 10-1 for skin are based on three reports and reflect wide differences in region and in procedure. Price (1938) counted serial rinses after scrubbing the hands with soap, and reported with inadequate detail that the count declined from 4.6×10^6 to 1×10^6 during an interval (of scrubbing?) of 14 minutes. Evans et al. (1950) chose the scapular and deltoid skin area as "non-special," and attempted to determine the deeper flora by grinding skin scrapings with alundum. They found the anaerobic diphtheroid *C. acnes* present in an average concentration of 5.5×10^4 per sq cm of skin as compared with 3.5×10^2 aerobes, most of which were staphylococci. The third set of values in Table 10-2 are those of Pachtman, Vicher, and Brunner (1954) for controls in a study of seborrheic dermatitis. They cultured scrapings made inside a 23-mm glass cylinder pressed against the naso-labial skin, and compared untreated skin with areas pretreated with 2 per cent Na_2CO_3 to liberate subsurface organisms. The treated skin yielded distinctly higher counts, totaling 3.2×10^6 (equaling approximately 7.6×10^5 per sq cm) for aerobes and 1.5×10^7 (equaling approximately 3.6×10^6 per sq cm) for anaerobes, among which *C. acnes* and other corynebacteria again accounted for the greatest part.

Counts of the upper respiratory mucous surfaces are represented in Table 10-1 by the data of Grubb and Puetzer (1947) based on nasal washings of 5 subjects taken by a standardized technique and plated aerobically on blood agar, and by the findings of Watson et al. (1962), in which washings taken by the same procedure were plated both aerobically and anaerobically. Ranges and averages for the aerobic counts reported by the 2 groups were, respectively, 70 to 38,200, average 4,320; and 30 to 8,220, average 1,050. One of 5 subjects studied by the former group contributed all counts above 13,000; without this subject the average would have been 1,400. In the second study the anaerobic counts ranged from 90 to 17,000, averaging 3,500. The anaerobic count of a given sample of washings was consistently higher than its aerobic correlate, and the average for the anaerobic group was significantly higher than for the aerobic. Kaplan, Larkin, and Hotz (1957) suggested a relative quantitative method for the oropharynx utilizing a platinum loop, but no data based on this or other methods are known.

Total counts of saliva are discussed in Chap. 2, (see also Table 10-3, below) and of feces in Chaps. 4 and 5, and below (see Table 10-4).

The data in Table 10-1 for urine, as suggested above, reflect the flora of the anterior portion of the urethra. They are based on studies whose principal focus has been to assess the clinical significance of positive urine cultures. The upper limit lacking pathologic significance, for catheterized or clean-voided midstream urine samples, has been set at 10^5 to 10^6 per ml by Kass and Finland (1956), at 10^5 per ml by Kaitz and Williams (1960), and at 10^4 per ml by Beeson (1958), Clark and Joress (1960), and Clabaugh, Rhoads, and Adair (1960). [See also Switzer (1961) and O'Sullivan et al. (1961).]

Biotas of the Different Areas

The distribution of species or groups of bacteria, fungi, and protozoa in the different inhabited skin or mucous membrane areas of man are summarized in Table 10-2. Data are given in the table in three ways as available: (1) the incidence as percentage of subjects studied given as a range of averages taken from different reports; (2) the concentration (colony count) per unit of surface, volume, or weight, as a range given roughly in $logs_{10}$; and (3) where neither of the preceding is available, an indication in terms of $\pm$, $1+$ or $2+$ of the occurrence and prominence of the organisms in the areas. Spaces left blank usually indicate absence of information, but in some instances (e.g., the occasional finding of coliforms on skin) the data are omitted as "special" (in this instance, probably representing fecal contamination). In others, the statement in the literature made directly or by implication that a given species is normally absent [e.g., *Klebsiella* or *H. influenzae* in the nose, Jacobson and Dick (1941)] does not seem definitive enough to warrant inserting a zero in the corresponding space. Indeed, except in the few instances in which an incidence of 100 per cent is noted in the table, either alone or as the top of a range (and perhaps even in some of these) the presence of a given organism in any area cannot be considered invariable, and its absence is even less significant. It is a major theme of this book that the indigenous biota is not haphazard but like the rest of the natural world is reducible to order. It is nevertheless abundantly clear that the distribution of indigenous microorganisms is subject to great variation, and hence that the effort to deal with the subject even by the crude quantitation of Table 10-2 must be made and also interpreted with caution.

One of the uses of this kind of table, nevertheless, is that it exposes gaps in our knowledge that may be worth filling; and some of these may be emphasized in passing. Conspicuous gaps are found in rows assigned to nonsporulating anaerobes, and more often reflect failure to look for the organisms than their absence. As a few examples, one would expect *Corynebacterium acnes* to occur in the external auditory canal; and this organism is probably much more widespread on mucous membranes than the data in the table suggest. It also seems likely that the distribution of anaerobic streptococci, *Veillonella, Actinomyces israelii, Leptotrichia buccalis,* and the anaerobes of group E (in Table 10-2) is wider than is indicated. Further search for members of the moraxella-mima group and for the lesser hemophili might also be rewarding. Other deficiencies in our information will emerge as we proceed to consider the separate areas and to compare them.

The Skin

The resident bacterial microbiota of the skin seems to consist mainly of *Corynebacterium acnes* and coagulase-negative aerobic staphylococci [Evans et al. (1950); Pachtman, Vicher, and Brunner (1954)], accompanied by aerobic diphtheroids [Pachtman et al. (1954); Pillsbury and Rebell (1952)]. Anaerobic micrococci were found on skin occasionally by Evans et al. (1950). Unspecified, presumably nonhemolytic, streptococci were reported by Flandin and Duchon (1938) as occurring exceptionally on skin, and hemolytic streptococci as never occurring there. These findings are probably accurate in terms of the true indigenous flora; but Rebell (1947) recovered hemolytic streptococci from as many as 4 per cent of normal skin areas. According to Cruickshank and Cruickshank (1931), *Mycobacterium smegmatis* may be found on skin. More prominent than these latter bacterial species in the skin biota are certain fungi, among which candidas other than *C. albicans* [Benham and Hopkins (1933); Croft and Black (1938)] and the fatty acid-utilizing *Pityrosporum* species [Emmons (1940); Gordon (1951); Di-Menna (1954)] seem most prominent.[2] Conspicuously lacking as true members of the biota of skin are neisseriae, hemophili, and anaerobes lacking iron-porphyrin enzymes. Enterobacteria and other mucous membrane microbes do not seem to be characteristic, but may be found as a result of autocontamination. The association of presence on skin with carriage in the nose in the instance of *Staphylococcus aureus* was stressed by Gillespie, Devenish, and Cowan (1939) and by Miles, Williams, and Clayton-Cooper (1940).

[2] In an early study by Fleming (1909), what appear to have been strains of *Corynebacterium acnes* capable of aerobic growth on agar showed markedly stimulated growth when 0.1 per cent oleic acid was incorporated in agar with 2 per cent glycerin. Pollock, Wainwright, and Manson (1949) described 5 oleic acid-requiring aerobic diphtheroids from skin. According to their fermentation reactions, 2 of these strains were *C. diphtheriae,* 2 were *C. hofmanni,* and 1 was *C. xerosis;* but stock strains of these species did not show the oleic acid requirement.

TABLE 10-2
MICROORGANISMS COMMONLY FOUND ON HEALTHY HUMAN BODY SURFACES*

Species or group	Skin: General	Skin: External auditory canal	Conjunctiva	URT: Nasal passages	URT: Nasopharynx	URT: Oropharynx-tonsil	Mouth: Predentulous	Mouth: Saliva-tooth surfaces	Mouth: Gingival crevice	Lower intestine: Upper levels	Feces: Infant	Feces: Adult	GU: External genitalia	GU: Anterior urethra	GU: Vagina
A. Gram-positive cocci:															
Coagulase-negative staphylococci	88-100 2-6/cm²	27-100	37-94	90	++	±†	+	75-100 1-4/ml		+	31-59‡	+ 2-4/Gm	+	++	34-78
Coagulase-positive staphylococci	5-24§	12-20	0-30	22-85 9-100^a	++	36-42		(16-35)¶		+	10-93^a	++§		±	5-15
Anaerobic micrococci	±				+	+				+					+
Str. mitis and undifferentiated α and γ streptococci	±0	0.2-23	0.9-1	±	24-99	100	++	100 6-8/ml	100 6/mg	+	14-32	+	+	±	10-21 47-50^b
Str. hominis (salivarius)					+	++	100	100 7/ml	++	+	0-6	+			+
Enterococci or group D streptococci						+^{c}	+	4-22^d	++	+	87 6-9/Gm	100 3-8/Gm	+	2-10	4.4-10^i
Str. pyogenes (usually group A unless noted)	0-4		0.3-2.5	0.1-5	0-9	5-66^e	+	12-68^f 3-6/ml^f			0.7-19^j	16^h	+		
Anaerobic streptococci						+	+	++	++ 6/mg			+	+		12-59
D. pneumoniae		+	0-5	0-17^j	0-50	8-71	+	26							±

318

B. Gram-negative cocci:

N. catarrhalis and other spp.	2.3		98		95-100 / 5-7/ml			+	+
N. meningitidis			++ / 10-97					+	+ / +
V. alcalescens		++	±		100 / 6-8/ml			+	+

C. Gram-positive bacilli:

Lactobacilli	53 / 5/cm² 45-100 / 6/cm² +	3-83	+		95ᵏ / 0-6/ml		60ᵏ / -7/Gm	+	49-73
Aerobic corynebacteria	86	++	+	+	59	10-21	6	+	44-74
C. acnes	+	+	±	±	±			±	
Mycobacteria				±	±		+		
Cl. perfringens, other spp.				+	+ / ++	13-19	+		
Cl. tetani					±		25-35 / 1-35		
Actinomyces bifidus					+	15-60ˡ / 90ᵐ / 7-11/Gmᵐ	+	+	26-72
A. israelii					++ / ++ / +				
Leptotrichia buccalis					0-3/ml			++	
L. dentium					+				±

±0, rare: ±, irregular or uncertain (may be only pathologic): +, common; ++, prominent.

* Boldface values (e.g., **31-59**) = range of incidence in per cent, rounded, in different surveys. Values given with units (e.g., 3–6/ml) = range of concentrations expressed as $\log_{10}$:6 = >5 × 10⁵ <5 × 10⁶.

† + in newborn; more common in school children than in adults.
‡ Predominant first day; decreasing during first month.
§ Associated with nasal carriage.
¶ Per cent of strains isolated.
a In infants and children; highest in hospital nursery infants.
b Children.
c In newborn.
d More common below age 20.
e More common in school children; see text.

f Associated with presence in throat.
g "Hemolytic"; Lancefield group not given.
h Groups B, C, F, and G; no A.
i Children; not group A.
j More common in children.
k Especially in dental caries.
l Bottle-fed infants.
m Breast-fed infants.

TABLE 10-2 (Continued)
MICROORGANISMS COMMONLY FOUND ON HEALTHY HUMAN BODY SURFACES

Species or group	Skin: General	Feet	External auditory canal	Conjunctiva	Nasal passages	Nasopharynx	Oropharynx-tonsil	Predentulous	Saliva-tooth surfaces	Gingival crevice	Upper levels	Feces Infant	Feces Adult	External genitalia	Anterior urethra	Vagina
D. Aerobic Gram-negative bacilli:																
Undifferentiated "coliforms"			4-8	2.1		21-23	+		65 / 0-3/ml		+	86-100 / 7-9/Gm	100 / 5-8/Gm	+	+	17-36[a] / 3-12
Escherichia coli			0.1-0.4	0.1		±			4.2		++	67-99	100		+	6[a]
"Intermediates"			+			±		+	31		++	28-52	+		++	+[a]
Klebsiella aerogenes			0.2-1	0.4			+++		52			19-48	33-68	±	+±	
Proteus mirabilis, other spp.					+	±±±	±	+				48	5-53 / -6/Gm		±	
Pseudomonas aeruginosa			0-1.3	±								0-2.1	3-11		5	
Alcaligenes faecalis			1.1-1.6	±±±					±				+			+
Vibrio alcaligenes													±			+
Moraxella lacunata													±±	±		+
Mima polymorpha																+
M. vaginicola															±	+[a]
Haemophilus influenzae				0.4-25	12	43-90	3-97		25-100						5	
H. parainfluenzae						5	20		25							+
Hemolytic hemophili						+	77		+							++[a]
H. aegyptius				+												
H. vaginalis															±	+

320

E. Anaerobic Gram-negative bacilli, vibrios, spirilla, and spirochetes; PPLO, etc.:

Organism	Values
Bacteroides fragilis, other spp.	± + 28–46[p] 4–6 +
B. nigrescens	± ± + +
Fusobacterium fusiforme	+ + + 6/mg + 4/mg + 14–88 3–5/ml +
F. girans	+ + + +
Spirillum sputigenum	+ +? ± ±
Vibrio sputorum	+ + ++ ++ ++ ++
Treponema dentium and Borrelia refringens	+ 28 60–88 6/mg +
PPLO, etc.	+ ± 18[o] + + +

F. Fungi:

Organism	Values
Candida albicans	28–46[p] 14–31 6–49 0–5/ml 6–28 ± 1–15
Other candidas	4–6 0–4/Gm. 1–4 3–10 ± +
Torulopsis glabrata	1–12 ± 100[q] ++
Pityrosporum ovale	+ +
P. orbiculare	+
Dermatophytes	± + 2–41

G. Protozoa:

Organism	Values
Entamoeba gingivalis	8.0–32.1[r] 0–72.6
Ent. coli	9.3–16.0
Endolimax nana	0.2–5.9
Dientamoeba fragilis	1.4–5.0
Iodamoeba bütschlii	4.0–33.8
Trichomonas tenax	0.3–4.1
T. hominis	+
T. vaginalis	2.9–14.7 17.6[n]
Giardia lamblia	9.9–24.9
Chilomastix mesnili	0.4–6.1
Enteromonas hominis	0.1–3.2
Retortomonas intestinalis	0.1–1.3

[n] Children.
[o] After the second week.
[p] C. stellatoidea.
[q] Especially scalp and nasal folds; also other skin areas.
[r] Values in this column are for North America and western Europe; see Chap. 8.

That different parts of the skin are inhabited by somewhat different biotas is supported by scattered observations. Exposed areas of skin are presumably more subject to environmental contamination than those usually covered by clothing. But this circumstance may have little importance, since the characteristic skin biota evidently resides in the deeper layers rather than on the surface, as is indicated by such findings as those of Pachtman, Vicher, and Brunner (1954), who liberated larger numbers of bacteria by treatment of skin with alkaline solutions. Evans and his coworkers (1950) found that bathing had little or no influence on the skin flora, and suggested that the sebaceous glands rather than the sweat glands are the site of their residence. Lovell (1945) showed that in portions of skin removed at operation, some of which had been painted with *Staphylococcus aureus*, after incubation for 6 hours followed by sectioning and staining for bacteria, the transient organisms appeared superficially, the indigenous forms deep in hair follicles and sebaceous glands.

That the hands may at any given moment be contaminated with whatever they have touched is obvious; and if a sampling of the microbiota of soil emerges from beneath a fingernail, especially of a child, the fact could hardly occasion surprise. Two skin areas that have been studied in recent years for specialized reasons are noted in parts of Table 10-2: the external auditory canal and the feet. The former has been examined especially with reference to inflammatory disease of the area, otitis externa, with results that suggest for the normal a difference from other skin areas only in that *Corynebacterium acnes*, as noted previously, has not been found or apparently looked for, and that a scattering of streptococci and enterobacteria have been recovered [see Hardy et al. (1954); Perry and Nichols (1956); Jones (1960)]. As for the feet, the occurrence of dermatophytes has been explored with reference to the epidemiology of tinea pedis (see Chap. 7) and their occurrence there in the absence of symptoms has been noted [Strickler and Friedman (1931); Downing, Nye, and Cousins (1937)].

The Conjunctiva

Numerous studies of the bacteria of the healthy conjunctiva seem to have been limited entirely to aerobic forms; they have been reviewed by Soudakoff (1954) and Smith (1954). There is general agreement that bacteria are absent in many instances, the percentage range of negative cultures in literature surveyed by the writer being from 17 [1,112 subjects; Khorazo and Thompson (1935)] to 49.4 [4,864 subjects; Smith (1954)]. Of the organisms found, coagulase-negative staphylococci (or the presumed equivalent as described) have been much the commonest [see Bachrach et al. (1953); Cason and Winkler

(1954); and the references cited above]. Coagulase-positive staphylococci appear more often than might be expected [Soudakoff (1954); Smith (1954)]. Aerobic diphtheroids, including *C. hofmanni* as well as *C. xerosis*, are described as second in frequency to staphylococci [Bachrach et al. (1953); Landau, Bachrach, and Gurevitch (1953)]. Neisseriae, streptococci, pneumococci, *H. influenzae*, and enterobacteria appear occasionally [Oeding (1946); Smith (1954); Soudakoff (1954); Pannarale and Huet (1959)]. The presence of *Moraxella* in the healthy conjunctiva was noted in tabular data without details by Smith (1954) for his own findings in 1 of 2 groups, and for the findings of 3 of 5 other workers. *M. lacunata* seems to have been recovered from healthy as well as from trachomatous subjects by Pannarale and Huet (1959). Bachrach et al. (1953) and Soudakoff (1954), on the other hand, agreed that *M. lacunata* is not found in the normal conjunctiva. Orfila and Courden (1960) isolated 18 strains of *Mima vaginicola* from the conjunctiva of 120 normal persons. Huet (1957) reported that 80 per cent of 184 strains of *Hemophilus* from the conjunctiva were *H. influenzae*, which he found in 25 per cent of healthy eyes; 12 per cent of the strains were *H. aegyptius* by the criteria of Pittman and Davis (1950); and 8 per cent were ambiguous. According to Bachrach et al. (1953), *H. aegyptius* is not found in the normal conjunctiva.

The Nose

The earlier literature on the flora of the nose was summarized by Küster (1929) and by Thomson and Thomson (1932). Thompson and Hewlett (1898) estimated that 1,500 to 14,000 microorganisms pass into the nose in an hour but found that few are recoverable except from the vibrissae. The vestibule is likely to harbor an abundant flora, and is perhaps comparable with the nails as a terminus for environmental saprophytes [see Shibley et al. (1926)]. In the nasal passages the flora is sparse. Both Küster (1929) and Thomson and Thomson (1932) mentioned that in their own studies occasional aerobic cultures proved sterile; but such a finding seems to be unusual, and several workers have reported that certain presumably normal subjects may show a copious flora [e.g., Neumann (1902)]. The predominant aerobic members of the nasal flora are diphtheroids and white staphylococci. On the other hand, nasal "carriers" of pathogens are well known: of coagulase-positive staphylococci [see Miles, Williams, and Clayton-Cooper (1940)]; of hemolytic streptococci [Hamburger, Green, and Hamburger (1945); Harvey and Dunlap (1961)] and of *Corynebacterium diphtheriae* [see Russell (1943)]. Other aerobic members of the nasal flora noted in Table 10-2 are occasional nonhemolytic streptococci [Lewis and Turner (1905); Jacobson and Dick (1941)]; pneumococci [Neumann (1902); Thomson and Thomson (1932); Masters et al. (1958); Kortekangas (1959); Harvey and Dunlap (1961)]; neisseriae [Arkwright (1907); Jacobson and Dick (1941)]; moraxellae [Henrikson (1958)]; and *Haemophilus influenzae* [Masters et al. (1958); Kortekangas (1958); see also Lees and McNaught (1959); Harvey and Dunlap (1961)]. The occurrence of smegma bacilli in the nose was noted by Topley and Wilson (1936).

It was mentioned above that Watson and her coworkers (1962) recovered anaerobes from the nasal passages and found them to outnumber aerobes by a factor of more than three. Among these forms was an organism closely resembling *Corynebacterium acnes*. Despite the ventilation of the area it is probable that other anaerobes may find suitable growth conditions there in deep or protected regions or in the reducing environment provided by association with aerobic bacteria.

The Pharynx

According to Cruickshank and Cruickshank (1931), aerobic cultures from the upper part of the posterior nares, if taken with care to avoid contamination from mouth or throat, are usually sterile. This, however, is the area in which the meningococcus has frequently been found in healthy carriers [see Wilson and Miles (1955)]. The biota of the pharynx seems in general to intergrade between a pattern similar to that of the nasal passages in its upper portion and one hardly distinguishable from that of the mouth in the tonsillar area.

The biota of the *nasopharynx* differs from that of the nose in being more copious, and the presence of obligate anaerobes seems established. Coagulase-negative staphylococci, streptococci, especially of the *mitis* group, corynebacteria, and neisseriae are the most prominent aerobes [Park, Williams, and Krumwiede (1921); Noble, Fisher, and Brainard (1928); Burky and Smillie (1929)]. *Staph. aureus, H. influenzae*, and pneumococci have been recovered frequently [for *H. influenzae* and related hemophili see also Fleming and MacLean (1930)]. These "pathogens" have been found in this area in low-grade viral infections when they were not found in the oropharynx [Commission (1949)]. Enterobacteria appear irregularly in the nasopharynx. Noble, Fisher, and Brainard (1928) found Friedländer's bacillus in 3 per cent of cultures made from 8 normal subjects [for other coliforms see Lees and McNaught (1959) and Harvey and Dunlap (1960)]. The presence of members of the Moraxella–Mima group in the nasopharynx has not been noted specifically, but since they appear in the nose and elsewhere in the respiratory tract it is assumed that they occur in this area as well.

References to the occurrence of anaerobes in the nasopharynx are scattered and appear only in the older literature. What is apparently

Veillonella alcalescens was observed by Wilson (1928), Wilson and Smith (1928), and Branham (1928); see also Garrod (1928). Gram-negative anaerobic bacilli, spirilla, and vibrios, usually described as passing Berkefeld V and N filters, and including the somewhat equivocal *Bacteroides pneumosintes* (see Chap. 5), were recovered in studies of influenza by Olitsky and Gates (1921, 1922*a,b*) and of the common cold by Olitsky and McCartney (1923), Mills, Shibley, and Dochez (1928) and Thomson and Thomson (1924–25). These organisms are listed in Table 10-2 under *Bacteroides* spp., *Spirillum sputigenum*, and *Vibrio sputorum.*

The *oropharynx*, including the posterior portion of the soft palate, the tonsillar area, and the posterior wall—all of which are assumed in the word "pharynx" or "throat" used without qualification—has the mixed biota to be expected of its character as a crossroads of the upper respiratory and alimentary tracts. White staphylococci are no longer prominent, perhaps reflecting low concentrations rather than low incidence, as in the mouth. The nonhemolytic (γ and α) streptococci are universal and apparently the same as the oral forms. Neisseriae and aerobic diphtheroids appear to be common to the whole oropharyngeal region [see Kaplan et al. (1957); also Bezjak (1958)]. The presence of *Mycobacterium smegmatis* in the tonsil was mentioned by Topley and Wilson (1936). Enterobacteria occur irregularly as in contiguous regions [see Lees and McNaught (1959); Rajkovic (1959); Harvey and Dunlap (1960); Jones (1960)]. The finding of *Proteus* strains and *Pseudomonas aeruginosa* in this area [Rajkovic (1959); Jones (1960)] may not necessarily imply abnormality. Likewise, the occurrence of *Moraxella* and both *Mimae* in the throat or other parts of the respiratory tract [Oliver and Wherry (1921); Schaub and Hauber (1948); Ferguson and Roberts (1950); Piéchaud et al. (1951); Henrikson (1952)] cannot be unequivocally associated with pathologic conditions.

H. influenzae and related species, including hemolytic hemophili prominently, have been recovered from the throat, including the tonsil [Fleming and Maclean (1930); Stillman (1945); Kaplan et al. (1957); Masters et al. (1958); Lees and McNaught (1959); Kortekangas (1959); Elmes, Dutton, and Fletcher (1959); Harvey and Dunlap (1960)]. Harvey and Dunlap (1961) found *H. influenzae* more universally present in the healthy nose and throat than pneumococci or hemolytic streptococci.

Coagulase-positive staphylococci are less often looked for in the oropharynx than in the nose and are apparently somewhat less common in the throat [Commission (1949); Lees and McNaught (1959); Kortegangas (1959); Jones (1960)]. Masters et al. (1958) found them, together with hemolytic streptococci, most common in the throats of school children. Pneumococci have been recovered from the healthy throat during recent years by Kaplan and his coworkers (1957), Lees and McNaught (1959), Kortegangas (1959) and Harvey and Dunlap (1960, 1961), among others.

The relevant literature pertaining to hemolytic streptococci, most of which is concerned with *Str. pyogenes*, group A, is too extensive to be reviewed here. Some of the earlier references were given by Hamburger et al. (1945) and by Duguid (1946). More recent studies have emphasized especially children of school age largely in relation to the problem of rheumatic fever. The carrier rate has been found highest in this age group [see Quinn et al. (1957, 1961); Masters et al. (1958); Saslaw et al. (1959); Zanen, Ganor, and Van Toorn (1959); Brumfitt, O'Grady, and Slater (1959); Cornfeld and Hubbard (1961a)]. Cornfeld et al. (1961b) found that approximately half of a large group of children in 3 schools in Philadelphia yielded positive throat cultures on one or more occasions during each of 2 years. The average monthly carrier rate for the 3 schools during 1955 to 1959 ranged from 7.4 to 28.8 per cent. Routine cultures from healthy children accounted for the great majority of the positive findings.

Among anaerobes, Foubert and Douglas (1948) recovered both Gram-negative (*V. alcalescens*) and Gram-positive cocci (*M. anaerobius*) from tonsils. While no specific reference to anaerobic streptococci in the tonsil is known, their presence there may be assumed as part of the fusospirochetal complex. *Actinomyces israelii* was found in tonsils by Lord (1910) and by Emmons (1938) [see also Marotta (1953)]. As with the anaerobic streptococci, the presence of bacteroides, as well as of anaerobic vibrios and spirilla, in the healthy tonsillar crypts may be assumed from their occurrence in disease of the area [see, e.g., Veillon and Zuber (1897, 1898); Guillemot (1898); Guillemot, Hallé, and Rist (1904); Lemierre (1936); Lemierre et al. (1938)]. *B. nigrescens* was recovered from tonsils by Burdon (1928); see also Varney (1929). Fusobacteria and spirochetes were found in the throat by Pilot and Brams (1923) and by Pratt (1927).

Members of the PPLO group have been recovered from the throat by Dienes et al. (1948) and by Smith and Morton (1951). The data in Table 10-2 for *Candida* species in the throat are taken from Brygoo (1952) and from DiMenna (1954) as complied in Table 7-3; those for *Torulopsis glabrata* are also from DiMenna. Tumka (1957) has reported finding both *Trichomonas tenax* and amebas thought to be larger than *E. gingivalis*, in the tonsils in chronic tonsillitis.

Gundel and Schwarz (1932) suggested that the flora of both mouth and upper respiratory tract in infants is derived from the oral flora of attendants, perhaps especially the mother. They based this opinion on the occurrence of oral organisms in the nose and throat during the first few days of life, including mouth streptococci and fusiform rods; and they were able to show that pneumococci recovered from the infant were of the same serologic type as that found in the mother's mouth. There is much circumstantial evidence that throughout life respiratory contamination of man emanates as much from the mouth as from the nose of donors in sneezing as well as in kissing [see Jennison (1942); Hamburger et al. (1945); Duguid (1946)]. In this process, of course, interchange must be assumed to occur between mouth and respiratory tract in both directions. Williams, Appleton, and Polevitzky (1952) observed that the flora of mouth and pharynx are more similar to each other than either is to that of the nose.

Harvey and Dunlap (1960) have reported an interesting study of the nose and throat aerobes of 75 married couples as recovered on 24-hour horse blood agar plates. Cultures were taken once each month for about 15 months. Principal attention was given to the more pathogenic species or to those considered less characteristic of the local flora, including coliform organisms and "yeasts." None of the members of this selected group was recovered from all couples, and the findings suggested continual but intermittent interchange rather than consecutive maintenance. The species most frequently recovered were *H. influenzae* and *H. haemolyticus,* each of which appeared in 67 (89 per cent) of the couples at one time or another; but *H. influenzae* was found in only one spouse in 16 of the 67 couples, and *H. haemolyticus* in only one spouse in 19. In only 55 and 54 per cent of the positive couples, respectively for the 2 hemophili, was the organism recovered simultaneously from both spouses. For the other species, in decreasing order of prevalence, the values for simultaneous occurrence in percentage of positive couples were staphylococci, 19; hemolytic streptococci, 14; pneumococci, 9; coliform bacteria, 7; and yeasts, 23. Host conditions ("immunity") were suggested by Harvey and Dunlap as the basis of these differences.

The Mouth

The mouth is the first mucous membrane area of the body to develop a microbiota after birth, as noted above. For many obvious reasons, including those applicable to childhood that led Freud to speak of the oral phase of human development, the mouth is of all body areas, perhaps excluding the hands, most subject to contamination throughout life. The mouth is also the most accessible of the mucous membrane regions for purposes of investigation, and both the saliva and other parts of its contents can be dealt with quantitatively. The evidence available suggests that the microbiota of the mouth is the most varied of all, although less numerous than that of the lower intestinal tract. Opportunities for contamination make it likely that any microbic species, parasitic, saprophytic, or even autotrophic, may turn up in a given sample of mouth material.

The more evanescent forms can be eliminated from the category of indigenous microbes by the irregularity of their appearance; but some nonindigenous saprophytes—such as many of the fungi found on skin —may possibly appear often enough to give a false impression of survival and multiplication in the mouth. It is possible that some of the species that have not been found elsewhere in the indigenous biota— *Leptotrichia dentium*, so called, or certain nocardiae—belong in this category. The similarities between the oral biota and that of other areas suggest the need for caution in attributing indigenous status to some of the more unusual forms sometimes observed in mouth material. It is nevertheless likely that certain truly indigenous organisms—especially anaerobes—are present but have thus far resisted adequate characterization, such as the "test-tube brush" forms described by Beust (1908) and others [see Rosebury (1944*b*)] which appear to have been cultured anaerobically by Tunnicliff and Jackson (1930) from tonsillar granules and named *Vibriothrix tonsillaris*. If such forms are true species their characteristics would permit their undetected presence in other sites as well as in the mouth and throat.

From Table 10-2 it appears that *Streptococcus mitis*, *Str. hominis*, neisseriae, and *Veillonella alcalescens* are universally present in the healthy adult mouth. Universality is probable also for coagulase-negative staphylococci, anaerobic streptococci, *Leptotrichia buccalis*, and *Hemophilus influenzae*. The following are probably not more than occasionally absent: aerobic lactobacilli (mainly absent in the caries-free), *Actinomyces israelii*, bacteroides, *Fusobacterium fusiforme*, *Spirillum sputigenum*, *Vibrio sputorum*, and spirochetes. Additional forms probably present in at least 25 per cent of instances are coagulase-positive staphylococci, *Streptococcus pyogenes*, pneumococci, aerobic diphtheroids, coliforms perhaps principally of the *K. aerogenes* intermediate varieties, *H. parainfluenzae* and *H. haemolyticus*, *Candida albicans*, *Entamoeba gingivalis*, and *Trichomonas tenax*. Conspicuously absent from this list—and probably found in the mouth (as compared with other indigenous loci) only rarely—are clostridia, proteus, pseudomonads, and *Alcaligenes faecalis*. The moraxella-mima group has not been looked for in the mouth; its absence cannot be assumed. References to the oral flora (see also Table 10-1 and 10-3) will be found in Rosebury (1944*a,b,c*), Rosebury and Sonnenwirth (1958), Berger (1958), and Bissett and Davis (1960). See also, for staphylococci, Jordan, Fitzgerald, and Faber (1956) and Taplin and Goldsworthy (1958, 1959); for *Str. pyogenes*, Hamburger (1944), Duguid (1946), and Massler and

Macdonald (1950); for enterococci, Hugh, Klopp, and Ryschenkow (1959) and Williams et al. (1950); for diphtheroids and leptotrichia, Hemmens, Blayney, and Harrison (1941); for coliforms, Nolte and Swineford (1957) and Chang and Foltz (1960); for hemophili, Fleming and Maclean (1930); for PPLO, Morton, Smith, and Keller (1952); for candidae, DiMenna (1954), Fox and Ainsworth, (1958) and Marples (1960); for *Torulopsis glabrata*, DiMenna (1954), and for protozoa, Wantland and Wantland (1960) and Chap 8.

It is generally agreed that aerobic forms, in particular the streptococci, are most characteristic of the smooth mucous surfaces such as cheeks, palate, and areolar gingival areas, and that they are among the first microorganisms to appear in the mouth following birth, hence among the first settlers of the indigenous biota as a whole. Lewkowicz (1901) found streptococci and "nonpathogenic pneumococci" to be the first colonizers after the initial sterile phase. Braïlovsky-Lounkevitch (1915) found in the mouths of infants by the tenth postnatal hour, when bacteria were just beginning to appear in the intestine, a well-developed flora of aerobic cocci and bacilli, including salivary streptococci, hemolytic streptococci, pneumococci, micrococci, and lactobacilli, as well as enterococci and *K. aerogenes*-like forms (*B. acidilactici*). By the second day the number of bacteria had increased, and *coli-aerogenes* forms, proteus, and staphylococci were present in addition to the other forms. Yeasts were found at the end of the second week. By the twelfth day, according to this observer, *Str. salivarius* became prominent and remained constant during the first year; other species were intermittent. Braïlovsky-Lounkevitch found strict anaerobes rare in nurselings, but Lewkowicz (1901) had noted the presence in 3-month-old infants of *A. bifidus*, anaerobic streptococci, *Leptotrichia buccalis*, and *V. alcalescens* (*Micrococcus gazogenes alcalescens*), which this worker discovered, as well as filamentous bacteroides-like forms.

More recently, Berger et al. (1959) reconfirmed the presence of *V. alcalescens* occasionally as early as the first day of life and regularly at the end of the first week. He found fusobacteria sometimes in the early weeks, regularly after the fifth month. But *Spirillum sputigenum* and anaerobic vibrios were seen only occasionally in the predentulous mouth, while spirochetes appeared only after the teeth had begun to erupt. These forms are, of course, characteristic of the gingival crevice. Their dependence on the teeth was noted as early as 1891 by Podbielskij and again in 1906 by Oshima. Berger et al. (1959) suggested that the tonsillar area may be the site of development for anaerobes in the predentulous period. It is possible that the tonsillar crypts and the gingival crevices provide the exacting anaerobic conditions needed for growth especially of spirochetes. These anaerobes are less characteristic of the dorsum of the tongue, the flora of which seems to differ little from that of the smooth oral surfaces, with cocci constant, spirochetes and filaments variable, and vibrios rare [Braïlovsky-Lounkevitch (1915)].

With complete loss of teeth, changes occur which include a modified tendency to revert to an aerobic flora. Simple dependency on surfaces or on forms such as those provided by teeth is suggested by the finding that lactobacilli tend to disappear in the edentulous mouth and to return in the presence of artificial dentures, as shown by Bradel and Blayney (1940) and confirmed by Lilienthal (1950), who found the same to be true of *Candida albicans*. Both organisms, perhaps especially the latter, are of course present in the predentuous mouth. Typical anaerobes, especially spirochetes, are uncommon but apparently not absent in the edentulous mouth [Kostecka (1924); Rosenthal and Gootzeit (1942)]. Pejrone (1935) reported total bacterial colony counts in aerobic blood agar plates for 20 men and 30 women edentulous patients without artificial dentures. The average values per milliliter were, for the men, 2.0×10^7 and for the women, 1.4×10^7, the combined average being 1.6×10^7, which compared with an average for normals of 2.0×10^7. Pejrone regarded the lower average for the edentulous group, especially that for women, as significant.

Table 10-3 presents a listing of average values as given by several authors for total bacterial counts and counts of separate bacterial groups, for saliva and gingival scrapings; all pertain to healthy mouths. The data of Dale et al. (1961), thus far available only as a brief abstract, indicated that "no significant differences were found between the counts per gram from normal gingivae and those from periodontal disease" but gave no data for sample weight. The amount of material obtainable from the healthy gingival area is, of course, very much less than the sometimes massive gingival exudate of periodontal disease; the suggestion that the gingival biota increases in disease without change in the proportion of its components (or of those listed by Dale et al. and given in Table 10-3) is of interest. It may be seen that in the few instances in which the same category is represented in both saliva and gingival counts (total anaerobic and aerobic viable counts, aerobic streptococci, and fusobacteria) the paired values are proportional to a degree that may well be within experimental error. More data of this kind are needed. The table indicates that we can at present account in separate cultures for only roughly one-half of the bacteria that appear in anaerobic (blood agar) plates. The concentration of spirochetes (given as a microscopic count for the gingival crevice) is evidently not high enough to affect the total markedly, making the discrepancy all the more striking. It would be useful to know how much of this discrepancy

TABLE 10-3

ESTIMATED CONCENTRATIONS OF BACTERIAL GROUPS
OF THE ORAL BIOTA

	Saliva, per ml	Gingival crevice, per mg[a]
Total, microscopic		1.6×10^8
Total, anaerobic viable	$1.1 \times 10^{8\,b}$	3.6×10^7
Total, aerobic viable	$4.0 \times 10^{7\,b}$	1.5×10^7
	$2.5 \times 10^{7\,c}$	
Staphylococci	$5 \quad \times 10^{3\,b}$	
Aerobic streptococci	$1.0 \times 10^{7\,c}$	2.5×10^6
	$1.8 \times 10^{7\,b}$	
Str. hominis	$5.1 \times 10^{6\,c}$	
	$1.1 \times 10^{7\,b}$	
Anaerobic streptococci		3.0×10^6
Veillonella alcalescens	$5.3 \times 10^{7\,d}$	
	$3.3 \times 10^{7\,e}$	
	$1.7 \times 10^{7\,b}$	
Neisseriae	$2 \quad \times 10^{6\,b}$	
Fusobacteria	$5.6 \times 10^{4\,b}$	4.3×10^4
Bacteroides nigrescens		9.5×10^5
Spirochetes (microscopic)		$8 \quad \times 10^5$
Miscellaneous and unidentified	$.7 \quad \times 10^{6\,b}$	
Total accounted for, approximate	6.5×10^7	7.3×10^6
Not accounted for (from total viable)	4.5×10^7	8.7×10^6

[a] Dale et al. (1961).   [d] Douglas (1950).
[b] Richardson and Jones (1958).   [e] Rogosa (1956).
[c] Kraus and Gaston (1956).

would be made up if the gaps in the table were filled: for saliva, especially the anaerobic streptococci and the bacteroides; and for gingival bacteria especially veillonellae and neisseriae, and perhaps bacteroides other than B. *nigrescens*.

The Lower Intestinal Tract

As we saw earlier in this chapter, the gastrointestinal tract between the oropharynx and the ileum or cecum seems to harbor few microorganisms, and such forms as are found in the small intestine are thought of as derived from the mouth [Cregan and Hayward (1953)]. It is of interest, nevertheless, that the accumulated flora above an obstruction in the small intestine was found by Bishop and Allcock (1960) to consist largely of fecal forms: *E. coli*, "paracolon" organisms, bacteroides, enterococci, and proteus, admixed with *Cl. perfringens* as well as with veillonellae and candidas, and the more typical oral streptococci

(*Str. mitis*). Since the flora below the obstruction was found by these workers to be scanty and transient, they considered their findings to represent ingested microorganisms rather than the effects of retrograde spread.

Cregan and Hayward (1953) studied both aerobic and anaerobic cultures of syringe-aspirated material from the small intestine of 14 patients undergoing gynecologic operations, with no intestinal disease. In 12 the upper jejunum was sterile; one yielded a lactobacillus, the other *C. albicans*, both scantily. In 10 the midportion (lower jejunum or upper ileum) gave no growth; the other 4 contained scanty growths of the same 2 microbes and also of oral streptococci, *V. alcalescens*, and, in one instance, *E. coli*. Seven of fourteen samples from the lower ileum were also sterile. From the others, in addition to the species found in the higher sections, *Str. faecalis*, *Cl. perfringens*, *Staph. aureus*, *K. aerogenes*, and a bacteroides were each recovered once, while oral streptococci, *E. coli*, and *V. alcalescens* were each recovered in three or four instances. Few of these microbes were considered to be resident in the small intestine.

The findings of several investigators [Duncan et al. (1954); Schwabacher et al. (1959); see especially Goudie and Duncan (1956)] suggest that the *Clostridium perfringens* often found in the stool proliferates in the cecum and colon and perhaps even in the small intestine (see Chap. 3). According to Parr (1923) the spirochetes of feces inhabit the cecum particularly.

Our knowledge of the microbiology of *feces* of healthy adults is surprisingly meager. No general study or review of the subject is known to the writer; nor, apparently, is the matter considered in texts, old or new, of gastroenterology, proctology, or rectal surgery. Biochemistry texts [e.g., White et al. (1954)] state that bacteria make up approximately 25 per cent of the dry weight of feces. Strasburger (1902) estimated that a normal person excretes 8 Gm of bacteria per day, representing a quarter to a third of the fresh fecal material. Lissauer (1906) estimated that the average bacterial content of feces of man was 8.7 per cent of total solids on a dry weight basis. Riddell, Morton, and Murray (1953) presented the only data the writer has seen on total bacterial counts of feces, including both aerobic and anaerobic viable counts. Unfortunately, the subjects presented were not normal; but some of the data for 2 subjects with cancer of the sigmoid may not depart from the normal range. These data are as follows, in numbers of viable bacteria per gram of wet feces: for total aerobes, 1×10^7 to 2.5×10^9; for total anaerobes, 1.5×10^9 to 2×10^{12}; for coliforms, 1×10^7 to 9×10^8; for aerobes other than coliforms, 3×10^6 to 2×10^9; and for strict anaerobes, 1.5×10^9 to 2×10^{12}. The highest of these values (2×10^{12}), found on 1 day for 1 subject, was made up of "anaerobic lactobacilli" [unbranched Gram-positive rods, following Skerman (1949); see also Skerman (1959)], bacteroides and *Str. lanceolatus* (*Str. putridus?* see Chap. 2) each of which appeared on that day in concentration given as approximately 10^{11} per Gm.[3]

Turning to Table 10-2, we find that the predominant bacteria in adult feces are anaerobes, among which the bacteroides are known to be conspicuous, although few quantitative data for other anaerobes are available. Eggerth and Gagnon (1933), who included both Gram-positive and Gram-negative anaerobic nonsporulating bacilli as *Bacteroides*, stated that the anaerobic colony count of feces was frequently 300 times as high as the aerobic count; that of 60 stool samples, 55 contained 50 per cent or more of anaerobes and 31 contained more than 90 per cent anaerobes. His anaerobic colony counts per gram of wet feces ranged from 4.7×10^{7} to 9.6×10^{9}. Misra (1938) reported that 24 of 26 strains of bacteroides from human feces were Gram-negative, and found them 3 to 170 times as numerous as coliforms. Ruebner (1957) presented graphical data on 6 presumably normal subjects and 15 with cirrhosis of the liver; in the former the counts of *bacteroides*, based on Fildes peptic blood-digest medium [Schwabacher and Michison (1947–48)] ranged approximately from 10^{8} to 7×10^{9} per Gm, in the latter approximately from 4×10^{7} to 4×10^{10} per Gm. This worker's values for *E. coli* in the same subjects were approximately, for the normal subjects, 10^{7} to 5×10^{8} per Gm, and for the group with liver disease, 10^{7} to 6×10^{9} per Gm. Loh and Baker (1955) reported values for *E. coli* ranging from 1.5×10^{5} to 6.9×10^{8} per Gm of wet feces, with an average for 18 subjects of 10^{7} per Gm or slightly lower. The data given by Slanetz and Bartley (1957) utilizing membrane filters, range from 1.0×10^{4} to 2.6×10^{8} per Gm, with an arithmetic mean of 1.9×10^{7} and a geometric mean of 2.1×10^{6} per Gm of feces. Data for *enterococci* given presumably for the same specimens by these workers showed an even wider range, from 1×10^{3} to 2.7×10^{8} per Gm, with arithmetic and geometric means, respectively, of 3.0×10^{7} and 1.1×10^{6}. There was a marked tendency for a high count of 1 microbic group to be correlated with a high count of the other, and vice versa. Loh and Baker (1955) also reported wide variation in enterococcus counts of feces. The data for *staphylococci* in Table 10-2 are taken from the latter report.

Other quantitative data found in the literature have been omitted

---

[3] Subsequent values for the same patient, under dihydrostreptomycin treatment, of 10^{13} and 10^{14} for organisms of the same groups must be taken with skepticism and cast doubt on the other values. Given a density of 1 and a minimum bacterial volume of 0.2 μ^{3}, 1 Gm = 1 cm^{3} = 10^{12} μ^{3}; solidly packed bacteria could not exceed 5×10^{12} per Gm (see also Chap. 2).

from the table as pertaining to single subjects or having probable pathologic import. The data given by Ruebner (1957) indicate normal counts
of *proteus* and of *lactobacilli* of less than 5×10^6 and 5×10^7 per Gm
respectively in the groups studied. Riddell et al. (1953) found in the one
subject with cancer of the sigmoid mentioned above, before treatment
with dihydrostreptomycin, values for *E. freundii* of 10^5 and 10^8 per
Gm, for *B. nigrescens* of 10^4, and for *Cl. perfringens* of 10^4 and 10^6. Loh
and Baker (1955) implied that the count of *pseudomonads* in wet feces
without antibiotic medication was below 10^6 per Gm.

The frequency data and qualitative notations in Table 10-2 for adult
feces are taken from the following sources: *Staph. aureus*, Ridley
(1959), Hancock, Dulaney, and Caldwell (1959) and see Chap. 2;
viridans streptococci, Rodaniche, Palmer, and Kirsner (1943), Berens
and Chapman (1944); hemolytic streptococci of groups other than D
and A, Smith and Sherman, (1938); lactobacilli, Harrison and Opal
(1940), and see also Ruebner (1957); corynebacteria, Dudgeon (1926);
clostridia, Dudgeon (1926), Duncan et al. (1954), Goudie and Duncan
(1956); *Cl. tetani*, Tenbroeck and Bauer (1922), Kerrin (1928); *K.
aerogenes* and intermediate forms, Shidlovsky, Prigot, and Turell
(1957–58), Orskov (1955); proteus, Rustigan and Stuart (1945), Loh
and Bagley (1956), and see Chap. 4; pseudomonads, Ringen and Drake
(1952), Lowbury and Fox (1954); fusobacteria and spirochetes, Parr
(1923), Dudgeon (1926); PPLO, Dienes and Madoff (1953), Nicol and
Edward (1953); candidas, Ashford (1929), Schnoor (1939), Felsenfeld (1944), DiMenna (1954), Reiersöl (1958); *T. glabrata*, DiMenna
(1954). The data for intestinal protozoa in Table 10-2 are taken from
Chap. 8.

Table 10-4 presents the principal findings as reported by H. W. Smith
and Crabb (1961) of a quantitative study of the fecal flora of 10 human
adults and of equal numbers of 10 other animal species. The data were
published after Table 10-2 was assembled and are not included in it.
The studies of man provide quantitative information for *Cl. perfringens*
which was not previously available. Otherwise, the data agree generally
with those in Table 10-2 except for the high values for lactobacilli given
by these workers. It is noted that lactobacilli were identified on plates
incubated in anaerobic jars. In response to a question, H. W. Smith
(1961) offered the impression that these organisms were, in the main,
typical members of the genus, with many different kinds present, not
identified beyond colonial and cellular morphology. These findings suggest the need for further studies of human fecal lactobacilli by modern
taxonomic methods. The additional data in Table 10-4 show striking
differences between host species, differences for which no easy explanation seems at hand. Smith and Crabb remarked on the close resemblance

TABLE 10-4

NUMBERS OF VIABLE BACTERIA FOUND IN THE FECES OF TEN
ADULT ANIMALS OF EACH OF ELEVEN SPECIES
(AFTER SMITH AND CRABB, 1961)

	E. coli	Cl. perfringens	Strepto-cocci	Bacteroides	Lactobacilli[†]
	Logarithm of viable count per Gm feces*				
Cattle	4.3 (1.7–5.8)	2.3 (0–3.3)	5.3 (4.3–6.4)	0 (0)	2.4 (0–5.6)
Sheep	6.5 (5.2–8.0)	4.3 (1.7–5.9)	6.1 (5.0–7.5)	0 (0–6.4)	3.9 (0–5.4)
Horses	4.1 (3.0–5.4)	0 (0–2.3)	6.8 (3.7–8.3)	0 (0–7.4)	7.0 (5.7–8.0)
Guinea pigs	0 (0–2.7)	0 (0–2.3)	0 (0–5.7)	0 (0)	8.2 (7.4–9.3)
Pigs	6.5 (5.2–7.6)	3.6 (2.8–5.7)	6.4 (5.7–8.2)	5.7 (0–8.0)	8.4 (6.0–9.2)
Chickens	6.6 (4.0–7.6)	2.4 (0–4.4)	7.5 (0–8.7)	0 (0–9.0)	8.5 (6.5–9.1)
Rabbits	2.7 (0–6.7)	0 (0)	4.3 (0–5.6)	8.6 (7.3–9.1)	0 (0–6.4)
Dogs	7.5 (6.2–8.9)	8.4 (4.7–9.0)	7.6 (5.7–10.1)	8.7 (6.5–9.6)	4.6 (0–9.0)
Cats	7.6 (5.2–9.0)	7.4 (5.5–9.0)	8.3 (4.1–8.9)	8.9 (8.0–10.0)	8.8 (4.3–10.0)
Mice	6.8 (4.8–8.9)	0 (0–2.6)	7.9 (6.4–8.9)	8.9 (0–10.3)	9.1 (7.8–10.9)
Man	6.7 (5.7–8.5)	3.2 (0–5.9)	5.2 (3.4–9.4)	9.7 (8.3–10.1)	8.8 (7.3–10.0)

* Median values, with range of counts in parentheses for individual animals.
† Counted on Rogosa agar incubated anaerobically in 95% hydrogen and 5% CO_2.

in the variety of fecal bacteria within each host species and on the comparatively small effects of changes in diet—for example, a diet of grass as compared with one consisting mainly of cereal in rabbits, or a change from meat to cereals in dogs. More marked changes occurred in pigs following consumption of large quantities of food after enforced fasting than by altering the composition of the diet. The little we know on this subject reveals the vastness of our ignorance.

The following bacterial groups found elsewhere in the normal flora are *not* known to occur in adult feces: anaerobic micrococci, pneumococci, neisseriae, veillonellae [but see Bishop and Allcock (1960)[4]], actinomycetes (including A. *bifidus*), leptotrichiae, moraxellae, hemo-

[4] H. W. Smith and Crabb (1961) found anaerobic Gram-negative cocci in the feces in 1 of 10 adults.

phili, and anaerobic vibrios. The techniques commonly employed for cultures of feces might well hide the presence of some or all of these groups if they were present in low concentrations. The occurrence of actinomycosis of abdominal origin suggests that *A. israelii*—an elusive bacterium—may not actually be absent; and the presence of other characteristic members of the fusospirochetal flora makes it likely that the even more elusive *Vibrio sputorum* could be disclosed by suitable procedures. Brown and Moore (1960) recovered from the feces of man, rabbit, and horse an anaerobic butyric-acid-producing vibrio (*Butyrivibrio fibrosolvens*) previously found in the bovine rumen (see Chap. 5).

Development of the Fecal Flora. In 1899 Tissier reported that the predominant bacterium in the feces of nursing infants was not a variant of the colon bacillus, as Escherich thought, but a Gram-positive strictly anaerobic bacillus which he isolated and named *Bacillus bifidus communis*. He noted that this organism forms nearly the whole of the normal intestinal flora of nurselings, and that its numbers diminish in diarrhea. In the following year, Tissier (1900) furnished additional details of this organism and described the sequence of bacteriologic events observed by the examination of feces from the time of birth. The initial "aseptic phase" lasts 10 to 20 hours, followed by a "phase of developing infection." Very few organisms were found before the inception of feeding; these were mainly cocci in smears and coliforms in cultures. But after alimentation bacteria increased, becoming most numerous by the third day. Tissier found at this time streptococci, sarcinae, and various rods, including spore-bearers. During an interval of 12 to 24 hours terminating with the end of the fourth day or earlier, a "phase of transformation" leads to the emergence of the bifid bacillus. In breast-fed babies only, there then ensues a "constant phase" during which only *B. bifidus* is seen microscopically, accompanied in cultures by scattered coliforms and enteric streptococci, with other forms, including aerobic lactobacilli, appearing only abnormally. In bottle-fed infants, on the other hand, a mixed flora persists, with *B. bifidus* present but accompanied by yeasts, coliforms, enterococci, aerobic lactobacilli, staphylococci, and other forms with much variation from infant to infant [see also Tissier (1905)].

The general validity of these findings has been confirmed repeatedly, but with interesting quantitative differences. Snyder (1940), who reviewed the earlier literature, found the organism we now call *Actinomyces bifidus* in the feces of 20 of 21 breast-fed infants, in 12 of 19 on supplemented feeding, and in only 12 of 142 weaned infants. In the breast-fed group coliforms and enterococci were frequently but irregularly present, while other forms, such as oral or hemolytic streptococci, staphylococci, diphtheroids, clostridia, aerobic lactobacilli and yeasts, were rare or absent. Except for a slight increase in the incidence of staphylococci and *Cl. perfringens*, the findings in the infants on supplemented feeding were not strikingly different; but in weaned infants there appeared a distinct increase in the prevalence of *Str. mitis* and *Cl. perfringens* as well as the preponderance of coliforms.

Barbero et al. (1952) confirmed the finding that *A. bifidus* accounts for more than 90 per cent of the fecal flora of breast-fed infants, as well as the presence of the same organism in lesser proportions in bottle-fed babies. By intubation at various levels between the sigmoid and the duodenum these workers found that the difference between the 2 groups develops distally to the cecum and is associated with progressively decreasing pH toward the rectum in breast-fed babies. More recently, Gyllenberg and Roine (1957) have found that counts of *A. bifidus* may actually be higher in infants fed cow's milk than in nurselings, and that the principal difference between breast- and bottle-fed infants, associated with low and high fecal pH, respectively, is that in the latter the concentration of other bacteria—enterococci and coliforms—increased disproportionately (see Table 3-2, Chap. 3).

Other findings for infant feces, underlying notations under this head in Table 10-2, are as follows. Sharpe (1952) studied the aerobic fecal flora in 78 specimens from 65 healthy infants, of which 63 were from breast-fed babies, 13 from babies on bottle or supplementary feeding and 2 with feeding of unknown type. Streptococci, which in 94 per cent of infants positive for this group proved to be group D, were recovered from 77.8 per cent of the breast-fed and from 92.3 per cent of the bottle-fed groups, coliforms from 85.7 and 100 per cent, and micrococci from 58.7 and 30.8 per cent, respectively. For rectal carriage of coagulase-positive staphylococci in infants see Moustardier et al. (1956). Digeon and Raynaud (1952) found anaerobic pigmented micrococci frequent in infant feces. Snyder (1940) found a scattering incidence of *Corynebacterium hofmanni* in the feces of both breast-fed and weaned infants but *C. xerosis* appeared in only one of 142 of the weaned group. Additional data on coliforms and other Gram-negative aerobes in infant feces were given by Hall and O'Toole (1934) and by Moustardier, Bentegeat, and LeNoc (1956). The occurrence of pathogenic serotypes of *E. coli* in the feces of infants in nurseries has been reported on by Gamble and Rowson (1957), Gareau et al. (1959), and Cooper et al. (1959). Parr (1923) reported finding spirochetes in the feces of 17.6 per cent of children between the ages of 14 days and 14 years, but not in 33 babies less than 2 weeks old. *Candida albicans* and other yeastlike forms have been found in infant feces by Moustardier et al. (1956) and by Serpa (1957).

H. W. Smith and Crabb (1961) in the paper referred to above, also presented findings on the fecal flora of a baby examined repeatedly from the second day to the end of the first year of life, and on 4 other infants during the first 4 to 9 days after birth. The data were compared with findings for the fecal flora of newborn calves, lambs, piglets, and rabbits. As in the studies of adults given above (Table 10-4), lactobacilli, recovered anaerobically, were prominent; they showed no clear relationship to breast feeding. A striking finding was a tendency, evidenced especially by *Cl. perfringens*, to appear in high concentrations during the first few days and then diminish, in the instance of this bacterium often to zero, over the course of a few weeks. A more gradual reduction in concentration of *E. coli* was "a general feature of ageing" during the first few months of life in all the animal host species studied including the baby; and a similar but less consistent trend appeared among the fecal streptococci. Feces of the baby, but not that of any of the animal subjects, showed *Staph. aureus* in 24 of 58 examinations in concentrations of 10^3 to 10^6 per Gm.

The Genitourinary Tract

The writer has seen no recent studies of the biota of the *external genitalia*. Smegma from the preputial sac or the clitoris has been found to contain *Mycobacterium smegmatis* [Alvarez and Tavel (1885)], and in smears has shown large and small spirochetes and fusiform bacilli from both sexes and, from women, in addition, various cocci, Gram-negative bacilli, Gram-positive rods including diphtheroids, and yeasts [Pilot and Kanter (1923)]. It is probable that microbes found in endogenous infections of the deeper genital tract are among the flora of the vulva; namely, bacteriodes [Hallé (1898); Harris and Brown (1927)], including *B. nigrescens* [Patocka and Sebek (1947)], and anaerobic streptococci [Colebrook (1930, 1931); Schwarz and Brown (1936)]. Carter et al. (1959) recovered several species of *Candida* from the vulva, and Rieth (1958) found *Torulopsis glabrata* commonly in clinical specimens from both vulva and vagina. Urethral as well as vaginal organisms would be expected in this area, including the more pathogenic urethral forms that seem to be derived from the rectum. The data of Patocka and Sebek (1947, 1948), seen by the writer only in abstracts, suggest a vulval anaerobic flora (said to be vaginal) similar to that of the mouth, with veillonellae, vibrios, leptotrichiae, and *Fusobacterium girans* as well as spirochetes of both *T. dentium* (*T. minutum*) and *T. refringens* types, bacteroides, and various streptococci, among other forms [see also Wegelius (1909) and Küster (1929)].

A pattern of development of the biota of the *vagina* is associated with maturation, the deposition of glycogen in the vaginal epithelium, and the presence of a comparatively simple group of actively acidogenic and aciduric microorganisms. The microorganism most directly involved in acidogenesis, and hence most characteristic of the healthy adult vaginal flora, has long been identified as the aerobic lactobacillus described in 1892 by Döderlein (see Chap. 3); but the true picture may not be quite so simple. Miura (1928) noted a relationship between ovarian function and the occurrence of vaginal glycogen. Cruickshank and Sharman (1934) reported that glycogen, associated with a deep, many-layered epithelium, is demonstrable in the fetal vagina, in infants up to the third or fourth week of life, and in women during the reproductive period. Glycogen is absent before puberty and absent or scanty following menopause. These workers found that Döderlein's bacillus appears in the vagina soon after birth and remains associated with the presence of glycogen in the wall and with a simple vaginal flora and a highly acid secretion. After the first month of life the vaginal flora is more varied but remains sparse, and the scanty secretion is alkaline. At puberty a sudden reversion occurs to the simple aciduric flora (largely bacilli and candidas) and highly acid secretion, which persists in health until the menopause, when a sparse varied flora and scanty alkaline secretion return.

Cruickshank (1934) found that lactobacilli isolated from the vagina were able to ferment glycogen with production of lactic acid. He and Sharman (1934) suggested that the acidity of the secretion in vivo reaches a sufficient concentration to permit only acid-resistant bacteria such as Döderlein's bacillus to survive and multiply, and that the consequent inhibition of "foreign and possibly harmful bacteria" constitutes a defense mechanism in the vagina. Much evidence for this view has accumulated and it has come to be generally accepted [see Rosebury (1944c); Laughton (1948)]. Pérez-Miravete and López (1958) reported that Döderlein's bacillus inhibits E. coli at pH 5 and Str. faecalis at pH 4.5.

Hardy (1941) found the vaginal canal at birth packed with desquamated glycogen-filled epithelial cells. The pH of a suspension of these cells was less than 5.0. Bacteria appeared as early as the twelfth hour, with Gram-positive cocci at first, followed by a great profusion and variety gradually diminishing after the second week, and reaching the phase of scanty flora with only traces of glycogen and a pH of about 7 after the first year. In a group of 129 infants including clinic and hospital patients and premature infants, all with nonpurulent vaginal secretions (with leukocytes rare or absent in smears), Hardy found, in decreasing order of percentage incidence, diphtheroids (60 per cent), white staphylococci (60), γ streptococci (50), E. coli (36), and Döderlein's bacillus, yeasts and Gram-negative cocci (each 22), with a scattering of other Gram-negative bacilli and other forms. In a study of aerobic blood agar cultures of the vagina of 46 older children, aged 14 months to 11 years, Pettit and Hitchcock (1933) also found diphtheroids predominant; streptococci—γ, α, a few enterococci and occasional hemolytic forms— were more numerous than staphylococci, most of which were *Staph. albus; E. coli* appeared in 10 of 60 cultures and a scattering of neisseriae and proteus were found, but no lactobacilli.

In a study of the vaginal flora of 114 pregnant women and 100 gynecologic patients, all apparently free from inflammatory disease, Carter and Jones (1937) again found diphtheroids predominant, occurring in 70 to 74 per cent of the subjects. Döderlein's bacillus occurred in 49 and 73 per cent of the obstetric subjects and in 22 and 36 per cent of the gynecologic subjects, and yeasts in only 36 and 21 of the first and in 14 per cent of the second. The following appeared in the percentage frequency given: *Staph. albus*, 48 to 78; anaerobic streptococci, 30 to 54; γ streptococci, 20 to 44; and α streptococci, 8 to 12. Hite, Hesseltine, and Goldstein (1957) reported a study in which both aerobic and anaerobic cultures were made of a group that included 61 normal prenatal vaginal samples. In this group the commonest organisms were aciduric rods, found in 63.9 per cent; and in decreasing order of percentage frequency, diphtheroid rods, 44.2; *Staph. albus*, 34.4; candidas, 22.9; α streptococci, 16.4; γ streptococci, 14.7; anaerobic streptococci, 11.5; *Staph. aureus*, 6.5; and lower percentages of coliforms and other cocci. These workers noted the absence of bacteroides or fusiforms in the normal vagina, although they found these organisms in disease and in the normal postpartum uterus.

The nature of Döderlein's lactobacillus, long associated vaguely with *Lactobacillus acidophilus* (see Chap. 3) has been clarified by recent studies. Hunter, Long, and Schumacher (1959) found the vaginal lactobacilli heterogeneous. Rogosa and Sharpe (1960) examined 35 strains of lactobacilli from the vagina of 21 normal nonpregnant women aged 21 to 40 and found about 25 per cent heterofermentative, including *L. fermenti* and *L. cellobiosus*. A variety of *L. casei* was also found; but 14 of 21 isolates studied in detail were *L. acidophilus*, and glycogen fermentation was observed as a variable character only in the last species.

That the source of vaginal acidity may be less simple than has been thought is also implied by the findings of Laughton (1950), who observed that some of the aerobic corynebacteria of the vagina are actively acidogenic and suggested that they may contribute to the high vaginal acidity of adult women before menopause, "as Corynebacteria appear to be commonly present, and even more frequent than Döderlein's vaginal bacillus." In an earlier study of 39 women in a fertility clinic [Laughton (1948)], lactobacilli were found more often and in greater proportion when the vaginal pH was lowest (4.4 to 4.6); diphtheroids were more uniformly present and more numerous at intermediate pH levels (5.6 to 6.2), while both lactobacilli and diphtheroids tended to be absent or scarce, and other bacteria to be numerous, at higher pH levels (6.8 to 7.8). In a few instances, however, lactobacilli were found in profusion in the presence of a vaginal pH level as high as 6.9 to 7.6.

The following additional data on the vaginal biota are noted in Table 10-2: Pérez-Miravete, Poujol, and Calderón (1959) and Bret et al. (1959) have found *Staph. aureus* in 14.9 and 15 per cent, respectively, the latter in 300 pregnant women. Gram-positive anaerobic micrococci were found in the vagina by Hite, Hesseltine, and Goldstein (1947), and strains of these organisms recovered from the vagina were described by Hare et al. (1952). Veillonellae have been recovered from the vagina by Hite et al. (1945), Trussell (1947), and Patocka and Sebek (1947). Hardy (1941) found group A hemolytic streptococci in the vagina in 2 of 129 instances among children. Hite and Hesseltine (1947) failed to find group A strains among 16 hemolytic streptococcal cultures mainly isolated from vaginitis in adults and from postpartum uteri under either normal or pathologic conditions. *Actinomyces bifidus* was recovered from the maternal vagina in 5 of 10 instances by Montagna and Cataldi (1944) and by Harrison et al. (1953), who reviewed earlier literature on this point. Leptotrichiae, regarded as different from those of the mouth, were found rarely in the vagina by Patocka and Sebek (1947). Both species of *Mima* were isolated by DeBord (1942) from the normal vagina, apparently before puberty. *H. influenzae* was reported in the vagina of 2 of 129 children by Hardy (1941). *H. vaginalis* has been found in the vagina apart from disease by Heltai (1959, 1960). The occurrence of anaerobic vibrios in the vagina was noted by Curtis (1913), Patocka and Sebek (1947), and Moore (1954). Salaman (1945) and Salaman et al. (1946) have reported on PPLO in the vagina. For *Candida* species see especially Jones and Martin (1938) and Halde and Aragon (1956); see also Bret et al. (1958), and Carter et al. (1959). Rieth (1958) reported that *Torulopsis glabrata* is commonly present in the vagina. *Trichomonas vaginalis* and *Candida albicans* have been found by Feo (1953) to survive in the presence of Döderlein's bacillus and the 3 forms may be found together in the vagina.

That the flora of the *anterior urethra*, as indicated principally in urine cultures, is evidently the same in men and women suggests that the area may be inhabited by a normal flora, and that the microbes found are not necessarily contaminants from skin, vulva, or rectum. Coagulase-negative staphylococci appear to be found most frequently, alone or with enterococci or α streptococci [Philpot (1956); see also

Shackman and Massent (1954); Merritt and Sanford (1958)]. On the other hand, *Staph. albus* is found in urinary tract infections less commonly than coliforms or proteus [Gillespie et al. (1960); see also Kass and Finland (1956)]. Shackman and Massent (1954) regarded the normal flora of the male urethra as consisting of staphylococci, enterococci, diphtheroids, coliforms, viridans streptococci, and proteus. They found midstream urine specimens sterile in 8 of 18 cases and recovered *E. coli* 4 times, *Staph. aureus* 3 times, *Staph. albus* and *Str. faecalis* each 2 times, and coliforms, diphtheroids, and other organisms each once. The results reported by O'Sullivan et al. (1961) were generally similar. Merritt and Sanford (1958) studied both clean-voided and catheterized samples from hospitalized women and recovered *E. coli* in 26 of 29 sets, *Staph. albus* in 10, proteus in 3, *Str. faecalis* and pseudomonads each in 2, and *Staph. aureus* in 1. Of 19 cases in which the total aerobic count in the catheterized specimen was less than 10^5 per ml, *Staph. albus* was found in 4, *E. coli* in 3, and proteus in 2; the other 10 showed no growth. In this series, *Str. faecalis, Ps. aeruginosa,* and *Staph. aureus* were recovered only when the count was high, while in most instances the presence of *E. coli* was also related to a high count. Kaitz and Williams (1960) found that all 53 of their group of 309 patients (17.2 per cent) who had bacteruria (defined as more than 10^5 "pathogens" per ml) showed Gram-negative bacilli; *E. coli* in 24, *K. aerogenes* in 8, proteus in 9, unidentified forms in 8 and mixed forms in 6. They considered *Staph. albus* nonpathogenic, and did not find *Staph. aureus.* Data for babies [James (1959)] and older children [Pryles et al. (1959); Straffon and Engel (1960)] are similar to those for adults.

Also found in urine under conditions presumed normal: neisseriae [Kass and Finland (1956)]; both moraxellae and mimae [Henriksen (1947); Brooke (1951); Philpot (1956)]; *Haemophilus vaginalis* [pathologically, Leopold (1953)]; PPLO [Beveridge (1943); Salaman et al. (1946); Freundt (1956)]; and candidas and *Torulopsis glabrata* [probably pathologic, Guze and Haley (1958)].

The Indigenous Biota in General

The hypothesis toward which the data in this chapter and, indeed, the material of this book as a whole, seems to point is that of a degree of unity of the microbiota of man which makes it possible to speak of it as one thing. The data are very incomplete, and the hypothesis will be useful if it stimulates attempts to fill the gaps in our knowledge. It may be suggested that the areas of the healthy human body that are inhabited by microorganisms present four kinds of environment for microbic growth: (1) extraneous pabulum is present in massive amounts and tends to favor the overgrowth of saprophytes (the lower intestine); (2) pabulum is relatively abundant, enriched by either or both extraneous material (ingested food residues) or accumulated cell debris, and crypts or recesses encourage anaerobic growth (the mouth, the oropharynx, and the female genitalia); (3) the conditions of the preceding areas diminish toward zero (other mucous membrane areas); and (4) a lower moisture content and a higher concentration of lipids tend to encourage or select somewhat different microorganisms (the skin).

These conditions are, of course, modified by differences in degree of exposure to contamination (which is lower, for example, in the eye than in the mouth or the nose), in ventilation (compare nose and intestinal tract), perhaps in the kinds and relative significance of host defensive mechanisms, and doubtless in other respects as well. But the selection of microbic immigrants that arrive at the body's portals from the outside world will tend toward uniformity for all areas—the seed is qualitatively although not quantitatively the same throughout. And differences in living conditions are actually superimposed on a basic uniformity of host tissue; the soil is also the same under its differences. Hence, it is reasonable to expect the data to point, as they seem to do, toward a general uniformity of the microbiota with diversity of detail. This idea provides a basis for examining the host-biota relationship as an aspect of physiology.

References

Alvarez and Tavel, 1885, *Arch. Physiol. Norm. Pathol.*, **6**:303.

Anderson, C. M., and Langford, R. F., 1958, *Brit. Med. J.*, **1**:803.

Arkwright, J. A., 1907, *J. Hyg.*, **7**:145.

Ashford, B. K., 1929, *J. Am. Med. Assoc.*, **93**:762.

Bachrach, U., Gurevitch, J., Landau, J., and Birnbaum, D., 1953, *Acta Med. Orient.*, **12**:10 (*Biol. Abstr.*).

Barbero, G. J., Runge, G., Fischer, D., Crawford, M. N., Torres, F. E., and György, P., 1952, *J. Pediat.*, **40**:152.

Beeson, P. B., 1958, cited by Rengarts (1960).

Benham, R. W., and Hopkins, A. McH., 1933, *Arch. Dermatol. Syphilol.*, **28**:532.

Berens, C., and Chapman, G. H., 1944, *J. Bacteriol.*, **47**:473.

Berger, U., 1958, *Die Treponemen der Mundhöhle und ihre Bedeutung für die Pathogenese der oralen Fusospirochätosen*, J. A. Barth, Leipzig.

————, 1959, *Z. Hyg.*, **145**:564.

Beust, T. B., 1908, *Dental Cosmos*, **50**:594.

Beveridge, W. I. B., 1943, *Med. J. Australia*, **2**:479.

Bezjak, V. 1958, *Acta Med. Yugoslav.*, **12**:270 (*Biol. Abstr.*).

Bishop, R. F., and Allcock, E. A., 1960, *Brit. Med. J.*, **1**:766.

Bisset, K. A., and Davis, G. H. G., 1960, *The Microbial Flora of the Mouth*, Heywood and Company, London.

Bradel, S. F., and Blayney, J. R., 1940, *J. Am. Dental Assoc.*, **27**:1601.

Braïlovsky-Lounkevitch, Z. A., 1915, *Ann. Inst. Pasteur*, **29**:379.
Branham, S. E., 1928, *J. Inf. Dis.*, **42**:230.
Bret, J., Coupé, C., Sollé, R., and Marchand, H., 1958, *Presse Méd.*, **66**:937.
———, ———, Pillet, J., Sollé, R., and Marchand, H., 1959, *ibid.*, **67**:216.
Brooke, M. S., 1951, *Acta Pathol. Microbiol. Scand.*, **28**:338.
Brown, D. W., and Moore, W. E. C., 1960, *J. Dairy Sci.*, **43**:1570.
Brumfitt, W., O'Grady, F., and Slater, J. D. H., 1959, *Lancet*, **2**:419.
Brygoo, E.-R., 1952, *Ann. Inst. Pasteur*, **83**:818.
Burdon, K. L., 1928, *J. Inf. Dis.*, **42**:161.
Burky, E. L., and Smillie, W. G., 1929, *J. Exptl. Med.*, **50**:643.
Carter, B., and Jones, C. P. 1937, *Southern Med. J.*, **30**:298.
———, ———, Creadick, R. N., Parker, R. T., and Turner, V., 1959, *Ann N.Y. Acad. Sci.*, **83**:265.
Cason, L., and Winkler, C. H., 1954, *A.M.A. Arch. Ophthalmol.*, **51**:196.
Chang, J. C. C., and Foltz, V. D., 1960, *J. Dental Research*, **39**:1120.
Clabaugh, G. F., Rhoads, P. S., and Adair, D. M., 1960, *Quart. Bull. Northwestern Univ. Med. School*, **34**:119 (*Biol. Abstr.*).
Clarke, B. G., and Joress, S., 1960, *J. Am. Med. Assoc.*, **174**:1593.
Colebrook, L., 1930, *Brit. Med. J.*, **2**:134.
———, 1931, *ibid.*, **2**:777.
Commission on Acute Respiratory Diseases, 1949, *Am. J. Hyg.*, **50**:331.
Cooper, M. L., Keller, H. M., Walters, E. W., Partin, J. C., and Boyle, D. E., 1959, *A.M.A. J. Diseases Children*, **97**:255.
Cornelison, J. L., Johnson, E. A., and Fisher, W. M., 1946, *Am. J. Obstet. Gynecol.*, **52**:797.
Cornfeld, D., and Hubbard, J. P., 1961a, *New Engl. J. Med.*, **264**:211.
———, ———, Harris, T. N., and Weaver, R., 1961b, *Am. J. Public Health*, **51**:242.
Cregan, J., Dunlop, E. E., and Hayward, N. J., 1953, *Brit. Med. J.*, **2**:1248.
———, and Hayward, N. J., 1953, *ibid.*, **1**:1356.
Croft, C. C., and Black, L. A., 1938, *J. Lab. Clin. Med.*, **23**:1259.
Cruickshank, J., and Cruickshank, R., 1931, in *A System of Bacteriology in Relation to Medicine* (*London*), **8**:334.
Cruickshank, R., 1934, *J. Pathol. Bacteriol.*, **39**:213.
———, and Sharman, A., 1934, *J. Obstet. Gynecol.*, **41**:190, 208.
Curtis, A. H., 1913, *J. Inf. Dis.*, **12**:165.
Dack, G. M., and Petran, E., 1934, *ibid.*, **54**:204.
Dale, A. C., Rosenthal, E., Bortnick, L. S., Axelsson, G. and Macdonald, J. B., 1961, *J. Dental Research*, **40**:716.
DeBord, G. C., 1942, *Iowa State Coll. J. Sci.*, **16**:471.
———, 1943, *J. Lab. Clin. Med.*, **28**:710.
Dienes, L., Ropes, M. W., Smith, W. E., Madoff, S., and Bauer, W., 1948, *New Engl. J. Med.*, **238**:509, 563.
———, and Madoff, S., 1953, *Proc. Soc. Exptl. Biol. Med.*, **82**:36.
Digeon, M., and Raynaud, M., 1952, *Ann. Inst. Pasteur*, **82**:362.
DiMenna, M. E., 1954, *J. Pathol. Bacteriol.*, **68**:89.
Dixon, J. M. S., 1960, *ibid.*, **79**:131.
Döderlein, A., 1892, *Das Scheidensekret und seine Bedeutung für das Puerperalfieber*, E. Besold, Leipsig.
Douglas, H. C., 1950, *J. Dental Research*, **29**:304.
Downing, J. G., Nye, R. N., and Cousins, S. M., 1937, *Arch. Dermatol. Syphilol.*, **35**:1087.

Dudgeon, L. S., 1926, *J. Hyg.*, **25**:119.
Duguid, J. P., 1946, *Brit. Med. J.*, **1**:265.
Duncan, I. B. R., Goudie, J. G., Mackie, L. M. and Howie, J. W., 1954, *J. Pathol. Bacteriol.*, **67**:282.
Eggerth, A. H., and Gagnon, B. H., 1933, *J. Bacteriol.*, **25**:389.
Elmes, P. C., Dutton, A. A. C., and Fletcher, C. M., 1959, *Lancet* **1**:1241.
Emmons, C. W., 1938, *Public Health Repts.*, **53**:1967.
———, 1940, *ibid.*, **55**:1306.
Evans, C. A., Smith, W. M., Johnston, E. A., and Giblett, E. R., 1950, *J. Invest. Dermatol.*, **15**:305.
Farrer, S. M., Russo, R., Bavara, C., and Werthamer, S., 1959, *J. Am. Med. Assoc.*, **171**:1072.
Felsenfeld, O., 1944, *Am. J. Med. Sci.*, **207**:60.
Feo, L. G., 1953, *Am. J. Obstet. Gynecol.*, **65**:1330.
Ferguson, W. W., and Roberts, L. F., 1950, *J. Bacteriol.*, **59**:171.
Flandin, C., and Duchon, L., 1938, *Bull. Soc. Française Dermatol. Syphilis.*, No. 6, p. 893 (abstr., 1939, *Bull. Inst. Pasteur*, **37**:505).
Fleming, A., 1909, *Lancet*, **1**:1035.
———, and Maclean, I. H., 1930, *Brit. J. Exptl. Pathol.*, **11**:127.
Foubert, E. L., Jr., and Douglas, H. C., 1948, *J. Bacteriol.*, **56**:25.
Fox, E. C., and Ainsworth, G. C., 1958, *Brit. Med. J.*, **2**:826.
Freundt, E. A., 1956, *Brit. J. Venereal Diseases*, **32**:188.
Gamble, D. R., and Rowson, K. E. K., 1957, *Lancet*, **2**:619.
Gareau, F. E., Mackel, D. C., Boring, J. R. III, Payne, F. J., and Hammett, F. L., 1959, *J. Pediat.*, **54**:313.
Garrod, L. P., 1928, *Brit. J. Exptl. Pathol.*, **9**:155.
Gillespie, E. H., Devenish, E. A., and Cowan, S. T., 1939, *Lancet*, **2**:870.
Gillespie, W. A., Linton, K. B., Miller, A., and Slade, N., 1960, *J. Clin. Pathol.*, **13**:187.
Gordon, M. A., 1951, *J. Invest. Dermatol.*, **17**:267.
———, 1951, *Mycologia*, **43**:524.
Goudie, J. G., and Duncan, I. B. R., 1956, *J. Pathol. Bacteriol.*, **72**:381.
Grubb, T. C., and Puetzer, B., 1947, *J. Lab. Clin. Med.*, **32**:566.
Guillemot, L. J. B., 1898, *Recherches sur la gangrène pulmonaire*, Thèse de Paris, G. Steinheil, Paris.
———, Hallé, J., and Rist, E., 1904, *Arch. Méd. Expér. et Anat. Pathol.*, **16**:571, 677.
Gundel, M., and Schwarz, F. K. T., 1932, *Z. Hyg.*, **113**:411.
Guze, L. B., and Haley, L. D., 1958, *Yale J. Biol. Med.*, **30**:292.
Gyllenberg, H., and Roine, 1957, *Acta Pathol. Microbiol, Scand.*, **41**:144.
Halde, C., and Aragon, G. T., 1956, *Am. J. Obstet. Gynecol.*, **72**:363.
Hall, I. C., and O'Toole, E., 1934, *Am. J. Diseases Children*, **47**:1279.
Hallé, J., 1898, *Recherches sur la bactériologie du canal génital de la femme*, Thesis, Paris, cited by Hite et al. (1945).
Hamburger, M., Jr., 1944*a*, *J. Inf. Dis.*, **75**:58.
———, 1944*b*, *ibid.*, **75**:71.
———, 1944*c*, *ibid.*, **75**:79.
———, Green, M. J., and Hamburger, V. G., 1945, *ibid.*, **77**:68, 96.
Hancock, J. C., Jr., Dulaney, A. D., and Caldwell, M. G., 1959, *Southern Med. J.*, **52**:1525.
Hardy, A. V., Mitchell, R. B., Schreiber, M., Hoffert, W. R., Yawn, E., and Young, F., 1954, *Laryngoscope*, **64**:1020.

Hardy, G. C., 1941, *Am. J. Diseases Children*, **62**:939.

Hare, R., Wildy, P., Billett, F. S., and Twort, D. N., 1952, *J. Hyg.*, **50**:295.

Harris, J. W., and Brown, J. H., 1927, *Bull. Johns Hopkins Hosp.*, **40**: 203.

Harrison, R. W., and Opal, Z. Z., 1940, *J. Dental Research*, **28**:1.

Harrison, W., Stahl, R. C., Magavran, J., Sanders, M., Norris, R. F., and György, P., 1953, *Am. J. Obstet. Gynecol.*, **65**:352.

Harvey, H. S., and Dunlap, M. B., 1960, *New Engl. J. Med.*, **262**:976.

————, and ————, 1961, *ibid.*, **264**:684.

Helmholz, H. F., 1950, *J. Urol.*, **64**:158.

Heltai, A., 1959, *Ann. N.Y. Acad. Sci.*, **83**:290.

————, 1960, *Gynaecologia*, **149** (Suppl. 3/4):80.

Hemmens, E. S., Blayney, J. R., and Harrison, R. W., 1941, *J. Dental Research*, **20**:29.

Henriksen, S. D., 1947, *Acta Pathol. Microbiol. Scand.*, **24**:184.

————, 1952, *J. Gen. Microbiol.*, **6**:318.

————, 1958, *Acta Pathol. Microbiol. Scand.*, **43**:157.

Herzog, V. H., and Schild, C. A., 1953, *Helv. Med. Acta*, **20**:375.

Hite, K. E., and Hesseltine, H. C., 1947, *J. Inf. Dis.*, **80**:105.

————, ————, and Goldstein, L., 1947, *Am. J. Obstet. Gynecol.* **53**:233.

Huet, M., 1957, *Arch. Inst. Pasteur Tunis*, **35**:55 (*Biol. Abstr.*).

Hugh, R., Klopp, C. T., and Ryschenkow, E., 1959, *Med. Ann. Dist. Columbia*, **28**:61.

Hunter, C. A., Jr., Long, K. R., and Schumacher, R. D., 1959, *Ann. N.Y. Acad. Sci.*, **83**:217.

Hurst, V., 1960, *Pediatrics*, **25**:11.

Jacobson, L. O., and Dick, G. F., 1941, *J. Am. Med. Assoc.*, **117**:2222.

James, U., 1959, *Lancet*, **2**:1001.

Jennison, M. W., 1942, in *Aerobiology*, A. A. A. S. Publ. No. 17, p. 106.

Jones, C. P., and Martin, D. S., 1938, *Am. J. Obstet. Gynecol.*, **35**:98.

Jones, M., 1960, *Arch. Otolaryngol.*, **72**:329.

Jordan, H. V., Fitzgerald, R. J., and Faber, J. E. Jr., 1956, *J. Dental Research*, **35**:404.

Kaitz, A. L., and Williams, E. J., 1960, *New Engl. J. Med.*, **262**:425.

Kaplan, S. M., Larkin, B., and Hotz, R., 1957, *J. Lab. Clin. Med.*, **50**:330.

Kass, E. H., and Finland, M., 1956, *Trans. Assoc. Am. Physicians*, **69**:56.

Kerrin, J. C., 1928, *Brit. J. Exptl. Pathol.*, **9**:69.

Khorazo, D., and Thompson, R., 1935, *Am. J. Ophthalmol.*, **18**:1114.

Kligler, I. J., 1915, *J. Allied Dental Soc.*, **10**:141, 282, 445.

Kortekangas, A. E., 1959, *Acta Oto-Laryngol.*, Suppl. 150.

Kostečka, F., 1924, *Dental Cosmos*, **66**:927.

Kraus, F. W., and Gaston, C., 1956, *J. Bacteriol.*, **71**:703.

Küster, E., 1929, in Kolle, W., Kraus, R., and Uhlenhuth, P., *Kolle und Wassermann Handbuch der pathogenen Mikroorganismen*, Gustav Fischer, Jena, **6**:366, 372.

Landau, J., Bachrach, U., and Gurevitch, J., 1953, *Acta Med. Orient.*, **13**: 226 (*Biol. Abstr.*).

Laughton, N., 1948, *J. Obstet. Gynecol.*, **55**:608.

————, 1950, *J. Hyg.*, **48**:346.

Lees, A. W., and McNaught, W., 1959, *Lancet*, **2**:1112.

Lemierre, A., 1936, *ibid.*, **1**:701.

————, Reilly, J., and Laporte, A., 1938, *Ann. de Méd.*, **44**:165 (abstr., 1939, *Bull. Inst. Pasteur*, **37**:729).

Leopold, S., 1953, *U.S. Armed Forces Med. J.*, **4**:263.

Lewis, C. J., and Turner, A. L., 1905, *Edinburgh Med. J.*, **18**:393.

Lewkowics, X., 1901, *Arch. Méd. Expér. et Anat. Pathol.*, **13**:633.

Lilienthal, B., 1950, *Australian J. Exptl. Biol. Med. Sci.*, **28**:279.

Lissauer, 1906, *Arch. Hyg.*, **58**:145, cited by Lusk, G., 1928, *The Elements of the Science of Nutrition*, 4th ed., W. B. Saunders Company, Philadelphia.

Loh, W.-P., and Bagley, E. P., 1956, *Am. J. Med. Technol.*, **22**:184.

————, and Baker, E. E., 1955, *A.M.A. Arch. Internal Med.*, **95**:74.

Lord, F. T., 1910, *J. Am. Med. Assoc.*, **55**:1261.

Lovell, D. L., 1945, *Surg. Gynecol. Obstet.*, **80**:174.

Lowbury, E. J. L., and Fox, J., 1954, *J. Hyg.*, **52**:403.

Marotta, U., 1953, *Rend. Ist. Super. Sanità*, **16**:236 (*Biol. Abstr.*).

Marples, M. J., 1960, *Trans. Roy. Soc. Trop. Med. Hyg.*, **54**:166.

Massler, M., and Macdonald, J. B., 1950, *J. Dental Research*, **29**:43.

Masters, P. L., Brumfitt, W., Mendez, R. L., and Likar, M., 1958, *Brit. Med. J.*, **1**:1200.

Merritt, A. D., and Sanford, J. P., 1958, *J. Lab. Clin. Med.*, **52**:463.

Miles, A. A., Williams, R. E. O., and Clayton-Cooper, B., 1940, *J. Pathol. Bacteriol.*, **56**:513.

Mills, K. C., Shibley, G. S., and Dochez, A. R., 1928, *J. Exptl. Med.*, **47**:193.

Misra, S. S., 1938, *J. Pathol. Bacteriol.*, **46**:204.

Miura, H., 1928, *Mitt. med. Akad. Kioto*, **2**:1, cited by Laughton (1948).

Montagna, C. P., and Cataldi, M. S., 1944, *Rev. Assoc. Argent. Dietol.*, **2**:47.

Monzon, O. T., Ory, E. M., Dobson, H. L., Carter, E., and Yow, E. M. 1958, *New Engl. J. Med.*, **259**:764.

Moore, B., 1954, *J. Pathol. Bacteriol.*, **67**:461.

Morton, H. E., Smith, P. F., and Keller, R., 1952, *Am. J. Public Health*, **42**:913.

Moscovici, C., and Maisel, J., 1961, *Am. J. Diseases Children*, **101**:771.

Moustardier, G., Bentegeat, J., and LeNoc, P., 1956, *Ann. Inst. Pasteur*, **90**:489.

Nadel, H., and Gardner, F. H., 1956, *Am. J. Trop. Med. Hyg.*, **5**:686.

Neumann, R. O., 1902, *Z. Hyg.*, **40**:33.

Nicol, C. S., and Edward, D. G., 1953, *Brit. J. Venereal Diseases*, **29**:141.

Noble, W. C., Jr., Fisher, E. A., and Brainard, D. H., 1928, *J. Prev. Med.*, **2**:105.

Nolte, W. A., and Swineford, L. R., 1957, *Prepr. Abstr. Intern. Assoc. Dental Research*, no. 120.

Oeding, P., 1946, *Acta Pathol. Microbiol. Scand.*, **23**:271.

Olitsky, P. K., and Gates, F. L., 1921, *J. Exptl. Med.*, **33**:713.

————, and ————, 1922a, *ibid.*, **35**:813.

————, and ————, 1922b, *ibid.*, **36**:501.

————, and ————, 1923, *Science*, **57**:159.

————, and McCartney, J. E., 1923, *J. Exptl. Med.*, **38**:427.

Oliver, W. W., and Wherry, W. B., 1921, *J. Inf. Dis.*, **28**:341.

Orfila, J., and Courden, B., 1960, *Ann. Inst. Pasteur*, **99**:929.

Orskov, I., 1955, *Acta Pathol. Microbiol. Scand.*, **36**:461.

Oshima, 1906, *Arch. Kinderheilk.*, **45**:21, cited by Kligler (1915).

O'Sullivan, D. J., FitzGerald, M. G., Meynell, M. J., and Malins, J. M., 1961, *Brit. Med. J.*, 1:786.

Pachtman, E. A., Vicher, E. E., and Brunner, M. J., 1954, *J. Invest. Dermatol.*, 22:389.

Pannarale, M. R., and Huet, M., 1959, *Arch. Inst. Pasteur Tunis*, 36:53 (*Biol. Abstr.*).

Park, W. H., Williams, A. W., and Krumwiede, C., 1921, *J. Immunol.*, 6:1.

Parr, L. W., 1923, *J. Inf. Dis.*, 33:369.

Patočka, F., and Šebek, V., 1947, *Ceskoslov. Gynaekol.*, 12:24 (*Biol. Abstr.*).

————, and ————, 1948, *Časopis Lékařů Ceských*, 87:99 (*Biol. Abstr.*).

Pejrone, G. M., 1935, *Dental Cosmos*, 77:800.

Perekhozheva, M. N., and Kalshteyn, L. I., 1956, *Trudy Stalinabad. Med. Inst.*, 18:75 (*Biol. Abstr.*).

Pérez-Miravete, A., and López, J. C., 1958, *Rev. Latinoamer. Microbiol.*, 1:267 (*Biol. Abstr.*).

————, Poujol, E., and Calderón, Y., 1959, *ibid.*, 2:15 (*Biol. Abstr.*).

Perry, E. T., and Nichols, A. C., 1956, *J. Invest. Dermatol.*. 27:165.

Pettit, H., and Hitchcock, G. H., 1933, *J. Inf. Dis.*, 53:372.

Philpot, V. B., Jr., 1956, *J. Urol.*, 75:562.

Piéchaud, D., Piéchaud, M., and Second, L., 1951, *Ann. Inst. Pasteur*, 80:97.

Pillsbury, D. M., and Rebell, G., 1952, *J. Invest. Dermatol.*, 18:173.

Pilot, I., and Brams, J., 1923, *J. Inf. Dis.*, 32:134.

————, and Kanter, A. E., 1923, *ibid.*, 32:204.

Pittman, M., and Davis, D. J., 1950, *J. Bacteriol.*, 59:413.

Podbielskij, A., 1890, Dissertation, Kazan. Abstr., 1891, *Zentr. Bakteriol. Parasitenk.*, *I Orig.*, 9:617.

Pollock, M. R., Wainwright, S. D., and Manson, E. E. D., 1949, *J. Pathol. Bacteriol.*, 61:274.

Pratt, J. S., 1927, *J. Inf. Dis.*, 41:461.

Price, P. B., 1938, *ibid.*, 63:301.

Pryles, C. V., Akin, M. D., Morse, T. S., and Welch, K. J., 1959, *Pediatrics*, 24:983.

Quinn, R. W., Denny, F. W., and Riley, H. D., 1957, *Am. J. Public Health*, 47:995.

————, and Martin, M. P., 1961, *Am. J. Hyg.*, 73:193.

Rajkovic, A., 1959, *Higijena*, 11:26 (*Biol. Abstr.*).

Rebell, G. C., 1947, *J. Invest. Dermatol.*, 8:13.

Reiersöl, S., 1958, *Antonie van Leeuwenhoek J. Microbiol. Serol.*, 24:23.

Rengarts, R. T., 1960, *Am. J. Med. Sci.*, 239:159.

Richardson, R. L., and Jones, M., 1958, *J. Dental Research*, 37:697.

Riddell, M. I., Morton, H. S., and Murray, E. G. D., 1953, *Am. J. Med. Sci.*, 225:535.

Ridley, M., 1959, *Brit. Med. J.*, 1:270.

Rieth, H., 1958, *Archiv. klin. exp. Dermatol.*, 207:413.

Ringen, L. M., and Drake, C. H., 1952, *J. Bacteriol.*, 64:841.

Rodaniche, E. C., Palmer, W. L., and Kirsner, J. B., 1943, *J. Inf. Dis.*, 72:222.

Rogosa, M., 1956, *J. Bacteriol.*, 72:533.

————, and Sharpe, M. E., 1960, *J. Gen. Microbiol.*, 23:197.

Rosebury, T., 1944a, *Medicine*, 23:249.

————, 1944b, Bacteriol. Revs.. 8:189.

————, 1944c, Arch. Pathol., 38:413.

————, and Sonnenwirth, A. C., 1958, in Dubos, R. J., ed., Bacterial and Mycotic Infections of Man, 3d ed., J. B. Lippincott Company, Philadelphia, p. 626.

Rosenthal, S. L., and Gootzeit, E. H., 1942, J. Dental Research, 21:373.

Ruebner, B., 1957, J. Pathol. Bacteriol., 73:429.

Russell, W. T., 1943, Med. Res. Council Sp. Rep. Series No. 247, p. 35.

Rustigan, R., and Stuart, C. A., 1945, J. Bacteriol., 49:419.

Salaman, M. H., 1946, Brit. J. Venereal Diseases, 22:47.

————, King, A. J., Bell, H. J., Wilkinson, A. E., Gallagher, E., Kirk, C., Howorth, I. E., and Keppich, P. H., 1946, J. Pathol. Bacteriol., 58:31.

Sanchez-Torres, L. E., Barocio-Lozano, L., Bolaños-Castellanos, G., Brüggemann-Schmidt, C., and Velasco-Hernández, N., 1959, Rev. Latinoamer. Microbiol., 2:63 (Biol. Abstr.).

Schaub, I. G., and Hauber, F. D., 1948, J. Bacteriol., 56:379.

Saslaw, M. S., Jenks, S. A., and Saul, M., 1959, J. Lab. Clin. Med., 54:151.

————, and Streitfeld, M. M., 1959, J. Inf. Dis., 104:233.

Schnoor, T. F., 1939, Am. J. Trop. Med.. 19:163.

Schwabacher, H., Salsbury, A. J., and Loosemore, T. G. E., 1959, J. Clin. Pathol., 12:565.

Schwabacher, H., and Michison, D. A., 1947–48, ibid., 1:39.

Schwarz, O. H., and Brown, T. K., 1936, Am. J. Obstet. Gynecol., 31:379.

Schweinburg, F. B., and Sylvester, E. M., 1953, Proc. Soc. Exptl. Biol. Med., 82:527.

Schweitzer, B., 1919, Zentr. Gynäkol., 43:641, cited by Cruickshank and Cruickshank (1931).

Serpa, J., 1957, Ann. Fac. Med. Univ. Recife, 17:197 (Biol. Abstr.).

Shackman, R., and Massent, D., 1954, Brit. Med. J., 2:1009.

Sharpe, M. E., 1952, J. Hyg., 50:209.

Shibley, G. S., Hanger, F. M., Dochez, A. R., and Mills, K. C., 1926, Proc. Soc. Exptl. Biol. Med., 23:258.

Shidlovsky, B. A., Prigot, A., and Turell, R., 1957–58 Antibiotics Ann., p. 651.

Skerman, V. B. D., 1949, Bacteriol. Revs., 13:178.

————, 1959, A Guide to the Identification of the Genera of Bacteria, The Williams and Wilkins Company, Baltimore.

Slanetz, L. W., and Bartley, C. H., 1957, J. Bacteriol., 74:591.

Smith, C. H., 1954, Brit. J. Ophthalmol., 38:719.

Smith, F. R., and Sherman, J. M., 1938, J. Inf. Dis., 62:186.

Smith, H. W., 1961, personal communication.

————, and Crabb, W. E., 1961, J. Pathol. Bacteriol., 82:53.

Smith, P. F., and Morton, H. E., 1951, Science, 113:623.

Snyder, M. L., 1940, ibid., 66:1.

Soudakoff, P. S., 1954, Am. J. Ophthalmol., 38:374.

Stillman, E. G., 1945, Yale J. Biol. Med., 18:37.

Straffon, R. A., and Engel, W. J., 1960, J. Am. Med. Assoc., 174:1377.

Strasburger, J., 1902, Z. klin. Med., 46:413, cited by Cruickshank and Cruickshank (1931).

Strickler, A., and Friedman, R., 1931, Arch. Dermatol. Syphilol., 24:430.

Switzer, S., 1961, New Engl. J. Med., 264:7.

Taplin, J., and Goldsworthy, N. E., 1958, *Australian J. Exptl. Biol. Med. Sci.*, **36**:289.

———, and ———, 1959, *Med. J. Australia*, I, **46**:259.

Tenbroeck, C., and Bauer, J. H., 1922, *J. Exptl. Med.*, **36**:261.

Thompson, St. C., and Hewlett, R. T., 1898, *Lancet*, **1**:86.

Thomson, D., and Thomson, R., 1924–25, *Ann. Pickett-Thomson Research Labs.*, **1**:229.

———, and ———, 1932, *ibid.*, **8**:30.

Tissier, H., 1899, *Compt. Rend. Soc. Biol.*, **51**:943.

———, 1900, *Récherches sur la flore intestinale des nourrissons (état normal et pathologique)*, Thèse, Faculté de Médecine de Paris, Carré, Paris.

———, 1905, *Ann. Inst. Pasteur*, **19**:109.

Topley, W. W. C., and Wilson, G. S., 1936, *The Principles of Bacteriology and Immunity*, 2d ed., The Williams & Wilkins Company, Baltimore, p. 288.

Torrey, J. C., and Reese, M. K., 1945, *Am. J. Diseases Children*, **69**:208.

Trussell, R. E., 1947, *Trichomonas Vaginalis and Trichomoniasis*, Charles C Thomas, Publisher, Springfield, Ill., p. 130.

Tumka, A. F., 1957, *Vestn. Oto-Rino-Laringol.*, **2**:78 (*Abstr. Sov. Med.*, 1958, B2, No. 545).

Tunnicliff, R., and Jackson, L., 1930, *J. Inf. Dis.*, **46**:12.

Varney, P. L., 1929, *Arch. Surg.*, **19**:1609.

Veillon, A., and Zuber, A., 1897, *Compt. Rend. Soc. Biol.*, **49**:253.

———, and ———, 1898, *Arch. Méd. Expér. et Anat. Pathol.*, **10**:517.

Wantland, W. W., and Wantland, E. M., 1960, *J. Dental Research*, **39**:863.

Watson, E. D., Hoffman, N. J., Simmers, R. W., and Rosebury, T., 1962, *J. Bacteriol.*, **83**:144.

Wegelius, W., 1909, *Arch. Gynäkol.*, **88**:249.

White, A., Handler, P., Smith, E. L., and Stetten, DeW., Jr., 1954, *Principles of Biochemistry*, McGraw-Hill Book Company, Inc., New York.

Williams, N. B., Appleton, J. L. T., and Polevitzky, K., 1952, *Bacteriol. Proc.*, p. 129.

———, Forbes, M. A., Blau, E., and Eickenberg, C. F., 1950, *J. Dental Research*, **29**:563.

Wilson, G. S., 1928, *J. Pathol. Bacteriol.*, **31**:477.

———, and Miles, A. A., 1955, *Topley and Wilson's Principles of Bacteriology and Immunity*, 4th ed., The Williams & Wilkins Company, Baltimore, **2**:1634.

———, and Smith, M. M., 1928, *J. Pathol. Bacteriol.*, **31**:597.

Zanen, H. C., Ganor, S., and Van Toorn, M. J., 1959, *Am. J. Hyg.*, **69**:265.

CHAPTER II

NONPATHOGENIC ACTIVITIES OF THE NORMAL FLORA

The microorganisms indigenous to human body surfaces evidently represent a selection of the multitude of microbic species in the environment. Since the microbiota is not haphazard but contains discernible elements of order, an orderly pattern of phenomena may be assumed to regulate the process of selection. The components of such a pattern would be expected to derive in part from activities of the host as well as of separate groups or members of the biota. It would also depend on the effects of interactions between host and biota and between different groups of the biota. The net effects of these interactions evidently include the rapid destruction or expulsion of most of the microbic species that arrive at a body surface. Other species survive more or less transiently or permanently. During these longer or shorter intervals, continual interaction must occur, with alterations in both host and microbes which are encompassed within the broad definition of *infection* developed in Chap. 1. Infection implies modification or damage to the host (as well as to the microbes), and overt damage or disease is one of the resultant possibilities; but it is one of many. Effects discernibly beneficial to the host may also occur; and in between lies a range of resultants which may include (1) both damage and benefit induced by (different) interactions of the host with a single species (e.g., *Streptococcus mitis*, whose activities against other bacterial species will be considered in this chapter, but which also "causes" subacute bacterial endocarditis); (2) effects that may be obvious but not easily evaluated by standards of good or evil (e.g., the balance or coexistence entailed in the maintenance of many indigenous species); and (3) effects not yet recognized because means for their isolation and measurement are not available. It is the purpose of this chapter to look into this general question: to examine the pattern of phenomena concerned with selection of the typical microbiota, and those interactions of the biota with the host whose effects are discernible and take forms other than disease.

It is sufficient justification for this book that this problem affects man intimately, that it is inordinately complex, and that only bits and pieces of the information needed for its analysis are at hand. The problem of the relation of the normal flora of man to his economy may be compared with the similar relationship of microorganisms in the rumen of sheep and cattle. The latter problem is simple only by contrast, or possibly by hindsight—its working out is a model of elegance [see Hungate (1960)]. The rumen problem as it has been dealt with is essentially or exclusively one of microbic metabolism of food ingested by the ruminant animal. As such it has no exact parallel in man or other nonruminant animals, although microbic metabolism, directed against a different diet and not confined to a biological "fermentation vat," is one of the activities we must deal with. That phenomena in the rumen overlap with microbic digestion of man's food is suggested directly by the concurrence of some of the same microbic genera in both hosts (e.g., *Bacteroides, Veillonella, Lactobacillus*). But processes occur in the rumen that are unimportant or absent in man (e.g., cellulose digestion); while the activities of the normal flora in general, in areas other than the rumen in ruminants, as well as in man, ramify far beyond those of digestion.

The topics to be dealt with in this chapter are (1) the relationship of the indigenous biota to the nutrition of the host under normal conditions; (2) interactions of the biota with the host in general, and with particular reference to the formation and possible significance of antibodies formed by the host against indigenous species; (3) interactions within the biota itself and their effects on the biota and on the host (exclusive of pathogenesis); and (4) germfree animals, and the light they may cast by negative inference on the effects of the indigenous biota on the host. The last topic will be dealt with serially for the most part, for the sake of its contributions to the others.

The fact that certain mammalian and avian species can now be reared and maintained germfree in a state of apparently complete health, and that some of these—chickens, rats, and mice—can be bred in the germfree state through successive generations—indicates that for these species (and perhaps potentially for all others) the indigenous biota is not essential to the existence of the host. In man, an actual germfree state is probably neither attainable nor desirable, for humanitarian as well as technical reasons. It may therefore be useful to extrapolate from animal studies to the assumption that the indigenous biota is not essential to human life. Neither is the wheel—whose useful and destructive effects on man make the analogy perhaps less outrageous than it may at first seem. Our indigenous biota is, in fact, part of the environment in which we live. We need to accept its existence. Acceptance, however, need not be passive or resigned; the biota is no less subject than the rest of our environment to manipulation for human benefit.

The Indigenous Biota in Host Nutrition

It is known that certain microbic species of the normal flora, particularly the nutritionally nonfastidious enterobacteria, are capable of synthesizing vitamins in concentrations in excess of their own metabolic needs; and it is probable but not unequivocally clear that such vitamins may be absorbed by man. Mickelsen (1956), reviewing intestinal synthesis of vitamins in nonruminant animals, including man, concluded that such animals secure only a few vitamins by direct absorption after intraintestinal synthesis by bacteria. The rat apparently obtains folic acid, biotin, and vitamin K in this way, and perhaps other vitamins. Under normal circumstances, man may satisfy his requirement for biotin and vitamin K by such intestinal synthesis, and human adults (but not infants) may secure part of their pyridoxine and vitamin B_{12} by this mechanism. Yamaguchi (1959) has presented evidence for synthesis of pantothenic acid in the human intestine. Some of the vitamin production in the lower gut (apparently mainly in the cecum) may be diverted by vitamin-requiring bacteria [e.g., lactobacilli, Johansson and Sarles (1949); Johansson, Peterson, and Dick (1953)], or in the instance of ascorbic acid, by bacterial decomposition [Young and James (1942); Young and Rettger (1943)]; but Mickelsen (1956) has pointed out that such destruction in the intestine is probably insignificant in the presence of glucose.

Ambiguous findings on the need of germfree animals for vitamins seem to suggest, as might perhaps be anticipated from the assumption of inessentiality of the normal flora, that microbic synthesizing activity is supplementary or contributory rather than indispensable. Luckey (1959a) reported that germfree chicks seemed to require folic acid which, however, is synthesized by the germfree rat [for evidence to the contrary, see Gustafsson and Fitzgerald (1960)]. Germfree rats appear to require biotin [Wostmann (1959a)]. Horton and Hickey (1961) have reported that a complete diet sterilized by ionizing radiation was satisfactory for conventional but not for germfree guinea pigs, and suggested that unidentified or additional growth factors are contributed in this animal by its intestinal flora. Ambiguity on this general question is especially prominent with respect to vitamin K in germfree animals. This nutrient is readily synthesized by many bacteria and is known to be formed in feces [see Almquist, Pentler, and Mecchi (1938); Mickelsen (1956)]. Indications of vitamin K deficiency in weanling germfree rats were reported by Gustafsson (1948) and also by Luckey and

Reyniers (1954). But in subsequent studies by the latter workers [Luckey, Pleasants, and Reyniers (1955); Luckey (1959a)], a transient increase in blood clotting time in germfree chickens on vitamin K deprivation rapidly reverted to normal without dietary change; negative results under similar circumstances were also obtained with rats. Gustafsson (1959) has more recently reported that 42 of 44 germfree rats deprived of vitamin K showed signs of severe hypoprothrombinemia; 35 of these showed bleeding tendencies and 12 died. The symptoms did not appear in conventional animals given the same diet and could be cured in germfree rats either by feeding vitamin K_1 or by transferring the animals to contaminated surroundings. Mickelsen (1956) noted that earlier animal experimentation in this field had led to the belief that man obtains a considerable amount of his vitamin K from intestinal synthesis.

Brief mention may be made of vitamin synthesis in certain non-ruminant animals associated with coprophagy. Fridericia et al. (1927) designated as *refection* a phenomenon seen originally in rats, in which certain animals on a starch-containing diet deficient in B vitamins thrived and produced white bulky feces in which unchanged starch and B vitamins were present, the latter apparently synthesized by fecal bacteria. Resistance to deficiency disease was associated with coprophagy and could be "transmitted" by feeding feces of refected rats to young rats on a deficient diet. Mickelsen (1956) reviewed studies indicating interference with refection by sulfonamides and suppression of refection on feeding brewer's yeast. The process appears to depend on the presence of a poorly digested carbohydrate. It may be found in chicks and mice as well as in rats, but is doubtful or absent in other animals. Rabbits and poultry, on the other hand, seem able to make up vitamin B deficiencies by consuming their feces, in which vitamins apparently continue to be synthesized for an interval after their excretion [Lamoreux and Schumacher (1940)]. Barnes and Fiala (1959) [see also Barnes and Fiala (1958)] observed signs of vitamin K deficiency in rats in which coprophagy had been prevented by a plastic cup covering the anus and tail [Barnes et al. (1957)]. Gustafsson and Fitzgerald (1960) reported that when coprophagy was prevented by this means in rats, the fecal concentration of lactobacilli fell markedly, pointing to the importance of this practice in maintaining the normal flora of the gut. That other nutritional phenomena in the rat in which the fecal flora is thought to participate are independent of coprophagy is suggested by the finding of Rechcigl et al. (1959) that the growth-stimulating effect of urea in rats continued despite the use of tail cups.

Additional suggestive evidence that the intestinal biota helps to maintain nutritional balance in the host—in man as well as in experimental

animals—is to be found in the literature on the effects of chemotherapeutic drugs and need be only briefly mentioned. Some of the early
experimental studies of bacterial synthesis of vitamins in the intestine
depended on the use of sulfonamides [see Mickelsen (1956)]. The
incorporation of antibiotics in commercial animal feeds [Stokstad and
Jukes (1950); Stokstad (1953)] is thought to be based on a mechanism
involving the intestinal flora [Biely and March (1951)]. The appearance in man, under antibiotic therapy for infectious disease, of symptoms suggestive of vitamin B deficiency is usually explained in part by
disturbance of the intestinal flora [for references, see Rosebury
(1952)]. Finally it has been suggested that severe dietary deficiency itself, in man notably the form of protein malnutrition known as kwash-
iorkor [Williams (1953); Scrimshaw et al. (1957)], may include a
disturbance of the intestinal flora as part of its pathogenesis [Smythe
(1958)].

Host-Biota Interactions Not Leading to Disease

General

Effects of the Indigenous Biota on Man. Either beneficial or neutral
effects of the biota on man, other than those suggested in the preceding
section, and the antibiotic effects to be considered later, may be inferred
but can rarely be specifically indicated. Whenever a given microbic
species is found regularly and in appreciable numbers in an indigenous
locus, it may be assumed that its metabolic activity directly or indirectly
influences the host. In most instances left unexplored, the end result is
not—usually—disease, but it may range from subtle damage through
gradations of neutrality to benefit not less significant for being unrecognized, or it may combine such effects simultaneously or under different conditions. An example mentioned in earlier chapters is that of
Veillonella alcalescens, the anaerobic coccus present characteristically
in high concentration in saliva, having the peculiar ability to dissimilate
lactate anaerobically (and participating actively and by virtue of this
property in rumen metabolism)—whose effect on man is unknown.
Mazzarella and Shklair (1960) attempted to test the hypothesis that
disposal of lactic acid in the mouth might constitute a defense against
dental caries, but found the concentration of veillonellae higher in the
presence of caries than in its absence—a direct consequence, in their
view, of the higher substrate level in the carious lesions.

The probable role of unspecified skin microorganisms in producing
rancid odors from apocrine sweat has been explored by Shelley, Hurley,
and Nichols (1953). Scheimann et al. (1960) reported that after application of tripalmitin to skin, treatment with tetracycline partially in-

hibited fatty acid production. They suggested that fungi as well as bacteria may participate in lipolysis on the skin surface (see also *C. acnes*, Chap. 3; *Pityrosporum*, Chap. 7; and under host factors in skin, page 359).

Specific effects of the biota on the host that cannot be classified as harmful may be inferred from certain studies with germfree animals. In rats, mice, and especially in guinea pigs reared in the absence of microorganisms, a curious phenomenon of cecal distension has been described [Phillips, Wolfe, and Gordon (1959)]. This is said to be the only significant anatomical abnormality in the germfree guinea pig. The wall of the cecum, tough and thick in the normal animal, is more elastic and very thin; peristalsis, which normally mixes the mass of food and bacteria and forces it on to the large intestine, in the germfree animals distends the thin wall to the limits set by other abdominal organs and only then urges the contents into the colon. In germfree rats and mice, Gordon (1959) noted a fourfold to sixfold increase of the cecal contents and a twofold to threefold increase in weight of the cecal sac. That the enlargement is due to "the absent flora" was indicated by a rapid reversion toward normal weight values after "exposure to normal bacterial flora." Monocontamination with lactobacilli alone also brought about a considerable reduction in cecum weight. Gordon suggested that "some of the shortcomings" of germfree animals, such as retarded growth and adrenal enlargement, may be associated with this cecal abnormality, and that factors other than the germfree state itself may influence it.

Borgström et al. (1959) found that in germfree rats trypsin and invertase were present in the feces in amounts, respectively, of 1 to 6 mg and 12 to 25 units per day, whereas conventional animals did not have measurable amounts of either enzyme in the feces. Contamination of the germfree animals with a suspension of feces from normal animals led to disappearance of fecal trypsin within 24 hours; the fate of invertase under these conditions was apparently not determined. This group of workers [Gustafsson and Lanke (1960)] has also confirmed in germfree rats the view of earlier workers that intestinal bacterial action is responsible for the presence of reduction products of bilirubin in feces. They found such substances absent in germfree rat feces; after fecal contamination the exgermfree animals produced "urobilins" which reached "normal" concentrations on the third day. Germfree rats monocontaminated with a "clostridium-like" organism from rat feces produced small amounts of urobilins; further contamination with *E. coli* increased the fecal level but it remained lower than in animals subjected to full fecal contamination.

Additional reports on studies of germfree animals suggest that the normal flora may confer nonspecific resistance against certain diseases by unexplained mechanisms: an encephalomeningeal syndrome of unknown etiology in chicks [Gordon et al. (1959)], and experimental *Trichomonas vaginalis* infection in guinea pigs [Newton, Reardon, and DeLeva (1960)]. The chick disease appeared spontaneously throughout lots of newly hatched birds including both germfree chicks and those apparently unintentionally monocontaminated with *Streptococcus faecalis* or with an unidentified Gram-negative rod. Attempts to modify the disease by dietary or other means, and limited attempts to transmit it, were unsuccessful. In the studies of Newton and his coworkers, an axenic culture of *T. vaginalis* from a case of symptomatic trichomoniasis produced large abscesslike lesions containing gas and viable protozoa on subcutaneous inoculation of germfree guinea pigs but had little or no effect when injected similarly into conventional animals. Also of interest in this context is the report of Dineen (1960) that mice whose intestinal flora had been reduced by treatment with neomycin were much more susceptible to intravenous staphylococcus infection than untreated littermate controls. Taylor, Rooney, and Blundell (1961), moreover, have reported that 5-week-old germfree rats were very much more susceptible than conventional rats to intradermally inoculated *B. anthracis* spores. In the conventional rats resistance to anthrax was found to develop rapidly in early life and was thought to be associated with environmental bacteria. The high susceptibility of the germfree animals could not be correlated with their serum γ-globulin levels measured electrophoretically. Attempts to elucidate the basis of these curious findings are in their infancy. Developments will be awaited with interest.

Effects of the Host, Particularly Man, on the Indigenous Biota. This subject falls largely into the broad area of natural resistance and can be given only brief treatment here. Those aspects of the subject that bear most directly on the question of disease associated with indigenous microorganisms are deferred for treatment in a separate volume of this work. The effects of such agencies as lysozyme (cf. Chap. 9), and of properdin and other substances in serum and tissues, are considered at length in standard works. What needs to be noted here, especially with a view to presenting sources, are the less clearly defined phenomena, all presumably nonspecific, which seem to help the human host restrain and confine the indigenous biota.

The majority of studies in this area have been concerned with the mouth and upper respiratory tract. In some instances, inhibitory effects against certain microorganisms formerly attributed to the host [e.g., via the saliva—the "inhibin" of Dold and Weigmann (1934) and many later workers] have been shown to be antibiotic effects induced by members of the biota itself, and are considered under that head on page 375.

A similar mechanism may be found by future research to explain some of the phenomena to be considered here.

Bloomfield (1920, 1922) reported that a variety of bacteria (*E. coli, Staph. albus, Sarcina lutea, H. influenzae, K. aerogenes*, and hemolytic streptococci) when swabbed on the tongue or nasal septum, usually disappeared within 24 hours. Introduced into the tonsillar crypts they could be recovered for somewhat longer intervals, but no permanent carrier state resulted and none of the cultures produced disease. Bloomfield postulated a "definite mechanism" consisting principally of mechanical transport of the bacteria backward to the esophagus, perhaps assisted by a destructive effect of saliva. Caminiti (1939) found that aqueous extracts of human tonsils inhibited the growth of diphtheria and typhoid bacilli and *Brucella melitensis*. It may be noted that Vanna and Pollice (1947) failed to find lytic antibodies for pathogenic enterobacteria or phages for pseudomonads in normal nasal mucus or in mucus from cases of ozena.

The effects of functional and other movements in the mouth, such as those incident to eating a meal or brushing the teeth, on the number of bacteria in mouth rinsings have been reviewed and studied by Appleton (1950). A "diurnal tide" of bacteria in the mouth has been defined, with reductions at mealtimes, increases in the interprandial intervals, and a maximum count on awakening in the morning. The alternations seem to depend mainly on mechanical effects culminating in swallowing, abetted by toothbrushing, with presumably detergent contributions from dentifrices largely independent of commercially touted variations in their composition, as shown repeatedly by dental students in the writer's classes. Maximum reduction following a single event (e.g., brushing with a dentifrice), measured in aerobic nutrient agar pour plates, is of the order of 80 per cent. Small additive effects have been observed when brushing was followed by eating or vice versa [Weiss and Weinberger (1940)]. The effects of mastication and of toothbrushing on removal of organisms introduced by chewing a commercial yeast cake have been studied by Knighton (1942), with reductions as high as 99 per cent.

The presence in saliva of inhibitory factors that are not dependent on salivary bacteria was suggested by the earlier studies of Zeldow (1955) and others, and has been demonstrated by Kerr and Wedderburn (1958) and in Zeldow's more recent findings (1959, 1961) with parotid and submaxillary saliva drawn aseptically from the ducts. Both secretions, as well as whole saliva, were uniformly active against *M. lysodeikticus, Lactobacillus casei, L. plantarum*, and *L. acidophilus*, and in a majority of trials against *Str. hominis*. Kerr and Wedderburn found sterile saliva from both sources also active against *Staph. aureus* and

Staph. albus, whereas whole saliva was usually inactive against staphylococci. Williams and Powlen (1959) have found that aseptically collected parotid saliva served as sole nutrient medium for survival or less than optimal growth of *Staph. aureus, Str. faecalis, Aerobacter cloacae, Candida albicans, Bacillus subtilis,* and *B. cereus;* but lactobacilli, hemolytic and viridans streptococci, and *Corynebacterium diphtheriae* diminished in numbers in this medium over a 72-hour period.

Ostrom, Wolochow, and James (1958) have described attempts to recover *Serratia marcescens* from the mouth, nose, and pharynx after exposing human subjects to aerosols of the organism. Swabs, mouthwash samples, and nose washings taken by the method of Grubb and Puetzer (1947), all within 5 minutes after exposure via face masks in a closed system, were more often positive and gave larger yields as the cloud concentration to which the subjects were exposed increased from less than 5,000 to 10,000 organisms per cu ft; the highest frequency and concentrations were found in mouthwash samples.

The sterilizing effect of gastric acidity has been studied by Arnold and Brody (1926), who found in healthy dogs that *Ps. aeruginosa* and *S. marcescens* introduced into the empty stomach could not be recovered from the cecum unless given with alkaline buffers. Cregan, Dunlop, and Hayward (1953), however, have presented evidence that the scarcity of bacteria in the human small intestine does not depend on free acid in the stomach. Dack and Petran (1934) [see also Dack and Woolpert (1932)] suggested from their findings in monkeys and dogs that the antibacterial mechanism of the small intestine depends largely on mechanical action due to peristalsis aided physically by the mucus secretion [see also Florey (1933)]. Dixon (1960) inoculated a mixture of 4 bacterial species (*E. coli, S. marcescens, Ps. aeruginosa,* and a staphylococcus) with a suspension of Cr^{51}-labeled human red blood cells, into a subcutaneously transposed loop of small intestine in unanesthetized rats. He then traced the cells by means of the unabsorbed radiochromium, and the bacteria by colony counts, in corresponding segments of gut removed from the animal after intervals of 25 to 100 minutes. The results indicated that the bacteria were rapidly moved onward and soon expelled from the small intestine by peristaltic action with no indication of a bactericidal effect.

Neutralizing activity against *Cl. perfringens* α-toxin was found in feces of many subjects by Goudie and Duncan (1956) and reported to behave like a tryptic enzyme by Goudie (1959).

Host factors acting in skin against both indigenous and nonindigenous microbes have been reviewed by Rebell et al. (1950). Marchionini and his coworkers (1928–39) presented evidence that alkalinity resulting from NH_3 production by bacteria in sweat favors proliferation of skin bacteria, and that the rate of disappearance of *S. marcescens* applied to skin is greater in normally acid than in normally alkaline areas [see also Arnold (1942)]. Burtenshaw (1942) reported that the unsaturated fatty acids of skin are bactericidal for hemolytic streptococci, pneumococci, and diphtheria bacilli, and suggested their importance in the hygiene of skin [see also Krehl and Liao (1951), and Chap. 10]. Nathanson (1960) found that certain long-chain unsaturated fatty acids of skin, especially linolenic acid, showed distinct inhibitory action in vitro against *Trichophyton rubrum*. Other workers, including Norton and Novy (1931, 1932), Cornbleet and Montgomery (1931), and Rebell et al. (1950) have emphasized desiccation as the principal agency acting against bacteria on skin.

Antibody Formation against Indigenous Microorganisms

As would be expected, antibodies against species of the normal flora have been looked for in man principally in relation to disease in which such species were implicated; and much of the information in the following paragraphs comes from the fortunate inclusion in such studies of control subjects not afflicted with the disease in question. It is of interest that such antibodies have usually been found when looked for, although often in only a fraction of the sample of subjects, and generally in comparatively low concentrations. Almost nothing definite is known of their significance. They would be expected to occur when the microbe in question is present frequently or in large numbers, or as a function of infection in the broad sense—i.e., as a measure of the host's reaction to the presence of microbic antigens in tissues rather than on body surfaces. And on general principles the participation of such antibodies in phenomena of immunity would be expected to be at least as variable as is that of antibodies to overtly pathogenic bacteria. Antibodies capable of assisting in the process of blood or tissue clearance of bacteria would be expected to play a role in maintaining the balance between host and indigenous biota, but such a role may not be obvious.

Germfree Animals. Although our concern is with man, the bearing on this topic of relevant findings in germfree animals is apparent and worthy of examination at the outset. These findings have helped to strengthen the emerging view that antibodies all result from immunization which is chemically but not necessarily biologically specific. This view is opposed to the essentially metaphysical notion of "normal" or "natural" antibodies thought to have a distinct and unknown mode of origin. The latter idea was questioned in this context by Ingalls in 1937, and for isoantibodies by Wiener (1951). Evidence for the existence of γ-globulin that is not an antibody has, however, been presented by Franěk, Říha, and Šterzl (1961). The findings with germfree animals leave little doubt that antibodies to indigenous microorganisms result from immunization, but they do not as yet point clearly to any role played by such antibodies in the economy of the host.

Wagner (1955) reported that the serum of germfree chicks did not show the antibodies to intestinal bacteria found in normals, although both groups responded to immunization. Gordon (1955) found that eighth generation germfree rats appeared normal in all respects except that the gastrointestinal tract and associated lymph nodes weighed less than in control animals; the lymphocyte content of the ileocecal tonsil in the former group was one-tenth that of the controls. Appropriate exposure of germfree animals to contaminants led to a rapid increase in lymphocytes. Miyakawa (1959) confirmed the early findings of Glimstedt (1936) that active or germinal centers ("secondary nodules") are not found in the lymphoid tissue of germfree guinea pigs. Thorbecke (1959), on the other hand, found secondary nodules in the spleens of germfree rats and occasionally in their lymphoid tissue elsewhere. These findings are paralleled by the occurrence of antibodies in germfree animals. Wostmann (1959b) reported that the principal difference between normal and germfree chickens was in the γ-globulin fraction of their serum, which was markedly lower in the latter group and failed to show the increased concentration with age found in normal stock, associated with a rise in antibody titer to coliforms and staphylococci. Similar findings were obtained in rats and mice; in germfree guinea pigs certain γ-globulin fractions were entirely absent.

The presence of small amounts of antibody to indigenous bacteria in germfree animals has been explained on the basis that dead organisms find their way into the diets and may be seen in the feces [Luckey (1959a)]; presumably some are absorbed. Wagner (1959) found that germfree and conventional chickens and rats had equivalent titers of complement, properdin, and agglutinins to certain heterologous erythrocytes. However, there were marked differences in agglutinins to most bacterial antigens. In chickens, agglutinins to "Paracolobactrum aerogenoides," found in normal animals to a titer of 1:128 at 15 to 170 days, failed to develop in germfree birds in more than 200 days. Normal agglutinins to Staph. albus (Micrococcus epidermidis) developed later and in lower titer in germfree than in conventional chickens. Germfree chickens responded normally with antibody production to killed P. aerogenoides administered by feeding and to beef serum or killed Salmonella pullorum injected intravenously. Germfree rats had no agglutinins in their serum at 250 days to E. coli, Str. faecalis, or heterofermentative lactobacilli; whereas conventional animals showed such agglutinins usually in low titer, but in titer as high as 1:125 for Str. faecalis. With staphylococci, on the other hand, although one group of germfree rats was negative, another gave serum titers (up to 1:64) not markedly lower than those found in conventional animals (maximum 1:256). Rats monocontaminated (inoculated orally with a pure culture at weaning) with *Str. faecalis* or *Str. liquefaciens* showed much higher titers at 100 to 250 days (1:64 to 1:2,048 and 1:1,024 for the 2 species, respectively) than conventional animals (1:2 to 1:256 and 1:2 to 1:128, respectively). Similar monocontamination with a heterofermentative lactobacillus yielded a titer (1:8) no higher than that of normal rats, while monocontamination with either of 2 unidentified bacilli with which normal animal serum did not react failed to elicit a demonstrable antibody response. The occurrence or titer of antibodies would appear to depend on something in addition to the mere presence of the species as a "contaminant." Persistent and continued proliferation of the microbe and its absorption into (and interaction with) host tissues—in short, the processes of infection—may be assumed to be necessary.

The degree to which such infection is prevented from becoming disease by antibodies is not yet clear. There have been suggestions that germfree animals may succumb after contact with ordinarily harmless microbes, but they apparently need not do so. Reyniers (1946) noted that "when a germ-free animal is suddenly brought to the outside without exercising care as to the contaminations with which it comes in contact," it usually dies; and Taylor (1959) mentioned that *Sarcina lutea* and *Bacillus subtilis* may be pathogenic to germfree animals. Reyniers (1959) remarked that a 50 to 60 per cent fatality, apparently from mixed bacterial infection, occurred within 48 hours when germfree C3H mice were exposed to the contaminated laboratory environment; but that " . . . with the germfree rat it is generally true that exposure to a conventional laboratory environment has little effect on survival." Again, Luckey (1959*b*) stated his "impression" that:

. . . rats taken directly from a germfree environment to the conventional animal colony will die in 3 or 4 days. Consequently I used to take such animals routinely into my office for 3 or 4 days before introducing them into the conventional colony, and I never experienced difficulties . . . . On the other hand, the germfree chicken appears to show no effect, as far as fatal infections are concerned, when . . . introduced directly to an environment containing conventional chicks.

The capacity of separate species of the normal flora to produce disease in germfree animals has evidently not been studied. Thorbecke and Benacerraf (1959) showed that in germfree and control mice the rate of clearance of *E. coli* from the blood is determined largely by the concentration of circulating antibodies, as would be expected from a great deal of earlier work with conventional animals [see Sebestyen, Schlossman, and Benacerraf (1958)]. Gordon (1959) was evidently able to expose germfree rats to contamination with feces of normal rats without injury; and disease presumably did not result from his experiments and those of Wagner, mentioned above, which involved monocontamination with lactobacilli, enterococci, and unidentified bacilli.

Antibodies to the Normal Flora in Man. Staphylococci. The data pertain exclusively to coagulase-positive or pathogenic staphylococci. Antibodies or phenomena attributed to antibodies have been demonstrated in normal serum by their effect on colony form [Finkelstein and Sulkin (1958)], by gel-precipitation [Jensen (1958)] and agglutination [Jensen (1958, 1959); Boger, Frankel, and Gavin (1960); see also Pereira (1961)]; as antistaphylolysin [Richou, Quinchon, and Richou (1959)]; by hemagglutination and various modifications of it [Neter et al. (1959b, 1960)]; by mouse-protection tests [M. W. Fisher (1959), S. Fisher (1960)]; by immune adherence [Turk (1959)]; and by a fluorescence method [Cherry, Goldman, and Carski (1960)]. Jensen demonstrated antibody, to a polysaccharide in pathogenic staphylococci, in normal cord blood and in colostrum; he found that the titer decreased in milk and also in serum during the first 3 or 4 months of life, and then increased up to the age of about 25 years. He reported that the polysaccharide was toxic for normal guinea pigs and that the toxic effect was neutralized by normal human serum as well as by the serum of immunized rabbits, which showed a reaction of identity when paired with normal human serum in Ouchterlony plates. Neter, Rajnovich, and Gorzynski (1960) also found antistaphylococcal antibodies, by hemagglutination techniques, in cord blood and in the corresponding maternal blood, and showed a pattern of development in adults similar to that described by Jensen; but Neter et al. considered the antibody to be nonspecific, corresponding to that described by Rantz and his coworkers (1952, 1956). The mouse-protective antibody described by S. Fisher (1960) was held to be different from antibody active in vitro.

Nonhemolytic Streptococci. Antibodies to α or γ streptococci, all presumably members of the viridans group, have been reported in the serum of patients with subacute bacterial endocarditis [Kreidler (1926); Sachs (1942)] and also by skin tests in healthy subjects or patients with nonspecific illness [Howell and Corrigan (1928); Nye and Seegal (1929)]. Agglutinins to the strain of streptococcus known as MG, which occur in high titer in viral pneumonia, have been found in similar titers in subacute bacterial endocarditis [Thomas et al. (1943)], in a presumably viral gastroenteritis [Keitel (1950)], and in low titer in other subjects [Thomas et al. (1943)]. The statement, made without detail by these latter workers, that with "numerous other strains of indifferent streptococci . . . agglutination has either failed to occur or has occurred to an equal degree in both acute-phase and convalescent sera" (from primary atypical pneumonia) suggests that there is more to be learned on this question.

Schottmüller (1924) and Lehman (1926) found that nonhemolytic streptococci were destroyed or grew very slowly in human defibrinated blood. Colebrook, Lowbury, and Hurst (1960), on the other hand, reported that 2 of 4 strains of viridans streptococci grew in fresh human serum when either small or large inocula were used; whereas 2 others did not.

Lactobacilli. Jay, Crowley, and Bunting (1930, 1932) observed positive skin tests to lactobacillus antigens in children, especially but not only those with dental caries; while cariesfree children had serum agglutinins in higher titer (up to 1:640) than did those with caries. Dietz, Williams, and Lawton (1943) also reported a somewhat higher frequency of positive serum agglutination tests to lactobacilli in caries-free subjects (76 per cent) than in those with the disease (71 per cent); high lactobacillus counts in saliva were generally but not strikingly associated with low serum titers. Gillespie et al. (1950a) were unable to demonstrate precipitins to *L. acidophilus* in the serum of a single human subject even after feeding the organism in milk cultures over a 14-month period.

Actinomyces israelii. Mathieson et al. (1953) tested vaccines of 4 strains of this species by the intradermal route in human subjects. One of the 4 strains gave positive responses in all of 13 normal subjects, but only weak positives in 2 of 5 patients with actinomycosis, including a negative in the patient from whom the strain had been isolated. Heated tricresol-treated whole vaccine, and a Berkefeld-filtered unheated preparation, gave generally similar results. Two other strains failed to react and one gave weak reactions. By contrast, Holm and Kwapinski (1959), using hemagglutination and complement fixation with polysaccharide and nucleoprotein fractions of *A. israelii*, reported positive findings in 12 of 16 cases of actinomycosis. Lower proportions of positive reactions to these antigens were found in nonspecific disease (tuberculosis and streptococcal infections) and in one of 6 serums positive in serum tests for syphilis. Only 1 of 20 serums from healthy blood donors was reactive with the nucleoprotein antigen; all were negative with the polysaccharide. The highest titers with both antigen fractions (1:240 and 1:480) were found in the serums from clinical actinomycosis.

Escherichia coli. Gibson (1930), in a study of "natural agglutinins," tested 5 strains of *E. coli* against serums from man and a range of animals, and found agglutinins in all but 1 strain in human subjects, usually to very low titers (maximum 1:32). These antibodies were completely absorbed by the homologous strain with a variable lowering of titer for unrelated organisms. Agglutinins were also found in animal serums, especially those of ox, horse, and pig. Stetson (1955) suggested that the Shwartzman phenomenon may be due to a tuberculin-type hypersensitivity to somatic antigens or endotoxins of enterobacteria in "normal" rabbits. Gibson had found only weak and irregular "natural" agglutinins in rabbit serum to *E. coli* but stronger reactions to *K. aerogenes*. Gillespie, Steber, and Waugh (1950*b*) found 1 to 5 rabbit serums moderately reactive in agglutination against *E. coli* isolated from human feces.

In other studies in which *E. coli* was included among the bacterial species tested, Needell et al. (1955) found titers higher by hemagglutination than by the usual agglutination procedure in urinary tract infections; and Turk (1959) reported *E. coli* titers of 1:64 by the immune adherence method both with normal serum and with Cohn's fraction $III_{123} + I$, and suggested that the antibody is a fraction of the β-globulin. Cherry, Goldman, and Carski (1960) stated that antibody to *E. coli* could be demonstrated in the serum of normal persons by fluorescent techniques.

Several reports that include tests for antibodies to *E. coli* in normal serum have appeared in recent years, particularly in relation to the pathogenic serotypes. Although Gillespie et al. (1950*a,b*) did not use the serologic typing methods then newly available, they did examine the reactivity of a few normal human subjects and several animals with a large number of coliform and other cultures. Serums from the human sources of the strains were tested as well as from other human subjects. Agglutinin titers as high as 1:1,280 were reported for one subject with many homologous isolations of *E. coli* and other coliforms, and these high titers were found to persist essentially unchanged over a 4-year period. Other homologous strains failed to react with this subject's serum, and ingestion of killed suspensions of 2 such native strains failed to elicit a demonstrable antibody response. The second subject yielded lower titers (maximum 1:320). Serum from the first subject also gave high titers with strains isolated from the second; while, conversely, serum of the second subject again reacted only weakly in crosses. Similar results were obtained with other human serum; a few seemed much more reactive than the others.

Control data supplied in connection with the experimental feeding of pathogenic *E. coli* serotypes indicate the presence of antibody to such strains in low titer in certain subjects, and comparable titers somewhat more widely distributed against "normal" strains. The feeding of such normal strains has been found to have little or no effect on the titer. Such studies, using agglutination, have been reported by Ferguson and

June (1952) and by June, Ferguson, and Worfel (1953), and using hemagglutination, by Neter, Zalewski, and Ferguson (1953) and Wentworth et al. (1956). Cascio, Purpura, and Priolisi (1959) have reported the presence of antibody to a range of pathogenic serotypes of *E. coli* in healthy children as well as in those with gastroenteritis. Among 128 serum specimens from the healthy group, no reactivity was found at birth even though mothers tested had titers of 1:128 or higher. Thirty per cent of samples from babies 20 days to 3 months old were positive, 60 per cent in the 3- to 6-month age group, 66 per cent in the 6- to 12-month age group, 91.6 per cent at 1 to 2 years. All of 12 children more than 2 years old were positive. Neter et al. (1959*a*) found antibodies to pathogenic *E. coli* serotypes by direct and indirect hemagglutination in γ-globulin pools from the United States, Japan, and India.

Studies of the bactericidal activity of normal human serum against *E. coli* have been reported by Waisbren and Brown (1959), Roantree and Rantz (1960), Colebrook and his coworkers (1960), Muschel (1960), and Michael and Landy (1961). Colebrook et al. found that 4 strains of *E. coli*, not identified serologically, failed to grow in fresh human serum from inocula greater than 10^5; when 10^4 organisms or less were inoculated, they died within 24 hours. The bactericidal effect was impaired by heating at 56° for 1 hour or by trypsin treatment, more markedly by a combination of both treatments. Muschel, who studied a wide range of both normal and pathogenic serotypes of *E. coli*, found that they could not be distinguished as to virulence by their resistance to the bactericidal action of normal serum. Serum resistance was associated with O inagglutinability. This worker has concluded that the bactericidal effect of normal serum against enterobacteria is probably due to specific antibody, perhaps augmented slightly by the properdin system [see also Osawa and Muschel (1960)]. In the more recent studies of Michael and Landy (1961), variants of *E. coli* serotype O26:B6, selected for resistance to the bactericidal action of normal serum, were more active producers of endotoxin and of O antigenicity than their serum-sensitive counterparts. Similar results were obtained with *Shigella dysenteriae*.

Other Enterobacteria. Hirst (1917) recorded agglutinin titers for *Alcaligenes faecalis* in patient's serum, from his own and previous studies, ranging from 1:50 to 1:2,000. Weinstein and Wasserman (1951) noted a rise in specific agglutinin titer to *A. faecalis* in a patient with specific bacteremia complicating infectious mononucleosis and fusospirochetal angina. Gibson (1930) reported maximum agglutinin titers in normal human serum of 1:8 for *Proteus* X-19 and 1:256 for *Klebsiella aerogenes*. Hemagglutination reactions with proteus and "paracolobactrum" in infections of the urinary tract have been reported by Needell et al. (1955). In the studies of Colebrook, Lowbury, and Hurst (1960) referred to previously, 4 strains of proteus showed differences from one to another when incubated in fresh human serum. One strain that was killed under these conditions within 6 hours grew well in heated or trypsinized serum, better in serum both trypsinized and heated. Bregman and Kirsner (1960) reported hemagglutination reactions of uncertain specificity with serum from ulcerative colitis patients tested against peptic digests of colon mucosa containing cell-wall material of proteus (DAP or lysozyme digests).

Pseudomonas aeruginosa. Agglutinins to *Ps. aeruginosa* were reported by Lilley and Bearup in 1928 at titers of 1:5 to 1:20 in 72 of 100 normal serum samples from hospital cases not involving specific disease, and in 5 of 8 cases of generalized pseudomonas infections at a titer of 1:80. Gibson (1930) noted the presence of this organism among those reacting with "natural" agglutinins, in this instance to a maximum titer of 1:32. In 6 of 11 patients from whose urine this organism was recovered, Sandiford (1937) found serum agglutinins at titers of 1:50 to 1:250. Needell et al. (1955) has shown antibodies to *Ps. aeruginosa* in infection of the urinary tract by hemagglutination. Fox and Lowbury (1953) reported agglutinin titers to *Ps. aeruginosa* of 1:160 to 1:640 in all of 12 normal subjects when a saline antigen was used, but much lower titers (less than 1:80) with alcohol-treated antigen. Gaines and Landy (1955) found hemagglutination titers up to 1:960 in nearly 100 per cent of serum specimens from normal subjects over the age of 2 years. Vargues and Grenier (1960) have reported agglutinin titers of 1:4 and 1:32 in 80 of 124 normal serums, 63 of which had titers of 1:4 or 1:8. In hypergammaglobulinemic serums, antibodies to this species were found in 76 of 106 subject with titers ranging slightly higher (maximum 1:64); but in this group, 38 of the positive serums had titers of 1:16 or higher.

Haemophilus influenzae. Glynn (1959), using species-specific antigen extracts of *H. influenzae* [Tunevall (1953)], recorded hemagglutination titers ranging from 1:125 to 1:2,000 to 4,000 in 12 of 50 control subjects. A somewhat higher proportion of reactors (11 of 33) at similar titers were found among asthmatics, and a still higher proportion (69 of 90) at titers ranging up to 1:8,000 to 16,000 among patients with bronchitis.

Bacteroides funduliformis. Complement-fixing and agglutinating antibodies were reported by Dack, Dragstedt, and Heinz (1936) and by Dack et al. (1939) in normal subjects, but more often in patients with ulcerative colitis. Dragstedt, Dack, and Kirsner (1941), however, stated that such antibodies were found only in patients with colitis, not in normal subjects. Bregman and Kirsner (1960), in the paper referred to above, were able to use this organism as well as proteus in hemagglutination reactions with ulcerative colitis serum. Feldman, Hester, and Wherry (1936) reported the presence of agglutinins to *B. funduliformis* in animal and in certain human serums with a maximum titer of 1:50; they observed a maximum titer of 1:100 in ulcerative colitis serum.

Fusobacterium fusiforme. Dicker (1938) reported complement fixation with this organism by the serum of a patient with empyema from whom the organism was recovered. Lahelle (1945) mentioned other instances in which serum antibodies accompanied disease attributed to this species, and himself reported positive agglutination and complement fixation with serum of 3 of 4 patients with fusospirochetal disease.

Indigenous Spirochetes. Antibodies to these microorganisms have been reported in normal subjects by Beck (1939); Kolmer, Kast, and Lynch (1941); and Robinson and Wichelhausen (1946) (see Chap. 6).

Candida albicans **and other** *Candida* **Species.** Todd (1937) found agglutinins in normal serums to a maximum titer of 1:640 in 259 of 1,150 subjects (22.5 per cent). Only 35 of these had a titer of 1:160 or higher. The presence of agglutinins was related to the occurrence of the organism in the mouth or throat (see Table 7-4). A similar relationship of positive serum (complement-fixation) tests to positive throat cultures for *C. albicans* has been reported more recently by Gargani (1958); see also Gargani, Carloni, and Pin (1959). Drake (1943) found 88 of 100 human serums positive for *C. albicans* by slide agglutination; 21 were positive for *C. krusei*. Agglutinin titers for *C. albicans* of 1:5 to 1:320 were reported by Norris and Rawson (1947) in 299 of 464 serum samples (64.5 per cent) submitted for serum tests for syphilis. In this series, the highest titer recorded among 13 serum samples from children was 1:10. Brody and Finch (1960), using the technique of immune adherence, showed a marked relationship of titer to age, with serum dilutions as great as 1:4,096 in cord blood, falling at 1 to 4 months to a maximum of 1:256 and rising again progressively to more than 1:4,096 at age 30 and above. These data have been drawn from a chart in the original which suggests that all serums tested were positive with a minimal titer of 1:32 (in the 1 to 4 month group); the data are those of a control group in a study concerned principally with lymphoma and related disease, and were not fully reported. They may be compared with the findings of Jensen and of Neter et al. for staphylococci, and with those of Cascio and his coworkers for *E. coli*, given in preceding paragraphs. Additional data pertaining to an age-related effect of serum on *C. albicans*, not clearly attributed to antibody, have been reported by Roth et al. (1959), who found that the serum of normal adults inhibits growth of this fungus. A much lower inhibitory activity was found in cord serum, with significant levels not attained until the third month of life. In a later paper, Roth and Goldstein (1961) reported similar but less marked growth inhibition of other *Candida* species; they also found the inhibitory effect diminished in most serums from patients with acute leukemic disease but not in chronic leukemia or other disease. The effect was impaired only slightly by heating the serums at 56° for up to 2 hours.

Peck et al. (1955) and Winner (1955) also presented data on antibodies to *C. albicans* (see Chap. 7). According to Tomšíková and Wagner (1958), both complete and incomplete antibodies to this organism and also to *C. tropicalis*, *C. pseudotropicalis*, *C. krusei*, and *C. parapsilosis*, were demonstrated by an agglutination technique in healthy persons and in those with candidiasis, in the latter more often at higher titers.

Interactions of Indigenous Microorganisms

It may safely be assumed that wherever in nature two or more species of microorganisms (or, for that matter, macroorganisms) grow in intimate association, each will interact with the others; and if, as in the present instance, the microorganisms grow upon a host organism, then the host will be in some way influenced by the interactions: "mere toleration is biologically and statistically improbable" [Lucas (1949)]. The problem is one of ecology, and while progress has been made in studying the microbial subject apart from man—in soil and in the bovine and ovine rumen, for example [see Thornton (1952); Hungate (1960)]—the ecology of the indigenous microbiota of man is in its earliest infancy. In man the problem is less accessible, much broader in its ramifications, and economically less urgent; indeed at present we can only guess at its practical significance.

The principal experimental approach to it is via the study of culture mixtures for their distinctive biochemical products or the stimulatory or inhibitory effects of each culture on the others. The study of culture pairs—especially in terms of population changes—presents formidable difficulties that are likely to become forbidding as the number of species is increased beyond two [see Topley and Fielden (1922); Annear and Hayes (1950); Rosebury, Gale, and Taylor (1954)]. Perhaps it will become more accessible with the aid of modern computer techniques. Nevertheless, enough scattered information has come from such studies to support the a priori hypothesis that members of the indigenous biota engage in a multitude of phenomena of microbic species interaction; and in some instances the mechanism of the effect is known or partly known. But the data are made up essentially of minutiae in great diversity, and the present treatment can hardly aim to do more than attempt to classify the data and provide sources. Brief reviews of the general subject have been presented previously by Rosebury, Gale, and Taylor (1954) and Rosebury and Sonnenwirth (1958).

The references given in the preceding paragraph embody such general principles as the literature affords. It may be worth emphasizing that cooperative as well as competitive interactive phenomena are found, and moreover, that both of these tend as a general rule—with exceptions—to be beneficial rather than harmful to the human host. This question of "benefit" and the meaning of "symbiosis" and similar terms in ecology is well analyzed in some of the papers in the Thornton symposium on symbiosis [see especially Gregory (1952); Baker (1952)].

Cooperative Interactions

Cooperative microbic interactions entail the sharing between species of metabolic mechanisms, although the category might be broadened to include genetic interchanges between forms not regarded as members of the same species [e.g., pneumococci and streptococci, Bracco et al. (1957); Pakula et al. (1958, 1959); *Escherichia* and salmonellae, Baron et al. (1959, 1960); Brinton and Baron (1960); Zinder (1960)]. The provision by the growth of aerobes of reducing conditions permitting the growth of anaerobes is a well known example of metabolic cooperation. *Satellitism*, in which 1 species grows in a nutritionally deficient medium in the neighborhood of another which synthesizes the missing nutrilites or, more generally, the provision by 1 species of growth factors required by another, is also well known. Examples of satellitism are the classic relation of *Haemophilus influenzae* to *Staphylococcus aureus* [Grassberger (1897)], of *H. parainfluenzae* to *Str. faecalis* [Pickett and Stewart (1953)], of a streptococcus to *Actinomyces israelii* [Negroni and Daglio (1949)], of *E. coli* to *Candida albicans* [Rosebury, Gale, and Taylor (1954); see Fig. 11-3*a* to *d*], and of *Bacteroides nigrescens* to *Staph. aureus* or other bacteria [Gibbons and Macdonald (1960); see also Shifrine and Biberstein (1960)]. Rosebury, Gale, and Taylor (1954) also found that growth of a strain of *Neisseria catarrhalis* was stimulated by any of the following: *Str. mitis, Str. faecalis, Staph. albus, E. coli,* and *Candida albicans.* A microaerophilic diphtheroid not otherwise identified was found by Nevin, Hampp, and Duey (1960) to stimulate the growth of *Borrelia vincenti.* Stimulation of lactobacilli in vitamin-deficient media by *Candida albicans* has been described by Young, Krasner, and Yudofsky (1956) and by Koser et al. (1960); see also Wilson and Goaz (1959, 1960) and Nakamura and Hartman (1961). Krieg and Pelczar (1961) studied "syntrophic" growth of *Str. faecalis* and *Lactobacillus plantarum*. Enhancement of both growth and pathogenicity of tubercle bacilli by a polysaccharide-like substance from *C. albicans* has been reported by Mankiewicz, Stackiewicz, and Liivak (1959) and Mankiewicz and Liivak (1960). Other synergistic phenomena involving *C. albicans* and enterobacteria are noted below in the category of inhibitory effects of the latter group.

Nurmikko (1954, 1955) has reported combined growth of mixtures of lactobacilli and *Leuconostoc* species and *Str. faecalis*, with synthesis of amino acids and vitamins, on media inadequate for pure culture growth. Other studies of synthesis in culture mixtures have been reported by Doctor and Couch (1954); see also Nurmikko (1957). A remarkable example of sharing of nutrients—affecting in this instance 2 mutants of the same species, *E. coli* (strain K-12), was detailed by Umbarger and Mueller (1951) and Umbarger and Magasanik (1951). One mutant required isoleucine, the other both isoleucine and valine; but the second could grow when supplied with the corresponding keto acids. Grown together in a medium deficient in both amino acids, the first mutant was able to synthesize enough of the keto acids to initiate growth of the second, which by converting the excess of the keto acid analogue to isoleucine in turn enabled the first to grow.

In other metabolic activities thought by their authors to have a bearing on the pathogenicity of mixed indigenous bacteria in the mouth, Schultz-Haudt and Scherp (1955) reported that *Fusobacterium fusiforme*, when grown aerobically in mixture with any one of a group of aerobes or microaerophiles, produced phenolsulfatase, for which the chondroitin sulfate of gingival tissue was suggested as a possible substrate. Thonard and Scherp (1958) observed that mixtures of unidentified mouth bacteria reversibly inhibited the collagenase of *Clostridium histolyticum*.

A sharing of hydrolytic enzymes in conventional fermentation reactions was observed by Castellani (1925–1927), who studied various microbic mixtures, including combinations of typhoid or Flexner bacilli or staphylococci with *Proteus vulgaris* or *P. morganii*. He showed the formation of gas in the presence of disaccharides fermented to acid by the former species alone and not affected in pure cultures of the second [see also Holman and Meekison (1926)].

Competitive Interactions

Interactions recognized by the adverse effect of one microbic species on the population growth of another would be expected to depend on either or both of two general principles: the removal from the environment by one species (the "effector") of concentrations of one or more substances, or of limiting conditions, required for survival of multiplication of the other ("test") species; or the production by the effector of toxic or inhibitory substances or states. It is curious that the former mechanism, insofar as interactions between species are concerned, has been difficult to establish. The phenomenon of *staling* or *direct antagonism*, in which a test species is seeded into or streaked on a medium containing an old culture of the effector, seems to depend on viability of the latter. Similar but not identical findings have been interpreted by Lockhart and Powelson (1953) and Charlton (1955) as dependent on depletion of nutrients, and by Wynne and Norman (1953) as induced by labile diffusible antibiotic substances. Lockhart and Powelson contended that inhibition of one species by another under these conditions is analogous to the stationary phase of the growth curve of a pure culture.

Competition for nutrients was probably one of the mechanisms operating in the early experiments of Topley and Fielden (1922). Broth cultures inoculated with a loopful of feces from man or mouse and incubated continuously were plated at intervals on MacConkey agar until no growth appeared or until the bacilli were entirely replaced by enterococci, which often happened. In many instances, only lactose fermenters appeared, but when nonfermenters developed, whether early or late, they tended to replace the fermenters over a period of 10 to 21 days. The nonfermenters were *P. vulgaris, P. morganii* and *Alcaligenes faecalis* from human and *Salmonella enteritidis* from mouse feces. In other experiments, in which pure cultures of enterobacteria were inoculated together and handled as before, a variety of results emerged. In one instance, inoculated typhoid bacilli, *S. paratyphi*, and Shiga and Flexner bacilli never appeared in subcultures. Proteus tended to predominate; *E. coli* suddenly appeared on the thirteenth day and later disappeared.

More recently, Dixon (1959) has studied nutrient broth mixtures of pairs of enterobacteria under varying conditions of inoculum concentration. When 1 of 5 pathogenic *E. coli* serotypes was mixed with 1 of 5 nonpathogenic serotypes of the same species in ratios from 3,000:1 to 1:200,000, the ratios found after growth in broth for 18 hours at 37° tended to approach 1:1; final values were 80:1 to 1:135. Similar results were obtained when one pathogenic serotype was mixed with 4 nonpathogens (initial ratios 1:45 to 1:600; final ratios 1:20 to 1:50). The equalizing tendency continued progressively during incubation for 168 hours, and was found to be slightly more marked at 44° than at 37°. Addition to the mixture of *Pseudomonas aeruginosa* or

S. typhimurium or both seemed to have little effect at 37°; at 44° these latter species tended to disappear at 18 hours. Dixon suggested that nutrient broth enrichment cultures be used for isolation of pathogens outnumbered in feces.

Most competitive microbic interactions reported are known or thought to be due to the production by the effector of either a pH unfavorable for growth of the test species or, more commonly, an antibiotic substance. The early history of this subject has been reviewed by Florey (1946). It is of course closely associated with the search for therapeutically or commercially useful antibiotic substances. Some reports, however, have been concerned with a possible mechanism of resistance to a particular disease, including diphtheria in early studies [Mühlenbach (1939)] and shigellosis more recently [Friedman and Halbert (1960)]. Still others, notably most studies of colicines (see page 382), seem to have had no comparable motivation. It is of passing interest that the search for useful antibiotics among indigenous effectors has been entirely fruitless, even though one species we have included among the group—*Pseudomonas aeruginosa*—provided the earliest example of a serious attempt to introduce an antibiotic, pyocyanase, in medicine [Emmerich and Löw (1899); see Florey (1946)].

The influence of low pH induced by certain bacterial species as an inhibitor of the growth of others may not be so simple as is commonly assumed. As we saw in Chap. 3, the effectors concerned, all originally regarded as lactobacilli, may include *Actinomyces bifidus* in the nurseling intestine and acidogenic corynebacteria in the adult vagina. The original evidence consisted in the finding of acidogenic bacilli and few other organisms in these locations. Torrey and Kahn (1923) found that *L. acidophilus* inhibited the putrefactive activity of clostridia in mixed cultures, and that the effect seemed to be due entirely to acid; although lactic acid appeared more inhibitory than hydrochloric acid at equivalent pH levels. Upton (1929) presented evidence that inhibition of *E. coli* and enterococci by bacterial filtrates of *A. bifidus* was dependent in part on acetic and formic acids—less so on lactic acid—as well as on the low pH.

Young, Krasner, and Yudkofsky (1956) found that lactobacilli, although stimulated by *Candida albicans* when grown with the yeast, produced excess lactic acid which depressed growth of the candida. Similar findings were presented by Koser et al. (1960). From other recent studies with lactobacilli referred to below, it appears that additional substances besides acid and hydrogen ions may participate in the inhibitory phenomena they effect. Richardson and Schmidt (1959), however, attributed inhibition of *Leptotrichia dentium* by viridans streptococci to acid production; and Perez-Miravete and Flores (1960), who studied viable counts of mixed cultures in broth of Döderlein's bacillus with several other bacterial species and *Candida*, found that after a variety of phenomena in the earlier growth phases, a logarithmic decline of the test organism usually appeared at a critical pH level different for each test species.

The following discussion deals with inhibitory phenomena known or thought to be due to antibiotic substances produced by the effector species. The data are classified by effector species, including only effectors regarded as indigenous to man.

Antibiotic Effects of Staphylococci. Dujardin-Beaumetz (1932) observed inhibition of *C. diphtheriae*, other corynebacteria and *Nocardia* spp. by occasional strains of staphylococci isolated from nasal mucus; the effect appeared only on solid media before growth of the test species started. Similar findings were reported by Duliscouët (1935), but this worker noted that some staphylococci, characterized as *Staph. aureus*, favored growth of corynebacteria while other strains were inhibitory. Su (1948*b*) gave the name "micrococcin" to a substance from an aberrant strain of micrococcus; the substance was reported as heat stable, dialyzable through cellophane, soluble in alcohol or chloroform but not in ether and only very sparingly in water. It exerted mainly bacteriostatic effects against *Bacillus subtilis*, staphylococci, streptococci including *Str. faecalis*, *Corynebacterium diphtheriae*, *B. anthracis*, and streptomyces; it was less active against clostridia and the H37v strain of tubercle bacillus. An attempted assay of micrococcin was reported by Heatley, Kelly, and Smith (1952).

Halbert, Swick, and Sonn (1953) studied the antibiotics produced by 22 staphylococcal cultures from the conjunctiva and the palpebral margin, selecting active catalase-producers. Nine different antibiotic agents were found, acting significantly only against Gram-positive test species, among them *C. hofmanni*, *Sarcina lutea*, *Mycobacterium smegmatis*, streptococci other than enterococci, *Bacillus* spp., clostridia, and staphylococci themselves. In a later study, Halbert, Sonn, and Swick (1954) reported that the staphylococci that inhibited *Clostridium septicum* in vitro also protected mice against experimental mixed infections. Liu (1954) found a yellow pigment-forming micrococcus that inhibited staphylococcal δ-lysin activity. *Staphylococcus aureus* has also been reported to inhibit lactobacilli [Ritter (1954)]; and 50 of 500 skin staphylococci, including both *albus* and *aureus* strains, were found by Lizgunova (1958) to inhibit a range of enterobacteria and both hemolytic and nonhemolytic streptococci. Inhibition of the fungus *Monosporum apiospermum* by both *Staph. aureus* and *Staph. albus* has been reported by Cormane, Plankensteiner, and Holland (1959). Berger and Prelle (1961) found that all of 10 strains of *Staphylococcus aureus* inhibited 28 of 30 strains of amphibiotic neisseriae.

Parker, Tomlinson, and Williams (1955) observed that nearly half the *Staph. aureus* strains recovered from impetigo inhibited corynebacteria, showing a narrow, sharply defined zone of inhibition on solid media. Fewer strains from other diseases or from nose and throat swabs had this effect. These workers noted, moreover, that most of the impetigo strains fell into phage type 71, and that nearly 90 per cent of this type, but few of other types, showed the sharply defined inhibitory zone effect. Further details and additional references were provided by Parker and Simmons (1959). *Staph. aureus*, phage type 71, certain closely related strains, but few others, inhibited *C. diphtheriae* and other corynebacteria (not *C. ulcerans, C. pyogenes,* or *C. haemolyticum*) with the typical sharply circumscribed zone. Other staphylococci inhibiting corynebacteria showed wider hazy zones. The sharp-zone effectors inhibited inactive or hazy-zone staphylococci. Hazy-zone inhibition persisted, but the sharp-zone effect was regularly lost in culture in a few months, accompanied by widening of susceptibility to lysis by typing phages.

Evans et al. (1950) mentioned the observation that *anaerobic micrococci* from skin inhibited *Corynebacterium acnes*.

Antibiotic Effects of Streptococci. A considerable literature that appeared especially during the 1930s detailing inhibitory effects of saliva on a variety of test bacteria included some effects attributable to lysozyme and others clearly dependent on the salivary streptococci. For this literature see Bibby, Clough, and Hine (1938); Thompson (1940); and Berger (1952). Colebrook, as early as 1915, described inhibition of *N. catarrhalis* and other neisseriae by streptococci and pneumococci. McLeod and Gordon (1922) attributed inhibition of staphylococci by pneumococci to hydrogen peroxide produced by the latter. Many workers have found that viridans streptococci inhibit *C. diphtheriae* or staphylococci in vitro [Besta and Kuhn (1934); Mühlenbach (1939); Holzl (1941); Thompson and Shibuya (1946); Annear and Hayes (1950); Hayes (1950); Annear (1951); Thompson and Johnson (1951); Rosebury, Gale, and Taylor (1954); Rosebury, Zeitinger, and Mogab (1956a); Myers (1959)]. Decreased virulence of diphtheria bacilli for guinea pigs when inoculated in broth mixture with streptococci was reported by Besta and Kuhn (1934) and by Holzl (1941). Evidence that the in vitro inhibitory effect is due to hydrogen peroxide has been presented by Bethge, Soehring, and Tschesche (1947); Hegemann (1950); Thompson and Johnson (1951); and Berger (1952). The effect is antagonized on media containing catalase from nonbacterial sources, e.g., erythrocytes or fresh potato juice; but it is of interest that the typical actively inhibited test species are themselves catalase producers. Failure to find measurable concentrations of hydrogen peroxide in saliva led Kraus et al. (1957) to con-

FIG. 11-1. Inhibition of *Staphylococcus aureus* by *Streptococcus salivarius* (*a,b*) *Str. mitis* (*c,d*) and a type I pneumococcus (*e,f*) on cross-titration plates. *a,c,e*, rabbit serum agar, photographed by transmitted light; *b,d,f*,

clude that this phenomenon is probably not significant in vivo. Although there is no direct evidence to the contrary, it may be desirable to leave the question open. Negative findings in vitro are hardly conclusive for processes in vivo, and the possibilities of microenvironments in the mouth may be worth exploring.

Viridans streptococci and enterococci have been found to inhibit many other test species, and not all of their effects can be attributed to hydrogen peroxide. Annear (1954) found that *Staph. aureus* was inhibited by *Str. faecalis* in broth mixtures. Rosebury, Zeitinger, and Mogab (1956a) listed the following as inhibited by *Str. mitis, Str. hominis,* and *Str. faecalis: Staph. aureus, Staph. albus, Micrococcus lysodeikticus, Sarcina lutea, Corynebacterium diphtheriae (gravis* and *mitis), C. xerosis, Neisseria meningitidis, N. catarrhalis, Str. pyogenes* group A, *Fusobacterium fusiforme* and, in a few tests, *E. coli* and *C. albicans.* Green and Dodd (1956) reported inhibition of lactobacilli by streptococci in roughly the following sequence of decreasing effector activity: *Str. mitis, Str. hominis, Str. faecalis, Str. lactis,* and (inactive), *Str. equinus.* Stark (1960) found that the hemolytic *zymogenes* variety of *Str. faecalis* and another enterococcus, *Str. durans,* inhibited *Clostridium perfringens* type A, *Cl. oedematiens,* and *Cl. septicum,* as well as pneumococci. The hemolytic form in particular also inhibited *Str. pyogenes.* Both Stark, and Green and Dodd (1956) observed the effects anaerobically as well as aerobically, the former worker also in catalase-containing media; hence they could not be attributed to hydrogen peroxide.

The importance of the interacting microbic concentrations in these phenomena was emphasized in the work of Annear and Hayes (1950); [see also Hayes (1950); Annear and Hayes (1951)] as well as in the studies of Dixon (1959) noted earlier. It has also been made clear in experiments in the writer's laboratory, which made use of a cross-titration of paired drops of effector and test species, each species being tested on a single plate in 4 concentrations usually at tenfold dilution intervals [Rosebury, Gale, and Taylor (1954); see Fig. 11-1]. Under these conditions a front of inhibition could be seen across the plate which appeared to be linear both in these tests and in many others in which the number of points was increased by using a dilution interval

---

rabbit blood agar, photographed by reflected light, showing antagonism of inhibition by blood in *b* and *f*, partial antagonism in *d*. Concentrations of streptococci and pneumococci (effector species) inoculated increase in columns from left to right by tenfold intervals; concentrations of staphylococcus (test species) inoculated increase similarly in rows from bottom to top. [*From Rosebury, Gale, and Taylor* (1954), *courtesy of J. Bacteriol.*]

of $\sqrt{10}$. Of particular interest in this connection was the finding of mutual inhibition between *Str. mitis* and *Str. pyogenes* group A, in which the higher concentrations of each species inhibited the lower concentrations of the other, both interactions appearing as separate linear fronts on the same plate (Fig. 11-2). This phenomenon, first described by the writer's group in the paper referred to (1954), was found on blood agar and appeared anaerobically as well as aerobically. The inhibition of the hemolytic by the greening streptococcus could also be demonstrated in broth and by a marked reduction of pathogenicity for mice [Rosebury, Zeitinger, and Mogab (1956b)] Imaizumi (1955) has reported that an enterococcus isolated from a mouse inhibited growth of a hemolytic streptococcus on blood agar. Bartels, Blechman, and Lorieo (1960) also reported inhibition of β streptococci by a streptococcus said to resemble *S. salivarius*, and stated that the effect was not due to hydrogen peroxide [see also Bartels, Blechman, and Wallach (1961)].

Sherwood et al. (1949) and Murray and Pearce (1949) have described inhibitory effects against hemolytic streptococci and pneumococci due to hyaluronidase produced by other β streptococci or other

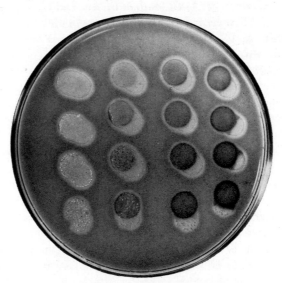

Fig. 11-2. Mutual inhibition of *Streptococcus mitis* and *Str. pyogenes* group A. Cross titration on rabbit blood agar incubated anaerobically. Concentration gradients as in Fig. 11-1. Where the *Str. mitis* inoculum concentration was highest and that of *Str. pyogenes* lowest—in the lower right corner—growth of the hemolytic form is restricted to a narrow zone below the effector; where the inoculum concentrations were reversed—in the upper left corner—the greening form is largely or entirely inhibited.

bacterial species. Both of these groups of workers also observed other antibiotic effects between strains of hemolytic streptococci which seemed to depend on a distinct substance called by the former workers "strep-tostasin." Antibiotic substances from lactic streptococci have been described by Oxford (1944); Hirsh (1946); Mattick, Hirsch, and Berridge (1947); Hirsch and Wheater (1951); and Briggs and Newland (1953).

Effects of Lactobacilli. Lactobacilli have been found to exert antibiotic effects apart from those due to acid and mentioned in an earlier paragraph. The "lactobacillin" described by Wheater, Hirsch, and Mattick (1951) as acting against *Staphylococcus aureus*, seemed to the same workers in a later paper (1952) to be hydrogen peroxide. More recently, Vincent, Veomett, and Riley (1959) described as "lactocidin" a nonvolatile, nondialyzable substance from *L. acidophilus* that inhibited a range of enterobacteria, saprophytic mycobacteria, fungi, and other organisms.

Inhibitory effects induced by corynebacteria, apparently not including indigenous species as effectors, have been described by Thibaut (1949), Munch-Peterson (1954), and Thibaut and Fredericq (1956).

Antibiotic Activity of Pseudomonads. *Ps. aeruginosa*, as we have seen, was the first microorganism among those we list as indigenous to disclose antibiotic effects [Bouchard (1889)]. Florey (1946), in a lecture on the history of antibiotics, stated that "Interest in the products of *Ps. pyocyanea*, as it is now called, is considerable at the present time, for Doisy and his colleagues have recently isolated four crystalline antibiotics from it and work on other substances produced by this organism is in progress in Sweden." These remarks were undocumented and the writer has not discovered references to correspond; presumably the products were not found commercially useful. Emmerich and Löw (1899) applied the name "pyocyanase" to an extract of an old culture of this organism, thinking of it as an enzyme, and found it active in vitro against *B. anthracis*, *Vibrio cholerae*, *S. typhi*, *C. diphtheriae*, *Pasteurella pestis*, and staphylococci. Porter (1946) listed "pyocyanase" as a thermostable agent with activity due largely to unsaturated fatty acids. Schoenthal (1941), who gave much of the earlier literature, noted that the enzymic nature of "pyocyanase" had been questioned, and himself described 3 antibacterial substances isolated from chloroform extracts of *Ps. aeruginosa:* (1) the blue pigment *pyocyanin,* said to be the first phenazonium compound discovered in nature, found moderately active against *V. cholerae* and *Staph. aureus,* and toxic for mice; (2) α-oxyphenazine, strongly bactericidal toward the same test species and inhibitory to a long list of other species, including the diphtheria, anthrax, Shiga, and Friedländer bacilli, *Shigella sonnei,* the meningococcus, pneumococcus type I, β streptococci, *Salmonella typhosa*, *S. schottmülleri*, and *Proteus vulgaris*, with toxicity reported as low; (3) an almost colorless bacteriolytic agent also active against cholera vibrios. Klite and Gale (1961) found that a substance produced in broth cultures of *Ps. aeruginosa* inhibited the growth of *Candida albicans* and other fungi (see also enterobacteria-candida interactions, below).

Studies of the inhibitory effects of extracts or products of *Ps. aeruginosa* have also been reported by Stokes, Peck, and Woodward (1942); Sternini (1956); and Chernomordik (1959). Hamon (1956) has described the production by 10 of 15 strains of *Ps. aeruginosa* of *pyocines* analogous to *colicines* in that they act against members of the producing group (in this instance, other pseudomonads). These substances were reported to be protein or to contain a protein fraction and to differ from other antibiotic substances produced by this microorganism. They have been employed in conjunction with specific bacteriophages for type classification of *Ps. aeruginosa* [Holloway (1960); see Chap. 4].

Antibiotic Effects of Enterobacteria. Several coliform organisms, including prominently *E. coli* itself, as well as proteus and other members of this broad group, have been found active both against distinct species or groups and against members of the species or group producing the agent. These effects may be subdivided into those involving (1) *Candida* spp., (2) various heterologous species, and (3) enterobacteria themselves.

Enterobacteria-Candida Interactions. Inhibition of a strain of candida —in this instance *C. krusei*—by *E. coli* was first reported by Paine (1952) in broth mixtures. Martin (1953) found that a saprophytic lactose-negative coliform rod inhibited the growth of several fungi including *C. albicans*. Inhibition of 2 strains of *C. albicans* by each of 3 strains of *E. coli* was observed on agar in the cross-titration experiments of Rosebury, Gale, and Taylor (1954) mentioned above (see Fig. 11-3e,f), and confirmed in broth mixtures. Akiba and his coworkers [Akiba and Iwata (1953, 1954); Akiba, Iwata, and Mochizuki (1954)] have described a saprophytic organism with properties suggestive of both *Proteus vulgaris* and *Serratia marcescens* which lyses *C. albicans* and other fungi. Inhibition and partial lysis of *Candida albicans* by proteus has been reported by Bizot (1955). Banič (1960) has also found that *E. coli* and, in addition, *K. aerogenes*, inhibit *C. albicans*. On the other hand, Staib and Ata (1957) have reported mutual inhibition of *E. coli* and *C. krusei*; and Emmanouilidou-Arseni and Soultani (1960) have noted briefly that on Sabouraud's glucose agar a high proportion of strains of *C. ablicans*, and smaller proportions of other candidas, inhibit *E. coli*, and also inhibit *Staph. aureus*, *P. vulgaris*, and

Ps. aeruginosa. As noted above, Klite and Gale (1961) have reported inhibition of *C. albicans* by *Ps. aeruginosa.*

Gale and Sandoval (1957) observed that injection of *E. coli* and *C. albicans* into mice in different ways resulted in either protection or enhancement of infection. When a prior injection of a nonlethal dose of *E. coli* was given intravenously or intraperitoneally, it protected mice against otherwise lethal doses of *C. albicans* given intravenously. When the colon bacillus was injected after the yeast, the result was either a delay or an acceleration of death depending on the dose of *E. coli.* Killed *E. coli,* or as little as 1 μg of coli O antigen extracted by the Boivin method, enhanced *C. albicans* infection, perhaps by impairment of the properdin system. Yamabayashi (1958) has also reported enhancement of mouse pathogenicity of *C. albicans* in mixture with *Proteus vulgaris* or *Pseudomonas aeruginosa* attributed to inactivation of the properdin system by the zymosan-like polysaccharide of candida; in this instance *E. coli* was found less active.

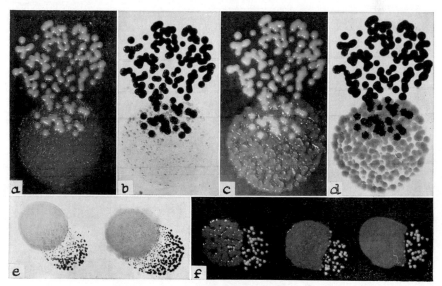

Fig. 11-3. Interaction on agar of *Escherichia coli* and *Candida albicans.* *a,b,c,d,* stimulation of *E. coli* (in lower drop) by *C. albicans.* The same pair of overlapping drops is shown in the four figures, photographed in *a* and *c* by reflected light and in *b* and *d* by transmitted light. Douglas lactate agar after incubation at 37° for 48 hours (*a,b*) and 72 hours (*c,d*); *E. coli* failed to grow independently on this medium during the same interval. *e,f,* inhibition of *C. albicans* (at right) by *E. coli. e,* Fildes (lactate-salts) agar plus 0.5 per cent yeast extract, transmitted light. *f,* infusion agar containing bromcresol green, reflected light. [*From Rosebury, Gale, and Taylor,* (1954), *courtesy of J. Bacteriol.*]

Petru (1956) has suggested that *Vibrio sputorum* may act in vivo (in the vagina) as an antagonist of *C. albicans*.

Antagonism of Other Groups by Enterobacteria. Antagonistic effects of *E. coli* and other enterobacteria against test species other than fungi and enterobacteria proper (especially *Escherichia* and *Shigella*) have been reported only sporadically. Heatley and Florey (1946) found that a colicine-producing strain of *E. coli* from cat feces inhibited *Staph. aureus, B. subtilis, Ps. aeruginosa,* and *Corynebacterium xerosis*—perhaps via hydrogen peroxide formed in the presence of glucose. Inhibition of *Staph. aureus* by *E. coli* has also been reported by Blackford, Parr, and Robbins (1951) and more recently by Banič (1960), who noted that *K. aerogenes* was also active and *Staph. albus (epidermidis)* also affected. Only doubtful inhibition by *E. coli* of *aureus* and *albus* staphylococci, as well as of *C. diphtheriae* strain PW8 and *Neisseria catarrhalis* (which was also stimulated on the same plate) was reported in the studies of Rosebury, Gale, and Taylor (1954).

Antagonism has also been described of *E. coli* toward human *Mycobacterium tuberculosis* [Gillissen and Carlson (1953)] and toward *Bacillus anthracis* [Gillissen (1953)], said to be dependent in both instances on intimate association in mixed culture. Sieburth, McGinnis, and Skinner (1952), in a study of the effects of antibiotics on the growth of turkey poults, were led to the finding that *Proteus mirabilis* is inhibited on agar as well as in vivo by *E. coli*. In studies mainly concerned with shigellosis, Halbert (1948a) listed in a table a series of Gram-positive and Gram-negative species, the latter including certain strains of *E. coli* and *Shigella*, in addition to other enteric and nonenteric forms (among them *Proteus* X-2), as having been "very slightly susceptible or completely resistant" to the action of living coliform organisms. Other *Shigella* and *E. coli* strains, but no other species, were moderately or highly susceptible. Blackford, Parr, and Robbins (1951) found that a strain of *Alcaligenes faecalis* showed varying activity against *Vibrio metchnikovii*. Freter (1956) has presented evidence of protection of mice and guinea pigs against infection with *Vibrio cholerae* (and also against *Shigella flexneri* infection) following introduction into the intestinal tract of a streptomycin-resistant strain of *E. coli;* but antagonism could not be demonstrated in vitro. By contrast, Sarkar and Tribedi (1953) reported that *V. cholerae* is actively antagonistic to *E. coli* in mixed broth culture.

Antagonism of Enterobacteria by Enterobacteria. Colicines. Antibiotic substances produced by enterobacteria, especially by *E. coli* strains and many *Shigella*, and acting upon members of the same group, were first described by Nissle (1916) and by Gratia (1925, 1932) and were given the name *colicines* by Fredericq (1946). The subject has generated a large literature that has been reviewed by Fredericq (1953, 1957) and requires only brief mention here. Colicines are produced by strains of *E. coli*, many *Shigella*, some *E. freundii*, and fewer *Salmonella* [Fredericq (1957)]; effectors have also been observed among the *Alcalescens-Dispar* group [Levine and Tanimoto (1954)], and in 1 of 27 strains of *Klebsiella* [Linton (1960)]. Test or indicator strains include certain *E. coli* strains (ϕ, B, C, or K-12) or any *Sh. sonnei* [Fredericq (1957)]. Since the antibiotics diffuse slowly in agar and are resistant to chloroform, tests are usually performed by stabbing the effector ("colicinogenic") strain usually at 8 points on a plate, incubating for 48 hours at 37°, sterilizing with chloroform vapor, and then seeding the indicator strain by various methods, such as applying for a few minutes a disk of filter paper soaked in the culture. After 24 hours' incubation, zones of inhibition are found around colicine-producing colonies.

Colicines comprise a varied group of antibiotic substances. At least 17 different colicines were accounted for by Fredericq in 1953, distinguished by spectrum of activity, form of the inhibition zone, diffusibility, heat resistance, and sensitivity to proteolytic enzymes. They have been called colicines A, B, C, etc. Particular interest has attached to the suggestion put forward by Gratia (1932) and by Fredericq (1953) [see also Lwoff (1953)] of resemblances between colicines and bacteriophages, although colicines do not appear to contain DNA and are known not to be transmissible [see also Ryan, Fried, and Mukai (1955); Mukai (1960)]. Goebel and his coworkers [(1956–1959); Amano, Goebel, and Smidth (1958)], after extensive studies of colicine K, found it associated with a protein fraction of the O antigen of the effector strain (*E. coli* K-235). Colicine K and the putatively corresponding phage T6 were shown to be chemically and serologically distinct. Papavassiliou (1961), moreover, has found in a study of 138 strains of *E. coli* that colicinogeny and lysogeny are not correlated but occur independently.

Halbert (1948*a,b*) has presented evidence that the development of colicine-producing organisms in the intestine during the course of shigellosis may contribute to recovery from the disease. Antibiotic-producing strains of *E. coli* growing in the peritoneal cavity and subcutaneous tissues of mice were found by Halbert and Swick (1950) to secrete, into local exudates and serum, antibiotics that seemed identical with those formed in vitro. Nonantibiotic-producing *E. coli* strains did not show these effects. More recently Friedman and Halbert (1960) reported that an antibiotic-producing *E. coli* strain inhibited *Shigella paradysenteriae* when given to adult mice as a mixed infection. With a similar mixture using a nonantibiotic-producing *E. coli*, both members of the mixture proliferated. Comparable inhibitory activity could not be demonstrated in newborn mice when the pathogen was a lethal *E. coli* strain. It seems of interest that Saphra and Wassermann (1954) explained a low frequency of healthy carriers of *Salmonella choleraesuis*, despite a high frequency of this organism in disease of man, on the ground that the pathogen is selectively suppressed in the intestinal tract. They found it to be almost completely overgrown by *E. coli* in mixed culture, whereas *S. anatum*, which showed a high carrier rate, grew well in vitro with *E. coli*.

Colicines have been used for typing enteropathogenic and other strains of *E. coli* and *Shigella sonnei* [Abbott and Shannon (1958); Hamon and Brault (1959); Cefalu and Bavastrelli (1959); Bavastrelli (1959); Linton (1960); Parr, El Shawi, and Robbins (1960)].

References

Abbott, J. D., and Shannon, R., 1958, *J. Clin. Pathol.*, **11**:71.

Akiba, T., and Iwata, K., 1953, *Japan. J. Bacteriol.*, **8**:951.

————, and ————, 1954, *ibid.*, **9**:1.

————, and ————, 1954, *Japan J. Exptl. Med.*, **24**:159.

————, ————, and Mochizuki, T., 1954, *Japan. J. Bacteriol.*, **9**:895.

Almquist, H. J., Pentler, C. F., and Mecchi, E., 1938, *Proc. Soc. Exptl. Biol. Med.*, **38**:336.

Amano, T., Goebel, W. F., and Smidth, E. M., 1958, *J. Exptl. Med.*, **108**:731.

Annear, D. I., 1951, *Australian J. Exptl. Biol. Med. Sci.*, **29**:93.

————, and Hayes, L., 1950, *ibid.*, **28**:183.

————, 1954, personal communication.

Appleton, J. L. T., 1950, *Bacterial Infection in Dental Practice*, 4th ed., Lea & Febiger, Philadelphia, p. 415.

Arnold, F. A., 1942, *Public Health Repts.*, **57**:1599.

Arnold, L., and Brody, L., 1926, *Am. J. Hyg.*, **6**:672.

Baker, F., 1952, *Proc. Roy. Soc. B*, **139**:204.

Banič, S., 1960, *Zentr. Bakteriol. Parasitenk., I Orig.*, **180**:27.

Barnes, R. H., and Fiala, G., 1958, *J. Nutrition*, **65**:103.

————, and ————, 1959, *ibid.*, **68**:603.

————, ————, McGehee, B., and Brown, A., 1957, *ibid.*, **63**:489.

Baron, L. S., Carey, W. F., and Spilman, W. M., 1959, *Proc. Nat. Acad. Sci.*, **45**:976, 1752.

————, Spilman, W. M., and Carey, W. F., 1959, *Science*, **130**:566.

————, ————, and ————, 1960, *J. Exptl. Med.*, **112**:361.

Bartels, H. A., Blechman, H., and Lorieo, D., 1960, *J. Dental Research*, **39**:687.

————, ————, and Wallach, G., 1961, *Oral Surg. Oral. Med. Oral Pathol.*, **14**:619.

Bavastrelli, L., 1959, *Riv. Ist. Sieroterap. Ital.*, **34**:172 (*Biol. Abstr.*).

Beck, A., 1939, *J. Hyg.*, **39**:298.

Berger, U., 1952, *Z. Hyg.*, **133**:371.

————, and Prelle, H., 1961, *Z. Immunitätsforsch.*, **122**:35.

Besta, B., and Kuhn, H., 1934, *ibid.*, **116**:520.

Bethge, J., Soehring, K., and Tschesche, R., 1947, Z. Naturforsch., 2b:12.
Bibby, B. G., Clough, O. W., and Hine, M. K., 1938, J. Am. Dental Assoc., 25:1290.
Biely, J., and March, B., 1951, Science, 114:330.
Bizot, M., 1955, Presse Méd., 62:1251.
Blackford, V. L., Parr, L. W., and Robbins, M. L., 1951, Antibiotics & Chemotherapy, 1:392.
Bloomfield, A. L., 1920, J. Am. Med. Assoc., 74:628, 1597.
——, 1922, Bull. Johns Hopkins Hosp., 33:145.
——, 1922, J. Am. Med. Assoc., 78:1751.
Boger, W. P., Frankel, J. W., and Gavin, J. J., 1960, Proc. Soc. Exptl. Biol. Med., 104:639.
Borgström, B., Dahlqvist, A., Gustafsson, B. E., Lundh, G., and Malmquist, J., 1959, ibid., 102:154.
Bouchard, C., 1889, Comp. Rend. Acad. Sci., 108:713.
Bracco, R. M., Krauss, M. R., Roe, A. S., and MacLeod, C. M., 1957, J. Exptl. Med., 106:247.
Bregman, E., and Kirsner, J. B., 1960, J. Lab. Clin. Med., 56:795.
Briggs, C. A. E., and Newland, L. G. M., 1953, J. Dairy Research, 20:189.
Brinton, C. C., Jr., and Baron, L. S., 1960, Biochim. et Biophys. Acta, 42:298.
Brody, J. I., and Finch, S. C., 1960, Blood, 15:830.
Burtenshaw, J. M. L., 1942, J. Hyg., 42:184.
Caminiti, F. P., 1939, Ann. Igiene, 49:654 (Biol. Abstr.).
Cascio, G., Purpura, R., and Priolisi, A., 1959, Giorn. Mal. Infettive e Parassit., 11:941, 942 (Biol. Abstr.).
Castellani, A., 1925–26, Proc. Soc. Exptl. Biol. Med., 23:481.
——, 1926–27, ibid., 24:511.
Cefalu, M., and Bavastrelli, L., 1959, Boll. Ist. Sieroterap. Milan, 38:86 (Biol. Abstr.).
Charlton, G., 1955, J. Bacteriol., 70:56.
Chernomordik, A. B., 1959, Zhur. Mikrobiol. Epidemiol. Immunobiol., 30:162 (Biol. Abstr.).
Cherry, W. B., Goldman, M., and Carski, T. R., 1960, Fluorescent Antibody Techniques in the Diagnosis of Communicable Diseases, U.S. Public Health Serv., Pub. No. 729, Atlanta.
Colebrook, L., 1915, Lancet, 2:1136.
——, Lowbury, E. J. L., and Hurst, L., 1960, J. Hyg., 58:357.
Cormane, R. H., Plankensteiner, R., and Holland, M. L., 1959, J. Invest. Dermatol., 33:75.
Cornbleet, T., and Montgomery, B. E., 1931, Arch. Dermatol. Syphilol. 23:908.
Cregan, J., Dunlop, E. E., and Hayward, N. J., 1953, Brit. Med. J., 2:1248.
Dack, G. M., Dragstedt, L. R., and Heinz, T. E., 1936, J. Am. Med., Assoc., 106:7.
——, Kirsner, J. B., Dragstedt, L. R., and Johnson, R., 1939, J. Inf. Dis., 65:200.
——, and Petran, E., 1934, ibid., 54:204.
——, and Woolpert, O., 1932, J. Preven. Med., 6:129.
Dicker, H., 1938, Zentr. Bakteriol. Parasitenk., I Orig., 141:37.
Dietz, V. H., Williams, N. B., and Lawton, W. E., 1943, J. Am. Dental Assoc., 30:838.
Dineen, P., 1960, Proc. Soc. Exptl. Biol. Med., 104:760.

Dixon, J. M. S., 1959, *J. Hyg.*, **57**:174.
———, 1960, *J. Pathol. Bacteriol.*, **79**:131.
Doctor, V. M., and Couch, J. R., 1954, *Arch. Biochem. Biophys.*, **51**:530.
Dold, H., and Weigmann, F., 1934, *Z. Hyg.*, **116**:158.
Dragstedt, L. R., Dack, G. M., and Kirsner, J. B., 1941, *Ann. Surg.*, **114**:653.
Drake, C. H., 1943, *J. Bacteriol.*, **46**:486.
Dujardin-Beaumetz, E., 1932, *Comp. Rend. Soc. Biol.*, **110**:1210.
Duliscouët, R., 1935, *ibid.*, **118**:1277.
Emmanouilidou-Arseni, A., and Soultani, D., 1960, *J. Bacteriol.*, **80**:137.
Emmerich, R., and Löw, O., 1899, *Z. Hyg.*, **31**:1.
Evans, C. A., Smith, W. M., Johnston, E. A., and Giblett, E. R., 1950, *J. Invest. Dermatol.*, **15**:305.
Feldman, W. H., Hester, H. R., and Wherry, F. P., 1936, *J. Inf. Dis.*, **59**:159.
Ferguson, W. W., and June, R. C., 1952, *Am. J. Hyg.*, **55**:155.
Finkelstein, R. A., and Sulkin, S. E., 1958, *J. Bacteriol.*, **75**:339.
Fisher, M. W., 1959, *Nature*, **183**:1792.
Fisher, S., 1960, *Australian J. Exptl. Biol. Med. Sci.*, **38**:339.
Florey, H. W., 1933, *J. Pathol. Bacteriol.*, **37**:283.
———, 1946, *Yale J. Biol. Med.*, **19**:101.
Fox, J. E., and Lowbury, E. J. L., 1953, *J. Pathol. Bacteriol.*, **65**:519.
Franěk, F., Říha, I., and Šterzl, J., 1961, *Nature*, **189**:1020.
Fredericq, P., 1946, *Schweiz. Z. allgem. Pathol. Bakteriol.*, **9**:385, cited by Fredericq (1957).
———, 1953, *Ann. Inst. Pasteur*, **84**:294.
———, 1957, *Ann. Rev. Microbiol.*, **11**:7.
Freter, R., 1956, *J. Exptl. Med.*, **104**:411, 419.
Fridericia, L. S., Freudenthal, P., Gudjounsson, S., Johansen, G., and Schoubye, N., 1927–28, *J. Hyg.*, **27**:70.
Friedman, D. R., and Halbert, S. P., 1960, *J. Immunol.*, **84**:11.
Gaines, S., and Landy, M., 1955, *J. Bacteriol.*, **69**:628.
Gale, D., and Sandoval, B., 1957, *ibid.*, **73**:616.
Gargani, G., 1958, *Sperimentale*, **108**:110 (*Biol. Abstr.*).
———, Carloni, M., and Pin, R., 1959, *Ann. Sclavo*, **1**:263 (*Biol. Abstr.*).
Gibbons, R. J., and Macdonald, J. B., 1960, *J. Bacteriol.*, **80**:164.
Gibson, H. J., 1930, *J. Hyg.*, **30**:337.
Gillespie, H. B, Steber, M. S., Scott, E. N., and Christ, Y. S., 1950*a*, *J. Immunol.*, **65**:105.
———, ———, and Waugh, M. H., 1950*b*, *ibid.*, **65**:115.
Gillissen, G., 1953, *Zentr. Bakteriol. Parasitenk., I Orig.*, **159**:187.
———, and Carlson, S., 1952, *Z. Immunitätsforsch.*, **109**:444.
Glimstedt, G., 1936, *Acta Pathol. Microbiol. Scand.*, Suppl. 30.
Glynn, A. A., 1959, *Brit. Med. J.*, **2**:911.
Goebel, W. F., and Amano, T., 1959, *Science*, **129**:1284.
———, and Barry, G. T., 1958, *J. Exptl. Med.*, **107**:185.
———, ———, and Amano, T., 1957, *Science*, **126**:1231.
———, ———, and Shedlovsky, T., 1956, *J. Exptl. Med.*, **103**:577.
Gordon, H. A., 1955, *Bull. N. Y. Acad. Med.*, **31**:239.
———, 1959, *Ann. N. Y. Acad. Sci.*, **78**:208.
———, Wagner, M., Luckey, T. D., and Reyniers, J. A., 1959, *J. Inf. Dis.*, **105**:31.
Goudie, J. G., 1959, *J. Pathol. Bacteriol.*, **78**:17.
———, and Duncan, I. B. R., 1956, *ibid.*, **72**:381.

Grassberger, R., 1897, *Wien. klin. Wochschr.*, **10**:485.
Gratia, A., 1925, *Comp. Rend. Soc. Biol.*, **93**:1040.
————, 1932, *Ann. Inst. Pasteur*, **48**:413.
Green, G. E., and Dodd, M. C., 1956, *J. Bacteriol.*, **72**:690.
Gregory, F. G., 1952, *Proc. Roy. Soc. B.*, **170**:202.
Grubb, T. C., and Puetzer, B., 1947, *J. Lab. Clin. Med.*, **32**:566.
Gustafsson, B. E., 1948, *Acta Pathol. Microbiol. Scand.*, Suppl. 73, 1.
————, 1959, *Ann. N. Y. Acad. Sci.*, **78**:166.
————, and Fitzgerald, R. J., 1960, *Proc. Soc. Exptl. Biol. Med.*, **104**:319.
————, and Lanke, L. S., 1960, *J. Exptl. Med.*, **112**:975.
Halbert, S. P., 1948a, *J. Immunol.*, **58**:153.
————, 1948b, *ibid.*, **60**:359.
————, Sonn, C., and Swick, L., 1954, *ibid.*, **73**:3.
————, and Swick, L. S., 1950, *ibid.*, **65**:675.
————, ————, and Sonn, C., 1953, *ibid.*, **70**:400.
Hamon, Y., 1956, *Ann. Inst. Pasteur*, **91**:82.
————, and Brault, G., 1959, *ibid.*, **96**:614.
Hayes, L., 1950, *Australian J. Exptl. Biol. Med. Sci.*, **28**:487.
Heatley, N. G., and Florey, H. W., 1946, *Brit. J. Exptl. Pathol.*, **27**:378.
————, Kelly, B. K., and Smith, N., 1952, *J. Gen. Microbiol.*, **6**:30.
Hegemann, F., 1950, *Z. Hyg.*, **131**:355.
Hirsch, A., 1946, *Proc. Soc. Appl. Bacteriol.*, p. 26 (*Biol. Abstr.*).
————, and Wheater, D. M., 1951, *Nature*, **168**:607.
Hirst, L. F., 1917, *J. Roy. Army Med. Corps.*, **29**:476.
Holloway, B. W., 1960, *J. Pathol. Bacteriol.*, **80**:448.
Holm, P., and Kwapinski, J. B., 1959, *Acta Pathol. Microbiol. Scand.*, **45**: 107.
Holman, W. L., and Meekison, D. M., 1926, *J. Inf. Dis.*, **39**:145.
Holzl, H., 1941, *Z. Hyg.*, **123**:500.
Horton, R. E., and Hickey, J. L. S., 1961, *Proc. Animal Care Panel*, **11**:93.
Howell, K. M., and Corrigan, M., 1928, *J. Inf. Dis.*, **42**:149.
Hungate, R. E., 1960, *Bacteriol. Revs.*, **24**:353.
Imaizumi, K., 1955, *Japan. J. Vet. Sci.*, **17**:30 (*Biol. Abstr.*).
Ingalls, M. S., 1937, *J. Immunol.*, **33**:123.
Jay, P., Crowley, M., and Bunting, R. W., 1930, *J. Dental Research*, **12**:429.
————, ————, and ————, 1932, *J. Am. Dental Assoc.*, **19**:265.
Jensen, K., 1958, *Acta Allergol.*, **12**:210.
————, 1958, *Acta Pathol. Microbiol. Scand.*, **44**:421.
————, 1959, Summary of Dissertation, Institute of Pathology, University of Copenhagen.
————, 1959, *Acta Allergol.*, **13**:89.
Johansson, K. R., Peterson, G. E., and Dick, E. C. 1953, *J. Nutrition*, **49**:135.
————, and Sarles, W. B., 1949, *Bacteriol. Revs.*, **13**:25.
June, R. C., Ferguson, W. W., and Worfel, M. T., 1953, *Am. J. Hyg.*, **57**:222.
Keitel, H. G., 1950, *J. Inf. Dis.*, **86**:219.
Kerr, A. C., and Wedderburn, D. L., 1958, *Brit. Dent. J.*, **105**:321.
Klite, P. D. and Gale, G. R., 1961, *Antibiotics & Chemotherapy*, **11**:256.
Knighton, H. T., 1942, *J. Am. Dental Assoc.*, **29**:2012.
Kolmer, J. A., Kast, C. C., and Lynch, E., 1941, *Am. J. Syphilis, Gonorrhea, Venereal Diseases*, **25**:300, 412.
Koser, S. A., Hodges, E., Tribby, I., and Stuedell, J. T., 1960, *J. Inf. Dis.*, **106**:60.

Kraus, F. W., Nickerson, J. F., Perry, W. I., and Walker, A. P., 1957, *J. Bacteriol.*, **73**:727.

Krehl, W. A., and Liao, S. J., 1951, *Ann. Rev. Microbiol.*, **5**:121.

Kriedler, W. A., 1926, *J. Inf. Dis.*, **39**:186.

Krieg, N. R., and Pelczar, M. J., Jr., 1961, *J. Gen. Microbiol.*, **25**:77.

Lahelle, O., 1945, *Acta Pathol. Microbiol. Scand.*, **22**:34.

Lamoreux, W. F., and Schumacher, A. E., 1940, *Poultry Sci.*, **19**:418, cited by Mickelsen (1956).

Lehmann, W., 1926, *Deut. Arch. klin. Med.*, **150**:127.

Levine, M., and Tanimoto, R. H., 1954, *J. Bacteriol.*, **67**:537.

Lilley, A. B., and Bearup, A. J., 1928, *Med. J. Australia*, **1**:362.

Linton, K. B., 1960, *J. Clin. Pathol.*, **13**:168.

Liu, P., 1954, *J. Bacteriol.*, **68**:718.

Lizgunova, A. V., 1958, *J. Microbiol. Epidemiol. Immunobiol.* (transl.), **29**:297.

Lockhart, W. R., and Powelson, D. M., 1953, *J. Bacteriol.*, **65**:293.

Lucas, C. E., 1949, in *Selective Toxicity and Antibiotics, Symposia Soc. Exptl. Biol.*, **3**:336.

Luckey, T. D., 1959*a*, *Ann. N. Y. Acad. Sci.*, **78**:127.

————, 1959*b*, *ibid.*, **78**:380.

————, Pleasants, J. R., and Reyniers, J. A., 1955, *J. Nutrition*, **55**:105.

————, and Reyniers, J. A., 1954, *Ann. N. Y. Acad. Sci.*, **57**:932.

Lwoff, A., 1953, *Bacteriol. Revs.*, **12**:269.

Mankiewicz, E., and Liivak, M., 1960, *Nature*, **187**:250.

————, Stackiewicz, E., and Liivak, M., 1959, *Can. J. Microbiol.*, **5**:261.

Marchionini, A., 1929, *Arch. Dermatol. u. Syphilis*, **158**:290.

————, 1938, *Klin. Wochschr.*, **17**:1831.

————, and Cerutti, P., 1932, *Arch. Dermatol. u. Syphilis*, **166**:354.

————, and Hausknecht, W., 1938, *Klin. Wochschr.*, **17**:663.

————, and Schmidt, R., 1938, *ibid.*, **17**:773.

————, and ————, 1939, *ibid.*, **18**:461.

————, ————, and Kiefer, J., 1938, *ibid.*, **17**:736.

Martin, H. L., 1953, *Antibiotics & Chemotherapy*, **3**:861.

Mathieson, D. R., Harrision, R., Hammond, C., and Henrici, A. T., 1935, *Am. J. Hyg.*, **21**:405.

Mattick, A. T. R., Hirsch, A., and Berridge, N. J., 1947, *Lancet*, **2**:5.

Mazzarella, M. A., and Shklair, I. L., 1960, *J. Dental Research*, **39**:685.

McLeod, J. W., and Gordon, J., 1922, *Biochem. J.*, **16**:499.

Michael, J. G., and Landy, M., 1961, *J. Inf. Dis.*, **108**:90.

Mickelsen, O., 1956, *Vitamins and Hormones*, **14**:1.

Miyakawa, M., 1959, *Ann. N. Y. Acad. Sci.*, **78**:221.

Mühlenbach, V., 1939, *Z. Hyg.*, **121**:569.

Mukai, F. H., 1960, *J. Gen. Microbiol.*, **23**:539.

Munch-Peterson, E., 1954, *Australian J. Exptl. Biol. Med. Sci.*, **32**:361.

Murray, R. G. E., and Pearce, R. H., 1949, *Can. J. Research, Sect. E*, **27**:254.

Muschel, L. H., 1960, *Proc. Soc. Exptl. Biol. Med.*, **103**:632.

Myers, D. M., 1959, *Am. J. Clin. Pathol.*, **31**:332.

Nakamura, L. K., and Hartman, P. A., 1961, *J. Bacteriol.*, **81**:519.

Nathanson, R. B., 1960, *J. Invest. Dermatol.*, **35**:261.

Needell, M. H., Neter, E., Staubitz, W. J., and Bingham, W. A., 1955, *J. Urol.*, **74**:674.

Negroni, P., and Daglio, C. A. N., 1949, *Mycopathologia*, 4:327.

Neter, E., Drislane, A. M., Harris, A. H., and Gorzynski, E. A., 1959a, *Am. J. Public Health*, 49:1050.

———, Gorzynski, E. A., Drislane, A. M., Harris, A. H., and Rajnovich, E., 1959b, *Proc. Soc. Exptl. Biol. Med.*, 101:484.

———, Rajnovich, E., and Gorzynski, E. A., 1960, *Pediatrics*, 25:21.

———, Zalewski, N. J., and Ferguson, W. W., 1953, *Proc. Soc. Exptl. Biol. Med.*, 82:215.

Nevin, T. A., Hampp, E. G., and Duey, B. V., 1960, *J. Bacteriol.*, 80:783.

Newton, W. L., Reardon, L. V., and DeLeva, A. M., 1960, *Am. J. Trop. Med. Hyg.*, 9:56.

Nissle, A., 1916, *Deut. med. Wochschr.*, 42:1181.

Norris, R. F., and Rawson, A. J., 1947, *Am. J. Clin. Pathol.*, 17:813.

Norton, J. F., and Novy, M. F., 1931, *Am. J. Public Health*, 21:1117.

———, and ———, 1932, *ibid.*, 22:193.

Nurmikko, V., 1954, *Ann. Acad. Sci. Fennicae Ser. A.*, II, 54:7.

———, 1955, *ibid.*, 60:216.

———, 1957, *Appl. Microbiol.*, 5:160.

Nye, R. N., and Seegal, D., 1929, *J. Exptl. Med.*, 49:539.

Osawa, E., and Muschel, L. H., 1960, *J. Immunol.*, 84:203.

Ostrom, C. A., Wolochow, H., and James, H. A., 1958, *J. Inf. Dis.*, 102:251.

Oxford, A. E., 1944, *Biochem. J.*, 38:178.

Paine, T. F., 1952, *Antibiotics & Chemotherapy*, 2:653.

Pakula, R., Fluder, Z., Hulanicka, E., and Walczak, W., 1958, *Bull. Acad. Polon. Sci. Sér. Sci. Biol.*, 6:319 (*Biol. Abstr.*).

———, Hulanicka, E., and Walczak, W., 1958, *ibid.*, 6:325 (*Biol. Abstr.*).

———, ———, and ———, 1959, *Schweiz. Z. allgem. Pathol. Bakteriol.*, 22:202 (*Biol. Abstr.*).

Papavassiliou, J., 1961, *J. Gen. Microbiol.*, 25:409.

Parker, M. T., and Simmons, L. E., 1959, *ibid.*, 21:457.

———, Tomlinson, A. J. H., and Williams, R. E. O., 1955, *J. Hyg.*, 53:458.

Parr, L. W., El Shawi, N. N., and Robbins, M. L., 1960, *J. Bacteriol.*, 80:417.

Peck, S. M., Bergamini, R., Kelcec, L. C., and Rein, C. R., 1955, *J. Invest. Dermatol.*, 25:301.

Pereira, A. T., 1961, *J. Pathol. Bacteriol.*, 81:151.

Perez-Miravete, A., and Flores, C. R., 1960, *Rev. Latinoam. Microbiol.*, 2:93 (*Biol. Abstr.*).

Petru, V., 1956, *Českoslov. Epidemiol. Mikrobiol. Immunol.*, 5:199 (*Biol. Abstr.*).

Phillips, B. P., Wolfe, P. A., and Gordon, H. A., 1959, *Ann. N. Y. Acad. Sci.*, 78:183.

Pickett, M. J., and Stewart, R. M., 1953, *Am. J. Clin. Pathol.*, 23:713.

Porter, J. R., 1946, *Bacterial Chemistry and Physiology*, John Wiley & Sons, Inc., New York, p. 337.

Rantz, L. A., Randall, E., and Zuckerman, A., 1956, *J. Inf. Dis.*, 98:211.

———, Zuckerman, A., and Randall, E., 1952, *J. Lab. Clin. Med.*, 39:443.

Rebell, G., Pillsbury, D. M., de St. Phalle, M., and Ginsburg, D., 1950, *J. Invest. Dermatol.*, 14:247.

Rechcigl, M., Kwong, E., Barnes, R. H., and Williams, H. H., 1959, *Proc. Soc. Exptl. Biol. Med.*, 101:342.

Reyniers, J. A., 1946, *Lobund Report No. 1*, University of Notre Dame, Ind.

——, 1959, *Ann. N. Y. Acad. Sci.*, **78**:378.

Richardson, R. L., and Schmidt, J., 1959, *J. Dental Research*, **38**:1016.

Richou, R., Quinchon, C., and Richou, H., 1959, *Ann. Sclavo*, **1**:407 (*Biol. Abstr.*).

Ritter, P., 1954, *Schweiz. Z. allgem. Pathol. Bakteriol.*, **17**:551.

Roantree, R. J., and Rantz, L. A., 1960, *J. Clin. Invest.*, **39**:72.

Robinson, L. B., and Wichelhausen, R. H., 1946, *Bull. Johns Hopkins Hosp.*, **79**:436.

Rosebury, T., 1952, in Dubos, R. J., ed., *Bacterial and Mycotic Infections of Man*, 2d ed., J. B. Lippincott Company, Philadelphia, p. 690.

——, Gale, D., and Taylor, D. F., 1954, *J. Bacteriol.*, **67**:135.

——, and Sonnenwirth, A. C., 1958, in Dubos, R. J., ed., *op. cit.*, p. 626.

——, Zeitinger, J. R., and Mogab, J. J., 1956a, *Proc. Intern. Assoc. Dental Research*, p. 54.

——, ——, and ——, 1956b, *Federation Proc.*, **15**:610.

Roth, F. J., Boyd, C., Sagami, S., and Blank, H., 1959, *J. Invest. Dermatol.*, **32**:549.

——, and Goldstein, M. I., 1961, *ibid.*, **36**:383.

Ryan, F. J., Fried, P., and Mukai, F., 1955, *Biochim. et Biophys. Acta*, **18**:131.

Sachs, H., 1942, *J. Pathol. Bacteriol.*, **54**:105.

Sandiford, B. R., 1937, *ibid.*, **44**:567.

Saphra, I., and Wassermann, M., 1954, *Am. J. Med. Sci.*, **228**:525.

Sarkar, J. K., and Tribedi, P. B., 1953, *Indian J. Med. Sci.*, **7**:403 (*Biol. Abstr.*).

——, and ——, 1954, *Indian Med. Gaz.*, **88**:206 (*Biol. Abstr.*).

Scheimann, L. G., Knox, G., Sher, D., and Rothman, S., 1960, *J. Invest. Dermatol.*, **34**:171.

Schoenthal, R., 1941, *Brit. J. Exptl. Pathol.*, **22**:137.

Schottmüller, H., 1924, *Münch. med. Wochschr.*, **71**:1009.

Schultz-Haudt, S. D., and Scherp, H. W., 1955, *J. Bacteriol.*, **69**:665.

Scrimshaw, N. S., Béhar, M., Viteri, F., Arroyave, G., and Tejada, C., 1957, *Am. J. Public Health*, **47**:53.

Sebestyen, M., Schlossman, S. F., and Benacerraf, B., 1958, *Proc. Intern. Congr. Microbiol.*, **7**:167.

Shelley, W. B., Hurley, H. J., and Nichols, A. C., 1953, *Arch. Dermatol.*, **58**:430.

Sherwood, N. P., Russell, B. E., Jay, A. R., and Bowman, K., 1949, *J. Inf. Dis.*, **84**:64.

Shifrine, M., and Biberstein, E. L., 1960, *Nature*, **187**:623.

Sieburth, J. McN., McGinnis, J., and Skinner, C. E., 1952, *J. Bacteriol.*, **64**:163.

Smythe, P. M., 1958, *Lancet*, **2**:724.

Staib, F., and Ata, S., 1957, *Zentr. Bakteriol. Parasitenk.*, *I Orig.*, **169**:275.

Stark, J. M., 1960, *Lancet*, **1**:733.

Sternini, G., 1956, *Riv. Ist. Sieroterap. Ital.*, **31**:404 (*Biol. Abstr.*).

Stetson, C. A., 1955, *J. Exptl. Med.*, **101**:421.

Stokes, J. L., Peck, R. L., and Woodward, C. R., 1942, *Proc. Soc. Exptl. Biol. Med.*, **51**:126.

Stokstad, E. L. R., 1953, *Antibiotics & Chemotherapy*, **3**:434.

————, and Jukes, T. H., 1950, *Proc. Soc. Exptl. Biol. Med.*, **73**:523.

Su, T. L., 1948a, *Brit. J. Exptl. Pathol.*, **29**:466.

————, 1948b, *ibid.*, **29**:473.

Taylor, A. R., 1959, *Ann. N. Y. Acad. Sci.*, **78**:102.

Taylor, M. J., Rooney, J. R., and Blundell, G. P., 1961, *Am. J. Clin. Pathol.*, **38**:625.

Thibaut, J., 1949, *Comp. Rend. Soc. Biol.*, **143**:1150.

————, and Fredericq, P., 1956, *ibid.*, **150**:1512.

Thomas, L., Mirick, G. S., Curnen, E. C., Ziegler, J. E., Jr., and Horsfall, F. L., 1943, *Science*, **98**:566.

Thompson, R., 1940, *Arch. Pathol.*, **30**:1096.

————, and Johnson, A., 1951, *J. Inf. Dis.*, **88**:81.

————, and Shibuya, M., 1946, *J. Bacteriol.*, **51**:671.

Thonard, J. C., and Scherp, H. W., 1958, *ibid.*, **76**:355.

Thorbecke, G. J., 1959, *Ann. N. Y. Acad. Sci.*, **78**:237.

————, and Benacerraf, B., 1959, *ibid.*, **78**:247.

Thornton, H. G., 1952, *Proc. Roy. Soc. B.*, **139**:170.

Todd, R. L., 1937, *Am. J. Hyg.*, **25**:212.

Tomšiková, A., and Wagner, V., 1958, *Z. Immunitätsforsch.*, **116**:239.

Topley, W. W. C., and Fielden, H. A., 1922, *Lancet*, **2**:1164.

Torrey, J. C., and Kahn, M. C., 1923, *J. Inf. Dis.*, **33**:482.

Tunevall, G., 1953, *Acta Pathol. Microbiol. Scand.*, **32**:258.

Turk, J. L., 1959, *Brit. J. Exptl. Pathol.*, **40**:578.

Umbarger, H. E., and Magasanik, B., 1951, *J. Biol. Chem.*, **189**:287.

————, and Mueller, J. H., 1951, *ibid.*, **189**:277.

Upton, M. F., 1929, *J. Bacteriol.*, **17**:315.

Vanna, F. de, and Pollice, F., 1947, *Giorn. Batteriol. e Immunol.*, **36**:115 (*Biol. Abstr.*).

Vargues, R., and Grenier, B., 1960, *Ann. Inst. Pasteur*, **98**:728.

Vincent, J. G., Veomett, R. C., and Riley, R. F., 1959, *J. Bacteriol.*, **78**:477.

Wagner, M., 1955, *Bull. N. Y. Acad. Med.*, **31**:236.

————, 1959, *Ann. N. Y. Acad. Sci.*, **78**:261.

Waisbren, B. A., and Brown, I., 1959, *J. Lab. Clin. Med.*, **54**:955.

Weinstein, L., and Wasserman, E., 1951, *New Engl. J. Med.*, **244**:662.

Weiss, A., and Weinberger, H., 1940, unpublished data from the author's laboratory.

Wentworth, F. H., Brock, D. W., Stulberg, C. S., and Page, R. H., 1956, *Proc. Soc. Exptl. Biol. Med.*, **91**:586.

Wheater, D. M., Hirsch, A., and Mattick, A. T. R., 1951, *Nature*, **168**:659.

————, ————, and ————, 1952, *ibid*, **170**:623.

Wiener, A. S., 1951, *J. Immunol.*, **66**:287.

Williams, C. D., 1953, *J. Am. Med. Assoc.*, **153**:1280.

Williams, N. B., and Powlen, D. O., 1959, *Arch. Oral Biol.*, **1**:48.

Wilson, T. E., and Goaz, P. W., 1959, *J. Dental Research*, **38**:1044.

————, and ————, 1960, *ibid.*, **39**:365.

Winner, H. I., 1955, *J. Hyg.*, **53**:509.

Wostmann, B. S., 1959a, *Ann. N. Y. Acad. Sci.*, **78**:175.

————, 1959b, *ibid.*, **78**:254.

Wynne, E. S., and Norman, J. O., 1953, *J. Inf. Dis.*, **93**:243.

Yamabayashi, H., 1958, *Med. J. Osaka Univ.*, **9**:11.

Yamaguchi, T., 1959, *J. Vitaminol.*, **5**:88 (*Biol. Abstr.*).

Young, G., Krasner, R. I., and Yudofsky, P. L., 1956, *J. Bacteriol.*, **72**:525.

Young, R. M., and James, L. M., 1942, *ibid.*, **44**:75.

———, and Rettger, L. F., 1943, *ibid.*, **46**:351.

Zeldow, B. J., 1955, *J. Dental Research*, **34**:737.

———, 1959, *ibid.*, **38**:797.

———, 1961, *ibid.*, **40**:446.

Zinder, N. D., 1960, *Science*, **131**:813.

AUTHOR INDEX

Pages on which references appear are given in parentheses.

Abbot, A., 298, (308)
Abbott, J. D., 384, (384)
Abboud, F., 15, (47)
Abe, Y., 129, (139)
Abernethy, T. J., 116, (140)
Abraham, R., 149, 151, 157, (180)
Abrams, A., 300, (306)
Abrams, R. Y., 301, (306)
Adachi, K., 86, (90)
Adair, D. M., 316, (344)
Adler, S., 279, 291, (293)
Adler, V. G., 10, (42)
Adriano, S. M., 244, (250)
Agius, E., 86, (97)
Aguilera, C. T., 240, 246, (253)
Ahearn, D. G., 232, (250)
Aiken, M. A., 113–115, 117, (135)
Ainsworth, G. C., 329, (345)
Ajello, L., 222, 223, 229, (250, 252, 254)
Akatsu, S., 190, 206, 210, 211, (216, 219)
Akhmedov, N. A., 27, 28, (40)
Akiba, T., 249, (250), 380, (384)
Akima, T., (44)
Akin, M. D., (348)
Aksjanzew-Malkin, S., 200, (216)
Aksoycan, N., 244, (250)
Aladame, N., (93)
Alberti, S., (95)
Albury, M. N., 48, 49, (95)
Alexenco, E., 13, (44)
Alford, J. A., 121, (135)
Allcock, E. A., 88, (90), 331, 335, (343)
Alleaux, V., 153, (180)
Allen, M. B., 122, (142)
Allen, T. D., (138)
Allibone, E. C., 135, (135)
Allison, P. R., 135, (135)
Almquist, H. J., 353, (384)
Alston, J. M., 154, (179)
Altenbern, R. A., 301, (306)
Al'tgauzen, V. P., 109, (135)
Altland, P. D., 30, (42)
Alvarez, 82, (90), 338, (343)

Amano, T., 383, (384, 386)
Amino, E., (254), 280, (294)
Amoureux, C., 131, (136)
Amsterdam, D., 124, (141)
Anaya, J. D. R., (183)
Anderson, C. M., 311, (343)
Anderson, E. S., 10, (40)
Anderson, K., 21, (40)
Anderson, T., 110, (136)
Anderson, T. B., 33, (40)
Anderson, T. F., 5, (8)
Andrews, J., 283, (295)
Angyal, T., 10, 24, (40)
Annear, D. I., 369, 375, 377, (384)
Ansel, M., 244, (250)
Aoi, H., (218)
Appleton, J. L. T., 327, (350), 358, (384)
Aragão, H. de B., 193, (216)
Aragon, G. T., 341, (345)
Arkwright, J. A., 324, (343)
Armen, D., 240, (254)
Armstrong, E. C., 239, (251)
Arndt, W. F., 300, (309)
Arnold, F. A., 360, (384)
Arnold, L., 359, (384)
Arroyave, G., (390)
Asaki, K., 300, (307)
Asami, K., 280, (291)
Asay, L. D., 128, (136)
Asheshov, E. H., 11, (40)
Ashford, B. K., 334, (347)
Assis-Lopes, L., (256)
Ata, S., 380, (390)
Atchley, F. O., (294)
Atwell, R. J., 84, (90)
Audureau, A., 112, 115, 119, (136)
Ausherman, R. J., (254)
Austrian, R., 127, (141)
Avery, R. J., 58, (90)
Axelrod, S. C., 246, (253)
Axelsson, G., (344)
Axenfeld, T., 111, 115, (136)
Ayliffe, C. A. J., (42)

393

Babbott, F. J., Jr., 265, 266, (291)
Babes, V., 145, (179)
Bach, A., (46)
Bachman, B. J., 297, (306)
Bachmann, W., 167, 171, (179)
Bachrach, U., 322, 323, (343, 346)
Baer, H., 108, (137)
Baer, R. L., 228, 229, (251, 255)
Baernstein, H. D., 280, (291)
Bagley, E. P., 90, (94), 334, (347)
Bahn, A. N., 29, 30, (40)
Bailey, R. W., 62, (90)
Baird-Parker, A. C., 54, 69, 72–75, 77, (90, 91), 167, (179)
Baker, E. E., 104–106, 126, (139, 141, 142), 333, 334, (347)
Baker, F., 370, (384)
Baker, H. J., (98)
Baker, R. D., 241, (254)
Bakerspigel, A., 239, (251)
Balamuth, W., 278, 279, (291)
Baldovin-Agapi, C., (41)
Baldwin, J. N., (44)
Ball, K. P., 30, (47)
Ball, R. A., (253)
Balows, A., (254)
Bamforth, J., 107, (136)
Bang, 145, (180)
Bang, B., 145, (179)
Banič, S., 380, 382, (384)
Banks, J., 14, (45)
Bannerjea, A., 109, (136)
Barban, S., 203, 205, (216)
Barbero, G. J., 60, 61, (90), 337, (343)
Barile, M. F., 304, 305, (306)
Barker, H. A., 70, 71, 73, (93), 169, 170, (182)
Barksdale, W. L., 79, (90)
Barkulis, S. S., 302, (308)
Barner, R. D., 111, (136)
Barnes, E. M., 28, (40)
Barnes, R. H., 354, (384, 389)
Barocio-Lozano, L., (46, 349)
Baron, L. S., 300, (306, 307), 370, (384, 385)
Barrett, M. T., 272, 281, (291)
Barron, M., 167, 170, (182)
Barrow, F. I., 15, (40)
Barrow, J., (295)
Barry, G. T., (386)
Barson, G. J., (95)
Bartels, H. A., 378, (384)
Bartley, C. H., 28, 29, (46), 103, (141), 333, (349)
Bass, C. C., 272, 281, (291)
Basserman, J., 298, (306)
Bastianini, L., 246, (252)

Bates, J. L., 129, (139)
Batista, A. C., 228, 239, (251)
Batty, I., 65, (90)
Bauer, A. C., 275, (291)
Bauer, J. H., 87, (97), 334, (350)
Bauer, W., (306, 344)
Baum, G. L., 239, (251)
Bavara, C., (41, 345)
Bavastrelli, L., 384, (385)
Beals, P. D., (46)
Beam, R. E., (94)
Beaman, A. J., (96)
Beard, C. W., (40)
Bearup, A. J., 129, (139), 367, (388)
Beatman, L. H., 272, 273, (291)
Beaver, D. C., 149, 157, (182)
Beck, A., 209–211, (216), 368, (384)
Beck, P. H., 77, (92)
Becker, J. R., 129, (140)
Beckman, H., 301–303, (309)
Beecher, H. K., 243, (252)
Beemer, A. M., 249, (251)
Beerens, H., 59, 61, 80, 88, (90), 148–153, 155–157, 160, 169, 171–173, (180, 181, 184)
Beeson, P. B., 316, (343)
Béhar, M., (390)
Beijerinck, M. W., 232, (251)
Belanger, M., 286, (295)
Belding, D. L., 258, 265, (291)
Bell, H. J., (308, 349)
Beloiu, I., (41)
Benacerraf, B., 362, 363, (390, 391)
Benham, R. H., 225, 227, 232, 234, 235, 237, 240, 243, (251, 255), 317, (343)
Bennett, I. L., Jr., 128, (137)
Bentegat, J., 337, (347)
Benton, D. A., (98)
Bequaert, J. C., (220)
Berendt, R. F., 22, (40)
Berens, C., 31, (40), 334, (343)
Berg, M. K., 243, (255)
Berg, R. L., 305, (306)
Bergamini, R., (254, 389)
Berger, U., 36, 37, 38, (40), 151, 159, 160, 167, 169, 171, 173, (180), 189, 191, 192, 196, 197, 200, 202, 203, 207, 212, 215, (216, 217), 328, 329, (343), 374, 375, (384)
Bernanke, D., 15, (45)
Bernhart, F. W., (93)
Berridge, N. J., 379, (388)
Berry, G., 195, (219)
Berry, G. P., 69, 73, 74, (90, 93), 167, (182)
Berthelot, A., 131, (136)
Bertrand, P., 287, (291)

Besta, B., 375, (384)
Bethge, J., 375, (385)
Beube, F., 145, (182)
Beust, T. B., 328, (343)
Beveridge, W. I. B., 304, (306), 342, (343)
Bezjak, V., 325, (343)
Bhat, M. L. A., 229, (252)
Bhattacharya, K., (137)
Bialkin, G., 85, (90)
Bibby, B. G., 69, 73, 74, 76, 77, (90, 92), 375, (385)
Biberstein, E. L., 370, (390)
Bichel, J., 248, (251)
Biehl, J. P., 127, (136)
Biely, J., 355, (385)
Bigger, I. A., 155, (184)
Biguet, J., 235, (251)
Billett, F. S., (42, 346)
Billing, E., 113, 116, 118, (136)
Bingham, W. A., (388)
Biocca, E., 57, (90)
Birnbaum, D., (46, 343)
Bishop, C. M., 241, (254)
Bishop, E. L., (294)
Bishop, R. F., 88, (90), 331, 335, (343)
Bisset, K. A., 49, 51, 54, 74, (90, 91), 174, (180), 328, (343)
Bizot, M., 380, (385)
Björksten, K. af, 59, (97), 300, (308)
Black, L. A., 237, (251), 317, (344)
Blackford, V. L., 382, (385)
Bladen, 166, (180)
Blagg, W., 265, (296)
Blair, J. E., 10, 11, 24, (40)
Blaizot, P., 195, (218)
Blanchard, R., 193, (217)
Bland, P. B., 243, 251, 275, (291)
Blank, F., 58, (90), 241, 247, (253)
Blank, H., (390)
Blau, E., (47, 350)
Blaurock, G., 62, (90)
Blaxland, J. D., 239, (251)
Blayney, J. R., 329, 330, (343, 346)
Blechman, H., 378, (384)
Bloomfield, A. L., 358, (385)
Blundell, G. P., 357, (391)
Blyth, W., 248, (251)
Böe, J., 37, (47), 69, 71–73, (90, 97), 151, 167, 169, 171, (180)
Boeck, W. C., 278, 279, (292)
Boger, W. P., 363, (385)
Böhme, H., 301, (308)
Boisvert, H., 173, (184)
Boivin, A., 125, (136)
Bojalil, L. F., 86, (90, 91)
Bolaños-Castellanos, G., 46, (349)

Boniece, W. S., (42)
Bonifas, V., 298, (307)
Bonner, D. M., 297, (306)
Borgström, B., 356, (385)
Boring, J. R., (138, 345)
Borko, W., 284, (293)
Borthwick, G. R., 88, (90)
Bortnick, L. S., (344)
Borts, I. H., 238, (254)
Botazzi, V., 53, (90)
Bouchard, C., 379, (385)
Bouchelle, McL., (94)
Bouffanais, A., 159, (185)
Boughton, J. E., 298, (308)
Bouma, C., 28, (43), 180
Bour, Y., 278, (294)
Bouvier, M., 172, (180)
Bowman, K., (390)
Boyd, C., (390)
Boyle, D. E., (344)
Bracco, R. M., 33, (40), 370, (385)
Brachman, P. S., (44)
Bradel, S. F., 330, (343)
Bradfield, J. R. G., 188, (217)
Bradley, E. G., 240, (252)
Brailoiu, A., (46)
Braïlovsky-Lounkevitch, Z. A., 193, (217), 312, 330, (344)
Brainard, D. H., 324, (347)
Brams, J., 170, (183), 194, (219), 326, (348)
Brandsaeter, E., 53, (90)
Branham, S. E., 325, (344)
Braude, A. I., 30, (40), 108, 129, (136)
Brault, G., 384, (387)
Braun, H., 131, (136)
Braun, W., 299, 300, (307)
Braunberg, B. C., 167, 169, (183)
Braunthal, S. D., 288, (293)
Bray, J., 109, (136)
Breaks, V. M., 155, 156, (180)
Breckon, D., (141)
Breed, R. S., 23, (40), 48, 63, 65, 69, 80, (91), 102, 111, 133, (136), 148, 160, 174, (180, 182)
Bregman, E., 367, 368, (385)
Brenner, S., 297, 300, 302, (306)
Bret, J., 14, (40), 248, (251), 312, 341, (344)
Bridson, E. Y., 29, 31, (40)
Briggs, C. A. E., 30, (45), 379, (385)
Brinkman, S., (254)
Brinton, C. C., Jr., 370, (385)
Brion, A., 65, (91)
Brisou, J., 105, 112–116, (136)
Brizio, P. D., 275, (292)
Brocard, H., 153, 157, 172, (180, 182)

Brock, D. W., (142, 391)
Brody, J. I., 368, (389)
Brody, L., 359, (384)
Brooke, M. M., (296)
Brooke, M. S., 112, 114, 117, 118, (136), 342, (344)
Brooks, B. E., 116, 119, (136)
Brown, A., (384)
Brown, D. W., 179, (180), 336, (344)
Brown, I., 366, (391)
Brown, J., 29, 31, (40)
Brown, J. H., 31, (40), 154, (181), 202, (217), 338, (346)
Brown, R., 250, (251, 253)
Brown, R. L., 265, (292)
Brown, T. K., 34, (40, 46), 338, (349)
Browne, H. G., 245, (254)
Browne, J., 78, (96)
Brownlee, I., 105, (141)
Broyles, E. N., (250)
Brüggeman-Schmidt, C., (46, 349)
Brumfitt, W., 108, (136, 138), 326, (344, 347)
Brumpt, 193, (217)
Brunner, M. J., 315, 317, 322, (348)
Bryant, M. P., 36, (40), 165, 166, 174, 176, 177, 179, (180), 195, 207, (217)
Bryant, T. R., Jr., (94)
Brygoo, E.-R., 237, 239, (251)
Bucca, M. A., 205, (217)
Buchbinder, L., 30, (40, 44), 49, 50, (96)
Buckle, G., (94)
Buetner, L. G., 30, (41)
Bühler, V. P., 85, 87, (91)
Buhr, A. J., 13, (40)
Bulleid, A., 74, (91)
Bulloch, W., 6, (7), 145, (180)
Bunting, R. W., 364, (387)
Burch, T. A., 272, 274–276, (292)
Burchall, J. J., 241, (253, 255)
Burdin, J.-C., (94)
Burdon, K. L., 151, 162–164, (180), 326, (344)
Burke, F. G., (254)
Burke, J. F., 22, (41)
Burkey, L. A., 176, 179, (180)
Burky, E. L., 324, (344)
Burnett, G. W., 53, (96), 305, (307)
Burns, R. P., 128, (136)
Burrows, R. B., 284, (292, 295)
Burrows, W., 31, (41)
Burtenshaw, J. M. L., 360, (385)
Burton, K. A., 230, 232, 241, (256)
Burton, M. O., 124, (136)
Bustea, C., (46)
Butler, M., 298, (306)

Buttiaux, R., 28, 29, (41), 56, (98), 121, 123, (136)
Bynoe, E. T., 11, (41)

Caffe, I., (41)
Cahn-Bronner, C. E., 131, (136)
Caille, B., 81, (91)
Cain, J. A., (139, 182)
Calandra, J. C., (40)
Calderón, Y., 341, (348)
Caldwell, M. G., 14, (42), 334, (345)
Caminiti, F. P., 358, (385)
Camp, E., (253)
Campbell, A., 289, (293)
Campbell, J. J. R., 124, (136)
Campbell, L. K., 243, (253)
Campbell, P. J., 247, (251)
Cannefax, G. R., 203, 211, (217)
Carey, 62
Carey, W. F., 300, (306, 307, 384)
Carlberg, G., 60, (92)
Carloni, M., 249, (252), 368, (386)
Carlson, S., 382, (386)
Carpenter, A. M., 239, 246, (251)
Carpenter, C. M., 79, (91)
Carr, M., 10, 11, (40)
Carrere, L., (306)
Carski, T. R., 363, 365, (385)
Carter, B., 238, (251), 338, 340, (344)
Carter, E., (347)
Carter, E. B., 240, (255)
Carter, E. E., (142)
Carter, H. F., 193, (218)
Carver, R. K., 265, (293)
Cary, S. G., 114, (136)
Cascio, G., 366, 368, (385)
Casey, D. W., 32, (43)
Casman, E. P., 134, (136)
Cason, L., 322, (344)
Castel, M. M., 149, 151, 157, (180)
Castellani, A., 148, (180), 193, 195, (217), 225, (251), 371, (385)
Cataldi, M. S., 62, (91, 95), 341, (347)
Cater, D. B., 188, (217)
Catlin, B. W., 37, (41)
Catterall, R. D., 275, 276, 277, 285, 286, 290, (292)
Cavier, R., 289, (292)
Cayer, D., 283, (294)
Cazemier, C., 250, (251), 290, (292)
Cazis, J., Jr., 246, (253)
Cefalu, M., 384, (385)
Censuales, S., 203, 211, (217)
Cerbón, J., 86, (90, 91)
Cerutti, P., (388)
Cesari, E., 153, (180)

Cetin, E. T., 114, 119, 120, (136)
Chabbert, Y., 119, 124, 131, (136)
Challice, C. E., (142)
Chalmers, A. J., 148, (180), 225, (251)
Chandler, A. C., 266, 270, 271, (292)
Chandler, F. A., 155, 156, (180)
Chang, J. C. C., 104, (136), 329, (344)
Chapman, G. H., 31, (40), 334, (343)
Chappaz, G., 287, (292)
Charlton, G., 54, (91), 372, (385)
Charter, R. E., 109, (142)
Chassignol, S., 113, 115, (136)
Chatterji, D. N., (136)
Cheeseman, G. C., 53, (91)
Cheever, F. S., 36, (41)
Cheng, W. F., 13, (41)
Chernomordik, A. B., 380, (385)
Cherry, W. B., 363, 365, (385)
Chia-Tung Pan, 278, (292)
Chick, E. W., 241, (254)
Chick, H., 195, (217)
Choffel, C., 172, (180)
Chowdhury, B., 131, (141)
Christ, Y. S., (138, 386)
Christiansen, A. H., 211. (217)
Christiansen, M., 153, (180)
Christie, A. O., 11, (41), 67, (91)
Christie, R., 121, (136)
Chu, H., 165, (180)
Ciaula, V., 275, (294)
Ciuca, M., 27, (41)
Clabaugh, G. F., 314, 316, (344)
Clado, 145, (185)
Clapper, W. E., 53, (94)
Clark, A. R., 63, 66, 69, 71, (96, 184), 194, (219, 220)
Clark, H. F., 28, 29, (43)
Clarke, B. G., 316, (344)
Clarke, R. T. J., 62, (90, 91), 239, (251)
Clayton-Cooper, B., 12, (44), 317, 323, (347)
Cleland, J. B., 193, (217)
Cleverdon, R. C., 131, (137)
Clough, O. W., 375, (385)
Cluff, L. E., 19, 20, (41, 42, 43)
Codd, S., 126, (137)
Coetzee, J. N., 54, (91)
Cohen, J., 163, 164, (181)
Cohen, J. O., 12, (41)
Cohen, J. R., (254)
Cole, R. M., 32, (45)
Colebrook, L., 34, (41), 338, (344). 364, 366, 367, 375, (385)
Collart, P., (292)
Collette, T. S., (182)
Collins, F. M., 125, (136)
Collis, L. R., 108, (141)

Combescot, C., 289, (292)
Comes, R., (217)
Comtois, R. D., 11, (41)
Conen, P. E., 17, (41)
Conklin, S. D., (182)
Conn, H. J., 131, (136)
Conn, N. K., 242, (251)
Connell, G. H., 5, (7), 223, 225, (251)
Conroy, D. A., 124, (136)
Conti, C. R., 19, 20, (41, 42, 43)
Cooper, M. L., 312, 337, (344)
Cormane, R. H., 374, (385)
Cornbleet, T., 360, (385)
Cornelison, J. L., 312, (344)
Cornfeld, D., 326, (344)
Corpron, D. O., (139)
Corrigan, E. A., 22, (41)
Corrigan, M., 363, (387)
Cort, 270, (292)
Cortner, J. A., 283, (292)
Cory, J. C., 243, (255)
Cosar, C., 290, (292)
Côté, G., 36, (43)
Cott, C. L., 132, (143)
Couch, J. R., (254), 371, (389)
Coulter, J., 21, (40)
Coupé, C., (40, 251, 344)
Courden, B., 323, (347)
Courtieu, A.-L., 113, 115, 116, 119, 124, 131, (136)
Cousins, S. M., 322, (344)
Couteau, M., 232, 239, 242, (252)
Coutts, W. E., 194, (217), 275, (292)
Couture, J., (292)
Cowan, S. T., 11, 12, (41, 42), 86, (97), 102, (136), 317, (345)
Cox, C. D., 189, (217, 218)
Crabb, W. E., 14, (46), 55, (96), 334, 335, 338, (349)
Craig, C. F., 209, (217), 265, (292)
Crawford, M. N., 90, (343)
Crawford, N., (95)
Crawford, Y. E., 300, (306)
Creadick, R. N., (344)
Crean, G. P., (251)
Cregan, J., 88, (91), 311, 314, 331, 332, (344), 359, (385)
Cressy, N. L., 159, (181)
Crockatt, H., 110, (136)
Croft, C. C., 237, (251), 317, (344)
Crowell, J., 135, (136)
Crowley, M., 364, (387)
Cruickshank, J., (7), 317, 324, (344)
Cruickshank, J. C., 89, (93)
Cruickshank, R., (7), 58, (91), 317, 324, 339, (344)
Cruz, J. C., 86, (91)

Csillag, A., 85, (91), 243, (252)
Csonka, G. W., 304, (306)
Cuckow, F. W., 298, (306)
Cummins, C. S., 26, (41), 58, 64, 65, 74, 78, 79, (90, 91)
Curnen, E. C., (44, 47, 391)
Curtin, J. A., 128, (137)
Curtis, A. H., 177, (181), 341, (344)
Cuttino, J. T., 86, (91, 92)
Czapelewski, E., 82, (91)
Czekalowski, J. W., 188, (217)

Dack, G. M., 89, (91), 148, 150, 153, 155–157, (181, 185), 311, (344), 359, 367, (385, 386)
Dacre, J. C., 53, (91)
Daggett, W., (306)
Daglio, C. A. N., 370, (389)
Dahlqvist, A., (385)
Dain, J. A., 27, (41)
Dale, A. C., 314, 330, 331, (344)
D'Alessandro, G., 203, 211, (217)
Dammin, G. J., 242, (255)
Dardanoni, L., 203, 211, 217, (219)
Dargelos, R., 278, (294)
Dark, F. A., (306)
Daufresne, M., (221)
Davis, B. C., 204, (217)
Davis, B. R., 103, (137)
Davis, C. H., 274, 275, (292)
Davis, D. J., 134, 135, (137, 141), 323, (348)
Davis, G. H. G., 48–51, (52), 55, 69, 72–75, 77, (90, 91, 93), 174, (180), 328, (343)
Davis, I., 125, (137)
Davis, J. E., 31, (46)
Dawbarn, M. C., 54, (91)
Dawson, I. M., (142)
De, S. N., 108, 109, (137)
Deacon, W. E., 115, 118, (137)
DeAlvarez, R. R., 127, (138)
Dean, K. F., 241, (252)
DeBord, G. C., 111, 112, 115–118, (137), 341, (344)
De Bruijn, J. H., 186, 211, (217)
DeCadore, F., 26, (45, 95)
DeFelip, G., (95)
Degaey, R., (251)
Dekhkan-Khodzhaeva, N. A., 284, (292)
De Klerk, H. C., 54, (91)
Delcourte, F., 89, (90)
De Leva, A. M., 282, 288, (294), 357, (389)
DeLey, J., 125, (137)
Delwiche, E. A., 53, (92)

Demain, A. L., 232, (255)
De Man, J. C., 54, (91)
DeMitri, T., 246, (252)
Demont, F., 80, (90)
De Moss, R. D., 124, (138)
Denault, L. J., 131, (137)
De Negroni, C. B., 240, (254)
Denny, F. W., (348)
Derbes, V. J., 230, (254)
Desai, S. C., 229, (252)
De Sipin, M., (95)
De St. Phalle, M., (389)
Devenish, E. A., 12, (42), 317, (345)
Dewar, M. R., 54, (91)
Dewey, M. E., (46)
Dexter, H. L. T., 116, 118, 120, (137)
Dexter, M. W., (137)
Diamond, L. S., 279, (292)
Dick, E. C., 57, (93), 353, (387)
Dick, G. F., 316, 323, 324, (346)
Dicker, H., 169, 171, (181), 368, (385)
Dickinson, L., 126, (137)
Dieckmann, W. S., 34, (46)
Dienes, L., 103, (137), 298, 300–302, 305, (306–309), 326, 334, (344)
Dietz, V. H., 364, (385)
Digeon, M., 26, (41), 337, (344)
DiMenna, M. E., 223–225, 227, 228, 237, (252), 317, 326, 329, 334, (344)
Dineen, P., 250, (253), 357, (385)
Disraely, M. N., (96), 156, 170, (181, 183)
Dixon, J. M. S., 311, (344), 359, 372, 373, 377, (386)
Dmochowski, L., 5, (7)
Dobell, C., 6, (7), 145, 146, (181), 187, 193, (217), 259, 278, 280, (292)
Dobias, B., 250, (252)
Dobson, H. L., (347)
Do Carmo Sousa, L., 223, 228, 239, (256)
Dochez, A. R., 160, (183), 325, (347, 349)
Doctor, V. M., 371, (389)
Dodd, M. C., 377, (387)
Dodd, R. L., 33, (41)
Döderlein, A., 55, (91), 339, (344)
Doetsch, R. N., 36, (45), 62, (92), 165, 166, (180, 181)
Dold, H., 357, (386)
Domenech, A., 289, (292)
Don, P. A., (142)
Doudoroff, M., 125, (137)
Douglas, H. C., 25, 31, 38, 39, (41), 80, 81, (91), 326, 331, (344, 345)
Dowling, H. F., 12, 13, 20, 24, (44)
Downing, J. G., 322, (344)

Dragstedt, L. R., 155, 157, (181), 367, (385, 386)
Drake, C. H., 126, (141), 248, (252), 334, (348), 368, (386)
Draper, J. W., 277, (292)
Drbohlav, J., 278, 279, (292)
Drew, A. H., 272, (292)
Drislane, A. M., (389)
Drouhet, E., 232, 239, 242, (252)
Dubos, R. J., 83, (95), 178, (181), 204, (217)
Duby, D., (95)
Duchon, L., 317, (345)
Dudgeon, J. A., 107, (136)
Dudgeon, L. S., 334, (345)
Duey, B. V., 370, (389)
Duguid, J. P., 326–328, (345)
Dujardin-Beaumetz, E., 374, (386)
Dukes, C. D., 134, 135, 137, (138)
Dulaney, A. D., 14, (42), 334, (345)
Duliscouët, R., 374, (386)
Dulong de Rosnay, C., (44)
Duncan, E. H. L., 230, (252)
Duncan, I. B. R., 88, 89, (91, 92), 332, 334, (345), 359, (386)
Duncan, J. T., 248, (252)
Dunlap, M. B., 324–327, (346)
Dunlop, E. E., 311, (344), 359, (385)
Dunn, M. S., (220)
Du Pasquier, P., (44)
Durbin, G. T., (93)
Durel, P., 290, (292)
Dutton, A. A. C., 18, (41), 311, 325, (345)
Dyer, R. F., 135, (137)
Dyer, W. R., 21, (47)

Eagle, H., 30, (42), 204–206, (217, 219, 220)
Eagles, B. A., 124, (136)
Eaves, G., 188, (217)
Eberson, F., 80, (91)
Edebo, L., 103, 106, (137)
Edgecomb, J. H., (137)
Edmondson, J. E., (93)
Edmunds, P. N., 134, (137)
Edsall, J., 304, (306)
Edward, D. G., 298, 305, (306, 308), 334, (347)
Edwards, C. L., (218)
Edwards, L. B., 82, 84, (91)
Edwards, P. R., 100–103, (137)
Egan, J. B., 126, (139)
Eggerth, A. H., 148–150, 152, (181), 333, (345)
Ehrenberg, C. B., 187, (217)

Ehrenhaus, J., 213, (217)
Ehrenworth, L., 108, (137)
Eickenberg, C. F., (47, 350)
Eisenberg, G. M., 106, (137, 142)
Eisman, P. C., 245, (252)
Elder, R. H., 11, (41)
Elek, S. D., 9, 17, 23, 24, (41)
Elford, W. J., (142)
Elliott, S. D., 27, (41)
Ellis, E. M., 118, (137)
Ellis, R. H., 54, (91)
Ellison, S. A., 178, (183, 184, 220)
Elmes, P. C., 311, 325, (345)
Elsden, S. R., 28, (46)
Elser, W. J., 37, (41)
El Shawi, N. N., 103, (140), 384, (389)
Elvehjem, C. A., (96, 98)
Emard, L. O., 54, (92)
Emmanouilidou-Arseni, A., 380, (386)
Emmerich, R., 373, 379, (386)
Emmons, C. W., 68, (92), 222, 225, (252, 254), 317, 326, (345)
Engel, S. G., 69, (96, 184, 219, 220)
Engel, W. J., 342, (349)
Engelhard, W. E., (139, 182)
English, M. P., 229, 230, (252)
Ennever, J., 68, (92)
Entner, N., 125, (137)
Epifanio, A., (291)
Epps, L. J., 63, 66, (96)
Epstein, S. S., 102, 108, (137)
Eriksen, K. R., (41)
Erikson, D., 63, 67, 80, (92)
Erlandson, A. L., Jr., 30, (41)
Escherich, T., 336
Estrada-Parra, S., 106, (137)
Ethier, J., 287, (295)
Evans, C. A., 24, 26, (41), 314, 315, 317, 322, (345), 375, (386)
Evans, J., 125, (142)
Evans, J. B., 30, (41)
Evans, W. E. D., 243, (252)
Ewing, W. H., 100–103, 112, (137)
Eyre, J. W., 111, (137)

Faber, J. E., Jr., 24, 36, 37, (43, 45, 47), 114, (136), 328, (346)
Faber, V., 10, 15, 16, (41)
Fahlberg, W. J., 245, (253)
Faia, M. de M., (256)
Fallon, N., 245, (254)
Farinha, M., 223, (256)
Farmer, E. D., 32, (41)
Farrer, S. M., 16, (41, 44), 312, (345)
Fasquelle, R., (306)
Faure, M., 211, (219)

Faust, E. C., 258, 265, 269, 270, (292)
Faust, J., 118, (137)
Favour, C. B., 132, (141)
Featherstone, J. L., 54, 55, (92)
Fedukowicz, H., 117, (137)
Fekety, F. R., (44)
Feldman, G. L., (254)
Feldman, W. H., 157, (181), 368, (386)
Felisati, D., 246, (252)
Felix, A., 103, (142)
Fell, J. W., (250)
Felsenfeld, O., 265, 284, (296), 334, (345)
Fenner, F., 85, (94)
Feo, L. G., 275, 277, 285, 290, (292), 341, (345)
Ferguson, T. M., (254)
Ferguson, W. W., 109, 110, 112, 114, 117, 118, (137, 139, 140), 325, (345), 365, 366, (386, 387, 389)
Fetter, T. R., (292)
Fiala, G., 354, (384)
Fielden, H. A., 369, 372, (391)
Fife, M. A., 101, 102, (137)
Finch, S. C., 368, (389)
Fincham, I. H., 239, (251)
Finegold, S. M., 10, (41), 148, 160, (181)
Fink, E. B., 213, (220)
Finkelstein, R. A., 363, (386)
Finland, M., 11, (47), 127, 130, 135, (138, 143), 311, 314, 316, 342, (346)
Finnerud, C. W., 243, (252)
Firestone, B. Y., 241, (252)
Fischer, D., (90, 343)
Fisher, A. M., 155, 158, 159, (181)
Fisher, E. A., 324, (347)
Fisher, I., 223, 237, (254)
Fisher, J. H., 272, (292)
Fisher, M. W., (41), 363, (386)
Fisher, S., 363, (386)
Fisher, W. M., 312, (344)
FitzGerald, M. G., (140, 348)
Fitzgerald, R. J., 24, 39, 40, (41, 43), 49, (96), 192, 202, 212, 216, (217, 218), 328, (346), 353, 354, (387)
Fitzgerald, W. A., 298, (306)
Fitz-James, P. C., 303, (306)
FitzPatrick, F. K., 86, (92)
Flanders, R. M., (95)
Flandin, C., 317, (345)
Fleisher, M. S., 79, (92)
Fleming, A., 317, 324, 325, 329, (345)
Fletcher, C. M., 311, 325, (345)
Fletcher, D. W., 223, 227, 232, 237, 240, 241, (255)
Flint, J. C., 157, (182)
Flippin, H. F., 106, (137, 142)
Flores, C. R., 373, (389)

Florey, H. W., 359, 373, 379, 382, (386, 387)
Florman, A. L., 81, (92)
Fluder, Z., (389)
Foley, G., 195, 199, 200, 213, 216, (219, 220)
Foley, G. E., 27, (41), 159, (181), 235, 247, (256)
Foltz, V. D., 104, (136), 329, (344)
Forbes, G. B., 13, (41)
Forbes, M. A., (47, 329)
Forbus, W. D., 83, (92)
Forkner, C. E., Jr., 127, (137)
Formal, S., 112, 113, 116, (142)
Forney, C. E., 246, (252)
Forsyth, B. R., 15, (45)
Forsyth, H., 54 (91)
Fortner, J., 200, (217)
Foster, 62
Foster, E. M., 165, (185), 207, (221)
Foster, W. D., 17, 18, 21, (41)
Foster, W. P., 135, (141)
Foubert, E. L., Jr., 25, 38, 39, (41), 326, (345)
Fox, E. C., 329, (345)
Fox, J. E., 126, 128, 129, (137, 139), 334, (347), 367, (386)
Fox, J. P., 5, (8)
Francis, S., 149, (184)
Franěk, F., 360, (386)
Frank, F. P., 300, (306)
Frank, H. A., 59, 80, (92)
Frank, H. G., 290, (293)
Frank, L. H., 124, (138)
Frank, L. J., 242, 243, (252)
Frankel, J. W., 363, (385)
Franklin, J. G., 54, (96)
Franklin, R., 108, (138)
Franks, A. G., 239, 250, (252, 254)
Fraser, D., 301, (307)
Frazier, 62
Frazier, C. N., 204, (221)
Fred, H. L., 116, 118, 120, (138)
Fredericq, P., 379, 382, 383, (386, 391)
Free, E. J., 121, 123, 131, (138)
Freeman, V. J., 78, (92)
Frei, E., (137)
Freimer, E. H., 302, 303, (306)
Freter, R., 382, (386)
Freud, S., 7, 327
Freudenthal, P., (386)
Freundt, E. A., 298, 299, 305, (306, 307), 342
Fridericia, L. S., 354, (386)
Fried, P., 383, (390)
Friedheim, E. A. H., 124, (138)
Friedman, D. R., 373, 383, (386)

Friedman, J., 245, (252, 255)
Friedman, L., 230, 244, 250, (254)
Friedman, R., 228, 229, (255), 322, (349)
Fritz, M. A., 14, (43), 290, (294)
Frostell, G., 73, (97)
Frühwald, F., 145, (181)
Frühwald, R., 276, (293)
Frye, W. W., 266, 278, (291, 295)
Fukazawa, Y., 235, 241, (256)
Fuller, J. E., 29, (43)
Fulton, J. K., 106, (138)
Funigiello, F., 241, (253)
Furnari, D., 240, (255)
Furness, G., 304, (306)
Fusillo, M. H., 10, (41)
Fusita, H., (139)

Gaby, W. L., 121, 123, 131, (138)
Gaehtgens, W., 203, 209, 210, (217)
Gagliardi, L. A., (41)
Gagnon, B. H., 148–150, 152, (181), 333, (345)
Gagnon, P., 121, (136)
Gaines, S., 129, (138). 367, (386)
Gale, D., 67, (92), 369, 370, 375, 377, 380–382, (386, 390)
Gale, E. F., 30, (42)
Gale, G. R., 380, 381, (387)
Gall, L. S., 4, (8), 161, 172, 174, 176, 177, (182)
Gallagher, E., (308, 349)
Gallai, Z., 273, 286, 287, (293, 295)
Gamble, D. R., 110, (138), 337, (345)
Ganor, S., 326, (350)
Garber, E. D., 108, (138)
Garber, M. J., 265, (292)
Gardner, F. H., 311, (347)
Gardner, H. L., 134, 135, (137, 138)
Gareau, F. E., 105, (138), 312, 337, (345)
Gargani, G., 249, (252), 368, (386)
Garré, C., 17, (42)
Garrod, L. P., 63, 64, 68, (92), 150, 158, 159, 161, (181), 325, (345)
Garson, W., 203, 211, (217)
Gaston, C., 31, (43), 314, 331, (346)
Gates, F. L., 147, 148, 160, 161, (183), 200, (217), 325, (347)
Gauhe, A., 60, (92)
Gaumont, R., 172, (180)
Gauthier, C., 244, (250)
Gavin, J. J., 363, (385)
Gebhardt, L. P., 247, (253)
Gebicki, J. M., 300, (307)
Geftic, S. G., 245, (252)
Gelfand, H. M., 5, (8)
Georg, L. K., 229, 242, (252, 254)

Gerard, A., 59, 61, (90)
Gerber, P., 193, (217)
Gerhardt, M. R., (46)
Gerhardy, P., (306)
Gesner, B. M., 156, (181)
Getz, M. E., 229, (250)
Ghon, A., 37, (47)
Gibbons, R. J., 62, (92), 163, 164, (181, 184), 370, (386)
Giblett, E. R., (41, 345, 386)
Gibson, C. D., Jr., 15, (42)
Gibson, H. J., 129, (138), 364–367, (386)
Gibson, M. D., 229, 230, (252)
Gilbert, A., 146, (181)
Gillem, H. C., (143)
Gillespie, E. H., 12, (42), 317, (345)
Gillespie, H. B., 109, (138), 364, 365, (386)
Gillespie, W. A., 10, 22, (42), 342, (345)
Gillissen, G., 382, (386)
Gilmore, E., 305, (307)
Gilmour, C. M., 125, (142)
Gilmour, M. N., 69, 73, 76, 77, (92)
Giminez, J., 116, (136)
Gins, H., 173, (181)
Ginsburg, D., (389)
Girling, J. A., (46, 47)
Girot, C., (292)
Glacy, J., (137)
Gledhill, A. W., 30, (42)
Glick, M. C., 60, (92)
Glimstedt, G., 361, (386)
Glynn, A. A., 367, (386)
Go, K., (44)
Goaz, P. W., 371, (391)
Gochenour, W. S., Jr., 121–123, (142)
Goebel, W. F., 383, (384, 386)
Goldman, M., 265, (293), 363, 365, (385)
Goldstein, L., 24, 26, 34, (42), 78, 87, (93), 104, (138), 238, (253), 340, 341, (346)
Goldstein, M. I., 369, (390)
Goldsworthy, N. E., 14, (46, 47), 52, 67, (97), 328, (350)
Goode, C. S., (254)
Goodey, T., 272, (293)
Gootzeit, E. H., 194, (220), 330, (349)
Gordon, D. L., (307)
Gordon, H. A., 356, 357, 361, 363, (386, 389)
Gordon, J., 39, (42), 201, (218), 375, (388)
Gordon, J. E., 266, (291)
Gordon, M. A., 225–227, 235, 240, 241, (252), 317, (345)
Gordon, R. E., 86, (92)
Goret, P., (91, 95)

Gorts, I. C., (253)
Gorzynski, E. A., 363, (389)
Goshi, K., 19, (42, 43)
Goslings, W. R. O., (251, 292)
Goudie, J. G., 88, 89, (91, 92), 332, 334, (345), 359, (386)
Gould, J. C., 12, 20, (42), 126, (138)
Goulden, J. D. S., 53, (92)
Graber, C. D., 131, (138)
Gracheva, N. M., 249, (252)
Graffenreid, C. von, 229, (252)
Graham, A. B., (252, 255)
Graham, J. H., 250, (256)
Graham, L., 189, (218)
Grainger, R. M., (183, 218)
Grant, V. Q., 240, (252)
Grassberger, R., 370, (387)
Gratia, A., 382, 383, (387)
Graudel, H., 28, (42)
Gray, D. M., 14, (44)
Gray, J. D. A., 88, (90)
Green, G. E., 377, (387)
Green, L. B., (95)
Green, M. J., 323, (345)
Greene, M. R., (220)
Gregor, H., 167, 171, (179)
Gregory, F. G., 370, (387)
Gregory, F. J., (255)
Grelland, R., 78, (93)
Grenier, B., 367, (391)
Gresham, G. A., 248, (256)
Grieves, N., 10, (44)
Griffin, U. D., 272, (292)
Griffith, R. S., 20, 24, (42)
Griffiths, J. D., (47)
Griffits, J. J., 134, (137)
Griner, L. A., 157 (182)
Groel, J. T., 250, (255)
Groman, N. B., 78, (92)
Grootten, O., (140)
Grossman, M., 11, 20, 22, (43)
Grott, J. W., 284, (293)
Grubb, R., 49, (92)
Grubb, T. C., 314, 315, (345), 359, (387)
Grumbach, A., 170, (181)
Guadalupe Mayer Tanguma, M., 12, (42)
Gudjounsson, S., (386)
Guilbeau, J. A., 304, (308)
Guillaume, J., 59, 61, (90), 151, 156, 165, 169, 172, (181)
Guillemot, L. J. B., 146, 147, 161, (181), 326, (345)
Guillot, N., 56, (92)
Guimaraes, J., (254)
Gundel, M., 326, (345)

Gunderson, W. B., 78, (92, 93)
Gunsalus, I. C., 125, (138, 307)
Gunter, S. E., 80, 81, (91)
Gurevitch, J., 323, (343, 346)
Gustafson, B. A., 227, (252)
Gustafsson, B. E., 353–356, (385, 387)
Gutekunst, R. R., 53, (92)
Gutierrez, J., 28, (43), 80, 81, (92)
Guze, L. B., 118, (141), 342, (345)
Guzman, M. G., 240, 243, (253)
Gyllenberg, H. G., 59–62, (92, 97), 313, 337, (345)
György, P., 60, 61, 90, (92, 93, 95, 97, 343, 346)

Haaland, M., 12, 13, 22, (47)
Habs, I., 126, (138)
Hackett, A. J., 108, (138)
Hadley, C., 123, 131, (138)
Hadley, F. P., 53, 54, (93)
Hagedorn, H., 58, (93)
Haggerty, R. J., 135, (138)
Hajek, J. P., 37, (45)
Halbert, S. P., 373, 374, 382, 383, (386, 387)
Halde, C., 341, (345)
Hale, C. M. F., 49, 51, 75, (91)
Halevi, C., (46)
Haley, L. D., 241, (252), 342, (345)
Hall, H. E., 108, (138)
Hall, I. C., 26, 38, (42), 337, (345)
Hall, J. A., 239, (251)
Hall, J. W., 131, (138)
Hall, M. W., 161, (181)
Hallé, J., 146, (181), 326, 338, (345)
Halphen, E., 82, (94)
Hamada, Y., 259, 288, (293)
Hamburger, M., 127, (136), 323, 326–328, (345)
Hamburger, V. G., 323, (345)
Hamilton, R. D., 70–73, (93)
Hamlin, L. J., 165, (181)
Hammett, F. L., (345)
Hammond, C., 213, (220, 388)
Hamon, Y., 380, 384, (387)
Hampp, E. G., 38, 39, (44, 45), 170, 171, (181, 183), 191, 192, 195, 196, 200–202, 207, 208, 211, 212, 215, 216, (217, 218, 219), 370, (389)
Hancock, J. C., Jr., 14, (42), 334, (345)
Handler, P., (350)
Hanford, V. L., 33, (44)
Hanger, F. M., (349)
Hanke, M., 152, (182)
Hano, J., 205, (220)

Hara, H. J., 135, (138)
Harding, H. B., 33, (42)
Hardy, A. V., 104, 126, 127, (138), 322, (345)
Hardy, E. C., 127, (139)
Hardy, G. C., 339, (346)
Hare, R., 25, 35, (42), 341, (346)
Harley, J. D., 15, (42)
Harper, A. E., (96, 98)
Harrell, E. R., 239, (253)
Harris, A. H., (389)
Harris, H., 58, 64, 65, 74, 78, 79, (90, 91)
Harris, J. W., 154, (181), 338, (346)
Harris, M., (140)
Harris, M. M., 21, (47)
Harris, N. McL., 146, 154, (182)
Harris, T. N., (344)
Harrison, A. P., 159, 160, (185)
Harrison, R., (388)
Harrison, R. W., 50, 53–55, (93), 213, (218), 329, 334, (346)
Harrison, W., 60, 62, (93), 341, (346)
Hart, D., 21, (42)
Hartman, P. A., 371, (388)
Hartmann, M., 191, 193, 197, (219)
Hartmann, O., 69, 71, 72, (97)
Harvey, H. S., 324–327, (346)
Harvey, T. S., (95)
Hasenclever, H. F., (46), 227, 235, 242, 244, (252)
Hassal, J. E., 15, (42)
Hassinen, J. B., 60, (93)
Hatch, R. E., 61, (93)
Hatcher, G. W., 15, (46)
Hauber, F. D., 112, 114, 116–119, (141), 325, (349)
Hauduroy, P., 85, (93, 306)
Hausknecht, W., (388)
Havez, R., (251)
Hay, D. R., 15, 16, (42)
Hayashi, J. A., 302, (308)
Hayes, L., 369, 375, 377, (384, 387)
Haynes, B. W., Jr., 15, (42)
Haynes, W. C., 121, 123, 131, (138)
Hayward, A. C., 49, 50, 52, 55, 56, (91, 93)
Hayward, N. J., 88, 90, (91, 93), 311, 314, 331, 332, (344), 359, (385)
Hazard, E. C., (46)
Hazen, E. L., 80, (93), 250, (251, 252, 253)
Heatley, N. G., 374, 382, (387)
Heck, W. E., 159, (182)
Hedrick, L. R., 246, (252)
Hegemann, F., 375, (387)

Hehre, E. J., 32, (42), 148, 152, (182)
Heidelberger, M., 164, (182)
Heidrick, P. J., (139, 182)
Heinrich, S., 69, (93)
Heinz, T. E., 155, (181), 367, (385)
Hellinger, E., 124, (138)
Helmholz, H. F., 311, (346)
Heltai, A., 134, (138), 341, (346)
Hemmens, E. S., 31, (41, 93), 213, (218), 329, (346)
Hempstead, B. A., (140)
Henderson, J. L., 248, (254)
Henrici, A. T., (388)
Henricson, T., 154, 157, (182)
Henriksen, S. D., 78, (92, 93), 112, 113, 115, 117–120, (138), 152, 172, (182), 325, 342, (346)
Henry, B., 245, (253)
Henry, M., 77, (93)
Henthorne, J. C., 149, 150, 152, 154, 157, (182)
Heptinstall, R. H., 108, (136, 138)
Herbst, S., 274, (293)
Hermann, G. I., 79, (93)
Hersey, D. F., 115, (142)
Herter, C. A., 49, (93)
Herzog, V. H., 311, (346)
Heseltine, W. W., 247, (251)
Hessel, H. L., (138)
Hesseltine, H., 289, (293)
Hesseltine, H. C., 24, 26, 29, 31, 34, (42), 78, 87, (93), 104, (138), 215, (218), 238, 243, (253, 254, 256), 340, 341, (346)
Hester, H. R., 157, (181), 368, (386)
Hewitt, W. L., (181)
Hewlett, R. T., 323, (350)
Hickey, J. L. S., 353, (387)
Higaki, M.-A., 239, (253)
High, R. H., 250, (253)
Highman, B., 30, (42)
Hijams, W., 300, 302, (307, 308)
Hill, D. W., 247, (253)
Hillegas, A. B., (253)
Hindle, E., 188, 193, (218)
Hine, M. K., 73, (93), 167, (182), 375, (385)
Hinshaw, H. C., 272, 279, 281, (293)
Hinton, N. A., 12–15, 21, (42, 44)
Hirsch, A., 379, (387, 388, 391)
Hirsch, H. A., 135, (138)
Hirsch, M. M., (43)
Hirschfeld, I., 145, (182)
Hirst, L. F., 131, 132, (138), 366, (387)
Hitchcock, D. J., 265, (293)
Hitchcock, G. H., 340, (348)
Hitchens, A. P., 69, (91)

Hite, K. E., 24, 26, 29, 31, 34, (42), 56, 78, 87, (93), 104, (138), 215, (218), 238, (253), 340, 341, (346)
Hlava, 32, (42)
Hobbs, B. C., 89, (93)
Hobbs, G., 90, (97)
Hobson, P. N., 38, (42), 177, (182)
Hodges, E., (387)
Hodges, R. M., 127, (138)
Hoelling, 167
Hofferd, R. M., 195, (218)
Hofferer, M. J., 123, (140)
Hoffert, W. R., (138, 345)
Hoffman, H., 162, (182)
Hoffman, N. J., (97, 350)
Hoffmann, E., 187, 192, 193, (218, 220)
Hofstad, T., 21, 22, (42)
Hogan, J., 131, (142)
Hogue, M. J., 194, (218)
Holdsworth, D. E., 135, (138)
Holland, M. L., 374, (385)
Holloway, B. W., 126, (139), 380, (387)
Holloway, W. J., 15, (42)
Holm, P., 69, (93), 364, (387)
Holman, R. A., 39, (42), 201, (218)
Holman, W. L., 38, (42), 371, (387)
Holmes, D. H., (42)
Holmes, J. R., 135, (137)
Holt, C. J., 282, 283, (295)
Holtzman, C. F., (138)
Holzel, A., 248, (253)
Holzl, H., 375, (387)
Homma, Y., 305, (307)
Honigberg, B. M., 259, 279, 288, (293)
Hood, F., (254)
Hood, M., 118, (137)
Hoogerheide, J. C., 250, (254)
Hoover, J. R. E., (92)
Hopkins, A. M., 227, 237, (251), 314, (343)
Hopkins, J. G., 228, (253)
Horikawa, T., 126, (139)
Horsfall, F. L., 33, (42, 44, 47, 391)
Horton, R. E., 353, (387)
Horwich, H., 117, (137)
Hotchin, J. E., (142)
Hotz, R., 315, (346)
Houwert, K. A. F., (251, 292)
Howard, B. H., (181)
Howard, D. H., 78, 79, (91, 93)
Howe, P. R., 61, (93)
Howell, A., Jr., 59, 64, 65, 67, 69, 73, 74, 76, 77, (92, 93, 95)
Howell, K. M., 265, 284, (293), 363, (387)
Howie, J. W., (91, 345)
Howitt, B. F., 38, (42), 279, (293)

Howorth, I. E., (308, 349)
Hoyer, B. H., 67, (96)
Hoyt, H. H., (253)
Huang, N. N., 250, (253)
Hubbard, J. P., 326, (344)
Huebner, R. J., 5, (8)
Huet, M., 134, 135, (139), 323, (346, 348)
Hugh, R., 28, 30, (42), 111, 116, 121, (139), 329, (346)
Huhtanen, C. N., 4, (8), 161, 172, 174, 176, 179, (182)
Huijsmans-Evers, A. G. M., 305, (307)
Hulanicka, E., 33, (45, 389)
Hülphers, G., 154, 157, (182)
Hummer, W. K., (46)
Humphries, J. C., 108, (138)
Hungate, R. E., 165, 179, (181, 182), 280, (293), 352, (387)
Hunter, C. A., Jr., 56, (93), 340, (346)
Hunter, C. J. W., (47)
Hunter, P. A., 74, 76, (92)
Huntoon, F. M., 37, (41)
Huppert, M., 229, 241, 246, (253, 256)
Hurley, H. J., 355, (390)
Hurst, L., 364, 367, (385)
Hurst, V., 11, 14, 20–22, (43), 312, (346)
Hurwitz, C., 299, (307)
Hutchinson, W. G., 300, (307)
Hutner, S. H., 278, 280, (293)
Hutt, M. S. R., 17, 18, (41)
Hvid-Hansen, N., 68, (93)
Hyams, D., 128, (142)
Hyde, B., 106, (139)
Hyde, L., 106, (139)

Ides, D., 290, (295)
Illenyi, A., 167, (182)
Imaizumi, K., 378, (387)
Ingalls, M. S., 360, (387)
Ingalsbe, C. K., 108, (140)
Ingram, F. R., (43)
Innes, A. G., 10, (43)
Ino, J., 120, (139)
Inoki, S., 259, 288, (293)
Inouye, S., 249, (250)
Ironson, E. J., (255)
Irwin, J., 27, (43)
Ishida, M., 243, (253)
Israel, J., 63, (98)
Israel, S. L., 14, (43)
Ito, S., 304, (307)
Ivey, M. H., 279, (293)
Iwahara, I., (256)
Iwai, 288, (293)
Iwata, K., 249, (250), 380, (384)

Jablon, J. M., (46)
Jackins, H. C., 70, 71, 73, (93), 169, 170, (182)
Jackson, G. G., 12, 13, 20, 24, (44), 246, (253)
Jackson, J. L. W., 11, (46)
Jackson, L., 147, (185), 328, (350)
Jacob, F., 5, (8)
Jacobelli, G., 116, 118, (142)
Jacobs, L., 288, (295)
Jacobson, L. O., 316, 323, 324, (346)
Jaffurs, W. J., 10, (41)
Jahnel, 209
James, A. M., 300, (307)
James, H. A., 359, (389)
James, L. M., 353, (392)
James, R. C., 19, (43)
James, U., 342, (346)
Janes, H., (141)
Jann, G. J., 78, (93)
Jay, A. R., (390)
Jay, P., 364, (387)
Jaynes, M. H., (306)
Jeffery, G. M., 265, 267, 268, (293)
Jeffrey, J. S., 15, (43)
Jenkin, C. R., 156, (181)
Jenks, S. A., (46, 326)
Jennison, M. W., 327, (346)
Jennison, R. F., 287, (296)
Jensen, K., 363, 368, (387)
Jensen, R., 157, (182)
Jensen, R. G., 50, 56, (93)
Jepps, M. W., 272, (293)
Jessen, O., (41), 106, (139)
Jevons, M. P., (47)
Jeynes, M. H., 175, (183)
Jindrich, J., (293)
Jira, J., 276, (293)
Jirovec, O., 290, (293)
Johansen, G., (386)
Johansson, K. R., 57, (93), 353, (387)
Johns, A. T., 38, 39, (43)
Johns, F. M., 272, 281, (291)
Johnson, A., 375, (391)
Johnson, A. H., 29, (44)
Johnson, E. A., 312, (344)
Johnson, F. T., 105, (139)
Johnson, G., 280, 281, (293, 295)
Johnson, J. E., 19, (42, 43)
Johnson, R., (181, 385)
Johnson, R. F., (40)
Johnson, S. A. M., 240, 246, (253)
Johnson, V., 32, (43)
Johnston, E. A., (41, 345, 386)
Johnstone, H. G., 272, 278, 279, 281, (293)
Joiner, M., (42)

Joliff, C. R., 130, (139), 160, (182)
Jones, C. P., 232, 237, 238, (251, 253), 340, 341, (344, 346)
Jones, D., 26, (43)
Jones, M., 24, 25, 30, 31, 34, 38, 39, (43, 45), 54, (96), 104, (139, 141), 314, 322, 325, 331, (346, 348)
Jones, M. M., 240, (255)
Jones, V., 15, (42)
Jonsen, J., 153, 155, 156, (182)
Jordan, F. T. W., 239, (253)
Jordan, H. V., 24, (43), 209, (219), 328, (346)
Joress, S., 316, (344)
Joubert, L., (91, 95)
Juhlin, I., 84, 85, (93)
Jukes, T. H., 355, (391)
Julou, L., 290, (292)
June, R. C., 109, 110, (137, 139), 365, (386, 387)

Kabler, P. W., 28, 29, (43), 118, (139)
Kagan, B. M., 130, (140)
Kahn, M. C., 373, (391)
Kaitz, A. L., 316, 342, (346)
Kalina, G. P., 297, (307)
Kaliski, D. J., 194, (219)
Kalshteyn, L. I., 311, (348)
Kamen, M. D., 39, (43)
Kamijo, K., (256)
Kanda, D., 276, (295)
Kandler, O., (306)
Kanter, A. E., 170, (183), 194, (219), 338, (348)
Kapicka, L., 241, 247, (253)
Kaplan, S. M., 315, 325, 326, (346)
Kapovits, M., 38, (40)
Kapral, F. A., 23, (43)
Karapetyan, A. E., 280, (293)
Kasai, G. J., 71, 73, (93)
Kasai, K., 195, (218)
Kass, E. H., 311, 314, 316, 342, (346)
Kassel, R., 79, (93)
Kast, C. C., 210, 211, (218), 368, (387)
Katz, Y. J., 153, (182)
Kauffmann, F., 103, 105, 109, (139)
Kaufman, L., 90, (94)
Kawakita, S., 235, 241, (256)
Kawata, T., 188, (218), 300, 301, (307)
Kaye, D., 30, (43)
Kayser, L., (142)
Kean, B. H., 265, 287, 288, (293)
Keeney, E. L., 229, (250, 253)
Keitel, H. G., 363, (387)
Kelcec, L. C., (254, 389)
Kellenberger, E., 298, (306, 307)

Keller, H. M., (344)
Keller, R., 329, (347)
Kelly. B. K., 374, (387)
Kelly, D. R., 287, (295)
Kelly, J., 241, (253)
Kelly, J. P., 241, (253)
Kemp, G., 228, 235, 250, (253)
Kendall, A. I., 49, (93)
Kendall, F. E., 164, (182)
Kenner, B. A., 28, 29, (43), 118, (139)
Keogh, E. V., 11, (41)
Keppich, P. H., (308, 349)
Kernohan, J. W., 284, (293)
Kerr, A. C., 358, (387)
Kerrin, J. C., 87, (94), 334, (346)
Keutel, H. J., 273, 276, (293)
Key, I. D., 278, (295)
Khorazo, D., 322, (346)
Kibayashi, Y., 129, (139)
Kiefer, J., (388)
Kilpatrick, D., 54, (91)
King, A. B., 158, (182)
King, A. J., (295, 308, 349)
King, E. O., 113, 115–117, 120, 125, 132, (135, 139)
King, J. W., 59, (94)
King, S., 63, 80, 81, (94)
Kingsbury, K. R., (46)
Kinnaird, D. W., 15, (46)
Kirby, H., 259, (293)
Kirby, W. M. M., 106, (139)
Kirchheiner, E., 153, 156, 171, (183)
Kirk, C., (308, 349)
Kirn, A., (309)
Kirschner, L., 189, (218)
Kirsner, J. B., 31, (45, 91), 151, (181), 334, (348), 367, 368, (385, 386)
Kitaziri, K., (139)
Kitchin, P. C., (92)
Kiuru, V. J. T., 54, (94)
Kjellander, J., 28, 29, (43)
Klieneberger, E., 298, (307)
Klieneberger-Nobel, E., 297–300, 302, 304, 305, (306, 307)
Kligler, I. J., 69, 73, 77, (94), 314, (346)
Kligman, A. M., 243, 250, (255)
Klinge, K., 123, (139)
Klite, P. D., 380, 381, (387)
Klopp, C. T., 30, (40), 329, (346)
Kneeland, Y., 127, (139)
Knight, B. C. J. G., 298, (306)
Knight, V., 127, (139)
Knighton, H. T., 237, 245, (253), 358, (387)
Knipschildt, H. E., 109, (139)
Knoll, E. W., 265, 284, (293)
Knoll, M. L., (182, 183), 215, (218)

Knorr, M., 167, (182)
Knox, G., (390)
Kobayashi, R., 195, (218)
Koch, F., 209, (218)
Koch, G., 301, (309)
Koch, M. L., 15, 21, (43), 130, (139)
Koch, R., 128, (136)
Koenig, M. G., 30, (43)
Kofoid, C. A., 272, 278, 279, 281, (293)
Kohl, C., 163, 164, (184)
Kohler, W., 125, (139)
Kohn, A., 300, (307)
Kok, P. C., (251, 292)
Kolmer, J. A., 210, 211, (218), 368, (387)
Kopeloff, N., 54, (94)
Kortekangas, A. E., 311, 324–326, (346)
Korttila, K., 57, (94)
Koser, S. A., 53, (94), 241, (252), 371, 373, (387)
Koss, L. G., 275, (293)
Kostečka, F., 330, (346)
Kott, H., 279, 291, (293)
Kovacs, N., 123, (139)
Kozinn, P. J., 241, 248, (253, 255, 256)
Kramer, P. E., (98)
Krasner, R. I., 370, 373, (392)
Krasse, B., 49, (92), 238, (253)
Kraus, F. W., 31, 32, (43), 314, 331, (346), 375, (388)
Krause, R. M., 302, 303, (306)
Krauss, M. R., (40, 385)
Kreger-van Rij, N. J. W., 232, 234, (253)
Krehl, W. A., 360, (388)
Krembel, J., (309)
Krickler, M. S., 103, (139)
Kriedler, W. A., 363, (388)
Krieg, N. R., 371, (388)
Kristoffersen, T., 53, (94)
Kritchewski, B., 191, (218)
Krock, F. H., 38, (42)
Kroeger, W. H., 250, (255)
Krumwiede, C., 324, (348)
Krupp, P. J., 238, (253)
Kubica, G. P., 85, (94)
Kuchler, R. J., (96)
Kudo, K., 258, 260–262, (293)
Kuhn, H., 375, (384)
Kuhn, R., (92, 96)
Kuhns, D. M., 305, (309)
Kulp, W. L., 54, (94), 131, (137)
Kunert, H., 215, (218)
Kunkel, M. F., Jr., 39, (46)
Kunkel, P., (181)
Kuntz, R. E., 265–267, (294)
Kupferberg, A. B., 205, (220), 279, 280, (294, 295)
Kusano, N., 305, (307)

Kushner, D. S., 86, (94)
Küster, E., 7, (8), 323, 338, (346)
Kutscher, A. H., 240, 241, (253)
Kuzell, W. C., 304, (307)
Kwapinski, J. B., 364, (387)
Kwok-Kew Cheng, 305, (307)
Kwong, E., (389)

Laan, I. A., 279, (294)
Lachowicz, T., 12, (43)
Lagerborg, V. A., 53, (94)
Lahelle, O., 145, 148–150, 153, 155, 156, 158, 169, 171, (182), 368, (388)
Lahey, W. J., (181)
Laidlaw, P. P., 278, 280, (292)
Lamoreaux, L. F., (141)
Lamoreux, W. F., 354, (388)
Lancefield, R. C., 26, (43)
Lanceley, F., 275, 276, 285, 286, 289, (294)
Landau, J., 323, (343, 346)
Landau, J. V., 299, (307)
Landman, O. E., 301, (306)
Landsteiner, K., 146, (182), 187, 188, (218)
Landy, M., 129, (138), 366, 367, (386, 388)
Lang, W. R., 14, (43), 274, 289, 290, (294)
Langbehn, H. R., 265, (294)
Langford, G. C., Jr., 37, (43)
Langford, R. F., 311, (343)
Langston, C. W., 28, (43)
Lanke, L., 356, (387)
Laporte, A., 34, (43), 153, 157, (182, 347)
Larkin, B., 315, (346)
Larkin, E. P., 29, (43)
Larson, A. D., 189, (217, 218)
Larson, W. P., 167, 170, (182)
Laser, H., 82, (94)
Latrille, J., (44)
Laughlin, K. A., (295)
Laughton, N., 56, 78, (94), 339, 340, (346)
Laurell, G., 12, (43), 103, 104, 106, (137, 139)
Lautrop, H., 102, (139)
Lavergne, E. de, 63, (94)
Lawless, D. K., 265–267, (294)
Lawton, A., (137)
Lawton, W. E., 364, (385)
Lea, W. A., Jr., 239, (253)
Leach, R. W., 85, (94)
Leathers, W. S., (294)
LeBlanc, D. R., 5, (8)
Lederberg, E. M., 10, (43), 54, (94)

Lederberg, J., 10, (43), 54, (94), 297, 300, (307)
Ledin, R. B., (253)
Lee, A. M., 157, (184)
Lee, H. C., 179, (182)
Lee, J. J., 259, 279, (293)
Lee, Y. C., 116, (140)
Lees, A. W., 311, 324–326, (346)
Leeuwenhoek, A. van, 6, 145, 146, 173, 187
Lefebre, M., 36, (43)
Lehman, E. L., 79, (91)
Lehmann, W., 167, 364, (388)
Leifson, R., 111, 116, 121, (139)
Leiwant, B., 287, (295)
Lemierre, A., 34, (43), 326, (346, 347)
LeMinor, L., 244, (250)
LeMinor, S., 244, (250)
LeNoc, P., 132, (139), 337, (347)
Lenriot, A., (136)
Lentze, F., 69, (94)
Leonard, J., (137)
Leonard, V., 124, (140)
Leopold, S., 134, 135, (139), 342, (347)
Lepley, D., Jr., (43)
Lepper, M. H., 12, 13, 20, 24, (44)
Lessel, E. F., Jr., 174, (182)
Leulier, J., 287, (291)
Lev, M., 163, 166, (182)
Levaditi, C., 83, (94)
Levin, J. D., 240, (254)
Levine, M., 383, (388)
Levrel, J., (95)
Levy, M. N., (95)
Levy, P., 83, (94)
Lewis, C. J., 161, (182), 323, (347)
Lewis, F. S., 250, (253)
Lewis, K. H., 59, (94), 148, 149, 152, (182)
Lewkowicz, X., 35, 38, (44), 61, (94), 146, 154, (182), 329, (347)
Liao, S. J., 360, (388)
Lidwell, O. M., 14, 21, (44)
Liebermeister, K., 298, (307)
Liebovitz, A., 135, (139)
Liebow, A. A., 79, (94)
Liivak, M., 371, (388)
Likar, M., (347)
Lilienthal, B., 238, 245, (253), 330, (347)
Lilley, A. B., 129, (139), 367, (388)
Lilly, H. A., 90, (94)
Lindberg, R. B., 114, (136)
Linell, F., 83, 85, (94)
Lingard, A., 145, (182)
Linton, K. B., 103, (139, 345), 383, 384, (388)
Linton, R. W., 49, 50, (96)

Linzenmeirer, G., 79, (94)
Lippmann, A., 146, (181)
Lipsitz, P. J., (47)
Lissauer, 332, (347)
Liston, J., 133, (139)
Litsky, W., 29, (43)
Litt, J. Z., 251, (255)
Little, G. N., 80, (93)
Little, P. A., 203, 204, (218)
Littleton, B. J., 245, (254)
Liu, P., 240, (253), 374, (388)
Liu, P. V., 121, 126, 129, (139)
Liu, T. Y., 13, (41)
Live, I., 14, (44)
Lizgunova, A. V., 374, (388)
Locke, M., 215, (218)
Lockhart, W. R., 372, (388)
Lockwood, J. S., 90, (94)
Lodder, J., 232, 234, (253)
Lodenkämper, H., 149, 158, 159, (182)
Loeffler, F., 145, (182)
Loh, W.-P., 90, (94), 104, 106, 126, (139), 333, 334, (347)
Lohss, F., 301, (309)
Loken, K. I., 239, (253)
Lomuto, G., 275, (294)
Long, E. T., 15, (45)
Long, K. R., 56, (93), 340, (346)
Longeray, C., 113, 115, (136)
Longwell, F. H., (295)
Looke, E., 21, (40)
Loosemore, T. G. E., 88, (96, 349)
López, J. C., 339, (348)
Lopez Fernandez, J. R., 228, (253)
Lorch, L. von, (95)
Lord, F. T., 68, (94), 326, (347)
Lorieo, D., 378, (384)
Loube, S. D., 135, (136)
Louria, D. B., 245, 250, (253)
Lovell, D. L., 322, (347)
Lovestedt, S. A., 64, (97)
Löw, O., 373, 379, (386)
Lowbury, E. J. L., 15, (44), 90, (94), 126, 128, 129, (137, 139), 334, (347), 364, 367, (385, 386)
Lowe, A. E., (43)
Lubbers, G. J., (251, 292)
Lucas, C. E., 369, (388)
Lucas, D. R., 159, 162–164, (184)
Lucas, R. N., (139)
Lucero, E. M., (142)
Luckey, T. D., 353, 354, 361, 362, (386, 388)
Ludlam, G. B., 248, (254)
Ludovic, M. M., 195, (218)
Ludwig, T. G., 77, (94)
Lundh, G., (385)

Lundin, B.-M., 301, (309)
Lutz, A., 113, 117, 118, 120, 123, (140)
Lwoff, A., 5, (8), 111–113, 115, (140), 257, 278, (293, 294), 383, (388)
Lynau, 62
Lynch, E. R., 210, 211, (218), 368, (387)
Lynn, R. J., 298, (308)

Maccabe, A. F., (251)
McCabe, A. M., 86, (91)
Maccacaro, G. A., 301, (307)
MacCallum, P., 85, (94)
McCartney, J. E., 147, 160, (183), 325, (347)
McCarty, M., 302, 303, (306)
McClary, D. O., 241, (254)
McClellan, J. T., (254)
McClure, L. E., (220)
McCullough, M., 114, (141)
McCullough, N. B., 157, (181, 183)
MacDonald, E. M., 259, 290, 291, (294)
Macdonald, J. B., 69, 71, (96), 147, 152, 162, 163, 172, 173, 175–178, (181, 182, 183, 184), 188, 190, 194, 200, 201, 215, (218, 219, 220), 329, (344, 347), 370, (386)
McDonough, E. S., 223, (254)
McEntegart, M. G., 289, 291, (294)
McEwen, D. C., 257, 287, (294)
Macfie, J. W. S., 193, (218)
McGann, V., 112, 113, 116, (142)
McGehee, B., (384)
McGill, M. I., 290, (294)
McGinnis, J., 382, (390)
McGovern, J. J., 247, (254)
McGuire, J. M., (42)
McHenry, M. C., 157, (183)
Mackaness, G. B., 23, (44)
Mackay, E. S. M., 104, (140)
McKay, K. A., 299, (307)
Mackel, D. C., (138, 345)
Mackenzie, I., 77, (94)
Mackie, L. M., (91, 345)
McKillop, E. J., 12, 20, (42), 89, (94)
McKinlay, B. C., 106, (138)
MacKintosh, M. E., 38, 39, 40, (41, 45)
McKusick, V. A., 155, 158, 159, (181)
MacLaren, J. A., 240, (254)
Maclean, I. H., 324, 325, 329, (345)
Maclean, N., (251)
Maclean, P. D., 79, (94)
MacLennan, J. D., 34, (44)
MacLeod, C. M., 19, 40, (43, 385)
McLeod, J. W., 39, (42), 126, (138), 201, (218), 375, (388)
McMillen, S., 86, (94)

McMurray, C. M., 283, (294)
McNaught, R. C., 159, (182), 311, 324–326, (346)
McNutt, S. H., 287–289, (294, 295)
MacPherson, D. A., 246, (253)
McQuillen, K., 297, 300, 301, 303, (306, 307)
MacRae, T. F., (217)
McVay, L. V., Jr., 158, (183)
Madden, J., (306)
Madlener, E. M., 174–176, (183, 218)
Madoff, S., 300, 302, 305, (306, 307, 309), 334, (344)
Magara, M., 25, (44), 250, (254), 280, (294)
Magasanik, B., 371, (391)
Magath, T. B., 284, (293)
Magavran, J., (93, 346)
Magnin, F., (95)
Magnusson, M., 83, (94)
Mahler, H. R., 301, (307)
Maisel, J., 5, (8), 312, (347)
Malakatis, G. M., (294)
Malek, J., 167, (183)
Malins, J. M., (140, 348)
Malizia, W. F., (98)
Malkova, J., 167, (183)
Malmquist, J., (385)
Maltby, M. P., 109, (142)
Maltman, J. R., 21, (42, 44)
Manchester, P. T., 242, (254)
Manciaux, M., (94)
Mandel, M., 246, (254)
Mandoul, R., 278, (294)
Manfield, P. A., 14, 21, (44)
Manfre, A. S., 239, (254)
Mankiewicz, E., 371, (388)
Mankle, E. A., 304, (307)
Mankowski, W. J., 240, (254)
Mankowski, Z. T., 240, 245, (254)
Mann, S. O., 30, 38, (42, 44), 177, (181, 182)
Manoliu, N., (46)
Manson, E. E. D., 81, (95), 317, (348)
Mansson, I., 104, (140)
Manten, A., 250, (254)
Many, H., 230, (254)
Mao, F. N., 132, (141)
March, B., 355, (385)
Marchand, H., (40, 251, 344)
Marchionini, A., 359, (388)
Marchoux, E., 82, (94)
Marcus, S., 250, (254)
Marggraf, H., 216, (217)
Margolis, A. McC., (92)
Markham, N. P., 15, 22, (44)
Markson, L. M., 239, (251)

Marmell, M., 104, (140)
Marotta, U., 326, (347)
Marples, M. J., 329, (347)
Marques, W., (254)
Marschall, F., 57, (94)
Marshall, M. S., 163, 164, (184)
Marston, J., 300, 302, (307)
Martelly, 152
Martin, A. J. P., (217)
Martin, C. J., (217)
Martin, D. S., 232, 237, (253), 341, (346)
Martin, H. L., 380, (388)
Martin, M. K., (46)
Martin, M. P., 326, (348)
Martin, W. J., 157, (183)
Martin-Scott, I., 227, (254)
Marwin, R. M., 236, 237, (254)
Mashimo, P. A., 178, (183)
Mason, A., 250, (251)
Massent, D., 342, (349)
Massler, M., 328, (347)
Masson, F. M., 30, (44)
Masters, P. L., 324–326, (347)
Mathews, W. W., 300, (307)
Mathieson, D. R., 364, (388)
Matsuo, J., (218)
Matthias, J. Q., (46)
Matthiessen, M., 114, (140, 142)
Mattick, A. T. R., 49, (96), 379, (388, 391)
Mattman, L. H., 35, (44), 163, (184), 300, (307)
Maughan, E., 21, (47)
Maxcy, K. F., 266, (294)
May, J. R., 135, (140)
Mayer, E., (182, 184)
Mayer, M. M., 203, (219)
Mayer, R. L., 245, (252)
Mazzarella, M. A., 39, (40, 44), 355, (388)
Mead, T. H., 126, (140)
Meader, P. D., 124, (140)
Mecchi, E., 353, (384)
Medill, M. A., 300, (307)
Meekison, D. M., 371, (387)
Meiklejohn, G., 33, (44)
Meleney, F. L., 265, (294)
Meleney, H. E., 215, (218)
Melly, M. A., 23, (44, 45)
Memmer, R., 78, (92)
Mendel, J., 74, (94), 154, (183)
Mendez, R. L., (347)
Mendonca, J., (254)
Menduke, H., 289, 290, (294)
Menolasino, N. J., 10, (44)
Mercadante, J., (253)

Mercado, D. G., 171, (185)
Mergenhagen, S. E., 35, 39, (44), 171, (183), 212, 215, 216, (218)
Merilan, C. P., (93)
Merritt, A. D., 342, (347)
Merritt, C. D., 10, (46)
Mesrobeanu, L., 125, (136)
Metchnikoff, E., 48, 49, (95)
Meyer, E., 63, 80, 81, (94, 95)
Meyers, C. E., 54, (95)
Meyers, S. P., (250)
Meynell, M. J., (140, 348)
Michael, J. G., 299, 300, (307), 366, (388)
Michaels, L. M., 108, (138)
Michel, 195, (218)
Michel, M. F., 300, (307)
Michison, D. A., 333, (349)
Mickelsen, O., 353–355, (388)
Middlebrook, G., 83, (95), 178, (181)
Mihalco, F., (41)
Mikolajczyk, R. J., (142)
Miles, A. A., 7, (8), 12, 36, (44, 47), 88, (97), 108, (140), 317, 323, 324, (347, 350)
Miller, A., (345)
Miller, W. D., 6, (8), 145–147, 166, 174, (183), 191, (218)
Millian, S. J., 13, (44)
Millican, R. C., 129, (140, 141)
Mills, G. Y., 130, (140)
Mills, K. C., 147, 160, 161, (183), 325, (347, 349)
Minck, R., (309)
Mira, O. J., (252, 255)
Mirick, G. S., 33, (44, 47, 391)
Miroslav, P., (293)
Misra, S. S., 148, (183), 333, (347)
Mitchell, J. A., 49, 54, (96)
Mitchell, R. B., (138, 345)
Mitchell, W. O., 227, 235, (252)
Miura, H., 339, (347)
Miyakawa, M., 361, (388)
Miyasaki, F., (256)
Mochizuki, T., 380, (384)
Moeller, 101
Moffett, M., 290, (294)
Mogab, J. J., 375, 377, 378, (390)
Moll, T., 108, (140)
Monk, M., 126, (139)
Monro, J. A., 15, 22, (44)
Monson, W. J., (96)
Montagna, C. P., 62, (95), 341, (347)
Montana, J. A., 250, (254)
Montgomery, B. E., 360, (385)
Monzon, O. T., 311, (347)

Moore, B., 10, (44), 147, 177, 178, (182), 341, (347)
Moore, D. W., Jr., 59, 63, 81, (96)
Moore, H. B., 121, 131, 133, (140)
Moore, M., 236
Moore, S. F., Jr., 287, (294)
Moore, W. E. C., 179, (180, 182), 336, (344)
Morax, V., 111, 115, 119, (140)
Morichau-Beauchant, J., 112–116, (136)
Morishita, T., 50, (95)
Morris, E. O., 26, 29, (44), 63, 65, 68, 73, 74, (95)
Morse, T. S., (348)
Mortimer, E. A., (47)
Morton, H. E., (292), 299, 305, (307, 308), 326, 329, (347, 349)
Morton, H. S., (141), 148, (184), 332, (348)
Moscovici, C., 5, (8), 312, (347)
Moseley, F. T., 124, (142)
Mossion, X., 289, (292)
Mourad, S., 244, 250, (254)
Moureau, M., 149, (183), 191, 203, 206, 207, (218)
Moustardier, G., 28, (44), 337, (347)
Mucha, V., 146, (182), 187, 188, (218)
Mueller, J. F., 284, (294)
Mueller, J. H., 371, (391)
Mühlenbach, V., 373, 375, (388)
Mühlens, P., 147, (183), 191, 193, 197, (219)
Mukai, F., 383, (388, 390)
Mukherji, R. N., (136)
Müller, A., 62, (91)
Munch-Peterson, E., 379, (388)
Mundt, J. O., 29, (44)
Munoz, J., 125, (140)
Murphy, W. C., (93)
Murphy, W. H., Jr., (255)
Murray, E. G. D., 23, (40), 48, 63, 65, 69, 80, 81, (91), 102, 111, 133, (136, 141), 148, 160, (180, 184), 332, (348)
Murray, R. G. E., 378, (388)
Murray, T. J., 245, (256)
Murrell, M., 290, (295)
Muschel, L. H., 300, (306, 307), 366, (388, 389)
Muskatblit, E., 239, (254)
Myers, D. M., 10, (44), 375, (388)

Nadel, H., 311, (347)
Nadel, J., (142)
Nahmias, A. J., (46)
Nakabayashi, T., 259, (293)

Nakamura, L. K., 371, (388)
Nakamura, M., 278, 280, (294)
Nakanishi, K., 259, (293)
Namioka, S., 103, 108, (140)
Nathanson, R. B., 360, (388)
Nativelle, R., 150, (185)
Neal, A. L., 27, (41)
Needell, M. H., 365, 367, (388)
Negrin, J., Jr., 127, (139)
Negroni, P., 223, 237, 240, (254), 370, (389)
Neill, J. M., 33, (42)
Nelson, E. L., 129, (140)
Nelson, F. E., 53, (90, 94)
Nelson, J. B., 297, 303, 305, (308)
Nelson, J. D., 110, (140)
Nelson, R. A., Jr., 203, (219)
Nelson, T. S., 15, (45)
Nestoresco, N., 12, (44)
Neter, E., 109, (140), 363, 366, 368, (388, 389)
Neugebauer, D. L., (139)
Neumann, R. O., 322, 323, (347)
Nevin, T. A., 192, 208, (218, 219), 370, (389)
Newland, L. G. M., 30, (45), 379, (385)
Newton, A., 235, 240, (253, 254)
Newton, W. L., 212, (217), 282, 288, (294), 357, (389)
Nichols, A. C., 14, (44), 322, (348), 355, (390)
Nichols, H. J., 209, (217)
Nickerson, J. F., (388)
Nickerson, W. J., 58, (96), 240, (254)
Nicol, C. S., 273, 276, 277, 286, 287, (292, 295), 305, (308), 334, (347)
Ninomiya, J., 280, (294)
Nishikawa, Y., (256)
Nissle, A., 7, (8), 382, (389)
Niven, C. F., 30, 32, 33, (41, 44, 47)
Noble, W. C., Jr., 324, (347)
Nocard, E., 298, (308)
Nodake, Y., 280, (291)
Noguchi, H., 188, 190–194, 196–198, 206, 209–211, 213, (219)
Nolte, W. A., 329, (347)
Norden, A., 83, 85, (94)
Norman, J. O., 372, (391)
Norris, R. F., 59–61, (92, 93, 95, 97), 248, (254, 346), 368, (389)
Norton, J. F., 360, (389)
Novák, E. K., 228, 239, (256)
Novy, M. F., 360, (389)
Nurmikko, V., 371, (389)
Nyberg, C., 132, (140)
Nye, R. N., 322, (344), 363, (389)

Oag, R. K., 113, 119, (140)
Oakley, C. L., 89, (93)
Oates, J. K., 304, (308)
Obermeier, O., 187, (219)
O'Connell, D. C., (184, 219)
Oddo, F., 211, (217, 219)
Oeding, P., 11, 12, 20, (44), 114, 117, 119, 132, (140), 323, (347)
O'Grady, F., 326, (344)
Ogston, 145
Ohlsen, J. R., (139, 182)
Ohno, M., 259, (294)
Okabe, S., 194, 206, (219)
Olafsson, M., 116, 118, (140)
Olarte, J., 305, (308)
Old, J. W., 132, (143)
Olitsky, P. K., 147, 148, 160, 161, (183), 325, (347)
Olitzki, A. L., 134, (140)
Oliveira, D. de, 228, 239, (251)
Oliveira, P. V., (254)
Oliver, W. W., 69, 70, (97), 111, 117, 119, (140), 147, 151, 162, 164, (183), 325, (347)
Olmedo, R., (292)
Olszewski, B., 274, (293)
Omata, R. R., 167, 169, 170, (183), 207, 215, (219)
Omland, T., 106, (140)
Opal, Z. Z., 50, 54, 55, (93), 334, (346)
Oppenheimer, E. H., 127, (141)
Opsahl, T., Jr., 118, 120, (140)
Orbach, H., (137)
Orcutt, M. L., 153, (183)
Ordal, E. J., 39, (47)
Orfila, J., 323, (347)
Orita, Y., 288, (294)
Orland, F. J., 53, (95)
Orr, J. H., 12–15, 21, 22, (42, 44)
Örskov, I., 104, 106, (140), 334, (347)
Ory, E. M., (347)
Osawa, E., 366, (389)
Osebold, J. W., 14, (44)
Oshima, 329, (347)
Osler, A. G., 30, (40, 44)
Osterrieth, P., 299, 301, (309)
Osteux, R., 151, 169, (181)
Ostrom, C. A., 359, (389)
O'Sullivan, D. J., 105, (140), 316, 342, (348)
O'Toole, E., 337, (345)
Otto, 270, (292)
Owens, F. J., (91)
Oxford, A. E., 30, 38, (42, 44), 104, (140, 181), 379, (389)
Oyama, V. I., 204, 205, 208, (219, 220)

Pachtman, E. A., 314, 315, 317, 322, (348)
Padilla, E. A., (183)
Padula, J. F., 249, (256)
Pagano, J. S., 14, (44), 240, (254)
Page, R. H., (142, 391)
Paine, T. F., 380, (389)
Pakula, R., 33, (45), 370, (389)
Palmer, C. E., 82, 84, (91)
Palmer, E. D., 194, (219)
Palmer, W. L., 31, (45), 334, (348)
Pannarale, M. R., 323, (346, 348)
Panos, C., 302, (308)
Papageorge, C., (252)
Papavassiliou, J., 119, (140), 383, (389)
Pappas, N. C., 107, (141)
Parfentjev, I. A., 250, (254)
Parfitt, G. J., 54, (91)
Park, R. W. A., 175, (183)
Park, W. H., 324, (348)
Parker, M. T., 15, (45, 141), 375, (389)
Parker, R. T., (344)
Parr, L. W., 103, (140), 194, 195, (219), 332, 334, 337, (348), 382, 384, (385, 389)
Parramore, M. L., 39, 40, (41)
Parrott, R. H., (254)
Partin, J. C., (344)
Patočka, F., 77, 87, (95), 162, (183), 338, 341, (348)
Paton, A. M., 124, (140)
Patterson, M., 89, (95)
Paul, E., 197, (219)
Paul, F., (93)
Payne, F. J., (138), 284, (294, 345)
Payne, J. I., 300, (308)
Payne, J. M., 109, 110, (142)
Payne, P., 10, (44)
Pearce, R. H., 378, (388)
Peck, R. L., 380, (390)
Peck, S. M., 249, (254), 369, (389)
Pedersen, G. T., (46)
Pederson, C. S., 48, 49, (95)
Pedrycz, W., 284, (293)
Pejrone, G. M., 314, 330, (348)
Pelczar, M. J., Jr., 36–38, (43, 45, 47, 97), 204, (219), 285, (294), 371, (388)
Peloux, Y., 118, (140)
Penso, G., (306)
Pentler, C. F., 353, (384)
Peoples, D. M., (292), 299, (308)
Pepys, J., 249, (254)
Perch, B., 105, (139)
Pereira, A. T., 12, (45), 363, (389)
Pereira-Barreto, M., 238, (254)
Perekhozheva, M. N., 311, (348)
Perez, J. E., 162, (183)

Perez-Miravete, A., 29, (45), 106, (137), 339, 341, (348), 373, (389)
Perlman, E., 124, (141)
Perry, E. T., 322, (348)
Perry, J. D., 54, (96)
Perry, J. J., 105, (139)
Perry, K. D., 30, (45)
Perry, W. I., (338)
Pessin, S. B., 242, 247, (255)
Pestre, M., 289, (292)
Petersdorf, R. G., 15, (45), 128, (137)
Peterson, G. E., 57, (93), 353, (387)
Peterson, W. J., 259, (294)
Petit, H., 151, 156, (180)
Petit, P., 111, 112, (140)
Petran, E., 311, (344), 359, (385)
Petru, V., 238, (254), 382, (389)
Petruk, G. F., 132, (141)
Pettit, H., 340, (348)
Petuely, F., 60, 62, (95)
Pfeifer, G., 38, (40)
Phaff, H. J., 232, (255)
Phillips, B. P., 282, (294), 356, (389)
Phillips, J. McI., 195, (219)
Philpot, V. B., Jr., 104, 118, (140), 311, 314, 341, (348)
Pickett, J. P., 241, (254)
Pickett, M. J., 121, 131, 133, (140), 370, (389)
Pidcoe, V., (44)
Piéchaud, D., 112, 114, (140), 325, (348)
Piéchaud, M., 112, 115–119, (140, 141, 348)
Pike, E. B., 54, (90)
Pike, R. M., 114, 119, 120, (141)
Pillet, J., (40, 344)
Pillot, J., 211, (219)
Pillsbury, D. M., 4, (8), 317, (348, 389)
Pilot, I., 170, (183), 194, 195, (219), 326, 338, (348)
Pin, R., 249, (252), 368, (386)
Pincus, I. J., (251)
Pine, L., 59, 64, 65, 67, 77, (93, 95)
Piro, J. D., (253)
Pittman, M., 133–135, (137, 141), 323, (348)
Pitzurra, M., 300, 302, (308)
Plankensteiner, T., 374, (385)
Plass, E. D., 238, (253, 254), 287, 289, (295)
Plaut, H., 145, 147, 166, 174, (183)
Pleasants, J. R., 354, (388)
Plotkin, S. A., (44), 127, (141)
Plueckhahn, V. D., 14, (45)
Pochi, P. E., 82, (95)
Podbielskij, A., 329, (348)
Polevitzky, K., 327, (350)

Pollack, J. D., 235, 240, (254)
Pollak, A., 85, 87, (90, 91)
Pollice, F., 358, (391)
Pollock, M. R., 81, (95), 317, (348)
Pomeranz. N., 159, (185)
Popovici, M., 12, (44)
Porch, M. L., 29, (45)
Porteous, J. W., 63, 67, 80, (91, 92)
Porter, J. R., 379, (389)
Porter, R. J., 278, (294)
Porterfield, J. S., 33, (45)
Posada, H. V., 29, (45)
Potee, K. G., 127, 130, (143)
Poujol, E., 341, (348)
Pouliquen, E., 159, (184)
Powell, D. E. B., (42)
Powelson, D. M., 373, (388)
Power, D. A., 204, (219)
Powers, D. 105, (141)
Powlen, D. O., 359, (391)
Pramanick, K., (136)
Pratt, J. S., 170, 171, (183), 326, (348)
Pratt, P. C., 84, (90)
Prelle, H., 374, (384)
Prévot, A.-R., 25, 26, 35, 37, (45), 53, 65, 79–81, 87, (95), 112, 116, 146–148, 150, 152, 153, 159, 161, 162, 171–173, 177, 179, (183, 184, 185), 191–193, 203, 206, 207, (219)
Price, K. M., 127, (139)
Price, P. B., 314, 315, (348)
Prigot, A., 104, (140, 141), 334, (349)
Primosigh, J., 301, (309)
Princivalle, M., 53, (95)
Priolisi, A., 366, (385)
Pritchard, H. N., (98)
Privitera, F., 246, (255)
Prohaska, J. V., 15, (45)
Proske, H. O., 176, (184), 201, 215, (219)
Provasoli, L., 278, 280, (293, 294)
Provost, P. J., 36, (45)
Prowazek, S. von, 193, (218, 219)
Prozorovskii, S. V., 301, 304, (308)
Pryce, D. M., 249, (251)
Pryles, C. V., 312, 342, (348)
Puetzer, B., 314, 315, (345), 359, (387)
Pulvertaft, R. J. V., 299, (308)
Purpura, T., 366, (385)

Quabeck, G., 250, (255)
Quinchon, C., 363, (390)
Quinley, R. L., 29, (45)
Quinn, R. W., 326, (348)

Rahe, A. H., 49, (95)
Rai Chaudhuri, M. N., 284, (295)

Rains, A. J. H., 69, (95)
Rajkovic, A., 325, (348)
Rajnovich, E., 363, (389)
Rakoff, A. E., (251), 275, 289, (291)
Ramakrishnan, T., 241, (255)
Rambo, F. R., 250, (254)
Rammelkamp, C. H., (47)
Ramsey, C. H., 101, 102, (137)
Randall, E., (389)
Raney, D. E., 125, 132, (139)
Rankow, R. M., (253)
Rantasalo, I., 14, (45)
Rantz, L. A., 107, (141), 363, 366, (389, 390)
Rao, G. R., 241, (255)
Rassfeld-Sternberg, L., 89, (98)
Rastjapin, T., 195, (221)
Rauchfus, 145, (184)
Ravin, A. W., 3, (8)
Rawson, A. J., 248, (254), 368, (389)
Raynaud, M., 26, (41), 53, (95), 337, (344)
Read, C. P., 259, 280, 281, 290, (293, 295)
Reardon, L. V., 272, 282, 288, (292, 294, 295), 357, (389)
Rebell, G., 4, (8), 12, 24, (45), 317, (348), 359, 360, (389)
Rebell, G. C., (253), 317, (348)
Rechcigl, M., 354, (389)
Redner, W. J., (291)
Reece, M. W., 34, (47), 157, (185)
Rees, C. W., 272, (292)
Rees, R. J. W., 30, (42)
Reese, M. K., 312, (350)
Reeves, R. E., 278, (295)
Reichert, von, 187
Reid, D. W., (92)
Reid, J. D., 240, (255)
Reid, R. D., 285, (294)
Reilersöl, S., 334, (348)
Reilly, J., 34, (43, 347)
Reimann, H. A., 24, (45)
Rein, C. R., (254, 389)
Reiner, J. M., 299, (307)
Reiner, L., 290, (293)
Reiss, F., 240, (255)
Rendtorff, R. G., 282–284, (295)
Rengarts, R. T., (343, 348)
Repaci, G., 146, 147, 174, (184)
Resnick, H., 80, (93)
Rettger, L. F., 54, 59, 60, 73, (94, 95, 96, 97), 148–150, 152, 167, 169–171, (182, 185), 353, (392)
Reyniers, J. A., 354, 362, (386, 388, 389)
Reynolds, R. C., (40)
Rheins, M. S., (44)
Rhodes, D. H., 128, (136)

Rhodes, P. S., 316, (344)
Rhodes, R. A., 57, (96)
Ribadeau-Dumas, L., (184)
Rice, E. C., (254)
Richardson, R. L., 25, 31, 34, 38, (45), 54, 74, (96), 104, (141), 314, 331, (348), 373, (390)
Richart, R., 242, (255)
Richou, H., 363, (390)
Richou, R., 363, (390)
Riddell, M. I., 104, (141), 148, (184), 249, (251), 332, 334, (348)
Riddell, R. W., 249, (251)
Ridley, M., 14, (45), 334, (348)
Rieth, H., 225, 228, 231, 233, 238, (255), 338, (348)
Rifkind, D., 32, (45)
Rigdon, A. L., (94)
Rigdon, R. H., (94, 254)
Riggall, F. O., (254)
Rights, F. L., 216, (220)
Říha, I., 360, (386)
Riley, H. D., (348)
Riley, R. F., 379, (391)
Rimington, C., 159, 162–164, (184)
Ringen, L. M., 126, (141), 334, (348)
Rippon, J. E., 10, 11, (40, 47)
Rist, E., 146, 161, (181), 326, (345)
Ritter, C., 29, (45)
Ritter, P., 374, (390)
Ritts, R. E., 105, 132, (141)
Roantree, R. J., 107, 108, (141), 366, (390)
Robbins, M. L., 103, (140), 382, 384, (385, 389)
Roberts, H. B., (217)
Roberts, L. F., 112, 114, 117, 118, (137), 325, (345)
Robertson, M., 291, (295)
Robinow, C. F., 174
Robinson, E. L., 58, 60, (96)
Robinson, G. H., 124, (140)
Robinson, G. L., 107, (141)
Robinson, H. B. G., (92)
Robinson, I. M., 165, (180)
Robinson, L. B., 188, 193, 201, 202, 208, 211, (219), 368, (390)
Robinson, M., 58, (96)
Robinson, R. H. M., 33, (46)
Rocha, H., 118, (141)
Rodaniche, E. C., 31, (45), 334, (348)
Rodin, P., 290, (295)
Rodwell, A. W., 298, (308)
Roe, A. S., (40, 385)
Rogachefsky, H., (251, 255)
Rogers, D. E., 17, 23, (45)
Rogers, K. B., 110, 135, (141)

Rogers, M. R., 179, (182)
Rogoff, M. H., 125, (141)
Rogosa, M., 38, 39, (45), 48, 49, 52–56, 59, 73, 74, (91, 92, 93, 96), 156, (181), 331, 340, (348)
Roine, P., 61, 62, (92, 345)
Romano, A. H., 58, (96)
Romansky, M. J., 135, (137)
Roodyn, L., 15, 20, (45)
Rooney, J. R., 357, (391)
Ropes, M. W., 149, 150, 152, (184, 306, 344)
Rose, C. S., 60, 61, (92, 96, 97)
Rosebury, T., 3, 7, (8), 24, 26, 28, 33, 34, (46), 48–50, 52, 56, 59, 63, 66, 68–71, 73, (96, 97), 104, (141), 149, 151–153, 157, 162, 169, 171–177, (184), 188, 190, 194–197, 199–202, 213, 215, 216, (219, 220), 238, (255), 287, (295), 310, 314, 328, 339, (348, 349, 350), 355, 369, 370, 375, 377, 378, 380–382, (390)
Rosen, F. S., 107 (141)
Rosenbaum, H. D., 89, (95)
Rosenberg, A. A., 79, (94)
Rosenberger, R. F., 28, (46)
Rosenblum, E. D., 11, (46)
Rosendal, K., (41, 46)
Rosenthal, E., (344)
Rosenthal, S. A., 229, 240, (251, 255)
Rosenthal, S. L., 194, (220), 330, (349)
Rosenthal, S. M., 129, (141)
Ross, C. A. C., 110, (136)
Ross, S., (143, 254)
Roth, F. J., 245–247, (250, 252, 255), 369, (390)
Rothblat, G. H., 298, (308)
Rothman, A. H., 280, (295)
Rothman, S., (390)
Rottino, A., 79, (93)
Rountree, P. M., 11, 15, (42, 46)
Roux, E., 298, (308)
Roux, J., (306)
Rowley, D., 107, (141)
Rowson, K. E. K., 110, (138), 337, (345)
Rozansky, R., 13, 20, (46)
Rubin, A., (308)
Rubio-Huertos, M., (306)
Rudolf, P., (293)
Ruebner, B., 104, (141), 148, (184), 333, 334, (349)
Ruelius, H. W., (92)
Ruiter, M., 302, 304, 305, (308)
Runge, G., (90, 343)
Runnels, J. L., 10, (46)
Runyon, E. H., 84, 85, (96)
Rusca, H. G., 238, (256)

Russell, B. E., (390)
Russell, P. F., 258, (292)
Russell, W. T., 323, (349)
Russo, R., (41, 345)
Rust, J. D., 129, (140, 141)
Rustigan, R., 104, (141), 334, (349)
Ruys, A. C., 155, 159, (184), 298, 305, (308, 309)
Ryan, F. J., 383, (390)
Ryff, J. F., 78, (96), 157, (184)
Ryigas, E. M., 279, (295)
Ryschenkow, E., 30, (40), 329, (346)

Saavedra, J., (292)
Sabin, A. B., 305, (308)
Sabouraud, R., 222, (255)
Sacenti, M., 248, (255)
Sachs, H., 363, (390)
Sacks, T. G., 54, (91)
Saez, H., 239, (255)
Sagami, S., (390)
Sahab, K., 103, (141)
St. Clair, J., 207, (307)
St. John, J. H., 280, (295)
St. Romain, M. J., 238, (253)
Sakazaki, R., 103, 108, (140)
Sakurai, N., 11, (46)
Salaman, M. H., 304, 305, (308), 341, 342, (349)
Saloum, R., (141)
Salsbury, A. J., 88, (96, 349)
Salton, M. R. J., 303, (306, 308)
Salvin, S. B., 67, (96), 242–244, 249, (255)
Sanchez-Torres, L. E., 14, 22, (46), 312, (349)
Sanders, G. B., 15, (46)
Sanders, M., (93, 346)
Sandiford, B. R., 129, (141), 367, (390)
Sandivik, O., 126, (141)
Sandoval, B., 381, (386)
Sanford, J. P., 131, (142), 342, (347)
Saphra, I., 384, (390)
Saquis, J., (254)
Sarkar, J. K., 131, (137, 141), 382, (390)
Sarles, W. B., 54, 57, (91, 93, 96, 98), 353, (387)
Sarria, A., 250, (253)
Saslaw, M. S., 32, (46), 326, (349)
Sathavara, S., (142)
Saul, M., (46, 326)
Sawyer, S., 164, (184), 189, 201, (220)
Saxholm, R., 78, (96)
Savers, R. R., 176, (184), 201, 215, (219)

Schaeffer, A., 123, (140)
Schafter, A. J., 127, (141)
Schaub, I. G., 10, 31, (46), 112, 114, 116–119, (141), 304, (308), 325, (349)
Schaudinn, F., 187, 192, 193, (220)
Scheder, E. P., 20, (41)
Scheff, G. von, 205, (220)
Scheimann, L. G., 355, (390)
Scherago, M., 125, (140)
Scherp, H. W., 35, 39, (44), 171, (183), 216, (218), 371, (390)
Scherr, G. H., 232, 244, 247, (255)
Schieler, L., (220)
Schierbeek, A., 6, (8), 145, (184)
Schild, C. A., 311, (346)
Schloss, G. T., 284, (293)
Schlossman, S. F., 362, (390)
Schmidt, E. G., 53, (96)
Schmidt, J., 74, (96), 373, (390)
Schmidt, R., (388)
Schmitt, J., (94, 96)
Schmorl, G., 145, (184)
Schneiderman, A., 205, (220)
Schneierson, S. S., 124, (141)
Schnitzer, R. J., 287, (295)
Schnoor, T. F., 237, (255), 334, (349)
Schoenthal, R., 379, (390)
Schönfeld, J., 233, (255)
Schonfeld, J. K., 300, (308)
Schottmüller, H., 364, (390)
Schoubye, N., (386)
Schreiber, M., (138, 345)
Schroeder, C. M., (43)
Schuldberg, I. I., 116, 118–120, (141)
Schuler, R. W., 278, (295)
Schultz-Haudt, S. D., 371, (390)
Schultze, M. L., 114, (141)
Schulze, H. O., 208, (220)
Schumacher, A. E., 354, (388)
Schumacher, R. D., 54, (93), 340, (346)
Schuster, C. W., 125, (138)
Schuster, D. S., 239, (253)
Schwabacher, H., 88, (96), 151, 159, 162–164, (184), 332, 333, (349)
Schwarz, F. K. T., 326, (345)
Schwarz, J., 244, (250)
Schwarz, O. H., 34, (46), 338, (349)
Schweighofer, D., 300, (308)
Schweinburg, F. B., 311, (349)
Schweinfurth, D. I., 278, (295)
Schweitzer, B., 312, (349)
Scoma, J. L., 81, (92)
Scott, D. B., 170, (181), 195, (218)
Scott, E. G., 15, (42)
Scott, E. N., (138, 386)
Scott, J. C., 13, (40)
Scott-Gray, M., 290, (295)

Scrimshaw, N. S., 355, (390)
Sears, H. J., 105, (141)
Šebek, V., 77, 87, (95), 162, (183), 338
    341, (348)
Sebestyen, M., 362, (390)
Second, L., 37, (47), 112, 113, (140,
    142, 348)
Sedlak, J., 102, (141)
Seegal, D., 363, (389)
Seeley, H. W., 27, (41, 43), 53, (92)
Seeliger, H., 79, (96)
Seguin, L., (253)
Seguin, P., 147, 173, 174, (184), 190–
    195, 206, (218, 220, 221)
Selbie, F. R., 33, (46)
Seligmann, E., 245, 246, (255)
Sellards, A. W., 282, (296)
Sellers, W., (137)
Senda, T., (254)
Seneca, H., 290, (295)
Senos, G., 35, (44), 163, (184)
Seppilli, A., 57, (90)
Serpa, 337, (349)
Sery, T. W., 148, 152, (182), 250, (254)
Sevin, A., 148–150, 155, 156, 160, 169,
    (184)
Shackman, R., 342, (349)
Shaffer, J. G., 278, (295)
Shannon, R., 384
Shapiro, A. P., 30, (40), 108, 129, (136,
    141)
Sharman, A., 339, (344)
Sharp, J. L., 239, (255)
Sharp, J. T., 300, 302, (306, 308)
Sharpe, M. E., 27, 28, 30, (46), 48, 49,
    53, 54, 56, 59, (90, 91, 92, 96), 337,
    340, (348, 349)
Shattock, P. M. F., 26, 27, 28, (43)
Shattuck, G. C., (220)
Shaw, C., 102, (136)
Shaw, E. D., (254)
Shaw, F. W., 155, (184)
Shayegani, M. H., 23, (43)
Shedlovsky, T., (386)
Sheingorn, A., 305, (306)
Shelley, W. B., 355, (390)
Shepard, C. C., 86, 87, (96)
Shepard, M. C., 306, (308)
Sher, D., (390)
Sherago, M., 125, (140)
Sherman, J. M., 26, 28, 31, 32, (44, 46),
    334, (349)
Sherris, J. C., 123, (141)
Sherwood, N. P., 378, (390)
Shevky, M., 163, 164, (184)
Shibley, G. S., 160, (183), 323, 325,
    (347, 349)

Shibuya, M., 375, (391)
Shidlovsky, B. A., 104, 132, (140, 141),
    334, (349)
Shifrine, M., 232, (255), 370, (390)
Shikashio, T., (46)
Shiota, T., 39, (46)
Shklair, I. L., 39, (40, 44), 355, (388)
Shmamine, T., 172, (184), 197, (220)
Shoesmith, J. G., (141)
Shooter, R. A., 14, 15, 21, 22, (44, 46,
    47)
Shorb, M. S., (97)
Shpuntoff, H., 213, (220)
Shrewsbury, J. F. D., (95)
Shull, I. F., 29, (45)
Shumway, C. N., 109, (140)
Shuster, D. S., 239, (253)
Sieburth, J. McN., 247, (255), 382,
    (390)
Siedentopf, von, 187
Siegel, E. H., 145, (182)
Siemienski, J., 30, (40), 108, 129, (136,
    141)
Siewert, L. A., (181)
Silva-Inzunza, E., (217, 292)
Silveira, G., 228, 239, (251)
Silver, M. D., 89, (96)
Simmers, R. W., (97, 350)
Simmons, L. E., 375, (389)
Simon, G., 248, (252)
Simon, R. D., 33, (46)
Simonton, F. V., 272, (293)
Simpson, J. W., 287, (294)
Sina, B., 240, (255)
Sinski, J. T., 241, (255)
Sirsi, M., 241, (255)
Sissons, H. A., (94)
Skadhauge, K., 27, (46)
Skerman, V. B. D., 333, (349)
Skinner, C. E., 5, 7, 59, 80, (92), 223,
    225, 227, 232, 237, 240, 241, (255),
    382, (390)
Sklaroff, S. A., 15, (43)
Slack, J. M., 59, 63, 81, (96)
Slade, H. D., 26, (41)
Slade, N., (345)
Slajsova, M., 102, (141)
Slanetz, L. W., 28, 29, (46), 73, (96),
    103, (141), 167, 169, 170, (184), 333,
    (349)
Slator, J. D. H., 326, (344)
Small, N., 176, 179, (180)
Smidth, E. M., 383, (384, 386)
Smiley, K. L., 32, (44)
Smillie, W. G., 265, (293), 324, (344)
Smith, A. G., (92), 240, (256)
Smith, B. S. W., 300, (308)

Smith, C. H., 322, 323, (349)
Smith, D. T., 187, 195, 215, (220)
Smith, E. L., (350)
Smith, F. R., 334, (349)
Smith, H., Jr., 246, (253)
Smith, H. W., 14, (46), 55, (96), 334, 335, 338, (349)
Smith, I. M., 18, 24, (46)
Smith, K. L., (93)
Smith, M. B., (43)
Smith, M. E., 89, (93)
Smith, M. M., 86, (92), 325, (350)
Smith, N., 86, (97), 374, (387)
Smith, N. R., 23, (40), 48, 63, 65, 69, 80, (91), 102, 111, 133, (136), 148, 160, (180)
Smith, P. F., 298, 299, (307, 308), 326, 329, (347, 349)
Smith, W. E., 149, 150, 152, (184, 306, 344)
Smith, W. M., (41, 345, 386)
Smythe, P. M., 355, (390)
Sneath, P. H. A., 86, (97)
Snodgrass, W. G., (96)
Snyder, M. L., 336, 337, (349)
Snyder, R. A., 33, (42)
So, K., (44)
Sochard, M. R., (143)
Socransky, S. S., 175, 176, (183), 189, 190, 201, (220)
Soehring, K., 375, (385)
Sokolski, W. T., 105, (139)
Sollé, R., (40, 251, 344)
Solotorovsky, M., 228, 235, 244, 250, (253, 255)
Soltau, D. H. K., 15, (46)
Somerson, N. L., 305, (308)
Sompolinsky, D., 11, 20, (44)
Sonn, C., 374, (387)
Sonnenwirth, A. C., 3, 7, (8), 24, 33, 34, (46), 69, 104, (141), 150–153, 157, 161, 162, 164–166, 169, 175, (185), 215, (220), 310, 328, (349), 370, (390)
Soudakoff, P. S., 322, 323, (349)
Soultani, D., 380, (386)
Spaulding, E. H., 73, (97), 167, 170, 171, (185)
Spears, R. G., (96)
Spies, H. C., 54, (91)
Spilman, W. M., (384)
Spindler, 270, (292)
Spink, W. W., 23, (46)
Spivak, A., 106, (142)
Sprince, H., 205, (220), 279, (295)
Springer, G. F., 60, (92, 97)
Sprunt, D. H., 158, (183)
Spy, C., 148, 160, (182)

Stackiewicz, E., 371, (388)
Stahl, R. C., (93, 346)
Staib, F., 380, (390)
Stanier, R. Y., (307)
Stanley, M. M., 127, (142)
Stark, J. M., 377, (390)
Starlinger, P., 300, (308)
Staubitz, W. J., (388)
Steber, M. S., (138), 365, (386)
Steel, K. J., 102, (136)
Steen, E., 150, 162, (185)
Stefanesco, V., 18, (46)
Steffen, G. I., 30, (40, 44)
Steinman, H. G., 204, 205, 208, (217, 219, 220)
Stempen, H., 300, (308)
Stenderup, A., 22, (46), 248, (251)
Stephan, R. M., (93)
Stern, I. J., 125, (142)
Sternberg, T. H., 250, (256)
Sternini, G., 380, (390)
Šterzl, J., 360, (386)
Ste·son, C. A., 365, (390)
Stetten, DeW., Jr., (350)
Stevens, J., 128, (142)
Stevens, W. C., 159, 160, (185)
Stewart, M. J., 213, (220)
Stewart, R. M., 370, (389)
Stienen, G., 149, 158, 159, (182)
Still, J. L., 52, (97)
Stillman, E. G., 325, (349)
Stoddard, J. L., 194, (220)
Stojowski, A. J., (94)
Stokes, J. L., 380, (390)
Stokstad, E. L. R., 355, (390)
Stone, M. L., 34, (46)
Story, P., 103, 106, (142)
Stough, A. R., 250, (255)
Stovall, W. D., 242, 247, (255)
Straffon, R. A., 342, (349)
Strange, R. E., (306)
Strasburger, J., 332, (349)
Strauss, J. S., 82, (95)
Strauss, R. E., 243, (255)
Stribolt, 145, (180)
Strickler, A., 228, 229, (255), 322, (349)
Strittmatter, C. F., 53, (97)
Strong, R. P., 193, 195, (220)
Stuart, C. A., 104, 112, 113, 114, 116, (141, 142), 334 (349)
Stuedell, J. T., (387)
Stulberg, C. S., (142, 391)
Su, T. L., 374, (391)
SubbaRow, Y., 203, 204 (218)
Sugiyama, H., (91)
Sulitzeanu, A., 134, (140)
Sulkin, S. E., 363, (386)

Sullivan, B., 300, (306)
Sullivan, H. R., 52, 67, (97)
Sullivan, M. T., 238, (256)
Summerlin, 265
Sundman, V., 59, (97), 300, (308)
Supniewski, J. W., 205, (220)
Sussman, M., 128, (142)
Suter, L. S., 63, 80, (97), 155, (185)
Sutton, R. M., 162, (182, 183), 215, (218)
Suzuki, T., (139)
Suzuoki-Ziro, 280, (294)
Svec, M., 49, (97)
Svensson, R., 265, 269, 270, 278, (295)
Svihus, R. H., 118, (142)
Swain, R. H. A., 188, 189, 195–197, (220)
Sweeney, E. E., 10, (41)
Swerdlow, M. A., 284, (292, 295)
Swick, L. S., 374, 383, (387)
Swineford, L. R., 329, (347)
Switzer, S., 316, (349)
Sword, C. P., 23, (46)
Sword, M. G., (46)
Sylvester, E., 311, (349)
Sylvestre, L., 273, 286, 287, 290, (293, 295)
Syverton, J. T., 245, (252, 255)
Szita, J., 28, (46)
Szybalski, W., 300, 302, (307, 308)

Taffenel, J., 26, (45), 171, (184)
Tager, B., (217)
Taggart, J. G., 13–15, (42)
Takagi, A., 300, (307)
Takazoe, I., 73, (97)
Takeda, R., 124, (142)
Talbot, E. C. S., 21, (47)
Tanimoto, R. H., 383, (388)
Tanner, D. C., (139)
Taplin, J., 14, (46, 47), 328, (350)
Tardieux, P., 79, (95), 159, (184)
Tarshis, M. S., 83, 84, 85, (97)
Taschdjian, C. L., 239–241, 248, 250, (253, 254, 255, 256)
Tatum, A. L., 259, 290, 291, (294)
Taubeneck, U., 301, (308)
Taubert, H. D., 240, (256)
Tavel, 82, (90), 338, (343)
Taylor, A. C., 34, (47)
Taylor, A. R., 362, (391)
Taylor, D. F., 369, 375, 377, 380–382, (390)
Taylor, G. W., (47)
Taylor, J., 109, 110, (141, 142)
Taylor, M. J., 357, (391)

Tejada, C., (390)
Tenbroeck, C., 87, (97), 334, (350)
Tergis, F., 69, (96, 184, 219)
Thayer, J. D., (217)
Thibault, P., 37, (47), 113, 131, (142)
Thibaut, J., 379, (391)
Thiman, K. V., 53, (97)
Thjötta, T., 37, (47), 69, 71–73, (90, 97), 150, 153, 155, 156, 162, 169, (182, 185)
Thomas, E. E., 105, (142)
Thomas, J. L., 53, (94)
Thomas, L., 33, (44, 47), 363, (391)
Thomison, J. B., 23, (44)
Thompson, E. S., (253)
Thompson, L., 63, 64, (97), 149, 157, (182)
Thompson, P. E., 274, 278, 279, (293)
Thompson, R., 23, (47), 322, (346), 375, (391)
Thompson, St. C., 323, (350)
Thompson, W. L., 58, 60, (96)
Thomson, D., 160, (185), 323, 325, (350)
Thomson, R., 160, (185), 323–325, (350)
Thomson, S., 104, 109, (142)
Thonard, J. C., 371, (391)
Thorbecke, G. J., 361, 362, (391)
Thornley, M. J., 121, (142)
Thornton, H. G., 3, (8), 369, 370, (391)
Thorpe, G. A., 250, (252)
Thorsson, K. G., 299, (308)
Thouvenot, H., 26, (45)
Tilden, E. B., 49, (97)
Tissier, H., 58, (97), 152, 312, 336, (350)
Todd, R. L., 248, 249, (256), 368, (391)
Toh, C. C. S., 30, (47)
Tolhurst, J. C., (94)
Tomarelli, R. M., (93, 95)
Tomcsik, J., (306)
Tomlinson, A. J. H., 15, (45), 375, (389)
Tompsett, R., 23, (45)
Tomšíková, A., 249, (256)
Topley, W. W. C., 7, 82 (97), 324, 325, (350), 369, 372, (391)
Toreci, K., 114, 119, 120, (136)
Torrech, A., (183)
Torres, F. E., (90, 343)
Torrey, J. C., 312, (350), 373, (391)
Totter, J. R., 124, (142)
Toucas, M., 81, (91)
Townsend, F. M., 115, 118, (142)
Tramontano, A., 290, (295)
Tran Van Ky, (251)
Treick, R. W., (218)

Trejo, W., 240, (254)
Tribby, I., (387)
Tribedi, B. P., 131, (141), 382, (390)
Truscott, R. B., 299, (307)
Trussell, R. E., 273–276, 278, 279, 281, 284–290, (294, 295), 341, (350)
Tschesche, T., 375, (385)
Tsuchiya, H., 283, (295)
Tsuchiya, T., 228, 234, 235, 241, (256)
Tuckett, J. D., (98)
Tulasne, R., 299, 300, (309)
Tumbusch, W. T., 131, (138)
Tumka, A. F., 262, 281, (295), 326, (350)
Tuncman, Z. M., (306)
Tunevall, G., 367, (391)
Tunnicliff, R., 147, 169, 177, (185), 213, (220), 328, (350)
Tunstall, L. R., 300, (307)
Tuoti, F., 241, (253)
Turell, R., 104, (141), 334, (349)
Turk, J. L., 363, 365, (391)
Turnbull, R. B., Jr., 15, (47)
Turner, A. L., 323, (347)
Turner, V., (344)
Turri, M., 301, (307)
Turtetaub, R., (292)
Twort, D. N., (42, 346)
Tybeck, E., 53, (94)
Tynes, B. S., 157, (185)

Uden, N. van, 223, 227, 228, 239, (256)
Uento, T., 280, (291)
Ulrich, E. W., 155, (185)
Umbarger, H. E., 371, (391)
Updyke, E. L., (46)
Upton, M. F., 373, (391)
Urso, B., 242, (256)
Utz, P. J., (137), 157, (185)

Vahlne, G., 109, (142)
Vaisman, A., 83, (94)
Valadares-Prieto, J., (217)
Valina, F., 275, (295)
Van den Ende, M., 126, (140, 142)
Van Eseltine, W. P., 24, (47)
Van Iterson, W., 298, (309)
Van Leewen, D. P., (251, 292)
Van Lorch, L., (95)
Van Niel, C. B., 122, (142)
Van Toorn, M. J., 326, (350)
Van Zee, G. K., 304, (306)
Vanna, F. de, 358, (391)
Vargas-Salazar, R., (292)
Vargues, R., 367, (391)

Varney, P. L., 73, (97), 162, 171, (185), 326, (350)
Vaughan, B. F., 155, (185)
Vaughn, R. H., (54), 92
Vedel, R., 153, (185)
Veillon, A., 33, 34, (47), 146, 150, 161, 167, 170, (185), 197, (220), 326, (350)
Veillon, R., 172, (184)
Velasco-Hernández, N., (46, 349)
Veldkamp, H., 186, (220)
Veltre, F. A., 57, (97)
Velu, H., 159, (185)
Veomett, R. C., 379, (391)
Verdan, C., 170, (181)
Verder, E., 125, 130, (142)
Verges, P., 63, 80, (95)
Verheye, H., 276, (295)
Verneuil, A., 145, (185)
Vernon, L. P., 39, (43)
Veron, M., 37, (47), 113, 121, 125, (142)
Vestal, A. L., (94)
Veszpremi, D., 193, (220)
Vetto, R. R., 135, (142)
Vianna, G., 193, (216)
Vicher, E. E., 315, 317, 322, (348)
Villa, E., (254)
Villecourt, P., 116, 118, (142)
Vince, I., 248, (252)
Vincent, H., 145, 170, (185), 195, (220)
Vincent, J. G., 379, (391)
Vineyard, J. P., 131, (142)
Vinzent, R., 190–195, 206, (221)
Visco, G., 245, (256)
Viteri, F., (390)
Vivino, J. J., 23, (46)
Vogel, E. H., Jr., 131, (138)
Vogel, R. A., 244, 249, (256)
Vogelsang, T. M., 12, 13, 21, 22, 42, (47)
Volkert, M., 114, (142)
Vörös-Felkai, G., 228, 239, (256)

Waage, R., 119, (142)
Waddington, G., (137)
Wagner, B. M., 305, (309)
Wagner, M., 361, (386, 391)
Wagner, V., 249, (256)
Wainright, S. D., 81, (95), 317, (348)
Waisbren, B. A., 15, (47), 366, (391)
Waksman, S. A., 57, (97)
Walczak, W., 33, (45, 389)
Walker, A. P., (388)
Walker, E. L., 282, (296)
Walker, L., 241 (256)
Walker, P. H., 153, (185)

Wallach, G., 378, (384)
Wallach, R., 159, (185)
Wallmark, G., 11, 12, (43, 47)
Walter, E. L., (95)
Walters, E. W., (344)
Walters, S. L., 289, (293)
Wang, C. H., 125, (142)
Wantland, E. M., 259, 279, (296), 329, (350)
Wantland, W. W., 258, 279, (296), 329, (350)
Ward, M. K., 113, 115, 125, 132, (135, 139)
Warin, R. P., 230, (252)
Warner, G. S., 36, (47)
Warner, P. T. J. C. P., 126, (142)
Warrack, G. H., 89, (93)
Wasley, M. A., (294)
Wasserman, E. M., 132, (142), 366, (391)
Wasserman, M., 384, (390)
Watson, E. D., 80, 81, (97), 314, 315, 324, (350)
Watson, R. W., 300, (308)
Watson, S. J., 64, 67, (95)
Watt, J., 125, 130, (142)
Watt, J. A., 111, (142)
Watt, L., 287, (296)
Waugh, L. M., 238 (255)
Waugh, M. H., (138), 365, (386)
Weaver, R., (344)
Weaver, R. H., 90, (94), 125, (140), 232, 247, (255)
Wedderburn, D. L., 358, (387)
Wegelius, W., 338, (350)
Wegner, G. H., 165, (185), 207, (221)
Weibull, C., 297, 299–303, (306, 308, 309)
Weichselbaum, A., 37, (47)
Weidel, W., 301, (309)
Weigmann, F., 357, (386)
Weil, A. J., 85, (90)
Weil, E., 103, (142)
Weinberg, M., 150, 152, 171, (185)
Weinberger, H., 358, (391)
Weinberger, H. J., 298, 300–302, (306, 309)
Weiner, D., 265, (296)
Weinstein, H. J., 16, (47)
Weinstein, L., 56, (95, 97), 132, 135, (142), 157, (185), 366, (391)
Weir, J., 271, (296)
Weiser, H. H., (44)
Weiss, A., 358, (391)
Weiss, C., 164, 171, (185)
Weiss, J. E., 59, 60, (95, 97), 148–150, (185)

Weiss, W., 104, 106, 137, (142)
Welch, H., 131, (143)
Welch, K. J., (348)
Weld, J. T., 288, (293)
Wellings, A. W., 272, (293)
Wellisch, G., (46)
Wellman, W. E., 157, (183)
Wells, A. Q., 86, (97)
Wells, W. H., 265, (296)
Welsch, M., 299, 301, (309)
Wender, I., 125, (141)
Wenning, M. E., (294)
Wenrich, D. H., 258, 259, 272, 273, 275, 281, 285, (296)
Wensinck, F., 108, (142)
Wentholt, H. M. M., 302, 304, 305, (308)
Wentworth, F. H., 109, (142), 366, (391)
Werder, A. A., (252, 255)
Werner, H., 193, (221)
Werthamer, S., (41, 345)
Westphal, A., 272, 278, 279, 281, 284, (296)
Wetmore, P. W., 121–123, (142)
Wezel, M., 37, (40)
Wheater, D. M., 53, (96), 379, (387, 391)
Wheeler, F. M., 27, (41)
Wheeler, H. O., (254)
Wheeler, R. E., (220)
Wherry, F. P., 157, (181), 368, (386)
Wherry, W. B., 69, 70, (97), 111, 117, 119, (140), 147, 151, 162, 164, (183), 325, (347)
Whitaker, J. A., (140)
White, A., 22, (47), 332, (350)
White, E., 34, (47)
White, J. C., 33, (47)
White, V., 54, (94)
Whiteley, H. R., 39, (47), 204, (221)
Whittington, M. J., 304, (308)
Whittle, C. H., 248, (256)
Wichelhausen, O. W., 200, 205, 206, 208, 215, (221)
Wichelhausen, R. H., 188, 193, 200–202, 205, 206, 208, 211, 215, (219, 221), 368, (390)
Wick, W. E., (42)
Wickerham, L. J., 228, 230, 232, 241, (256)
Widra, A., 235, (256)
Wiener, A. S., 360, (391)
Wiener, H., (253)
Wildy, P., (42, 346)
Wilkins, M. P., 110, (142)

Wilkinson, A. E., 36, (47), 304, (308, 349)
Williams, A. W., 324, (348)
Williams, B. W., 88, (97)
Williams, C. D., 355, (391)
Williams, E. D., 128, (142)
Williams, E. J., 316, 342, (346)
Williams, H. H., (389)
Williams, J. R. B., 21, (47)
Williams, N. B., 29, (47), 53, 60, (97, 307), 327, 329, (350), 359, 364, (385, 391)
Williams, R., 128, (142)
Williams, R. E. O., 10, 12, 15, 32, (44, 45, 46, 47), 317, 323, (347), 375, (389)
Willis, A. T., 90, (97)
Wills, M. R., 34, (47), 157, (185)
Wilson, A. P., (46)
Wilson, F. W., 115, (142)
Wilson, G. S., 7, (8), 36, (47), 82, 87, (97) 324, 325, (350)
Wilson, J. B., 10, (46)
Wilson, M. E., (295)
Wilson, T. E., 371, (391)
Wilssens, A., 56, (98)
Winblad, S., 14, (47)
Winger, A., 59, 63, 81, (96)
Winkler, C. H., 322, (344)
Winner, H. I., 243, 245, 249, (252, 256), 369, (391)
Winogradsky, S., 4, (8)
Winsten, S., 245, 250, (255, 256)
Winter, W. F., 235, 247, (256)
Wiseman, R. F., 54, 57, (96, 98)
Witkow, A., (296)
Wittler, R. G., 79, (98)
Witz, M.-A., (140)
Wolbach, S. B., 194, (221)
Wolf, H. W., 21, (47)
Wolfe, P. A., 282, (294), 356, (389)
Wolfe, R. N., (42)
Wolff, M., 63, (98)
Wolinska, W. H., 275, (293)
Wolinsky, E., 21, 22, (47)
Wolochow, H., 359, (389)
Wood, M., 30, (47)
Wood, W. A., 125, (143)
Woodruff, P. W., 238, (256)
Woodward, C. R., 380, (390)
Woolpert, O., 359, (385)

Worfel, M. T., 109, (139), 366, (387)
Wostmann, B. S., 353, 361, (391)
Wright, E. T., 250, (256)
Wright, S. S., 127, 130, (143)
Wright, W. W., 131, (143)
Wyckoff, R. W. G., 170, (181), 195, (218)
Wynne, E. S., 132, (143), 372, (391)
Wypkema, W., (42)

Xalabarder, C., 84, (98)

Yaguchi, R., 304, (306)
Yakimoff, W. L., 195, (221)
Yakouti, E., (254), 280, (294)
Yamabayashi, H., 381, (391)
Yamaguchi, T., 353, (392)
Yawn, E., (138, 345)
Young, A. D., (94)
Young, F., (138, 345)
Young, G., 238, 245, 247, (256), 370, 373, (392)
Young, R. M., 353, (392)
Young, V. M., 109, (143), 265, 284, (296)
Yow, E. M., 106, 127, 130, (143, 347)
Yudofsky, P. L., 370, 373, (392)

Zago, H., (254)
Zahler, S. A., 70–73, (93)
Zalewski, N. J., (140), 366, (389)
Zaman, V., 290, (296)
Zanen, H. C., 326, (350)
Zegarelli, E. V., (253)
Zeissler, J., 89, (98)
Zeitinger, J. R., 375, 377, 378, (390)
Zeldow, B. J., 358, (392)
Ziai, M., 135, (138)
Zidek, Z. C., (93)
Ziegler, J. E., Jr., (47, 391)
Zilliken, F., 60, (92, 95, 96)
Zinder, N. D., 300, (309), 370, (392)
Zinnemann, K., 135
Zinserling, W. D., 213, (221)
Zsigmondy, 187
Zuber, A., 146, 150, 161, 167, 170, (185), 197, (220), 326, (350)
Zuckerman, A., (389)
Zykin, L. F., 106, (143)

SUBJECT INDEX

Italic page numbers refer to illustrations.

Achromobacter, 113, 121, 123, 131
Achromobacter lwoffi (anitratum), 116
Aciduric flora, 57, 238
Acinetobacter anitratum, 113, 116
Actinomyces, 57–69
  cell-wall composition of, 58, 64, 74
  relation of, to *Bacterionema matruchotii*, 77
Actinomyces baudetii, 65
Actinomyces bifidus, 57, 59–63
  distribution of, 60–62, 319
  history of, 58–60, 336–337
  L forms of, 300
  relation of, to *A. israelii*, 59, 67
    to anaerobic diphtheroids, 80
  var. *pennsylvanicus*, 59, 60
Actinomyces bovis, 63–65
Actinomyces israelii, 63–69
  antibodies to, occurrence of, 364
  distribution of, 68, 319
  relation of, to anaerobic diphtheroids, 80–81
Actinomyces naeslundii, 64, 65
Actinomyces odontolyticus, 65
Actinomyces pseudonecrophorus, 154
Actinomycetales, 57
Actinomycosis, 63–65, 68–69, 80, 364
Aerobacter aerogenes, 101, 102
Aerobacter cloacae, 101, 102, 106
  L form of, 300
Alcalescens-Dispar group, 101, 102
Alcaligenes, 121, 131–132
  relation of, to Moraxella-Mima, 111
Alcaligenes faecalis, 121–123, 131–133
  antibodies to, occurrence of, 365
  distribution of, 320
  L forms of, 300
Ameba (see *Entamoeba*, etc.)
Amphibiosis, 4, 5
Anaerobiosis, 39, 201
  in L forms, 302, 305
  in protozoa, 280
  in spirochetes, 188, 201
Animals, actinomyces in, 63, 65, 68
  anaerobes in, 145
  antibodies to *E. coli* in, 364–365

Animals, bacteroides in, 146, 152
  B. nigrescens in, 162
  Candida in, 223, 239, 247
  clostridia in, 87
  coliforms in, 103–105
  enterococci in, 28–30
  fecal flora of, 334–335, 338
  germfree (*see* Germfree animals)
  lactobacilli in, 56
  Mima vaginicola in, 118
  Moraxella in, 111, 117
  Mycobacterium smegmatis in, 82
  Pityrosporum ovale in, 227
  PPLO in, 298, 305
  protozoa in, 259, 278, 280
  Selenomonas species in, 174–175
  spirochetes in, 195, 213
  Staphylococcus aureus in, 14
  Torulopsis glabrata in, 228
  Veillonella alcalescens in, 38
Antibiotics, effect of, on intestinal vitamin synthesis, 355
  infection due to, with *Candida albicans*, 245–247
    with *Escherichia coli*, 105
    with Klebsiella, 106
    with mycobacteria, 83
    with Proteus, 106
    with *Pseudomonas aeruginosa*, 127–128
    with *Staphylococcus aureus*, 13, 15, 20, 22
    with *Torulopsis glabrata*, 228
Antibodies to indigenous microorganisms, 363–369
Antrum, maxillary, microorganisms in, 311
Arizona group, 101–102
  relation of, serologic, to *Candida*, 244
Assimilation tests, 232
Authochthony, criteria of, 4
Auxanographic method, 232
Axenic, 278
Axistyle of spirochetes, 189
Axostyle of protozoa, 259–260

B5W, 112, 116
Bacilli, fusiform, 145, 171–172
  motile, 162
  (See also *Fusobacterium girans*)
Bacillus, 87
Bacillus anthracis, effect of, on germ-
  free animals, 357
Bacillus bifidus communis, 58, 336
Bacillus megaterium, protoplasts and
  spheroplasts of, 300, 303
Bacteremia, *Alcaligenes faecalis* in, 131–
  132
  anaerobic streptoccal, 34
  Bacteroides funduliformis in, 157
  diphtheroids in, 79
  Fusobacterium fusiforme in, 170
  Proteus in, 106
  Pseudomonas aeruginosa in, 127
  Staphylococcus aureus in, 15–17
Bacterial concentrations, maximal values
  for, 32, 333
Bacterial flora, concentrations of, 28, 31,
  62, 104, 148, 313–316, 318–321, 330–
  336
Bacterionema matruchotii, 73–77, *75, 76*
Bacteriophage, relation of, to colicine, 383
  to *Corynebacterium diphtheriae*, 78
  to protoplasts and spheroplasts, 301–
  303
  typing, of enterococci, 27
  of *Pseudomonas aeruginosa*, 125–126
  of *Staphylococcus aureus*, 10–11, 18–
  21
Bacteriophages, for Alcaligenes-Vibrio,
  133
  for lactobacilli, 52–53
  for *Mima vaginicola*, 119
Bacterium anitratum, 112–113, 116
Bacterium melaninogenicum, 162
Bacterium pneumosintes, 160
Bacteroides, 148–166
  antibiotic sensitivity of, 158–160
  distribution of, 321
  in experimental fusospirochetal infection, 215
  growth of indigenous protozoa with,
  278
  history of, 145–148
  relation of, to fusobacteria, 167, 169
Bacteroides amylogenes, 165
Bacteroides amylophilus, 165
Bacteroides brevis, 166
Bacteroides fragilis, 149–152
  history of, 146
  relation of, to bacteroides of the
  rumen, 165–166
  to *B. pneumosintes*, 161

Bacteroides funduliformis, 150–160, *154*
  antibodies to, occurrence of, 157, 367–
  368
  in feces, 149
  history of, 146
  L forms of, 155, 300
  relation of, to *Fusobacterium fusi-
  forme*, 169–170
Bacteroides melaninogenicus (see *B.
  nigrescens*)
Bacteroides mortiferus, 154
Bacteroides necrophorus, 152–153
Bacteroides nigrescens, 147, 150–151,
  162–165
  relation of, to *B. pneumosintes*, 161
  to *B. putidus*, 152
Bacteroides pneumosintes, 148, 150–151,
  160–161
Bacteroides putidus, 150–152
Bacteroides ruminicola, 165
Bacteroides serpens, 146, 150–151, 161–
  162
Bacteroides succinogenes, 165
Bacteroides vulgatus, 152
Bang's bacillus, 145, 152
Battey bacillus, 84, 85
Bibby's bacillus, 73
Biliary tract, bacteroides in, 146
  Candida species in, 237, 239
Blastospore, *231*, 232
Blepharoplast, 258, 261
Blood, *Corynebacterium acnes* in, 80
  diphtheroids in, 79–80
  (*See also* Bacteremia)
Borrelia, *188*, 189, 191
Borrelia buccale, 192–193, 208
Borrelia refringens, 192–193, 203
  discovery of, 187
  metabolism of, 206–209
  morphology of, 196–197
  pathogenicity of, 212
  serotypes of, 211
Borrelia vincenti, 192–193, 197, 206, 208
  pathogenicity of, 212
Butyribacterium rettgeri, 59
Butyrivibrio fibrosolvens, 179, 336

Calculi, 69
  experimental, proteus in, 108
Candida, 230–250
  growth of *Giardia lamblia* with, 280
  interactions of, with enterobacteria,
  380–382, *381*
  occurrence of, 127, 224–225, 236–239
  relation of, to *Torulopsis*, 227–228
  serology of, 235, 241, 249

Candida, species of, antibodies to, occurrence of, 248–249, 368–369
differential characteristics of, 234–235
distribution of, 237
pathogenicity of, 242–244
Candida albicans, 231, 233, 234–250
antibiotic sensitivity of, 250
association of, with lactobacilli, 56, 238, 341
with *Trichomonas vaginalis,* 238, 290, 341
in disease, 239–250
identification of, 239–241
immunity to, 248–250
in nonspecific urethritis, 285
pathogenicity of, 241–245
transmission of, 248
Candida bovina, 227
Candida candida, 232
Candida guilliermondi, 230, 237, 242, 244
Candida krusei, 234, 237–239, 242, 244, 246, 250
Candida mortifera, 232
Candida parakrusei, 232
Candida parapsilosis, 234, 236, 237–239, 241–242, 244
Candida pinoyi, 232
Candida pseudotropicalis, 234, 242
Candida psilosis, 232
Candida sloofii, 227
Candida stellatoidea, 233, 234–235, 237–238, 241–242, 244, 250
status of, 232–235
Candida tropicalis, 233, 238–239, 241–242, 244–245
Capsularis, 148, 152
Caries (dental), *Actinomyces odontolyticus* in, 75
Candida in, 238
keratin in, *Candida* and, 247
lactobacilli in, 49, 54–55, 319
antibodies to, 364
Veillonella alcalescens in, 39, 355
Catenabacterium, 79
Children, antibodies to indigenous microorganisms in, 364, 366–368
antibodies to *Trichomonas vaginalis* in, 291
Candida in, 243, 248
coliform bacteria in, 104
dermatophytes in, 239
fungi in, 224
hemophili in, 135
lactobacilli in, 54

Children, microbiota of, 311, 318–321, 325–326, 340
PPLO in, 305
protozoa in, 264–267, 277, 284
Pseudomonas aeruginosa in, 128
spirochetes in, 194
sterility of maxillary antrum in, 311
Torulopsis glabrata in, 228
Chilomastix mesnili, 260–261, 265–271, 284
Chlamydospores of *Candida,* 231–232, 240
Citrobacter, 101
Cladothrix matruchoti, 77
Clostridia, 87–90
distribution of, 319
Clostridium bifermentans, 87
Clostridium perfringens, 87–90
in animal tissues, 311
Clostridium sporogenes, 87
Clostridium tetani, 87, 319
Colicines, 382–384
Coliform bacteria, antibodies to, occurrence of, 365
in disease, 105
distribution of, 104, 320
in hospital disease, 16, 109–110
relation of, in nutrition, to lactobacilli, 57
(*See also* Enterobacteria; *Escherichia coli,* etc.)
Colloides anoxydana, 112
Commensal, 3
Conjunctiva, *Alcaligenes faecalis* in, 132
hemophili in, 134–135
microbiota of, 318–321, 322–323
Moraxella-Mima in, 117
Moraxella lacunata in, 119
Coprophagy, 354
Cortisone, effect of, on mycobacteria, 86
in experimental infection, with *Candida albicans,* 245
with enterococci, 30
with *Pseudomonas aeruginosa,* 129
in pathogenicity of spirochetes, 212
Corynebacteria, 56, 77–83
cell-wall composition of, 64, 78
distribution of, 319
relation of, to actinomycetes, 58, 68
stimulation of, by oleic acid, 81, 317
Corynebacterium acnes, 80–82
distribution of, 319
relation of, to actinomyces, 64
Corynebacterium anaerobium, 80–81
Corynebacterium belfanti, 78
Corynebacterium diphtheriae, 77–78
distribution of, 323
Corynebacterium granulosum, 81

Corynebacterium haemolyticum, 78–79
Corynebacterium hofmanni, 77–78
Corynebacterium liquefaciens, 80–81
Corynebacterium pseudodiphtheriticum, 77
Corynebacterium pyogenes, 78–79
Corynebacterium ulcerans, 78
Corynebacterium xerosis, 77–78
Cul-pal spirochetes, 202–206, 209–211, 215
Cytostome, 259–261

Darkfield microscope, history of, 146, 187
Dermatophytes, 222–223, 228–230
Dialister, 160
Diarrhea, *Clostridium perfringens* in, 88–89
    infantile, *Escherichia coli* in, 109–110
    protozoa in, 284
    Pseudomonas aeruginosa in, 127
Dienes phenomenon, 103, 106–107
Dientamoeba fragilis, 262–263, 265–271, 277, 278, 284
Diphtheroids, aerobic, 77–79, 163
    L forms of, 299–300
    anaerobic, 79–82
    in putrid pleurisy, 146
    (*See also* Corynebacteria)
Diplococcus mucosus, 37, 113
Diplococcus pneumoniae, distribution of, 311, 318, 323, 326–329
    L forms of, 300
Dispar group, 101
Döderlein's bacillus, 55–56, 78, 339–340
    relation of, to *Trichomonas vaginalis*, 289–341

Ear, external, *Candida* in, 239
    enterobacteria in, 104
    microbiota of, 318–322
    Mima in, 118
    Pityrosporum ovale in, 227
    Proteus in, 106
    Pseudomonas aeruginosa in, 126–128
    middle, Klebsiella in infection of, 106
Embadomonas intestinalis, 261
Endamoeba buccalis, 261
Endocarditis, subacute bacterial, 23–24, 30, 32–33, 36, 39, 57
Endolimax intestinalis, 263
Endolimax nana, 262–263, 265–271, 278, 283
Endolimax williamsi, 263
Endotoxin, in *Bacteroides funduliformis*, 153
    in *Candida albicans*, 244

Endotoxin, effect of, on experimental staphylococcal disease, 20
    in *Fusobacterium fusiforme*, 171
    in pathogenicity of enterobacteria, 107
    in spirochetes, 216
    in veillonellae, 39
Entamoeba coli, 262–263, 265–271, 278, 282–283, 290
Entamoeba gingivalis, 261–262, 271–272, 277–279, 281
Entamoeba histolytica, 262, 264, 278, 280, 282
Entamoeba nana, 263
Entamoeba williamsi, 263
Enterobacteria, 99–110
    antibiotic effects of, 380–384
    distribution of, 103, 320
    in host nutrition, 57, 353
    interactions of, with candida, 380–382, 381
    L forms of, 300
Enterococci, 26–31
    distribution of, 28–30, 318
    in infant feces, 62
    relation of, in nutrition, to lactobacilli, 57
Enteromonas hominis, 261, 265–271, 278
Epidermophyton floccosum, 228
Escherichia coli, 101–105, 107–110
    antibodies to, occurrence of, 364–366
    distribution of, 320
    epidemiology of, 105, 109–110, 312
    L forms of, 300–302, 305
    occurrence of, in disease, 108–110, 127
    (*See also* Coliform bacteria; Enterobacteria)
Escherichia freundii, 101, 112

Fecal pollution, enterococcus counts and, 29
Feces, *Actinomyces bifidus* in, 58, 60–62
    Alcaligenes faecalis in, 132
    anaerobic streptococci in, 34
    anaerobic vibrios in, 179, 336
    Arizona organisms in, 101
    bacterial counts of, 28, 62, 104, 148, 314, 318–321, 332–335
    bacteroides in, 148–149
    Bacteroides fragilis in, 152
    B. nigrescens in, 162
    B. putidus in, 152
    Butyrivibrio fibrosolvens in, 179
    Candida in, 237, 248
    clostridial α-toxin neutralizing substances in, 89

Feces, *Clostridium perfringens* in, 87–88
  coliform rods in, 28
  enterobacteria in, 103–105
  enterococci in, 28–29, 62
  fungi in, 224
  Fusobacterium girans in, 172
  lactobacilli in, 54–55, 56
  microbiota of, 313–315, 318–321, 332–
    338
    development of, 336–338
    effect of diet on, 335
  Micrococcus niger in, 26
  Mima in, 118
  Mycobacterium smegmatis in, 82
  protozoa in (*see* Intestine)
  Pseudomonas aeruginosa in, 126–127
  spirochetes in, 194
  Staphylococcus aureus in, 13–14
  Torulopsis glabrata in, 228
  viridans streptococci in, 31
  vitamin synthesis in, 353–354
Feet, fungi on, 320–322
  (*See also* Dermatophytes)
Fluorescein, 124
Food poisoning, clostridia in, 89
  enterococci in, 30
Fungi, 222–250
  actinomycetes as, 57
  distribution of, 321
  PPLO from, 297
Fusiformis (see *Fusobacterium*)
Fusobacteria, 166–173
  cell-wall composition of, 74
  distribution of, 321
  in fusospirochetal disease, 212–215
  history of, 145–148
  relation of, to *Leptotrichia buccalis*,
    69, 73, 166–169, 171
Fusobacterium biacutum, 171
Fusobacterium fusiforme, 150–151, 167–
    172, *168*
  antibiotic sensitivity of, 158–160
  antibodies to, occurrence of, 171, 368
  history of, 145
Fusobacterium girans, 147, 150–151,
    172–173
  in actinomycosis of cats and dogs, 65
Fusobacterium hemolyticum, 172
Fusobacterium nucleatum, 167
Fusobacterium plaut-vincenti, 167
Fusospirochetal disease, *Alcaligenes
    faecalis* in, 132
  chemotherapy in, 216
  experimental, 171, 213–215
  Fusobacterium fusiforme in, 170
  history of, 145
  PPLO in, 305

Fusospirochetal disease, protozoa in, 272
  relation of, to trichomoniasis, 287
  spirilla and vibrios in, 173
  spirochetes in, 195, 212–216
    cultivation of, 197–199
Fusospirochetal exudate, *176*, *212*
  experimental, bacterial counts of, 171,
    213
Fusospirochetal flora, 187
  in periodontal disease, 194

Gaffkya tetragena, 24
Gastrcenteritis, adult, *Escherichia coli* in,
    109
  infantile, *E. coli* in, 108–110
  protozoa in, 284
Gastrointestinal tract, *Candida* in, 239
  spirochetes in, 194
Genitalia, *Bacteroides nigrescens* on, 162
  Candida in disease of, 243
  Fusobacterium fusiforme on, 170
  fusospirochetal disease of, L forms in,
    305
  microbiota of, 318–321, 338
  Mycobacterium smegmatis on, 82
  spirochetes on, 194
Genitourinary tract, anaerobes in, 146
  enterococci in, 29
  Haemophilus vaginalis in, 135
  microbiota of, 338–342
  Moraxella-Mima in, 117–118
  PPLO in, 304–305
  protozoa in, 273–277, 283–290
  spirochetes in, 194
  Torulopsis glabrata in, 228
  Trichomonas vaginalis in, 283–290
Germfree animals, abnormalities of, 356
  antibody formation in, 360–362
  effect of *Entamoeba histolytica* on, 282
  effect of spirochetes on, 212
  effect of *Trichomonas vaginalis* on,
    282, 288
  significance of, for man, 352
  susceptibility of, to infection, 282, 288,
    357, 362
  vitamin synthesis in, 353
Giardia intestinalis, 259
Giardia lamblia, 259–260, 265–271, 277,
    280, 282–284
Giardiasis, 283
Gingiva, microbiota of, 314, 318–321,
    329–331
  motile anaerobes in, 147
  Spirillum sputigenum in, 176
  spirochetes in, 193

Gingivitis, protozoa in, 272–273, 281
    spirochetes in, 187, 194

Habitat as taxonomic criterion, 7, 191
Hadley types of lactobacilli, 53
Haemophilus aegyptius, 133–135
Haemophilus haemolyticus, 133–134
Haemophilus influenzae, 133–135
    antibodies to, occurrence of, 367
    L forms of, 300, 305
    relation of, to *Bacteroides funduli-
        formis*, 154
Haemophilus parahaemolyticus, 133
Haemophilus parainfluenzae, 133–134
Haemophilus vaginalis, 133–135
Helminths and protozoa, relative in-
    cidence of, 268, 270–271, 284
Hemophili, 133–135
    distribution of, 134, 320
    relation of, to *Bacteroides nigrescens*,
        164
    to *Moraxella*, 112
Herellea caseolytica, 116
Herellea vaginicola, 112, 116
Hospitals, infection in, with *Candida
        albicans*, 248
    with *Escherichia coli*, 16, 109–110
    with Klebsiella, 106
    with Proteus, 106–107
    with *Pseudomonas aeruginosa*, 128
    with *Staphylococcus aureus*, 13–17,
        20–22
    mental, protozoa in, 264–265, 267–
        269, 277
Hypersensitivity, delayed, in experi-
    mental *Staphylococcus aureus* dis-
    ease, 19
    in infection with *Candida*, 243, 249

Immunity to indigenous microorganisms,
    362–363
Infants, *Actinomyces bifidus* in, 58, 60–
    62, 313–314, 336–337
    antibodies to indigenous micro-
        organisms in, 366, 368–369
    bacteroides in, 146
    Candida in, source of, 248
    enterococci in, 31, 62
    Escherichia coli in, 105, 108–110
    hemophili in, 135
    intestinal vitamin synthesis in, 353
    microbiota of, 318–321, 336–338
        development of, 312–313
    Micrococcus niger in, 26
    Pseudomonas aeruginosa in, 128
    spirochetes in, 194

Infants, *Staphylococcus aureus* in, 14, 16,
    21–22
    thrush in, 243
    vaginal flora of, 339
    Veillonella alcalescens in, 38
    viruses in, 312
Infection, definition of, 3
    mixed, in actinomycosis, 69
    anaerobic, 215–216
    anaerobic streptococci in, 34, 215
    anaerobic vibrios in, 215
    bacteroides in, 157, 162, 215–216
    Candida albicans and *Trichomonas
        vaginalis* in, 290
    Entamoeba coli, *Iodameoba büt-
        schlii*, and *Endolimax nana* in,
        283
    Entamoeba histolytica and tryp-
        anosomes in, 282
    enterobacteria in, 106, 383–384
    fusobacteria in, 215
    in germfree animals, 362
    microbic synergism in, 371
    spirochetes in, 213, 215
    Streptococcus faecalis in, 106
    Trichomonas vaginalis in, 289
Inhibin, 357
Interactions, microbial, competitive, 371–
        384
    in vivo, 374–375, 378, 381–383
    cooperative, 370–371
Intestine, *Actinomyces bifidus* in, 61
    aerobic vibrios in, 133
    anaerobes in, 145–146
    antibacterial effects in, 359
    Candida albicans in, establishment of,
        246
    Clostridium perfringens in, 88
    Fusobacterium fusiforme in, 170
    lactobacilli in, 60
    microbiota of, 331–338
        development of, 312
    PPLO in, 305
    Proteus in, 106
    protozoa in, 264–271, 281–285
    small, flora of, 311, 331–332
    spirochetes in, 194
    Torulopsis glabrata in, 228
    vitamin synthesis in, 353–355
    (*See also* Feces)
Iodamoeba bütschlii, 262–263, 265–271,
    278, 284

Kasan spirochete, 203, 206, 209–211
Klebsiella, occurrence of, in disease, 127
    pathogenicity of, 107–108

Klebsiella-Aerobacter-Serratia group, 101
Klebsiella aerogenes, 102–103, 106
  antibodies to, occurrence of, 365–366
  distribution of, 320
  L forms of, 300
Klebsiella friedlaenderi, 102
Klebsiella oxytoca, 101, 102
Klebsiella ozaenae, 102
Klebsiella pneumoniae, 101–102, 106
Klebsiella rhinoscleromatis, 101, 102
Kligler's bacillus, 73, 77
Koch-Weeks bacillus, 134–135
Koch's postulates, 6, 34, 284
Króo spirochete, 203, 209–210

L forms, 298–302, 304–305
Lachnospira multiparus, 179
Lactobacilli, 48–57
  antibiotic effects of, 379
  antibodies to, occurrence of, 364
  association of, with Candida, 56, 238
  cell-wall composition of, 64
  distribution of, 54–56, 319
  effect of coprophagy on, 354
  in host nutrition, 57, 353
  relation of, to actinomycetes, 58, 64, 68
    to Leptotrichia buccalis, 73
Lactobacillin, 379
Lactobacillus acidophilus, 49, 50–56, 51
  relation of, to Actinomyces bifidus, 59–60
Lactobacillus bifidus (see Actinomyces bifidus)
Lactobacillus brevis, 50–52, 51, 55
Lactobacillus buchneri, 52, 55
Lactobacillus casei, 50–56, 51
Lactobacillus cellobiosus, 52, 55–56
Lactobacillus fermenti, 50–56, 51
Lactobacillus parabifidus, 59–60
Lactobacillus plantarum, 50, 52, 55
Lactobacillus salivarius, 50, 55
Lactocidin, 379
Leptospira, 188–190
Leptospira trimerodonta, 193
Leptothrix, 73–74
Leptothrix anaerobius tenuis, 154
Leptothrix asteroide, 154
Leptothrix innominata, 69
Leptotrichia, 69–77
Leptotrichia buccalis, 69–73, 70, 71, 72
  distribution of, 319
  relation of, to fusobacteria, 69, 73, 166–169, 171

Leptotrichia dentium, 73–77, 75, 76
  distribution of, 319

Malleomyces, 121–123, 126
Mastigophora, 258–261
Meningitis, 106, 118, 127, 132, 135
Microbiota (indigenous), antibodies to, 360–369
  areas inhabited by, 310–312
  development of, 312–313
  ecology of, 369–370
  effect of host on, 357–360
  forms excluded from, 5
  history of, 6
  in host nutrition, 353–355
  interactions of, 369–384
  nonpathogenic activities of, 351–384
  sources of, 326–327
  as unit, 2, 7, 342–343
Micrococcin, 374
Micrococcus, 23–26
  anaerobic, 25–26
Micrococcus anaerobius, 25
  distribution of, 318
Micrococcus foetidus, 33
Micrococcus gazogenes, 38
Micrococcus lactilyticus, 38
Micrococcus lysodeikticus, 23
Micrococcus niger, 26
Micrococcus tetragenus, 24
Microsporum gypseum, 222–223
Miller's bacillus, 145
Mima, 110–120
  relation of, to Neisseria mucosa, 37
  (See also Moraxella-Mima)
Mima caseolytica, 116
Mima polymorpha, 112–113, 115–117
  relation of, to Alcaligenes faecalis, 131
Mima polymorpha var. oxidans, 115
Mima vaginicola, 116–117
Mimeae, 112
Monilia, 232
Moniliasis (see Candida)
Monoxenic, 278
Morax-Axenfeld bacillus, 111
Moraxella, relation of, to Neisseria mucosa, 37
Moraxella-Mima, 110–120
  distribution of, 117–118, 320
Moraxella duplex, 112, 115, 119
Moraxella duplex var. liquefaciens and non-liquefaciens, 112, 115
Moraxella glucidolytica, 112–113, 116
Moraxella lacunata, 112, 119
  distinguishing features of, 115, 117
  L forms of, 300

Moraxella lwoffi, 112–113, 115–116
Mouth, *Actinomyces bifidus* in, 61
  A. israelii in, 68
  anaerobes in, history of, 145
  anaerobic micrococci in, 26
  anaerobic streptococci in, 33–34
  anaerobic vibrios in, 177
  antibacterial phenomena in, 358–359
  bacteroides in, 146
  Bacteroides funduliformis in, 146
  B. nigrescens in, 162
  Candida albicans in disease of, 242–243, 248–249
    pathogenicity of, 245
  Candida species in, 235, 237–238
  coliform bacteria in, 104
  edentulous, microbiota of, 330
  enterococci in, 29
  fungi in, 224
  Fusobacterium girans in, 173
  F. fusiforme in, 170
  hemophili in, 134
  lactobacilli in, 49, 50–55
  leptospiras in, 190
  microbiota of, 314, 318–321, 327–331
    development of, 312, 325, 329–330
  Moraxella-Mima in, 118
  motile anaerobes in, 147
  neisseriae in, 36
  PPLO in, 305
  predentulous, microbiota of, 318–321, 329–330
  protozoa in, 271–273, 277–278
  Spirillum sputigenum in, 175–176
  spirochetes in, 190, 193–194
  Staphylococcus albus in, 24–25
  Streptococcus mitis in, 32
  Torulopsis glabrata in, 228
  Veillonella alcalescens in, 38
  (*See also* Saliva)
Mycobacteria, 82–87
  atypical, 83–87
    distribution of, 84, 319
  L forms of, 300
Mycobacterium avium, 86
Mycobacterium balnei, 83, 85–57
Mycobacterium fortuitum, 84, 86–87
Mycobacterium intracellularis, 86
Mycobacterium kansasii, 85
Mycobacterium phlei, 86–87
Mycobacterium smegmatis, 82–83, 86–87
Mycobacterium tuberculosis, 82–83, 86–87
Mycobacterium ulcerans, 85
Mycoplasma, 298

Nasopharynx, anaerobes in, 160
  meningococci in, 36
  microbiota of, 318–321, 324–325
  motile anaerobes in, 147
  Staphylococcus aureus in, 13–14
Necrobacterium, 148
Negroes, *Staphylococcus aureus* carrier rate in, 13
  Trichomonas species in, 272–273
  trichomoniasis in, 286
Neisseria, 36–38
  anaerobic, 37
  distribution of, 319
  L forms of, 305
  relation of, to Moraxella-Mima, 111
Neisseria catarrhalis, 36–37
Neisseria caviae, 37
Neisseria haemolysans, 37
Neisseria meningitidis, distribution of, 319, 324
Neisseria mucosa, 37, 113
Neisseria pharyngis, 36
Neisseria sicca, 36–37
Neisseria winogradskyi, 116
Nichols-Hough spirochete, 203, 210–211
Nocardia, 57–58, 74, 77, 328
Nocardia intracellularis, 86
Noguchi spirochete (cul-pal), 203, 209–211
Noma, 145, 213
  spirochetes in, 187
Nonphotochromogens, 85
Normal, meaning of, 2
Nose, *Alcaligenes faecalis* in, 132
  antibacterial effects in, 358–359
  bacterial counts of, 314–315
  Candida in, 239
  coliform bacteria in, 104
  Corynebacterium acnes in, 80
  hemophili in, 134
  microbiota of, 313–315, 318–321, 323–324, 327
    development of, 312
  Moraxella-Mima in, 117
  Mycobacterium smegmatis in, 82
  neisseriae in, 36
  Proteus in, 106
  Pseudomonas aeruginosa in, 126, 128
  spirochetes in, 194
  Staphylococcus albus in, 23
  Staph. aureus in, 13, 14, 15–16, 21
Nosocomial infection (*see* Hospitals)

Oidium, 232
Orange bacillus, 85

Oropharynx, microbiota of, 318–321, 325–327

Parabasal body, 259–260
Paracolobactrum, 100
Parasitism, 4
Pathogen, 2–3
Peptostreptococcus, 36
Perlèche, 242–243
Petit's bacillus, 111, 115, 117
Pharynx, Actinomyces israelii in, 68
 antibacterial effects in, 358–359
 Bacteroides nigrescens in, 162
 Candida albicans in, 248–249
 Candida species in, 237, 239
 coliform bacteria in, 104
 Corynebacterium ulcerans in, 78
 enterococci in, 30
 fungi in, 224
 Fusobacterium fusiforme in, 170
 hemophili in, 134
 microbiota of, 318–321, 324–327
  development of, 312, 326
 Moraxella-Mima in, 118
 neisseriae in, 36
 PPLO in, 305
 Proteus in, 106
 Pseudomonas aeruginosa in, 126, 128
 spirochetes in, 194
 Staphylococcus albus in, 23
 Staph. aureus in, 14, 21
 Streptococcus mitis in, 32
 Torulopsis glabrata in, 228
 (See also Tonsils)
Pityrosporum, 223
Pityrosporum orbiculare, 225–227, 226
Pityrosporum ovale, 225–227, 226
Photochromogens, 85
Pleuropneumonia of cattle, 298, 305
Pleuropneumonia-like organisms (see PPLO)
Pneumonia, 15, 33, 104, 106, 108, 128, 363
PPLO, 297–306
 distribution of, 304–306, 321
 in nonspecific urethritis, 285
 (See also L forms; Spheroplasts)
Propionibacterium, 59, 68
Proteus, 101–103, 106–108
 antibodies to, occurrence of, 366–367
 L forms of, 300–302
 occurrence of, in disease, 106, 127
Proteus mirabilis, 101, 106
 antagonism by, of Candida, 247
Proteus morganii, 101, 106
Proteus rettgeri, 101, 106

Proteus vulgaris, 101, 106
Protoplasts, 299, 302–303
 of spirochetes, 189, 197
Protozoa, 257–291
 autochthony of, 257, 264–277
 cultivation of, 278–280
 implantation of, 282–285
 incidence of, 264–278, 321
 indigenous, species of, 258–263
 metabolic studies of, 280–281
 pathogenicity of, 281–290
 selenomonads and spirilla as, 174, 175
 serology of, 290–291
Providence group, 101
Pseudomonads, classification of, 121–123
Pseudomonas, relation of, to Moraxella-Mima, 111, 113
 to Vibrio, 133
Pseudomonas aeruginosa, 121–122, 124–131
 antibiotic effects of, 379–380
 antibodies to, occurrence of, 129–130, 367
 distribution of, 126, 320
 in disease, 127–128
 L forms of, 300
 relation of, to Alcaligenes faecalis, 131
Pseudomonas fluorescens, 122–123
Pseudomonas ovalis, 122–123
Pseudomonas pseudomallei, 126
Pseudomonas pyocyanea, 121
Pseudomonas stutzeri, 122–123
Pseudomycelium, 231, 232
Pyelonephritis, experimental, 30, 108, 129
Pyocines, 126, 380
Pyocyanase, 373, 379
Pyocyanin, 124
 antibiotic effects of, 379
Pyorubin, 124

Ramibacterium, 79
Ramibacterium pleuriticum, 80
Ramibacterium tortuosum, 80
Refection, 354
Reiter spirochete, 203–206, 208–211
 relation of, to Borrelia refringens, 203
 to Treponema zuelzerae, 186
Respiratory tract, Alcaligenes faecalis in, 132
 anaerobic micrococci in, 25
 anaerobic vibrios in, 177
 bacteroides in, 146
 Candida in, 242
 hemophili in, 135
 Klebsiella aerogenes in, 104, 106

Respiratory tract, *Mycobacterium*
   smegmatis in, 82
   Proteus in, 106
   Pseudomonas aeruginosa in, 127
   spirochetes in, 190, 195
Retortomonas intestinalis, *261*, 265–271,
   284
Rhizobium-legume symbiosis, 3
Rhizopoda, 258, 261–263
Rickettsiae as normal flora, 5
Ristella, 148, 151–152, 173
Rumen, *Actinomyces bifidus* in, 62
   anaerobic spirilla in, 174–175
   anaerobic streptococci in, 36
   anaerobic vibrios in, 178–179
   autochthony in, 4
   bacteroides in, 165–166
   Bacteroides nigrescens in, 163
   Candida in, 239
   coliform bacteria in, 104
   Corynebacterium acnes in, 80
   enterococci in, 30
   fusobacteria in, 172
   lactobacilli in, 56
   microbiota of, compared with that of
     man, 352
   motile anaerobes in, 161
   protozoa in. 280
   spirochetes in, 195, 207
   Veillonella alcalescens in, 38–39
Ruminococcus, 36

Saliva, actinomyces in, 68
   antibacterial effects of, 357–359, 375
   bacterial counts of, 31, 314, 318–321,
     330–331
   Candida in, 238
   coliform bacteria in, 104
   enterococci in, 29–30
   Fusobacterium fusiforme in, 170
   lactobacilli in, 54
   mycobacteria in, 84
   spore-bearing bacilli in, 87
   Staphylococcus albus in, 24–25
   Staph. aureus in, 14
   Veillonella alcalescens in, 38–39
   viridans streptococci in, 31
Salmonella, serologic relation of, to
   Candida, 244
Salmonella-Arizona-Citrobacter group,
   101
Saprophyte, 3
Saprophytism and pathogenicity of
   fungi, 222
Sarcina, 25
Satellitism, 370

Scotochromogens, 85
Selenomonas palpitans, 174–175
Selenomonas ruminantium, 174, 176–177
Selenomonas sputigena, 174–175
Septicemia (*see* Bacteremia)
Serratia group, 101
Shwartzmann reaction, *Bacteroides*
   nigrescens in, 164
   enterobacteria in, 365
   Fusobacterium fusiforme in, 171
   veillonellae in, 39
Skin, *Actinomyces bifidus* on, 62
   anaerobic micrococci on, 25–26
   antimicrobial effects on, 359–360
   bacterial counts of, 314–315, 318–321
   Candida on, 237–239, 242–243
   Corynebacterium acnes on, 80–81
   dermatophytes on, 228–230
   diphtheroids on, 79
   fungi on, 223–225
   keratin in, *Candida* and, 247
   microbiota of, 314–315, 317–322
   microorganisms on, activities of, 355
   Mima on, 118
   mycobacteria on, 85
   oleic acid of, effect on corynebacteria,
     81
   PPLO on, 304–305
   Pseudomonas aeruginosa on, 126–128
   spirochetes on, 195
   Staphylococcus albus on, 23
   Staph. aureus on, 14
   Torulopsis glabrata on, 227
Soil, autochthony in, 4
   Candida albicans in, 223
   Clostridium perfringens in, 89
   Corynebacterium acnes in, 80
   fungi saprophytic in, pathogenicity
     of, 222
   Mima in, 118
   mycobacteria from, 83, 86
   spore-bearing bacilli in, 87
Sphaerophorus, 148, 156
Spherocillus, 162
Spheroplasts, 299–302
Spirilla, anaerobic, 173–177
   history of, 145–148
   saccharolytic, 179
Spirillum ruminantium, 176–177
Spirillum sputigenum, 145–147, 150–
   151, 174–176, *175*, *176*
   distribution of, 321
   in fusospirochetal exudate, *176*, *212*
   isolation of, 178
   relation of, to fusobacteria, 166, 169
     to *Spirillum ruminantium*, 176–177

Spirochaeta dentium, 191, 193, 210
Spirochaeta enterogyrata, 193–194, 206
Spirochaeta eurygyrata, 193–194
Spirochetes, 186–216
  antibiotic sensitivity of, 192, 216
  antibodies to, occurrence of, 210–211,
    368
  biochemical properties of, 206–209
  classification of, 188–193
  colony growth of, 200
  cultivation of, 190, 197–202, *198, 200*
  in fusospirochetal exudates, *176, 212*
  history of, 145–187
  occurrence of, 193–195, 321
  oral, *188, 196, 198*
  pathogenicity of, 212–216
  relation of, to fusobacteria, 166, 169
  serologic studies of, 209–211
  structure of, 188
  (See also *Borrelia; Treponema*)
Sputum, *Candida* in, 239
  flora of, 311
  Haemophilus influenzae in, 135
  Klebsiella in, 106
  motile anaerobes in, 147
  mycobacteria in, 84–85
  Proteus in, 106
  Pseudomonas aeruginosa in, 127
  Torulopsis glabrata in, 228
Staling, 372
Staphylococci, 9–25
  antibiotic effects of, 374–375
  distribution of, 318
  L forms of, 300–302, 304
Staphylococcus afermentans, 23
Staphylococcus albus, 9, 18–19, 23–25
Staphylococcus anaerobius, 25
Staphylococcus aureus, 9–22
  antibodies to, occurrence of, 363
  epidemiology of, 20–22, 312
  pathogenicity of, 17–20, 357
Staphylococcus epidermis, 23
Staphylococcus lactis, 23
Staphylococcus pyogenes, 9
Staphylococcus roseus, 23
Staphylococcus saprophyticus, 23
Stomach, antibacterial effects in, 359
  Candida in, 239
  Clostridium perfringens in, 88
  mycobacteria in, 84–85
  spirochetes in, 194
Streptococci, 26–36
  anaerobic, 33–36, 146
    distribution of, 34, 318
  antibiotic effects of, 375–379, *376, 378*
  distribution of, 318
  in fusospirochetal disease, 215

Streptococci, hemolytic, 317, 323, 325,
    327, 334, 341
  L forms of, 300, 302–303
  lactic, 28–29
  relation of, to anaerobic micrococci, 25
    to corynebacteria, 79
  viridans group of, 31–33
    antibodies to, occurrence of, 363–
      364
Streptococcus bovis, 27–30, 62
Streptococcus durans, 27
Streptococcus evolutus, 35
Streptococcus faecalis, 26–31
  in mixed infections, 106
Streptococcus faecium, 27–29
Streptococcus hominis, 32
Streptococcus lactis, 28
Streptococcus lanceolatus, 333
Streptococcus liquefaciens, 27, 29
Streptococcus micros, 35
Streptococcus mitis, 32
Streptococcus MG, 33
Streptococcus putridus, 35
Streptococcus pyogenes, occurrence of,
    318, 326, 328
Streptococcus salivarius, 31–32
Streptococcus sanguis, 33
Streptococcus s.b.e., 33
Streptococcus viridans, 31
Streptococcus zymogenes, 27, 29–31
Streptomyces, 57–58, 75
Succinivibrio dextrinosolvens, 179
Symbiosis, 3, 370
Synergism among indigenous microor-
    ganisms, 370–371
Syringospora, 232

Thrush, 243, 245, 248
Tinea pedis, 228–230, 322
Tissier's bacillus, 58–59, 61
Tongue, microbiota of, 330
Tonsils, actinomyces in, 63, 68
  anaerobic micrococci in, 25
  microbiota of, 325–326, 329
  motile anaerobes in, 147
  Mycobacterium smegmatis in, 82
  Pseudomonas aeruginosa in, 126
  spirochetes in, 194
Toothbrushing, antibacterial effects of,
    358
Torulopsis, occurrence of, 224, 225
Torulopsis glabrata, 225, 227–228
Torulopsis pintolopesii, 227
Treponema, *189*, 191
Treponema ambigua, 193, 207

Treponema calligyra, 193–194, 206, 209
Treponema comandoni, 193, 195, 207
Treponema dentium, 193, 195–197
  metabolic characteristics of, 206–208
  pathogenicity of, 212–216
  serotypes of, 211
Treponema macrodentium, 188, 193,
  195, 206–207, 210–211
Treponema microdentium, 188, 190–195,
  206–211
Treponema minutum, 193, 207
Treponema mucosum, 190, 193, 206,
  209
Treponema pallidum, culture strains of
  (*see* Cul-pal spirochetes)
  dimensions of, 195
  discovery of, 187
  relation of, to cul-pal spirochetes, 209
    to indigenous spirochetes, 190, 195–
    196, 208–209
  to *T. zuelzerae*, 186
Treponema phagedenis, 193, 207
Treponema skoliodonta, 193, 207
Treponema trimerodonta, 193, 207
Treponema zuelzerae, 186
Tricercomonas intestinalis, 261
Trichomonads, antibodies to, occurrence
  of, 291
Trichomonas buccalis, 258, 281
Trichomonas elongata, 258, 281
Trichomonas foetus, 259, 280, 288, 291
Trichomonas gallinae, 259, 288
Trichomonas homing, 258–259, 264–268,
  271, 279, 284–285, 291
Trichomonas tenax, 258–259, 271–273,
  277, 279, 281, 284, 291
Trichomonas vaginalis, 258–259, 285–
  291
  association of, with *Candida*, 238, 290,
  341
  cultivation of, 205, 278–279
  effect of, on germfree animals, 282,
  288, 357
  incidence of, 272, 273–277
  metabolic studies of, 280–281
  nutritional studies of, 279
Trichomoniasis, 285–290
  PPLO in, 304
Trichophyton gypseum, 228
Trichophyton interdigitale, 228
Trichophyton mentagrophytes, 228–230
Trichophyton rubrum, 228–230
Tuberculin, effect of, on experimental
  staphylococcal disease, 19
  of atypical mycobacteria, 84
  of *Mycobacterium smegmatis*, 83

Urethra, 311, 341
Urethritis, Moraxella-Mima in, 118
  nonspecific, PPLO in, 304–305
    Trichomonas vaginalis in, 285–286,
    290
Urinary tract, *Alcaligenes faecalis* in,
  132
  anaerobic streptococci in, 33
  Candida in, 239
  coliforms in, 105
  Klebsiella in, 106
  PPLO in, 305
  Pseudomonas aeruginosa in, 127
  spirochetes in, 194
  Trichomonas vaginalis in, 276
  viridans streptococci in, 31
Urine, bacterial counts of, 314, 316, 318–
  321, 342
  enterobacteria in, 104
  Haemophilus vaginalis in, 134
  microbiota of, 314, 316, 318–321, 341,
  342
  Micrococcus niger in, 26
  Mima vaginicola in, 118
  Proteus in, 106
  sterility of, 311
Uterus, anaerobic micrococci in, 25–26
  anaerobic streptococci in, 34
  anaerobic vibrios in, 147
  m:croorganisms in, 340
  Staphylococcus albus in, 24

Vagina, *Actinomyces bifidus* in, 62
  anaerobic micrococci in, 25–26
  anaerobic streptococci in, 34
  anaerobic vibrios in, 147, 177–178
  Bacteroides serpens in, 162
  Candida species in, 237–238
    C. albicans in disease of, 243, 248
    C. stellatoidea, 235
  clostridia in, 87
  coliform bacteria in, 104
  corynebacteria in, 56, 78
  lactobacilli in, 55–56
  maternal, as source of indigenous biota,
  312
  microbiota of, 318–321, 338–342
    development of, 339–340
  Mima vaginicola in, 118
  neisseriae in, 36
  PPLO in, 305
  protozoa in, 273–275
  Staphylococcus albus in, 24
  Staph. aureus in, 14
  Streptococcus putridus in, 35
  Torulopsis glabrata in, 228

Vagina, trichomoniasis of, 274–275, 277, 285–290
  viridans streptococci in, 31
Veillonella alcalescens, 38–40
  distribution of, 319
  significance of, 355
  in trichomoniasis, 285
Veillonella gazogenes, 38
Veillonellae, 38–40, 146
Vibrio, aerobic, 132–133
  anaerobic, 173, 177–179
    in fusospirochetal disease, *212*, 215
  history of, 145–148
  relation of, to protozoa, 175
Vibrio alcaligenes, 132–133
  distribution of, 320
Vibrio mulieris, 177
Vibrio percolans, 133
Vibrio sputorum, 147, 150–151, 177–178
  distribution of, 321
  relation of, to rumen vibrios, 179
Vibriothrix tonsillaris, 328

Viruses, as normal flora, 5
  in premature infants, 312

Water, actinomyes in, 68
  enterococci in, 29
  Mima in, 118
  mycobacteria in, 85
Wounds, anaerobic streptococci in, 34
  Mima in, 118
  Proteus in, 106
  Pseudomonas in, 127–128
  staphylococci in, 15

X-radiation in experimental infection,
  with *Proteus mirabilis*, 108
  with *Pseudomonas aeruginosa*, 129

Yeasts (see *Candida; Torulopsis*, etc.)
Yellow bacillus, 85, 87

Zuberella, 148, 162